D0014266

# Biotechnology in the Feed Industry

# Biotechnology in the Feed Industry

*Proceedings of*
*Alltech's Fifteenth Annual Symposium*

*Edited by TP Lyons and KA Jacques*

NOTTINGHAM
University Press

Nottingham University Press
Manor Farm, Main Street, Thrumpton,
Nottingham, NG11 0AX, United Kingdom

NOTTINGHAM

First published 1999
© Copyright Alltech Inc 1999

All rights reserved. No part of this publication
may be reproduced in any material form
(including photocopying or storing in any
medium by electronic means and whether or not
transiently or incidentally to some other use of
this publication) without the written permission
of the copyright holder except in accordance with
the provisions of the Copyright, Designs and
Patents Act 1988. Applications for the copyright
holder's written permission to reproduce any part
of this publication should be addressed to the publishers.

Editor's note: The opinions expressed herein are those of the authors
and do not imply endorsement of any product by the author or any
policy or claim on the part of the Symposium sponsor.

ISBN 1-897676-700

Typeset by The Midlands Book Typesetting Company, Loughborough, Leicestershire, England
Printed and bound by Redwood Books, Trowbridge, Wiltshire, England

# Table of Contents

# Section 3: Meat quality – The consumer's ultimate concern

# Section 4: Mannan oligosaccharide application in pig and poultry diets

## Section 8: Managing mycotoxin impact

## Section 9: New routes to genetic potential: Biopeptides

Contents

# NEW ALTERNATIVES AND NEW SOLUTIONS

# The search for new alternatives and new solutions: how do we build a culture for change within our industry and our companies for the next millennium?

PEARSE LYONS

*Alltech Inc., Nicholasville, Kentucky, USA*

## Introduction

We live in a world of high velocity change, a world where although it has taken 6-7 million years to grow to over 5 billion people, it will only take 50 years to create the next 5 billion. This growing crowd of people is armed as never before with technology, and this technology feeds upon itself. The Internet adds in six months the total population of what was once considered the center of the universe, Great Britain. Technology developments are never complete; they are perpetually in the exponential growth phase. The next millennium convenes within months, and it will be one of more people, more knowledge, more tools. If there appears to be a lot of change around you, then hold on tight. The bottom line for tomorrow is that *you have not seen anything yet*. Change will leave corporations behind, and it will ruthlessly destroy companies and people who cannot, or will not, adapt.

Response time in years gone by (1970s and 1980s) could be slower. Not so in the future, for there will be less time for recovery and fewer opportunities to catch our breath in the roller coaster ride. To survive, we must think differently, set short-term goals and prepare to jettison old habits and mindsets. The need to survive will demand that we do what works.

How then can a corporation cope in a world of constant new challenges and ever-changing rules? The modern world wants everything and wants it *now*; and it is a world where today's winner is tomorrow's nobody. The answer is simple to some, but impossible to many others. We cannot resist change, we cannot carry extra weight. We must simply search for different solutions and find better approaches.

How does all of this affect the feed industry? No industry is under as much scrutiny as our industry, yet few industries respond more slowly. This scrutiny is set against a rapidly changing background. In a short six weeks we saw the prestigious New York Times reporting that in the November 1998 US elections, the big loser was hogs. Not Democrats, not Republicans, but hogs. New laws against corporate farming cost a state

3

representative an election in North Carolina because of an association with farming. South Dakota, with a population of only 700,000 people in an area bigger than Britain, completely banned hog units larger than 400 sows. The state of Kentucky put a moratorium on all new pig and poultry units. Europe expects to ban feed antibiotics by June 30, 1999. Meanwhile the World Federation of Animal Health Industries has called for a new set of global principles to ensure continued prudent antibiotic use. In November of 1998 the US Food and Drug Administration distributed a new draft guideline explaining why it believes it must now re-evaluate the human impact of all antimicrobial animal drugs. Allied to all of the above is the whole issue of traceability through the food chain, a concept being championed by the supermarket chains. Clearly, our industry is under pressure, and pointing fingers is not going to help us: complaining is a 'cakewalk' at any time.

How then can our industry break out of its old routines and make radical changes? How can any organization do more with less, but do it better and faster? As Mark Twain once said "The world does not owe us a living-it owes us nothing-it was there first." What follows then is a case study, a game plan, an effort to build a culture of simplicity. Put simply, it is Alltech's plan to grow the company five-fold in 3–5 years. Ambitious, yes. Possible? Absolutely.

THE ALLTECH STRATEGY

Our strategy is a plan based on identifying six areas in which we have the scientific expertise to develop products that address some industry problems (Table 1). Each product has been assigned a technical champion and a commercial champion. Each product must first pass two tests. The first is scientific scrutiny. Does the product do what we expect? Are there sound data to support it? The second test, the task of the commercial champions, is whether the product can be produced at a cost that enables its use in animal feed at a good return. All six of the product areas we have chosen pass these tests and all six are non-genetically modified, non-chemical and consumer friendly. Whether these products bring about the five-fold increase in sales in such a short time remains to be seen. However, as Wayne Gretsky, perhaps the greatest ice hockey player of all time said, "Let's go for it. You miss 100% of the shots you never take". This strategy is our way of building a corporate culture flexible enough to change quickly and willing to take chances.

# Product area number I: Fibrozyme

Enzyme use in the feed industry is widespread, particularly where the raw material is barley or wheat and the animal is a non-ruminant. This technology dates back to the 1970s; however enzymes have often been tested unsuccessfully in ruminants. Invariably the enzyme was overwhelmed and

Table 1. The Alltech 'Blockbusters'.

| | |
|---|---|
| Fibrozyme[TM] | A rumen-protected enzyme |
| Sel-Plex[TM] | Natural organic selenium |
| Mycosorb[TM] | Scientifically proven mycotoxin adsorbent |
| Bio-Mos[TM] | A natural growth promoter |
| Vegpro[TM] | An enzyme to unlock the protein and energy in soy and other oilseed meals |
| Ultimate Protein[TM] Biopeptides | The next step in improving nitrogen metabolism |

degraded by rumen microbial enzymes. Through new technology for glycosylation developed at the Bioscience Center in conjunction with university researchers, the rumen stability problem for enzymes was overcome by protecting them against ruminal degradation long enough for them to be effective. The new product is called Fibrozyme. Unlike previous attempts with rumen enzymes, with Fibrozyme pre-treatment of forage is not required. In addition, the enzyme is stable to pelleting up to 95°C.

## THE SCIENTIFIC CASE: IS FIBROZYME EFFECTIVE?

A growing body of research and practical experience has clearly demonstrated the effectiveness of Fibrozyme in improving milk production. The initial research by Dawson at the University of Kentucky in conjunction with our own scientists demonstrated that Fibrozyme added to rumen fluid provided more usable substrate for rumen microbes (Figure 1) and prompted further studies related to volatile fatty acid (VFA) production. The change in propionate:acetate ratios in response to Fibrozyme (Table 2) aids in explaining the increase in energy available to the animal for milk production.

Table 2. Effect of Fibrozyme on *in vitro* acetate:propionate ratios[1].

| Component | Control | Fibrozyme |
|---|---|---|
| Fescue hay | 4.2 | 2.1 |
| Oat straw | 3.9 | 2.0 |
| Rolled barley | 3.5 | 1.3 |

[1]Tricarico *et al.*, 1998.

Fibrozyme response in *in vivo* trials has been equally successful. University of California researchers observed that Fibrozyme increased ruminal NDF digestion and feed protein digestion when added to diets fed duodenally-cannulated steers (Zinn and Salinas, 1999) (Table 3). Increasing the rate of fiber digestion improves the rate of passage and consequently intake, a process critical to increasing milk production in dairy cattle and gain in beef cattle. The same researchers found that

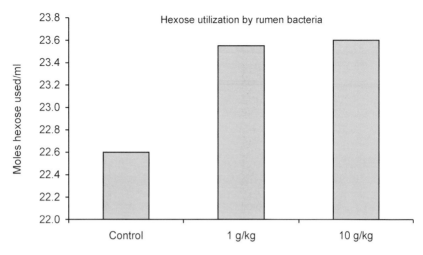

**Figure 1.** Changes in activities of ruminal microbes associated with Fibrozyme supplementation (Tricarico *et al.*, 1998).

Fibrozyme significantly increased average daily gain and feed intake when fed to steers (initial weight 225 kg) in a 64 day receiving trial (Figure 2). The 4.5% increase in dry matter intake was accompanied by an improvement in feed efficiency.

Results from research trials are reflected in response to Fibrozyme in commercial dairy herds. Increases in milk production have been measured in herds fed both high and low forage diets in Canada, US and South Africa. For example, cows fed diets containing barley silage and concentrate in Canada showed a 2.5 liter increase in daily milk production when supplemented with Fibrozyme. Cows in a California herd fed a corn silage-based total mixed ration (TMR) with Fibrozyme averaged 2.5 liters more milk per day over a 60 day trial. When Fibrozyme was removed from the diet the average drop in milk production was 1.5 liters (Figure 3). Finally, in a survey of 16 herds along the US eastern seaboard representing a wide range of management, feed and production levels (26 to 45 liters/day), average response to Fibrozyme was a 1 liter increase in daily milk production.

**Table 3.** Effect of Fibrozyme on ruminal digestion of nutrients (%) by steers[1].

|  | Control | Fibrozyme |
| --- | --- | --- |
| Organic matter | 60.97 | 63.16 |
| Starch | 79.99 | 81.47 |
| Neutral detergent fiber | 28.23 | 34.68 |
| Nitrogen | 66.65 | 69.75 |

[1]Zinn and Salinas, 1999.

6

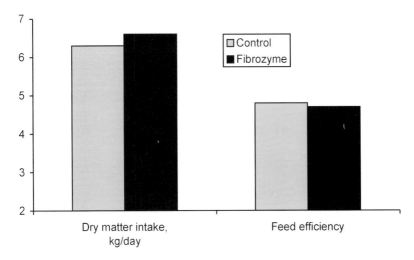

**Figure 2.** Effect of Fibrozyme on dry matter intake and feed efficiency of steers fed a 78% concentrate diet (Zinn and Salinas, 1999).

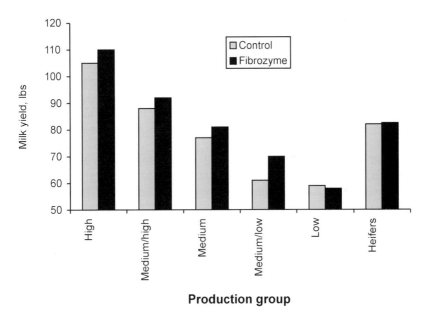

**Figure 3.** Effect of Fibrozyme on average production for the seven days before and after introduction in a herd fed in six production groups.

THE ECONOMIC CASE: DOES USING FIBROZYME PAY?

It is important to point out that Fibrozyme is neither a 'cure' for poor forage quality nor a replacement for quality nutrition or management. Fibrozyme is a biological tool designed to enhance fiber digestion through the action of protected hemicellulase and cellulase enzymes and results in improved meat and milk production. In its first year in the marketplace Fibrozyme has surpassed even our most optimistic forecasts. The return on investment for Fibrozyme to the dairy farmer has ranged from a low of 5:1 to a high of 10:1.

## Product area number II: Vegpro: an enzyme to maximize protein utilization

Economic and environmental pressures are pushing the food animal industries to improve dietary protein utilization. Protein remains the most expensive ingredient in food animal diets, and price could become more of an issue with removal of animal protein options owing to the BSE scare. Scarcity of some vegetable proteins may also affect price; and substitution of animal proteins in some diets with vegetable sources will require added synthetic amino acids. In addition, undigested protein excreted in manure contributes to odor problems and ground water pollution. The advantages of improving utilization of protein ingredients in livestock and poultry feeds are very quickly apparent.

THE SCIENTIFIC CASE: DOES VEGPRO INCREASE PROTEIN AND ENERGY AVAILABILITY?

Ironically, the solution to reducing feed protein waste comes from that bastion of genetic engineering, the Roslin Institute, home of Dolly, the cloned lamb. Although this solution is not the result of genetic modification, one of the Institute's senior scientists, McNab, found that a natural enzyme, $\alpha$-galactosidase, could release as much as 7% more energy and 7% more amino acids when added to legume proteins fed to broilers. Work in poultry with Allzyme Vegpro, the enzyme complement designed by Pugh at ADAS in Britain along with McNab and co-workers, has expanded into evaluations with other legume protein sources in broilers, layers and ducks (Table 4). Recently, work with pigs has demonstrated the potential to improve feed utilization of corn/soy diets in the grow/finish phase. Pluske and co-workers at the Massey Institute in New Zealand have demonstrated the increase in amino acid digestibility with Vegpro inclusion in pig diets containing a variety of vegetable proteins, including soybean meal and canola (Figure 4).

THE ECONOMIC CASE: WHAT'S THE RETURN?

To take full advantage of the improvement in energy and amino acid/protein digestibility gained when adding Vegpro, feed formulators should add a new ingredient to the matrix called 'Soy + Vegpro' with higher digestible amino acid and energy values. Reformulating to the same diet specifications provides the same animal performance with a less expensive diet: a savings of as much as 10 to 15 USD per ton.

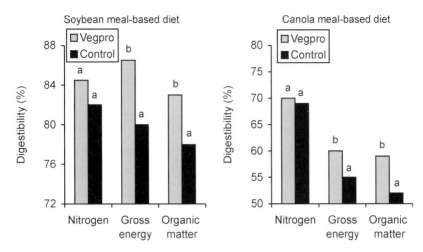

**Figure 4.** Effect of Allzyme Vegpro on nitrogen, energy and organic matter digestibilities of soybean meal and canola-based diets fed to pigs ([ab]P<0.01) (Pluske *et al.*, 1999).

Table 4.    **Response to Vegpro in research trials.**

| Species | Researcher | Response |
|---------|------------|----------|
| Broilers | McNabb and Bernard (1997) | Increased TME(n), amino acid digestibilities of soy |
| | Pugh and Charlton (1995) | Increased TME(n) of various legumes |
| | Swift *et al.* (1996) | Increased nutrient digestibility and growth |
| | Stanley *et al.* (1996) | Increased feeding value of cottonseed meal, soy |
| | Schutte and Pereira (1998) | Increased digestibility, production |
| | Schang *et al.* (1997) | Improved performance, efficiency |
| Layers | Considine (1997) | Increased egg production in diets containing wheat, sunflower meal and DDG |
| Ducks | Adeola (1997) | Increased AME, TME(n) of soy |
| Pigs | Lindemann *et al.* (1997) | Improved FCR in grow/finish |
| | Kitchen (1997) | Improved FCR |
| | Spring *et al.* (1998) | Improved FCR |
| | Pluske *et al.* (1999) | Improved digestibility of soy and canola-based diets |

# Product area number III: the move away from antibiotics

As early as the late 1940s, the growth-promoting properties of antimicrobial agents for farm animals were recognized. Since then, the practice of feeding subtherapeutic doses of these antibiotics has become an integral part of nutritional feeding programs worldwide. The publication of the Swann Report in 1968 was the earliest alarm bell that perhaps bacterial resistance to certain antibiotics might have potential to harm both animals and humans. This debate has continued to the present day; but the economic return from using these materials (typically on the order of 5–10:1) along with the absence of hard scientific data demonstrating resistance, led to their continued use. In the mid- to late 90s, the environment changed with the rise of public awareness of in-feed antibiotic use and the growing ability of consumer advocates to manipulate the media. Perception that the practice of antibiotic use is wrong often overrode the reality that there may be no scientific evidence to support the position.

In Europe, perception has won out with the banning of zinc bacitracin, spiramycin, virginiamycin and tylosin phosphate in pig and poultry rations (along with others already banned), and the deadline for European antibiotic use to cease completely is June 30, 1999. The pharmaceutical companies now face a dilemma. Do they (and some have) challenge the ban legally, or do they decide that the market is just not worth it?

The real question is how does the scientific community convince a skeptical audience? The consumers of the new millennium are too well informed and/or opinionated about feed antibiotics and the threat of human antibiotic resistance to even listen to the benefits of growth promoters in feeds. Against a background of BSE, salmonella and the controversy surrounding genetically-modified organisms, the pharmaceutical industry may find discretion to be the greater part of valor and that a gracious retreat may be advantageous.

The real question becomes if/when these antimicrobial additives are banned, what changes should we make in diet composition, especially for young animals? The most exciting direction in the marketplace is a compound our Bioscience Centers have been working on for eight years. It is based on mannan oligosaccharide and called Bio-Mos. Working as a 'functional food' instead of a bacteriocide or bacteriostat, this complex carbohydrate can accomplish some of the same goals as the in-feed antibiotic in that it beneficially affects the gut microbial population to result in improved growth and efficiency when added to livestock and poultry diets (Table 5).

Table 5.  Characteristics of chemical growth promoters and mannan.

| | Chemical growth promoters | Mannan |
|---|:---:|:---:|
| Positive effect on gut microbial populations | ✔ | ✔ |
| Conveys resistance | ✔ | – |
| Supports immune response | – | ✔ |
| Improves feed efficiency | ✔ | ✔ |

FUNCTIONS OF MANNAN OLIGOSACCHARIDES

Because many common intestinal pathogens also bind to the gut wall via mannose lectins, mannan in the diet helps maintain gut integrity and beneficial microbial balance by reducing binding opportunities for pathogens. Bacteria possessing Type 1 fimbria (mannose-bearing lectins) will agglutinate mannan from Bio-Mos. A significant number of commonly-occuring enteric pathogens possess such fimbria. In a survey of 250 coliform strains obtained primarily from commercial farms, 68% of the *E. coli* and 53% of the salmonella strains were found to have Type 1 fimbria. (Finucane *et al.*, 1999; Table 6). A secondary effect is the immuno-stimulatory properties of mannan. Bio-Mos has been shown to increase the reactivity of the intestinal lymphocytes as measured by the lymphoblast transformation and to enhance the phagocytic ability of white blood cells.

Table 6.    Incidence of *E. coli* and salmonella strains possessing mannose-sensitive adhesins (Type 1 fimbria)[1].

| Organism | No. Tested | No. with Type 1 fimbria |
|---|---|---|
| *E. coli* | | |
|    *poultry isolates* | 60 | 41 |
|    *others* | 17 | 10 |
| *Salmonella enteritidis* | 5 | 4 |
| *Salmonella typhimurium* | 6 | 4 |
| *Salmonella give* | 2 | 0 |
| *Salmonella montevideo* | 2 | 2 |
| *Salmonella pullorum* | 2 | 0 |
| *Salmonella senftenberg* | 2 | 0 |
| Salmonella others | 11 | 6 |

[1]Finucane *et al.*, 1999.

## THE SCIENTIFIC CASE FOR BIO-MOS: DOES IT WORK?

Assuming this approach to manipulating the gut microflora is effective, can mannan act to enhance performance, and are there scientific data to support its practical use? Research studies with mannan in a variety of species support its practical response, a few of which are summarized here.

### Bio-Mos for pigs: reducing copper sulfate

Copper sulfate and zinc oxide have been used for many years because of their antimicrobial effects in the intestine of pigs. Because high levels of these minerals in manure contribute to soil mineral profiles, alternatives are very much of interest. Recent work at the University of Arkansas (Maxwell, 1999) compared Bio Mos and copper sulfate in piglet diets in a segregated early weaning program. The study involved nine pens of six pigs per treatment. The pigs weighed 5.8 kg at the start of the trial. Pigs were fed four diets: control, copper sulfate at 250 ppm, Bio Mos at 2 kg/ton, and Bio Mos combined with copper sulfate. Pigs given diets supplemented with Bio-Mos were 1.42 kg heavier after the 38-day growing period (Figure 5).

### Bio-Mos response in broilers

The Danish Poultry Advisory Office conducted two trials with three non-antibiotic feed additives: a killed *Lactobacillus acidophilus* product, organic acids and Bio Mos. Both Bio-Mos and the lactobacillus product

11

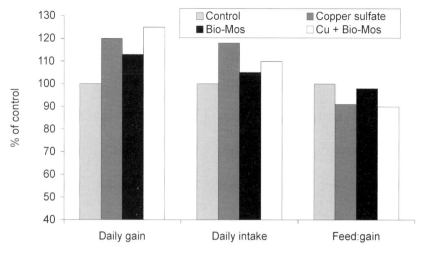

**Figure 5.** Effects of Bio-Mos and copper sulfate on performance of weanling pigs.

improved final body weight relative to the control; but Bio-Mos provided the best growth and feed conversion in both trials (Petersen, 1998; Figures 6 and 7). In addition, broilers given Bio-Mos had the lowest mortality.

### Bio-Mos for turkeys
Research conducted by Virginia Scientific, an independent research company in the US, compared effects of BMD and Bio-Mos or their combination in commercial tom turkeys grown to 18 weeks (Sims and Sefton, 1999). To assure a disease challenge, used litter was topdressed

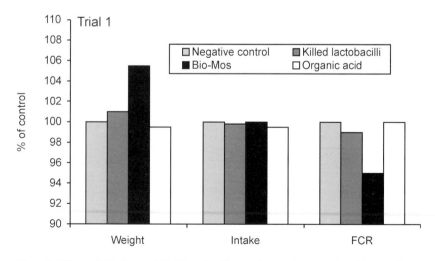

**Figure 6.** Effects of Bio-Mos, a killed lactobacillus product and an organic acid on performance of broilers relative to the control in Trial 1.

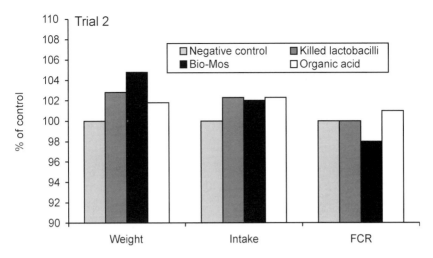

**Figure 7.** Effects of Bio-Mos, a killed lactobacillus product and an organic acid on perform-ance of broilers relative to the control in Trial 2.

on fresh pine shavings. Bodyweights of the control birds were significantly lower than all other treatments (Table 7). Weights for the Bio-Mos and BMD birds did not differ and were intermediate to the negative control and the Bio-Mos + BMD treatments. The combination treatment differed from, and was superior to, the negative control and BMD, but was not significantly different from Bio-Mos. There were no significant differ-ences in feed conversion before adjusting for mortality. After adjust-ing for mortality, the negative control had the worst feed conversion while the combined treatment was the most efficient. Bio-Mos and BMD were intermediate. *It was concluded that Bio-Mos and BMD had similar and additive effects on the performance of turkeys.*

**Table 7.   Effects of Bio-Mos and BMD on average liveweight of turkeys at 15 and 18 weeks[1].**

|  | Bodyweight (kgs) | | Feed efficiency | |
|---|---|---|---|---|
|  | Week 15 | Week 18 | Week 15 | Week 18 |
| *Control* | 9.348[b] | 11.868[c] | 2.805[b] | 3.370[b] |
| Bio-Mos | 9.698[ab] | 12.563[b] | 2.662[a] | 3.122[ab] |
| BMD | 9.716[ab] | 12.455[b] | 2.692[ab] | 3.154[ab] |
| Bio-Mos + BMD | 9.804[a] | 12.787[a] | 2.739[ab] | 2.974[a] |

[1]Sims and Sefton, 1999.
[ab]Means in a column with different superscript(s) differ (P≤(0.05).

13

THE ECONOMIC CASE FOR BIO-MOS?

Although these are but a few of the trials reported to date on this natural carbohydrate, the success in both field and controlled studies is increasingly convincing. Bio-Mos would appear to pass the scientific challenge of effectiveness. Furthermore, with increased production capacity it can now be produced at prices that make its standard inclusion economically attractive.

# Product area number IV: Sel-Plex, an organic form of selenium

USING NATURE'S MODEL TO REDEFINE SELENIUM SUPPLEMENTATION

Selenium is traditionally thought of as a component of the antioxidant glutathione peroxidase (GSH-Px) or more specifically selenium-dependent cytosolic GSH-Px. This is the best known selenoprotein and for many years was the only known physiological role of selenium. Classical selenium deficiencies are usually related to this enzyme and the deficiencies in livestock include liver necrosis (pigs), exudative diathesis in poultry and white muscle disease in ruminants. *However, recent studies have identified in excess of thirty selenoproteins including several forms of GSH-Px and other tissue specific selenoproteins with antioxidant activity.* Other selenoproteins include the deiodinase enzyme that activates thyroid hormone, (required for growth and cold adaptation) and a sperm selenoprotein thought to have a structural role.

Despite routine supplementation with inorganic selenium (selenite, selenate), selenium deficiency in domestic livestock is common and is associated with a range of practical and costly problems including infertility, lowered disease resistance and poor growth and efficiency. This is particularly true in regions where feed ingredients are low in naturally occurring selenium and producers must rely on inorganic supplements. Sel-Plex, an organic selenium supplement from yeast, offers a simple solution to selenium deficiency problems by placing the selenium in the same form that animals would receive if consuming grains and forages adequate in selenium.

THE SCIENTIFIC CASE FOR SEL-PLEX: WHY DR. MAHAN PREDICTED IN 1995 THAT *ALL* SELENIUM SUPPLEMENTATION WOULD ONE DAY BE IN ORGANIC FORM

### *Improved selenium status in animals*
Both yeast and higher plants incorporate selenium into amino acids such as selenomethionine. This organic selenium is uniquely suited to animal metabolism and is better able to protect against selenium deficiency than

inorganic forms. Organic dietary selenium, unlike inorganic sources, can be used in formation of other body proteins in addition to selenoproteins (Figure 8). In contrast, dietary inorganic selenium not used in selenoprotein formation is largely excreted via urine. As a result, organic selenium has two key advantages. First, selenium can be retained by the animal thereby allowing reserves to accumulate for periods of critical demand. The second major advantage of organic selenium metabolism is that the selenium content of other protein-bearing tissues including fetal tissues, meat, milk and eggs, is increased when selenoamino acids are incorporated (Mahan and Kim, 1996; Mahan and Parrett, 1996; Hemken *et al.*, 1998; Paton *et al.*, 1998; Mahan, 1999; Mahan *et al.*, 1999). Neonates are born with better selenium status (and lower incidence of white muscle disease) as more organic selenium is available during fetal growth.

In the calf, improved selenium status at birth affects both the potential for white muscle disease and ability to keep warm when born in cold weather owing to the role of selenium in thyroid hormone activity. The selenoprotein 5'deiodinase (ID I) converts inactive thyroxin ($T_4$) to active thyroid hormone ($T_3$). As a result, deficiencies in selenium result in lower circulating active thyroid hormone and render the newborn calf or lamb susceptible to cold stress. Kincaid and co-workers at Washington State University demonstrated that beef calves born to cows supplemented with Sel-Plex had higher $T_3$ concentrations at birth than calves from cows supplemented with an equal amount of selenium as selenite (Figure 9).

Antioxidant status also holds implications for the performance horse. The strenuous exercise that accompanies racing and endurance competition induces oxidative stress and free radical generation and can result in lipid peroxidation and tissue damage in respiratory and muscle tissues. This is particularly true if the animal has a deficient or impaired antioxidant status owing to low consumption of antioxidant cofactors; and less is known about the true requirements for these trace minerals in horses than in other species. Recently Pagan *et al.* (1999) examined selenium balance and blood levels in exercised Thoroughbreds given selenium in the form

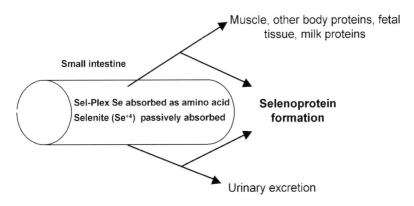

**Figure 8.** Organic and inorganic selenium are differently metabolized.

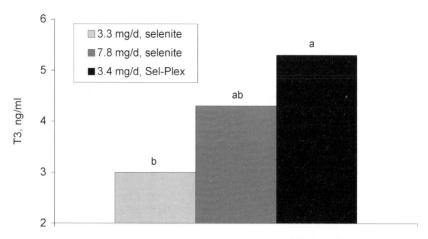

**Figure 9.** Effect of selenium source and level on active thyroid hormone concentrations in blood of calves at birth ([ab]$P<0.05$, Awadeh *et al.*, 1998).

of either selenite or Sel-Plex. They found that selenium retention was improved with Sel-Plex and that while selenium excretion and blood levels increased in general in response to exercise, horses given Sel-Plex retained higher plasma selenium at 24 hrs post-exercise (Figure 10). Essentially the horses given organic selenium lost less selenium in response to exercise stress.

### *Positive implications for human food nutritional value and meat shelf life*
A number of the selenoproteins in addition to GSH-Px contribute to antioxidant capacity, many in ways not yet understood. What is clear is that the improvement in antioxidant status in response to Sel-Plex has an impact on meat quality that will affect retail shelf life. Edens *et al.*

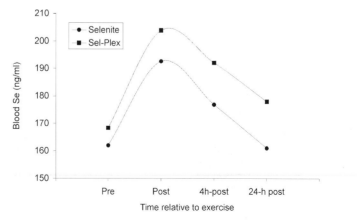

**Figure 10.** Effect of selenium form on plasma selenium in horses relative to exercise (Pagan *et al.*, 1999).

16

(1996) found that meat from broilers given Sel-Plex had lower drip loss (Figure 11). In pigs, Mahan *et al.* (1999) found that the pro-oxidant effects of selenite tended to increase drip loss while Sel-Plex had no such effect (Figure 12).

Sel-Plex organic selenium brings meat, milk and egg selenium content up to levels expected when livestock consume feed ingredients grown in selenium-sufficient regions. Because much of the world's major agricultural production is in selenium-deficient areas, human consumers benefit from the increased intake of this important antioxidant nutrient. Human selenium intake has long been an issue in regions such as northern Europe; and recently links between organic selenium supplementation and reduction in the incidence of human cancers has further focused interest in selenium nutrition. In addition, producers can benefit from the improved marketability of animal products whether it be a designer egg or meat produced using a human nutritionally-specific feeding program.

## THE ECONOMIC CASE: CAN WE AFFORD TO USE THE NATURAL FORM OF SELENIUM?

Sodium selenite is very inexpensive, costing only a few cents per tonne of feed to include. Organic selenium is relatively expensive; however with three modernized Alltech plants production is streamlined to the point that Sel-Plex can be included for USD$1–2 per tonne. It is also worth remembering that sodium selenite becomes extremely expensive if it is ineffective. Therefore, the real question is can we afford not to use organic selenium?

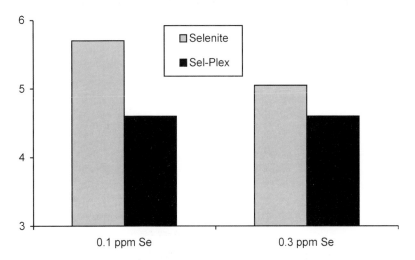

**Figure 11.** Effect of selenium level and form on drip loss from broiler meat.

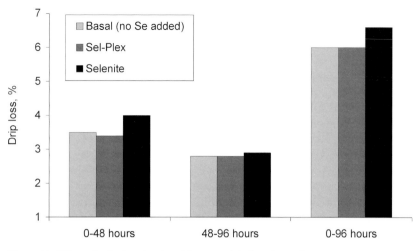

**Figure 12.** Effect of selenium level and form on drip loss from pig meat.

## Product area number V: Protection against mycotoxins

Today it is estimated that as much as 25% of the world's cereals are contaminated with known mycotoxins, while a higher percentage could be contaminated with toxins as yet unidentified. The impact on the consumer can be unexplained illness leading to a collapse in confidence in food and feed safety.

While drying grains to 12% moisture as soon as possible and good storage practices are key to minimizing the molds that produce mycotoxins, very often the feed manufacturer must deal with reality – namely, his grains are contaminated with mycotoxins. To counteract mycotoxins, various grades of clays are used including zeolites, bentonites and other aluminosilicate clays. Unfortunately, clays must be used at high rates (5–10 kg per ton); and recently a bentonite source was found to be responsible for elevated levels of dioxins in chickens.

Of major concern to the producer is the impact of clays on lagoon function. Clays are non-digestible and pass through the animal with the feces. Upon entry into the waste-handling system clays accumulate in the lagoon thereby contributing to accumulation of solids. Assuming expected animal numbers and feed consumption for a farm comprised of four 880-head finishing barns, it has been calculated that at an inclusion rate of 0.5% clay in the diet, 26,217 lbs of indigestible material go through the pigs into the lagoon each year: a staggering 65.5 tons in a five year period.

A LOW-INCLUSION, NATURAL NUTRITIONAL BINDER: THE SCIENTIFIC CASE FOR MYCOSORB

Over the past few years a number of scientists have evaluated a range of compounds with possible applications as mycotoxin-binding agents in

18

search of something that binds toxins without the need to add large amounts of indigestible substances or complicated chemicals to the diet. Few useful compounds exist; however results of studies with a new product based upon an esterified glucomannan derived from yeast are promising. The new product, Mycosorb, has been shown to absorb several mycotoxins in a variety of *in vitro* studies (Table 8). Aflatoxin is bound at highest rates followed by zearalenone. Ochratoxin and fumonisin are also adsorbed. In practice, 0.5 kg of the nutritional binder is as effective as 4 kg of clay. In addition, the new adsorbent removes other mycotoxins not affected by clays.

**Table 8.** *In vitro* **mycotoxin binding (% bound) by Mycosorb: a summary of research findings.**

| Researcher | Location | Bound by Mycosorb (%) |
|---|---|---|
| Newman | North American Biosciences Center, Kentucky, US | |
| Aflatoxin B$_1$ | | 95 |
| Don (Vomitoxin) | | 21 |
| Trenholm | University of Guelph, CA | |
| Aflatoxin B$_1$ | | 99.6 |
| Zearalenone | | 78.4 |
| Fumonisin | | 58.4 |
| DON (Vomitoxin) | | 8 |
| Sala | Argentina | |
| Aflatoxins | | 95 |
| DON (Vomitoxin) | | 30 |
| Zearalenone | | 68 |
| Mahesh and Devegowda, 1996 | University of Agricultural Sciences, India | |
| Aflatoxin in liquid media | | 80 |
| Aflatoxin in poultry feed | | 87 |

A unique feature of the glucan is its truly enormous surface area. Five hundred grams of esterified glucan has a surface area of some two hectares. Even the small amount of Mycosorb that a chicken would consume equates to 2.5 square meters of mycotoxin-binding surface area per day. In addition, different modifications of the glucan allow the product to be altered to bind specific toxins.

***Practical studies.*** *In vivo* data are also accumulating on Mycosorb. Whitlow and co-workers at the University of North Carolina found that Mycosorb reduced milk aflatoxin concentrations by 58% in dairy cows consuming aflatoxin-contaminated diets (Diaz *et al.*, 1999; Figure 13). A sodium bentonite product also reduced milk aflatoxin, however it required inclusion at 1.1% of the diet compared to 0.05% for Mycosorb. Activated charcoal had no effect.

Recently researchers in Italy examined the ability of Mycosorb to reduce

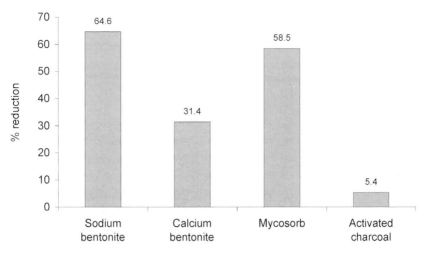

**Figure 13.** Effects of sequestering agents on milk aflatoxin residues (Diaz *et al.,* 1999).

aflatoxin impact on layers. Forty-eight laying hens (ISA Brown Golden, 2.2 kg mean body weight) were given a diet containing 2.5 ppm aflatoxin $B_1$ for 28 days. Twenty-four birds were assigned to the test group B, which was supplemented with 0.11% Mycosorb. All birds were clinically examined and the eggs were collected daily. At the end of the study hens were euthanized and livers collected to determine aflatoxin $B_1$ and $M_1$ levels by enzyme immunoassay. Birds on both treatments were healthy during the experiment and there was no apparent effect of the mycotoxin on feed intake, weight gain or egg production. In spite of this, results of liver tissue analysis confirmed the hepatotoxic effect of aflatoxin $B_1$. Significant differences were observed between the levels of aflatoxin in the control group and the group given Mycosorb (Figure 14). These data clearly demonstrate the efficacy of Mycosorb added to the diet in counteracting aflatoxin either by adsorption or degradation. It also represents the first of a new range of natural low-inclusion mycotoxin binders.

THE ECONOMIC CASE: CAN WE AFFORD TO USE MYCOSORB?

As with the other products, it is critical that Mycosorb be economic to include in practical feeds. Again, due to new production techniques it is now possible to produce Mycosorb for sale at a cost lower than clays. *Therefore a scientifically proven mycotoxin binder specific for a range of mycotoxins that will save money currently spent on a tonne of feed is now available.*

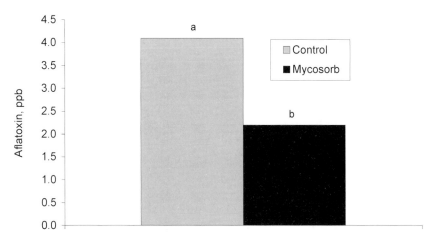

**Figure 14.** Effect of Mycosorb, an esterifed glucomannan, on liver aflatoxin content of layers ([ab]P<0.01, Rizzi *et al.*, personal communication).

# Product area number VI: Biopeptides

THE SCIENTIFIC CASE

Animals must obtain nourishment for health, growth and well being from their environment, but the mechanisms for this, and the relative importance of the various mechanisms, are still being discovered. For example, it was thought that most animals obtained their nitrogen needs for protein synthesis by intestinal absorption of amino acids. It is now accepted that significant absorption of nitrogen as larger peptide molecules is also very important. Peptides are molecules comprising between two and 50 amino acids. In recent years a large number of biologically active peptides have been isolated having diverse biological properties.

### Flavour peptides
Recent interest in food quality has led to an increase in the use of natural additives and renewed interest in the role of peptides. Different amino acid sequences can be used to create all four of the basic taste sensations (sweet, sour, bitter and acidic). Aspartame, for example, a dipeptide, is an intense sweetener. Peptides may be designed to improve palatability of feeds by mimicking, masking or enhancing flavors.

### Peptides for growth
Today's more environmentally aware producers are under pressure to reduce the quantity of nitrogen excreted from animals in intensive farming systems. One way of doing this is to lower the protein level of the diet while supplementing specific amino acids to closely match the animal's require-ments. However, the amount of protein that can be replaced by amino acids is limited and optimum growth is not achieved with supplemented

21

diets. It is thought that the transport systems required to carry amino acids across the gut membrane may become saturated thus limiting the total quantity absorbed. Peptides have an independent transport system and appear to be absorbed more rapidly, thus lower protein diets may be optimized by replacing the protein with peptides instead of amino acids.

### Ultimate Protein: Biopeptides

How can these biopeptides be extracted or produced? Over the last two years Alltech have been extensively researching the biopeptide manufacture process and have now established a dedicated facility at Turtle Lake, Wisconsin in the US. Here, vegetable ingredients comprise the key raw materials in the manufacturing process. Lessons learned from the BSE epidemic in Europe have been taken into account and no mammalian products are used thus ensuring biosecurity of this feed ingredient.

Termed Ultimate Protein 1672, this biopeptide product is designed specifically for weaning pigs. The tightly controlled process and quality assurance systems ensure that batch variation is kept to a minimum. Peptides have been characterized in human and animal nutrition and those present in Ultimate Protein 1672 are known to include:

- Dipeptide rich in glutamic acid to enhance palatability
- Easily absorbable tripeptides
- Nucleotide similar to specific proteins found in milk and colostrum
- Oligopeptide to help stimulate the proliferation of lactobacilli.

THE ECONOMIC CASE: WHAT SAVINGS CAN BE ACHIEVED?

Pig weaning diets in Canada, USA and Mexico have been incorporating Ultimate Protein 1672 for over 12 months with positive results. Early intake of solid food has been encouraged leading to increases in liveweight gain to bring pigs closer to genetic potential. In Manitoba in Canada, a field trial with segregated early weaning piglets (initial weight 5.5 kg) compared high milk (~20%) diets containing plasma protein (control) or Ultimate Protein 1672 both at 5% inclusion for 14 days post-weaning (Figure 15). Cost savings and increased gains were seen when using Ultimate Protein 1672.

Pigs reach market weights some 8-10 days earlier than controls. In other trials, diets including Ultimate Protein 1672 have achieved increased gains, resulting in overall economies during lifetime performance.

## Conclusions: toward the new millennium-a mind and culture shift

As we move into the 21st century, that we must move faster is surely a 'no-brainer'. The question is *"How can we make our organizations adjust?*

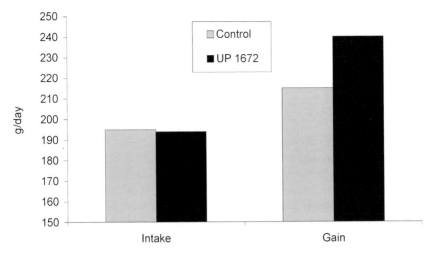

**Figure 15.** Effects of Ultimate Protein 1672 on post-weaning gain and intake of pigs.

*What can we do to make them more successful? What can we do to help grasp some of the opportunities present during worldwide industry upheaval?*
Specifically in the feed industry there are a number of key areas that must be addressed before an organization is to succeed. The organization must be built in such a way that change comes more easily. The feed industry must be able to respond to the marketplace at that moment.

The feed industry must grasp opportunities and employees must be trained to be flexible and change quickly with enthusiasm instead of resistance. We cannot fight against the future. If we do, we will find ourselves quickly with no customers. Individually we must take personal responsibility for embracing whatever new technology is present. We must become 'world-class adapters'.

Our own company, Alltech, sees our six new product areas as being the step forward to the next three to five years. Alltech will however, like Churchill, be constantly looking backward because as he said *"The further back you look, the further forward you see"*.

The six ideas put forward as products may never come to be the world-beaters we expect. They do, however, form focal points upon which to concentrate our energies. The challenge of the leaders for the six areas will be to retain flexibility and to adjust to an ever-changing marketplace. However, the organization must adapt, accelerate, innovate, learn and transform itself to fit the market's constantly changing conditions.

## References

Adeola, L. 1997. Effect of Allzyme Vegpro on apparent and true metabolizable energy (nitrogen-corrected) of soybean meal for ducks. Department of Animal Sciences, Purdue University, West Lafayette, Indiana, USA.

Awadeh, F.T., R.L. Kincaid and K.A. Johnson. 1998. Effect of level and source of dietary selenium on concentrations of thyroid hormones and immunoglobulins in beef cows and calves. J. Anim. Sci. 76:1204.

Considine, M. 1997. The response of ISA brown layers to the addition of Allzyme Vegpro in diets containing vegetable protein supplements. Proceedings of the 11th European Symposium on Poultry Nutrition. World's Poultry Science Association, August 24–28, Faaborg, Denmark. pp. 478–479.

Diaz, D.E., W.M. Hagler, Jr., B.A. Hopkins, J.A. Eve and L.W. Whitlow. 1999. The potential for dietary sequestering agents to reduce the transmission of dietary aflatoxin to milk of dairy cows and to bind aflatoxin *in vitro*. J. Dairy Sci. (Abstract) Southern Branch, American Dairy Science Association, February 1, 1999.

Edens, F.W., T.A. Carter and A.E. Sefton. 1996. Influence of dietary selenium sources on post-mortem drip loss from breast meat of broilers grown on different litters. Poult. Sci. 75(Suppl.1):60.

Finucane, M., P. Spring and K.E. Newman. 1999a. Incidence of mannose sensitive adhesions in enteric pathogens. Poster S179, Southern Poultry Science, Jan 18–21, Atlanta, GA.

Hemken, R.W., R.J. Harmon and S. Trammell. 1998. Selenium for dairy cattle: A role for organic selenium. In: Biotechnology in the Feed Industry. Proc. of the 14th Annual Symposium. (T.P. Lyons and K.A. Jacques, eds). Nottingham University Press, Nottingham, UK.

Kitchen, D.I. 1997. Enzyme applications in corn/soya diets fed to pigs. In: Biotechnology in the Feed Industry – Proceedings of Alltech's 12th Annual Symposium (T.P. Lyons and K.A. Jacques, eds.), Nottingham University Press, Nottingham, UK. pp. 101.

Lindemann, M.L., J.L. Gentry, H.J. Monegue and G.L. Cromwell. 1997. Determination of the contribution of an enzyme combination (Vegpro) to performance in growing/finishing pigs. J. Anim. Sci. 75 (Suppl. 1): 184.

Mahan, D. C. 1999. Effect of organic and inorganic selenium sources and levels on sow colostrum and milk composition. J. Anim. Sci. (submitted).

Mahan, D.C. and N.A. Parrett. 1996. Evaluating the Efficacy of Se-Enriched Yeast and Sodium Selenite on Tissue Se Retention and Serum Gsh-Px Activity in Grower and Finisher Swine. J. Anim. Sci. 74:2967–2974.

Mahan, D.C., and Y.Y. Kim. 1996. Effect of Inorganic or Organic Selenium at Two Dietary Levels on Reproductive Performance and Tissue Selenium Concentrations in First Parity Gilts and Their Progeny. J. Anim. Sci 74:2711–2718.

Mahan, D.C., T.R. Cline and B. Richert. 1999. Effects of dietary levels of selenium-enriched yeast and sodium selenite as selenium sources fed to grower-finisher pigs on resulting performance, tissue selenium, serum glutathione peroxidase activity, and carcass characteristics. J. Anim. Sci. (in press).

Mahesh, B.K. and G. Devegowda. 1996. Ability of aflatoxin binders to bind aflatoxin in contaminated poultry feeds – an *in vitro* study. In: Proc. XX World's Poultry Congress, New Delhi, India. 4:296.

Maxwell, C.V. 1999. Efficacy of Bio-Mos in improving gain and efficiency in early-weaned pigs. J. Anim. Sci. (submitted).

McNab, J.M. and K. Bernard. 1997. The effect of proteases (Vegpro) on the true metabolizable energy (TMEn) and true digestibility of amino acids in soybean meal. Poult. Sci. 76(Suppl. 1):133.

Pagan, J.D., P. Karnezos, M.A.P. Kennedy, T. Currier and K.E. Hoekstra. 1999. Effect of selenium source on selenium digestibility and retention in exercised Thoroughbreds. J. Equine Nutrition and Physiology (submitted).

Paton, N.D., A.H Cantor, M.J. Ford, B.T. Slaugh, A.F. Rizvi, and T.P. Karnezos. 1998. Effect of Providing Organic Selenium and Chromium as Yeast in Laying Hen Diets on Nutrient Composition of Eggs. Poultry Science 77(Suppl. 1):11.

Petersen, C.B. 1998. Comparative Effects of ZooLac, Bio-Mos and Bio-Pro on Performance of Broilers to 36 days. National Poultry Advisory Office, Skejby, Aarhus, Denmark

Petersen, C.B., Calleson and P. Spring. 1999. Comparative Effects of ZooLac, Bio-Mos and Bio-Pro on Performance of Broilers to 36 days. National Poultry Advisory Office, Skejby, Aarhus, Denmark. British Society of Animal Production (submitted).

Pluske, J.R., P.C.H. Morel, E.A.C. James and K.A. Jacques. 1999. Vegpro increases fecal digestibility coefficients in pigs fed soybean meal and canola meal. J. Anim. Sci. (submitted).

Pluske, J.R. 1998. Effect of Allzyme Vegpro on apparent digestibility of vegetable proteins by pigs, Monogastric Research Centre, Institute of Food, Nutrition and Human Health, Massey University, Palmerston North, New Zealand.

Pugh, R. and P. Charlton. 1995. Enzyme applications for plant proteins: time to look beyond cereals. In Biotechnology in the Feed Industry – Proceedings of Alltech's 11th Annual Symposium (T.P. Lyons and K.A. Jacques, eds.), Nottingham University Press, Nottingham, LE, UK. pp. 393–399.

Schang, M.J., J.O. Azcona and J.E.Arias. 1997. Effects of a soya enzyme supplement on performance of broilers fed corn/soy or corn/soy/full fat soy diets. Poultry Sci. 76(Suppl. 1):132.

Schutte, J.B. and A. Santos Pereira. 1998. Effect of an enzyme preparation (Vegpro) on broiler chick performance. Zootecnica, May 1998.

Sims, M. and A.E. Sefton. 1999. Comparative effects of a mannan oligosaccharide and an antibiotic growth promoter on performance of commercial tom turkeys. Southern Poultry Science, Jan 18–21, 1999, Atlanta, GA.

Spring, P., C. Wenk, A. Lemme, G. Bee and S. Gebert. 1998. Effect of an enzyme complex targeting soybean meal on nutrient digestibility and growth performance in weanling piglets. 1998. Institute for Animal Science, ETH Zurich, Switzerland. 14th symposium poster.

Stanley, V., C. Gray, H. Chukwu, and D. Thompson. 1996. Effects of enzyme treatment in enhancing the feeding value of cottonseed meal and soybean meal in broiler chick diets. Poultry Sci. 75(Suppl. 1):61.

Swift, M.L., M.A.G. von Keyserlingk, A. Leslie and D. Teltge. 1996. The effect of Allzyme Vegpro supplementation and expander processing on the nutrient digestibility and growth in broilers. Canadian Eastern Nutrition Conference, Halifax, Canada. May 15–17. p. 261.

Tricarico, J.M., K.A. Dawson and K.E. Newman. 1998. Effects of an exogenous microbial enzyme preparation (Fibrozyme) on ruminal digestion of fescue hay. J. Anim. Sci. 76(Suppl. 1):289).

Zinn, R.A., and J. Salinas. 1999. Influence of Fibrozyme on digestive function and growth performance of feedlot steers fed a 78% concentrate growing diet. J. Anim. Sci. (submitted).

# Yeast – could you base a business on this bug?

W. MICHAEL INGLEDEW

*Applied Microbiology and Food Science Department, University of Saskatchewan, Saskatoon, Canada*

## Introduction

As an academic, I would like to provide some background that will help you to appreciate yeast and what yeasts have done for science and for industry. At that point you might realize more fully why Alltech chose to base a good proportion of its business fully in the lap of the yeast, *Saccharomyces cerevisiae,* and on the applications of this and other microbes in both the alcohol and the feed/food industries.

The beginning of this story is rooted in history. Yeast (I will mainly confine my remarks to Saccharomyces yeasts: for a broader approach see Walker, 1998) is mankind's oldest and best understood microorganism. We know that around 6000 BC (Corran, 1975) yeast was used in beer-like beverages. Wine and bread making followed in the next thousand years and were well documented by the Egyptians in Thebes and later by the Romans. These forms of the 'art' of ethanol production were carried forward and spread throughout the world - mostly by religious orders - until science began in the 1600s to unravel the art and consolidate the science of yeast metabolism. The world's first microscopes helped van Leeuwenhoek in 1680 to see creatures described as 'animalcules' which some 150–200 years later were correlated with the biochemical observations of fermentation of sugars to alcohol. Cagniard de la Tour also observed yeast under the microscope, and was able to distinguish the budding process a short time after inoculation of yeasts into a fresh medium. Louis Pasteur in 1876 in his "Étude sur la bière" consolidated the thoughts of the day with some excellent observations, especially his treatise that "*la fermentation est la vie sans air*", in which fermentative (and respiratory) metabolism was described. Pasteur also described pure culture techniques that were perfected by Hansen and used in the brewing industry to obtain large volumes of pure culture yeast which were inoculated into beer wort. The 'propagators' as designed by Hansen remain to this day as an exhibit in the Carlsberg brewery. Somewhat later, the Buchners made cell free extracts of yeast (yeast zymase) by grinding yeast with diatomaceous earth. Their '*en zyme*' preparation (meaning 'in yeast', a term coined in 1897 by Buchner) was able to generate carbon dioxide from sugar. The word enzyme was adopted to describe protein isolated from living matter that would, in the absence of the cell which made it, catalyze a change in substrate to a product or products under physiological conditions. A complete new industry soon resulted based at first on amylases and proteases and their applications. Enzymes were first isolated from plants and animals and later from bacteria and fungi.

## Composition of yeasts

The composition of a microbe provides a clue as to why yeasts have value and applications exploitable by industry. Wide ranges of values for cellular components of baker's and brewer's yeasts are known. Table 1 is a compilation of values from industrial preparations of the two major Saccharomyces yeasts available to us in quantity.

Although scientists might quibble over the magnitude of the values reported in Table 1, the importance of these compositional analyses is in assessment of the utility of such yeast when harvested for potential industrial use. Such tables are useful guidelines. The constituents of each yeast vary extensively among strains as well as between yeast genera. Less well appreciated are the changes to composition caused by the nutritive status of the growth media used in production of the yeast strain. Using examples from our own work, brewer's yeasts harvested about 100 hours into a normal lager beer fermentation contained over 60% w/w carbohydrate, 2/3 of which was glycogen (Patel and Ingledew, 1973). When this yeast was harvested at the end of the fermentation, it had already decreased its carbohydrate levels to less than 50%. However, because of the high polysaccharide content, the yeast was still far below the protein content necessary for its potential use in animal feed preparations. For use as an animal feed protein source, brewers' yeast protein content must normally be at least 40% of dry weight. In order to meet such levels, the brewers' yeast slurry must be aged at elevated temperatures (~20°C) for a time to allow glycogen to be endogenously dissimilated, providing an apparent increase of protein in the cells (Ingledew *et al.*, 1977). Likewise, in baker's yeast production a ripening period in the process is carried out to allow the yeast to synthesize increased glycogen and trehalose with concomitant lowering of RNA and protein values. These changes influence in a positive manner the leavening ability, stability and viability of the yeast when it is stored.

A third example of the influence of nutrition in a medium on yeast composition was shown by O'Connor-Cox and Ingledew (1991) where an increase in the free amino acid nitrogen from 0 to 750 mg/l in a glucose medium led to an increased protein content in the harvested yeast through a range from 12.6 to 36.9% w/w. And as a further example, nutritional conditions are now known where *Saccharomyces cerevisiae* can produce

**Table 1.** Approximate composition of industrially produced baker's and brewer's yeasts.[1]

| Component | Baker's yeast | Brewer's yeast |
|---|---|---|
| | g/kg dry yeast | |
| Carbohydrate | 180–440 | 390–600 |
| Protein | 380–590 | 370–420 |
| Ash | 45–75 | 73–81 |
| Nucleic acid (DNA and RNA) | 52–95 | 39–43 |
| Lipids | 40–50 | |
| Phosphorus | 10–19 | 14–20 |
| Sulfur | 3.9 | |
| Potassium | 20–21 | 17 |
| Sodium | 0.12–0.3 | 0.7 |
| Calcium | 0.6–0.75 | 01.3 |
| Iron | 0.02–0.03 | 0.1 |
| Magnesium | 1.3–1.65 | 2.3 |
| Cobalt | 0.008 | 0.0002 |
| Copper | 0.008 | 0.033 |
| Manganese | 0.0059 | 0.0057 |
| Zinc | 0.170–0.197 | 0.0387 |
| Chromium | 0.0005–0.0025 | |
| Nickel | 0.003 | |
| Tin | 0.003 | |
| Molybdenum | 0.00004 | |
| Lithium | 0.000017 | |
| Vanadium | 0.00004 | |
| Selenium | 0.005 | |
| Pantothenate (Coenzyme A) | 0.065–0.10 | 0.110–0.120 |
| Choline (membranes) | 2.71–4.00 | 3.80–4.55 |
| Thiamin (Vit B1) | 0.090–0.165 | 0.092–0.150 |
| Riboflavin (Vit B2) | 0.040–0.100 | 0.035–0.045 |
| Nicotinic acid/niacin (NAD) | 0.30–0.585 | 0.450 |
| Pyridoxine (Vit B6) | 0.020–0.040 | 0.043–0.050 |
| Biotin (biocytin) | 0.0006–0.0013 | 0.001 |
| *p* – aminobenzoate (folic) | 0.160 | 0.005 |
| Inositol (phospholipids) | 3.0 | 3.9–5.0 |
| Folic acid (1–C transfer) | 0.013–0.015 | 0.010 |

[1]Adapted from Malony, 1998; Reed and Nagodawithana, 1991; Ingledew *et al.*, 1977; Patel and Ingledew, 1973; Peppler, 1970.

at least 23.8% v/v ethanol without selection or adaptation using commercial strains of active dry yeasts in batch fermentation with all the carbohydrate present at zero time (Thomas *et al.,* 1993). Yet millions of dollars have been spent in trying to obtain yeasts which are tolerant to more than 12–13% alcohol. We believe that changes in cell composition and in end product synthesis are influenced greatly by yeast nutrition and common physiological principles.

The message provided above is simple. The composition of yeast is influenced by the growth medium and by the environmental conditions chosen to propagate the cells. Not only can the concentration of the major components of yeast (carbohydrate, protein and nucleic acid) be influenced, but also the levels of minerals, the levels of enzymes made by the yeast, and the amounts of end products harvested from a medium. This information must not be forgotten in the current hysteria to produce genetically engineered yeasts with properties different from the yeasts we have come to know.

# Versatile applications of yeast

To demonstrate the versatility of Saccharomyces yeasts and the breadth of industrial opportunities available, all that is needed is to show both the historical development and current usage of these yeasts in industry.

BAKING INDUSTRY

The growth of baking yeast production from both a sales and technology standpoint is an interesting story. This industry propagates the largest amount of a single type of microbial biomass in all the fermentation industry. About 82,000 tonnes (dry) of baker's yeasts are now made annually (Reed and Nagodawithana, 1991). The technological aspects of their production and use are well documented by Rose and Yijayalakshmi (1993) and by Reed and Nagodawithana (1991). There are three major forms in which yeast is supplied: slurried yeast, compressed yeast and active dry yeast.

### *Slurried yeast*
This yeast preparation is also called 'cream yeast'. It is usually a 14–16% w/v suspension of yeast in water or in the medium or diluted medium in which it was grown. Yeast slurries are relatively hardy, but have to be kept at 4°C to maintain viability. They can be washed with acid to reduce bacterial contamination. They are delivered in refrigerated tanker trucks at or near 4°C.

### *Compressed yeast*
To prepare compressed yeasts, slurried yeast at 4°C with added salt is filtered in a cloth press or rotary drum vacuum filter. The resultant yeast is 27–33% dry weight and has the consistency of butter. It is then extruded into blocks and stored at 4°C where it looses 5–10% viability per week. It is best used within 30 days. It must be shipped and stored at refrigerated temperatures.

### *Active dry yeast*
This product is made by extruding compressed yeast in spaghetti-like strands which are placed in an appropriate dryer to remove moisture (Bayrock and Ingledew, 1997). The tiny cylindrical pellets of dry yeast produced in air lift (fluidized bed) dryers are relatively stable especially if stored under nitrogen gas. They require no refrigeration, and only lose ~1% activity per month under these conditions. This product is very useful

to small bakeries and those not located near the source for shipping of slurry or compressed product. For the home baking trade, active dry yeast is a miracle product. The viability of these preparations can be as high as $2.2 - 2.5 \times 10^{10}$ viable yeasts per gram. The traditional technique of saving a portion of the leavened bread dough for the next batch is a long forgotten part of the art of making bread.

A major benefit of the development of active dry yeasts in baking has been in spin-offs to other industries including brewing, enology and industrial alcohol production. Yeast companies are now making a number of active dry yeasts specially selected for each of these related industries. These are used as direct inocula for the corresponding fermentations, and have reduced significantly the need for yeast propagation, microbiological expertise and microbiological surveillance at the alcohol plants. Predictability of fermentation has been significantly increased. The major impact of these products has been in the smaller companies. In larger plants, active dry yeasts or selected company cultures are sometimes propagated in stages of increasing volume or conditioned prior to use. During this time a small increase in cell number occurs (anaerobically), preparing the yeast in advance for the medium used in fermentation and lowering slightly the cost of yeast procurement. The availability of a shelf-stable dried microbial inoculum where each gram contains $\sim 2.2 \times 10^{10}$ viable yeasts is a major biotechnological development. Other microbes are similarly being dried for the fermentation industry and for probiotics.

## ALCOHOL PRODUCTION (POTABLE AND FUEL/INDUSTRIAL)

*Saccharomyces cerevisiae* remains the most exploited microorganism known and is still the primary yeast species responsible for production of potable and industrial ethanol. Ethanol is quantitatively and economically the world's premier biotechnological commodity (Walker, 1998), produced at 24 billion liters per year (Dixon, 1999). The alcohol industry can be divided into potable and non-potable production. The former includes brewing, winery and distillery products. The yeasts used in these industries are different, and the handling procedures are not the same. In brewing, for example, worts are inoculated with from $5 \times 10^6$ to $2 \times 10^7$ yeasts/ml. There is a 3 to 8-fold growth of the yeast anaerobically as it makes alcohol from grain starch-derived sugars. This provides the brewer with a crop of yeast which is harvested, chilled and reused for the next batch as an inoculum. Because each fermentor produces an increase in cell number, there is always a purging of the oldest or least desirable crops, and they are usually incorporated into animal feed (via the spent grains from the process).

In winery and distillery technology, the yeasts are not reused. Presumably this is due only to the inability to collect them from the rest of the insoluble materials on tank bottoms, and the lowered viability of the harvested yeasts caused by the lower pH and higher alcohol levels of the final fermentation. In such fermentations, the peak yeast cell numbers in the fermentors can exceed $190 \times 10^6$ yeasts/ml. This figure will become relevant below.

North American fuel alcohol production now totals some 7 billion liters per year. Alcohol is made at about 12% concentration on average. Therefore about 60 billion liters of mash is fermented in North America. If peak yeast levels in fermentors average $190 \times 10^6$/ml for each of the 60 billion liters of mash in fermentation, over $1.14 \times 10^{22}$ yeasts would have been made. If we assume that 1 gram of yeast before any stresses are applied contains approximately $4.87 \times 10^{10}$ cells (K.C. Thomas, unpublished data; Bayrock and Ingledew, 1997)[1], then $2.34 \times 10^{11}$ grams of excess yeast or 234,000 tonnes of yeasts would be available in North America. At a conservative protein content of 38%, 88,920 tonnes of yeast protein would be distributed into the spent grains. Moreover, large amounts of growth factors, vitamins and beneficial minerals would be present. If production of 1 kL of ethanol leads to 0.86 tonnes of distiller's dried grains (DDG) (Lewis, 1997), then $7 \times 10^6$ kL of ethanol would lead to $6 \times 10^6$ tonnes of DDG. The contribution of yeast biomass to the weight of what would become distillers dried grains with solubles (DDGS) would be at least 3.9 %. The contribution of the yeast protein to the protein content of DDGS (of 28%) would be at least 5.3 %. The contribution of spent yeasts to overall vitamin content of DDG feed would be even higher as many of the vitamins from grain would have been scavenged by the yeast population during fermentation. Mash and thin stillage are collected after distillation, a process that leads to yeast death and denaturation of proteins. We believe that thin stillage and spent grains from the alcohol fermentation industry benefit animals more than most people realize owing to the nutrient content of yeast cells and the fact that a good portion of the yeast protein would be "by-pass" protein for the animal.

## SINGLE CELL PROTEIN FOR MAN AND ANIMALS

Some 80,000 tonnes of baker's yeasts (dry basis) are produced in the US alone annually. Most of this is used in baking and therefore is consumed in food, but a small amount, some 200–4,000 tonnes, is directly used in dried form for nutritional purposes. From breweries, ~14,000 tonnes of spent brewer's yeast is used for yeast extract and nutritional yeast purposes (Athnasios, 1996). Saccharomyces yeasts play a large part therefore in what could be called a segment of the single cell protein (SCP) market. Enormous quantities of Saccharomyces yeasts are available from the brewing industry. Unfortunately, a useful way of collecting and quickly processing such surplus yeast is not readily available;

---

[1] The total yeast cell number in compressed yeast is ~$4.87 \times 10^{10}$/gram dry weight. The best ADY preparations are ~$2.5 \times 10^{10}$ cells/gram dry weight. This indicates that even though the dryer is gentle to the yeast, ~50% of the yeasts do not survive the dehydration process (Bayrock and Ingledew, 1997). Our assumption is that one gram of any Saccharomyces yeast would contain at least $4.87 \times 10^{10}$ yeast cells/gram dry weight (viable and dead cells).

and some of this yeast may be contaminated with non-pathogenic lactic bacteria. Surplus yeast from the baker's yeast industry is similarly contaminated because it is not possible to produce a pure culture yeast in such large quantities without some bacterial and wild yeast contaminants present. Production of yeasts aerobically in the baking trade is done with an aeration rate exceeding one volume of air per volume of medium per minute, and a number of sequential propagations are done in increasing volumes of medium. Absolute sterility of equipment and media is not possible at this scale. The drying process for inactive dry yeast, however, kills the vast majority of viable non-yeast contaminants as well as the yeast itself, which is highly viable in the baker's or brewer's yeast preparations. The wine and distillery industries are largely unable to separate yeast from fruit or grain insolubles, and thusly this yeast is lost as a human food. Most remains with the discarded lees or spent grains to be consumed by animals or used as fertilizer or landfill.

The single cell protein (SCP) industry is a shadow only of past practices where many different yeast, bacteria and fungi were grown as primary cultures on a wide variety of industrial wastes to produce biomass destined to serve as food or feed for man and animals. This industry grew from the war efforts during World War I and World War II, but failed in part due to carcinogenic residues in SCP produced on paraffins and oils which led to closure of some superb facilities worldwide. Another factor leading to problems was the content of nucleic acid in SCP (7 times more than meat), a circumstance leading to uric acid (gout) buildup in the lower extremities of man and primates (and birds) due to the absence of the enzyme uricase. For man, this effectively limits the consumption of SCP to approximately 20 grams/day unless the RNA has been chemically extracted, a process that increases costs. Methods are available to extract RNA (Reed and Nagodawithana, 1991). The nucleic acid content is high enough in yeasts that scientists who measure the nitrogen content of yeast cells in order to calculate protein content now use the conversion factor of 5.5 (rather than 6.25). This directly corrects the protein efficiency ratio for yeast to a value higher than previously determined and nearer to 2.0 or 2.2 for extracted yeast protein (compared to the value of 2.5 calculated for casein). The amino acid content of yeast is high in lysine, and resembles soy protein. Interestingly, if methionine is supplemented into yeast protein, the protein efficiency ratio then exceeds casein (Reed and Nagodawithana, 1991). The correction on the constant used for protein estimation is needed due to the high RNA/DNA content of these fast-growing yeasts.

Although a large number of microbes have been employed in the manufacture of single cell protein over the years, the processes relying on paraffin oil, methanol, ethanol or methane have been mostly terminated. Since the middle of the 20th century, interest in SCP as a novel food source has waned. However, an immense volume of scientific and commercial data have been collected since World War I when *Candida utilis* and

*Saccharomyces cerevisiae* were grown in Germany and the Caribbean. Notable successes include the production of quorn protein in the UK (a Fusarium fungal product rather than a yeast), and pruteen, a bacterial animal SCP feed made from methanol. Design and engineering of these products contributed technology to the industry in the form of novel fermentor designs, genetic engineering, metabolic diversity, novel substrate use, methods of obtaining adequate aeration levels for strict aerobic growth, and extensive information on the feeding of SCP to man and animals. Saccharomyces yeasts still have a role to play in this technology because of the fact that they are secondary yeasts, i.e., produced as a by-product of the ethanol and baking yeast industries and sold for production of dietary vitamin (B vitamins and trace minerals) or protein supplements.

ENZYME PRODUCTION

Yeasts are used to produce commercially relevant quantities of alcohol dehydrogenase, hexokinase, lactate dehydrogenase, glucose-6-phosphate dehydrogenase, glyceraldehyde-3-dehydrogenase, as well as coenzyme A, diphosphopyridine nucleotides, and mono-, di- and tri-phosphates of adenine, quanine, cytidine and uridine (Athnasios, 1996). Three yeast-derived enzymes which have had significant industrial use in recent years are invertase, lactase and melibiase.

***Invertase***
The invertase enzyme (isolated from autolysed Saccharomyces yeasts) catalytically degrades sucrose into glucose and fructose. Saccharomyces yeasts constitutively synthesize this enzyme. Industrially, isolated invertase is used in the confectionery business to produce soft-centered chocolates. This is the secret as to how one can put the caramilk™ in the caramilk bar. It takes more than 79% w/w sugar to inhibit possible fermentation (and explosion) of chocolates by osmophilic yeasts. At that concentration, sucrose is not fully soluble. As a result, a creamy center cannot be obtained. However, if a hard sucrose center is treated with invertase just prior to coating with chocolate, after a suitable incubation time the insoluble sucrose center becomes fully liquid due to the conversion of the sucrose into more soluble glucose and fructose. Moreover, the water activity ($a_w$) of the chocolate decreases because the molecular weights of the monosaccharides are lower than the disaccharide. The reduced water activity improves the shelf life of the confectionery products. This is a method of food preservation. Invertase is also used to make high test molasses. Without enzyme addition, crystallization of the sucrose would occur.

***Lactase***
The enzyme ß-galactosidase (lactase) is now widely used in the dairy industry to prevent crystallization of lactose in ice creams and condensed products and to reduce the concentration of lactose in milk products for

lactose-intolerant people. This enzyme is often isolated from *Kluyveromyces lactis, Saccharomyces lactis, K. marxianus,* or *K. fragilis* yeasts which are grown in fermentors for the purpose of enzyme isolation.

### Melibiase

This enzyme, also found in yeast, degrades the disaccharide melibiose to glucose and fructose (or raffinose to galactose and sucrose). Raffinose in beet sugar juice is present in appreciable amounts and decreases the amount of crystallizable sugar from beet molasses during processing. For complete removal of raffinose, melibiase is required. Without it, when the molasses is used for alcohol manufacture, the extra raffinose is hydrolyzed to fructose and melibiose, the latter staying in the fermentation in an unfermentable form.

## SPECIALTY YEASTS

### Minerals: selenium and chromium from yeast

Yeasts accumulate varied amounts of most of the minerals present in their growth media. From Table 1, it can be seen that 7.5–8.1% ash is found in the yeast grown for baking or harvested from beer. Much of this ash is potassium phosphate, but yeast has the ability to accumulate other ions provided (but not necessarily needed) in high concentration. Therefore, the mineral content of cells harvested from a particular propagation medium can be adjusted to be of significance as nutritional or health supplements for animals or humans.

*Selenium.* Selenium is an essential nutrient in nutrition of all animals. Selenium appears to be most deficient in countries such as China, New Zealand and Finland; however the selenium content of crops and livestock feeds produced in many parts of the world is below levels optimum for health of animals or humans. Historically animal and human foods have been supplemented with inorganic selenium, chiefly sodium selenite. Although primary deficiencies can be corrected with selenite, the inorganic form is metabolized very differently than the organically-complexed selenium found in forages and grains. Recently yeasts have been used to produce an organic selenium for feed supplements that owing to its similarity to the form of the element found in nature is much more available for useful metabolism and storage. When sulfur-deficient, yeasts are able to incorporate selenium into the cells. If done in an incremental (fed batch) fashion, the selenium concentration in the medium never becomes toxic and the yeast can take up almost 1000 ppm (into selenomethionine, selenodiglutathione and selenocysteine) and then serve as a nutritional source of selenium for human or animal needs.

The organic selenium from yeast is digested and metabolized via the same routes as the sulfur-containing amino acids (Mahan, 1995). This means that in addition to being used for synthesis of selenoproteins such as glutathione peroxidase, selenoamino acids from organic sources can be used in synthesis of other body proteins including muscle and milk.

The practical health and productive benefits of organic selenium metabolism on the farm are numerous, however the ability to improve the nutritional value of animal products for humans is worth special note. The increase in selenium content of meat, milk and eggs in response to organic selenium supplements has been of particular interest to those concerned about antioxidant mineral content of human diets (Figures 1a,b and c).

*Chromium.* Trivalent chromium was first determined to be the active constituent of the glucose tolerance factor (GTF) isolated by Schwartz and Mertz in 1959. This substance could restore glucose tolerance in rats fed mineral deficient diets. This work and subsequent studies in both animals and humans suggested that chromium in GTF is a cofactor needed to potentiate insulin in moving glucose from circulation into peripheral tissues (Anderson and Mertz, 1977).

The ability of people to make GTF seems to decrease with age, making older people more susceptible to diabetes. Yeast GTF is able to reverse this deficiency. If correct, it may be that yeasts which can be induced to take up higher levels of chromium ion could be most useful in the treatment of humans to increase the GTF levels in blood.

Given that trivalent chromium serves as the cofactor for insulin, it is not difficult to see how supplementation of this trace element would be useful in animals. The primary roles of insulin are uptake of glucose and amino acids into insulin-sensitive tissues such as bone, liver, muscle and adipose tissue in order to provide cells with metabolic fuel. As such, GTF and its cofactor trivalent chromium are required for normal metabolism of carbohydrates, proteins and lipids. Once acquired by the cell, vital sugar is used for energy that, along with the anabolic actions of hormones such as growth hormone (GH) and insulin-like growth factor 1 (IGF–1), drives

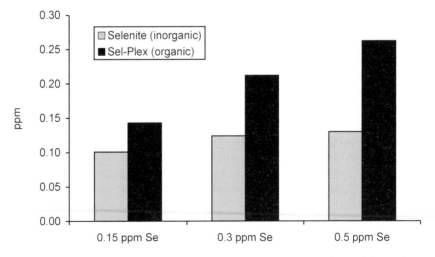

**Figure 1a.** Effect of selenium supplement form on selenum content of pork loin (Mahan and Parrett, 1996).

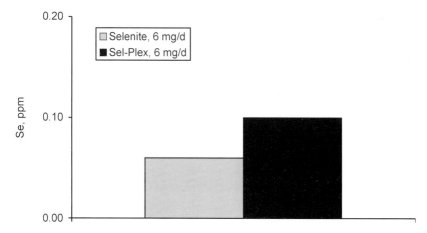

**Figure 1b.** Effect of selenium supplement form on selenium content of milk produced by Holstein cows (Hemken *et al.*, 1998).

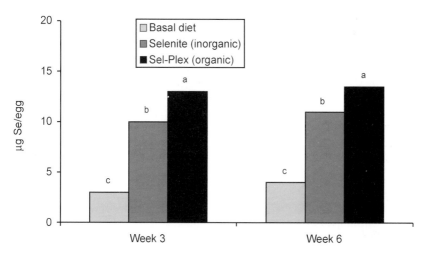

**Figure 1c.** Effect of selenium supplement form on selenium content of eggs (Cantor, 1997; [abc]P<0.005).

protein synthesis, lean growth and proper maintenance and function of all organs. Given modern nutrition and animal genetics it is little wonder that we are finding it necessary to ensure that diets contain adequate amounts of all the co-factor nutrients needed by the metabolic machinery. The faster growth rates, higher reproductive potential and the nutrient-dense diets that make production at modern levels possible require that nutrient metabolism be at peak efficiency.

It is also important to note that chromium deficiency is associated with poor immune response in livestock, especially those subjected to conditions of stress such as shipping, etc. Where chromium supplementation could increase effectiveness of vaccines and/or reduce the incidence of disease, we would benefit from less need for antibiotics (a growing problem in agriculture). The effects of mineral and vitamin malnutrition (chromium, zinc, selenium, Vitamin E) upon the immunity of farm animals is an emerging science (Mowat, 1994).

### Viable yeast culture: digestive aid for livestock diets

In ruminating livestock, live yeast cultures made from certain brewer's strains improve growth rates of beef cattle and yield of milk and components from dairy cattle. These responses are brought about primarily through stimulatory effects of the yeast culture on two key populations of rumen microbes, cellulolytic bacteria and bacteria that convert lactic acid to propionate. Increasing growth and activity of the cellulolytics is beneficial in that degradation rate of fiber is increased (and thus rumen turnover and intake) along with nutrient yield and microbial biomass (protein). Decreasing rumen lactic acid has a rumen-stabilizing effect of great importance to cattle on high concentrate diets. In addition, propionate is the volatile fatty acid most efficiently used for glucose production.

Progress has been made in recent years as to the mode of action of yeast culture in stimulating rumen microbes. Although the mechanism is yet to be fully elucidated, yeasts are well known to have an oxygen scavenging ability in fermentation, and therefore may work by enhancing the anaerobic environment in the rumen for the strictly anaerobic population. Girard and Dawson (1995) have identified a number of small stimulatory peptides in *Saccharomyces cerevisiae* strain 1026 which stimulate growth of *R. albus* that appear to be derived from specific yeast strains. Though it is not possible to assign specific metabolic roles to these peptides, the authors think it possible that the peptides serve as metabolic triggers or inducers that initiate the transition from a stationary phase to exponential growth (Figure 2, Dawson and Girard, 1997).

Another live Saccharomyces (*S. cerevisiae var. boulardii*) is also receiving attention in diets for humans, monogastric animals and poultry. When this organism was given to humans after a prolonged oral antibiotic therapy, the proliferation of pathogens in the compromised gut was prevented. The same findings are seen with livestock. Probiotics of this type are under test in a number of circumstances to determine their potential widespread use.

### Vitamins

The major vitamin complex found in inactive dry yeasts is the water soluble B group found to be useful for both human and animal nutrition. The 20 g/day suggested limit on yeast consumption (due to risk of gout) limits this food supplement to a substantial part (but not all) of the B complex vitamin daily requirements for man. Yeast also supplies a portion of a number of other vitamins or precursors needed for biochemical reactions in the cells (Table 1). No appreciable amounts of vitamins C, A, E, or K, however, are provided by yeast.

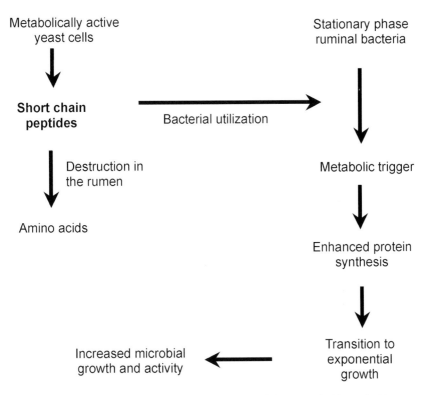

**Figure 2.** Possible metabolic role of yeast stimulatory peptides on ruminal bacteria (Dawson and Girard, 1997).

SPECIALTY PRODUCTS

*Autolysates and yeast extract*
Washed and debittered (if brewer's yeasts are used) ~15% w/v yeast cell slurries are autolysed when the temperature is raised above 45°C. Sometimes, exogenous proteases, glucanases and nucleases are added. The yeast cells are slowly killed at these temperatures; but the proteolytic enzymes contained in the cells begin to break down large molecular weight proteins to peptides and amino acids which are much more soluble. The process is monitored by analysis and terminated by separating the insoluble cell wall materials (see yeast hulls) from the solubles which are then evaporated to a self-preserving paste or spray-dried to a powder. Yeast extracts produced in this way are low in salt and are relatively soluble, and are formulated into many processed foods to increase their nutritional value and to add a meaty flavor. Examples include soups, soup cubes and gravies. About 31,000 tonnes of yeast extract are made annually worldwide from baker's (primary) and brewer's (secondary) yeasts. Yeast extracts are also used as yeast foods for fermentation processes, as nutrients for other microbes and for

39

microbiological media. Yeast extracts can also be made by addition of salt which initiates plasmolysis. The breakdown of proteins occurs in a similar fashion to the autolytic process, except that the salt concentration keeps bacteriological contamination at a low level but at the same time limits the use of the yeast extracts in foods. Extracts can also be made following the addition of acids like hydrochloric acid. Although not as useful, this process can be carried out on high solids yeast slurry which is low in viability (for example a dried yeast). The hydrolysate is then neutralized with sodium hydroxide and made into a paste. Pressurized equipment used in this process is expensive due to the highly corrosive hydrochloric acid. Salt content of these extracts is also a problem. Autolysates are produced as above but the insoluble wall/membrane fraction is not removed, leading to a less intense flavor than the corresponding extract and a product which does not dissolve. However, the wall components have excellent water holding capacity and they are also active as flavor carriers. This creates a demand for autolysates rather than extracts.

### Flavor enhancers

Notable also are the flavor enhancers derived from yeast RNA (not necessarily from Saccharomyces yeasts) achieved after chemical extraction and modification. Yeasts like *Candida utilis* can be grown with as much as 15% RNA and they are on the GRAS list of safe microbes for use in foods. Saccharomyces yeasts are lower in RNA but often used to make flavor active compounds. Inosine-5'-monophosphate and quanosine-5'-monophosphate are two such compounds which in combination with monosodium glutamate are used for flavor improvement of a number of processed foods and restaurant meals. They are extracted from aerobically-grown yeasts by hot alkaline sodium chloride followed by centrifugation and partial purification by ethanol precipitation of the RNA. The neutralized extract is spray-dried and the 5'-nucleotides are later extracted using 5'-phosphodiesterase enzymes prepared from fungi (immobilized). At least four fermentation plants in the world are involved with production of the flavor-active nucleosides, and monosodium glutamate is a well-studied fermentation product with a market of more than 400,000 tonnes per year (Ward, 1989).

### Yeast hulls

Yeast cell walls surround the yeast cell and are responsible for the rigidity of the cell shape and the protection of the cell membrane which functions for the diffusion and/or transport of nutrients into, and products out of, the cell. The cell wall may account for up to 20% of the cell weight and is composed of glucan, mannan, and smaller amounts of chitin (80–90%), protein (6–13%) and lipids (2–5.8%) (Fleet, 1991). Structural proteins are bound to the polysaccharides. Unsaturated fatty acids found are likely part of the cell membrane, which still adheres to the yeast cell wall. Yeast hulls are the ghosts or residuals (insolubles) from the production of yeast extract. They have a verified role as an additive in wine making where they stimulate stuck and sluggish fermentations. Although the mechanism of action of the hulls has been in dispute, the ghosts appear to act as nutrient sources for the oxygen substitutes which are needed by the yeast for sterol and unsaturated fatty acid components in newly synthesized membranes (daughter cells) (Munoz and Ingledew, 1990). We believe that justification of the use of hulls can only be made if oxygen input to juice is considered detrimental to color or flavor. This may not be the case (Long and Lindblom, 1986).

## Glucans

Yeast glucan is a component of the cell wall of yeast. Glucan has an ability to bind water, and because it is readily available, yeast companies have made isolates which have had use in the food industry as water binders, thickening agents or as fat replacers. Glucan is used in ice cream, meat products and salad dressings. Interestingly, in recent years, a good deal of attention to glucans has been given because of its enhancement of immunological reactions to antigens in animals, humans and fish. This enhancement is the result of a stimulation of the reticuloendothelial system which leads to an increased production of macrophages which destroy, by phagocytosis, any invading microbes or antigens. Glucans also have an effect in plants where low molecular weight antimicrobials called phytoalexins are made, and in invertebrates where glucans appear to activate a defense mechanism (polyphenoloxidase) (MacDonald, 1995). Yeast glucan also reduces blood cholesterol and may therefore reduce the risk of coronary heart disease.

## Mannans

Isolated mannanoligosaccharides have been used in poultry and pig diets to aid performance and health, especially in young animals (MacDonald, 1995; Spring, 1998). Though the mode of action in bringing about a performance response is not entirely known, dietary mannan is able to prevent attachment of bacterial pathogens with Type I fimbria to the gut wall and has been shown to reduce cecal colonization of salmonella in poultry (Spring, 1996). In addition to its role in binding potentially harmful bacteria, the complex is becoming of major interest in elicitation of enhanced immunological responses to bacteria, viruses, fungi and parasites in animals and in fish (Spring, 1998). This represents another nutritional route that can be used to aid intensively-reared animals in resisting disease and thereby reduce reliance on therapeutic and subtherapeutic antibiotics. Another significant use for modified glucomannan products occurs in the grain industry to adsorb mycotoxins. Compounds derived from yeast mannanoligosaccharide have been shown by Charmley et al. (1995) to bind mycotoxins.

### Therapeutic uses

Skin respiratory factor (SRF) used in hemorrhoidal preparations is a live yeast product which has wound-healing properties related to the uptake of oxygen by the preparation. Oxygen uptake (an increase in respiration) stimulates the healing of the wound. The exact component found in the yeast extract rich in SRF activity has not yet been identified, but scientists have proved the worth of the treatment. Another finding is that ß-proteins produced by the body as an early reaction to cancer cells can be detected by a yeast derived compound called coenzyme A-synthesizing protein. It is found in the particulate fraction of lysed baker's yeast and can be isolated in high purity for such a use. The molecular weight of the active fraction is only 400–1000 daltons (Bucovaz *et al.*, 1981).

### Colorants

Some yeasts of other genera than Saccharomyces are colored. For example, *Phaffia rhodozyma* is a yeast from which the pink pigment astaxanthin can be isolated. Astaxanthin is the natural color found in lobsters, shrimp, salmon and in flamingos. It is possible to feed the whole yeast to fish or crustaceans reared in captivity, where they rarely gain the natural color, thereby providing the characteristic flesh color to the salmon or seafood to improve marketability (Lyons *et al.*, 1993). At the same time, the other nutrients provided by the yeast are also of benefit to the fish. Lyons and coworkers (1993) have reviewed the production of this pigment.

GENETIC ENGINEERING

One of the miracles of modern science is the ability to alter microbes like Saccharomyces yeasts to permit them to make enzymes or end products that they did not have the ability to make prior to the manipulation. Because we know so much about the genetics and the use (and safety) of Saccharomyces, much of the genetic manipulation has been carried out with this microbe and with other yeasts which are somewhat better able to secrete proteins. The first targeted end products were ones with medical significance like hepatitis B vaccine, interferon and human insulin. A wide variety of other therapeutic proteins have been examined (Dixon, 1999), and the so-called second generation of value-added yeast-derived products are in limited production (Reed and Nagodawithana, 1991).

Other advances have been made which are not as newsworthy, but which have huge impact on the fermentation industry. For a detailed discussion on the practical exploitation of yeasts as producers of such biotechnological end products the reader is directed to the work of Walker (1998) and a recent editorial by Dixon (1999). Suffice it to say that modern and emerging applications of yeast are in a wide range of fields including biomedical research, biopharmaceuticals, biotransformations, biosensors, bioremediation, bioelectricity, biocontrol, biomass and bioethanol. Many of the advances will result due to the application of biotechnology. Saccharomyces and other yeasts may be the ideal hosts for the expression of foreign genes. Positive reasons for the utilization of yeasts have been reviewed in a concise and understandable way by Walker (1998), not the least of which is that we have the technology to grow yeasts on an industrial scale.

Recently, methodologies of modern biology have been used to determine the relatedness (lineage) of yeasts through the history of a brewery or the extent of cross-company transfer of baker's yeasts isolated and developed by one yeast company but adopted for use by a competitor. Polymerized chain reaction (PCR) techniques and immunological detection methods using flourescent monoclonal or polyclonal antibodies to detect contaminants in brewing and related fermentations have also been developed (Whiting *et al.*, 1992). Genetic modification of many microbes have been investigated in an agricultural context. This work may have profound influence in the nutrition of animals and in the fermentation industry. Modified *Saccharomyces cerevisiae* which hydrolyze maltodextrins in wort fermentation have been used to make beer in the UK for testing and limited consumption (with approval of the UK Government to the Brewing Research Foundation International). In fuel alcohol production, the potential exists for alternative yeasts or bacteria to be used in industrial processes where alternative substrates are available. Significant genetic modifications of other ethanol-producing microbes (*Zymomonas* and *E. coli*) have taken place with regard to use of alternate substrates and we may see these organisms industrially in the coming years. Alcohol tolerance, however, may be the biggest concern. Any new microbe in this industry will have to tolerate 12–14% v/v alcohol and contribute to the nutritional value of distiller's grains without concerns of animal health.

Molecular biology will eventually lead to genetic modification of proven Saccharomyces yeasts. In our experience, the major yeast problems in fuel alcohol production are the unexplained occurrence of cell death in the latter stages of fermentation and the effect of contaminating bacteria on batch and continuous fermentation yields. These are physiological problems rather than genetic ones. Tolerance to alcohol in our belief is also better solved through physiology and nutrition than by genetic means. However, genetic manipulation to produce proteolytic, fully amylolytic, ß-glucan degrading, and/or xylanolytic yeasts would lead to increased yields and new substrate possibilities.

## Conclusions

Could you base a business on this bug? It seems that a successful company requires a window on agriculture and the vision to go with it, a research team and research commitment (in yeast physiology, molecular biology and fermentation technology as well as an interface on animal nutrition and animal physiology), an international marketing team, and the cash flow and management philosophy to permit technology to develop to meet focused industrial objectives. Such objectives would be based primarily in the feed and alcohol sectors. Does Alltech have this? I certainly think so, and I think that is why the Biotechnology in the Feed Industry Symposium has continued to grow. In Walker's (1998) textbook in Yeast Physiology and Biotechnology there are two statements which allow us to gauge the future for the exploitation of yeasts. One states that "*It should also be stressed that yeast biodiversity is almost untapped from the industrial viewpoint and many yeast products have yet to be harnessed and commercialized*". The other is a quote from Fogel and Welch (1987) which states "*the gene pool in industrial and wild yeasts is wide, deep, and virtually unplumbed. To this we must add the gene pools of 500 other yeast species.*" This kind of opportunity will lead Alltech and related companies into the next millennium.

## References

Anderson, R.A. and W. Mertz. 1977. Glucose tolerance factor:an essential dietary agent. Trends Biochem. Sci. 2:277.

Athnasios, A.K. 1996. Yeasts. Ullmann's Encyclopedia of Industrial Chemistry. Fifth Edition. Eds. B. Elvers and S. Hawkins. VCH Verlagsgesellschaft, Cambridge UK. A28:461–474.

Bayrock, D., and W.M. Ingledew. 1997. Fluidized bed drying of baker's yeast: moisture levels, drying rates, and viability changes during drying. Food Research International 30:407–415.

Bucovaz, E.T., J.C. Morrison, W.D. Whybrew and S.J. Tarnowski. 1981. Process for the preparation of CoA-SPC from baker's yeast. U.S. Patent 4,284, 552.

Cantor, A.H. 1997. The role of selenium in poultry nutrition. In: Biotechnology in the Feed Industry, Proceedings of the 13th Annual Symposium (T.P. Lyons and K.A. Jacques, eds) Nottingham University Press, Nottingham, UK.

Charmley, L.L., H.L. Trenholm and D.B. Prelusky. 1995. Myotoxins: their origin, impact and importance: insights into common methods of control and elimination. In: Biotechnology in the Feed Industry. Proceedings of the 11th Annual Symposium, (T.P. Lyons and K.A. Jacques, eds) Nottingham University Press, Nottingham, UK.

Corran, H.S. 1975. A History of Brewing. David and Charles. Newton Abbot, London.

Dawson, K.A. and I. D. Girard. 1997. Biochemical and physiological basis for the stimulatory effects of yeast preparations on ruminal bacteria. In: Biotechnology in the Feed Industry, Proceedings of the 13th Annual Symposium (T.P. Lyons and K.A. Jacques, eds) Nottingham University Press, Nottingham, UK.

Dixon, B. 1999. Yeasts: rising stars in biotechnology. ASM News 65(1):2–3.

Fleet, G.H. 1991. Cell walls. In: The Yeasts Vol 4. Cell Organelles. (A.H. Rose and J.S. Harrison, eds). Academic Press, London.

Fogel, S. and J.W. Welch. 1987. Yeasts in Biotechnology. In: Biological Research on Industrial Yeasts. Vol 1. (G.G. Stewart, I. Russell, R.D. Klein and R.R. Hiebsch, eds). CRC Press. Boca Raton, FLA pp. 99–110.

Girard, I.D. and K.A. Dawson. 1995. Stimulatory activities from low-molecular weight fractions derived from *Saccharomyces cerevisiae* strain 1026. 23rd Biennial Conference on Rumen Function, Chicago, Ill, p. 23.

Hemken, R.W., R.J. Harmon and S. Trammell. 1998. Selenium for dairy cattle. A role for organic selenium. In: Biotechnology in the Feed Industry, Proceedings of the 14th Annual Symposium (T.P. Lyons and K.A. Jacques, eds) Nottingham University Press, Nottingham, UK.

Ingledew, W.M. and G.A. Jones. 1982. The fate of live brewer's yeast slurry in bovine rumen fluid. Journal of the Institute of Brewing. 88:18–20.

Ingledew, W.M., L.A. Langille, G.S. Menegazzi and C.H. Mok. 1977. Spent brewers yeast - analysis, improvement, and heat processing considerations. MBAA Technical Quarterly. 14:231–237.

Lewis, S.M. 1997. Value added enzyme applications for fuel alcohol production. 1997 Fuel Ethanol Workshop. Omaha, Nebraska, June 25–27.

Long, Z. and B. Lindblom. 1986. Juice oxidation experiments. Wines and Vines 67(11):44–49.

Lyons, T.P. 1995. Biotechnology in the feed industry. A look forward and backward. In: Biotechnology in the Feed Industry, Proceedings of the 11th Annual Symposium (T.P. Lyons and K.A. Jacques, eds). Nottingham University Press, Nottingham, UK. pp. 1–29.

Lyons, T.P., K.A. Jacques and K.A. Dawson. 1993. Miscellaneous products from yeast. In: The Yeasts. Vol 5. Yeast Technology. (A.H. Rose and J.S. Harrison, eds). Academic Press, New York.

Macdonald, F. 1995. Use of immunostimulants in agricultural applications. In: Biotechnology in the Feed Industry, Proceedings of the 11th Annual Symposium (T.P. Lyons and K.A. Jacques, eds). Nottingham University Press, Nottingham, UK. pp. 97–103.

Mahan, D.C. 1995. Selenium metabolism in animals: What role does selenium yeast have? In: Biotechnology in the Feed Industry, Proceedings of the 11th Annual Symposium (T.P. Lyons and K.A. Jacques, eds). Nottingham University Press, Nottingham, UK. pp.257–267.

Mahan, D.C. and N.A. Parrett. 1996. Evaluating the efficacy of Se-enriched yeast and sodium selenite on tissue Se retention and serum GSH-Px activity in grower and finisher swine. J. Anim. Sci. 74:2967–2974.

Maloney, D. 1998. Yeasts. In: Kirk-Othmer Encyclopedia of Chemical Technology. 4th Edition. (J. I. Kroschwitz and M. Howe-Grant, eds). John Wiley & Sons, New York, 761–788.

Mowat, D.N. 1994. Organic chromium: a new nutrient for stressed animals. In: Biotechnology in the Feed Industry, Proceedings of the 10th Annual Symposium (T.P. Lyons and K.A. Jacques, eds). Nottingham University Press, Nottingham, UK. pp. 275–282.

Munoz, E. and W. M. Ingledew. 1990. Yeast hulls in wine fermentations - a review. Journal of Wine Research. 1:197–209.

Newman, K. E. 1994. Mannan-oligosaccharides: Natural polymers with significant impact on the gastrointestinal microflora and the immune system. In: Biotechnology in the Feed Industry, Proceedings of the 10th Annual Symposium (T.P. Lyons and K.A. Jacques, eds). Nottingham University Press, Nottingham, UK. pp. 167–174.

O'Connor-Cox E.S.C. and W.M. Ingledew. 1991. Alleviation of the effects of nitrogen limitation in high gravity worts through increased inoculation rates. Journal of Industrial Microbiology 7:89–96.

Patel, G.B. and W.M. Ingledew. 1973. Internal carbohydrates of *Saccharomyces cerevisiae* during commercial lager brewing. Journal of the Institute of Brewing 79:392–396.

Peppler, H.J. 1970. Food Yeasts. In: The Yeasts, Vol 3. Yeast Technology. Academic Press, New York, 421–461.

Reed, G. and T.W. Nagodawithana. 1991. Yeast Technology 2nd Edition. AVI. Van Nostrand Reinhold, New York.

Rose, A.H. 1987. In: Biotechnology in the Feed Industry. Proceedings of the Alltech's Third Annual Symposium. Alltech Technical Publications (T.P Lyons, ed). Alltech Inc. Nicholasville KY pp. 113–118.

Rose, A.H. and G. Vijayalakshmi. 1993. Baker's Yeasts. Chapter 10. In: The Yeasts. Volume 5. Yeast Technology. 2nd Edition. (A.H. Rose and J.S. Harrison, eds). Academic Press, London. pp. 357–398.

Schwartz, K. and W. Mertz. 1959. Chromium (III) and the glucose tolerance factor. Arch. Biochem. Biophys. 85:292.

Spring, P. 1998. Mannanoligosaccharide. Its logical role as a feed additive for piglets. In: Biotechnology in the Feed Industry, Proceedings of the 14th Annual Symposium (T.P. Lyons and K.A. Jacques, eds) Nottingham University Press, Nottingham, UK.

Spring, P. 1996. Effects of mannanoligosaccharide on different cecal parameters and on cecal concentrations of enteric pathogens in poultry. Ph.D. Dissertation Thesis, Swiss Federal Institute of Technology Zurich, Switzerland.

Thomas, K.C., S.H. Hynes, A.M. Jones and W.M. Ingledew. 1993. Production of fuel alcohol from wheat by VHG technology. Effect of sugar concentration and fermentation temperature. Applied Biochemistry and Biotechnology. 43: 211–226.

Walker, G.M. 1998. Yeast technology. In: Yeast Physiology and Biotechnology. J. Wiley and Sons, Toronto. pp. 265–320.

Ward, O.P. 1989. Fermentation Biotechnology. Principles, Processes and Products. Prentice Hall, Englewood Cliffs, NJ.

Whiting, M., M. Chrichlow, W.M. Ingledew and B. Ziola. 1992. Detection of *Pediococcus spp.* in brewing yeast by a rapid immunoassay. Appl. and Environ. Microbiol. 58:713–716.

# NEW PERSPECTIVES ON ORGANIC MINERAL METABOLISM AND ANIMAL PRODUCTION

# Organic minerals for pigs: an update

WILLIAM H. CLOSE

*Close Consultancy, Wokingham, Berkshire, UK*

When we consider or calculate the nutrient requirements of the pig, we normally take into account the energy, protein and amino acid needs, as well as the macro minerals such as calcium and phosphorus, and some vitamins. A very important source of nutrients, the trace minerals, is often neglected. Their role is often underestimated, and their presence in the feed in adequate quantities taken for granted. However, they are necessary to maintain body function, to optimise growth and reproduction and for proper immune response. Trace mineral nutrition can therefore determine the health status of the animal. A deficiency of these trace elements can cause a considerable reduction in performance.

Mineral requirements are dependent upon the level of production and in the modern animal with its high level of performance, it has been suggested that the requirements may be higher than current recommendations. For example, in a recent trial (Mahan and Newton, 1995), the body mineral content of sows at the end of their third lactation was considerably lower when mean litter weight at 21 days was above 60 kg than when it was below 55 kg (Table 1). This suggests that considerable demineralisation of the sow's skeletal structure probably occurred during lactation to meet the needs of the higher-performing piglets. Although the animals were fed to normal recommendations, the losses from all body tissue were considerable when compared with non-pregnant animals of similar age. This raises questions about the actual mineral levels in the feed, as well as their availability to the animal.

Trace elements are present in most feed ingredients, but they are not routinely measured. Also, the content may vary considerably from region to region and there are doubts about the actual amounts in the complete feed, mineral bioavailability and bioactivity. As a result, trace elements are added in a commercial premix. Normally, inorganic salts such as sulphates, carbonates, chlorides and oxides are added to the diet to provide the correct levels to meet the animal's needs. These salts are then broken down in the digestive tract to form free ions and are absorbed. However, free ions are very reactive and can form complexes with other dietary

**Table 1.    The body mineral content of sows at weaning in parity 3[1].**

|  | Mean litter weight (kg) at 21 days | | % change |
|---|---|---|---|
|  | <55 | >60 | |
| Calcium, g | 1480 | 1262 | −14.7 |
| Phosphorus, g | 816 | 770 | −5.6 |
| Magnesium, g | 46 | 44 | −4.3 |
| Iron, g | 7.4 | 7.6 | +2.7 |
| Zinc, g | 4.2 | 3.7 | −11.9 |
| Copper, mg | 488 | 468 | −4.1 |
| Selenium, mg | 21 | 18 | −14.3 |
| Chromium, mg | 122 | 126 | +2.4 |

[1]Mahan and Newton, 1995.

molecules that are difficult to absorb. The availability of the trace mineral source to the animal therefore varies considerably and under extreme conditions it may be unavailable for absorption and therefore of little benefit to the animal.

As a consequence, there has been increasing interest in 'organic' or 'chelated' trace elements. In this form, the trace element is chemically bound to a chelating agent or ligand, usually a mixture of amino acids or small peptides. Indeed, this is the form that many minerals occur in nature. In the organic form the trace elements are protected from reacting with other chemicals during digestion, making them more soluble and therefore better absorbed. They are therefore more bioavailable and bioactive and provide the animal with a 'metabolic advantage' which often results in improved performance.

Specific organic trace elements of interest in pig nutrition are iron, copper and zinc, as well as selenium and chromium. The purpose of this paper is to provide an update on recent information; a more extensive review has been published (Close, 1998).

# Iron

Iron (Fe) is a component of haemoglobin and is therefore required for carrying oxygen and carbon dioxide in the blood as well as being vital to cellular and whole body metabolism. Iron is involved in several enzyme systems in the body and is essential for good health and the prevention of anaemia.

Except for the newborn piglet, the requirement for iron can generally be met through the diet. However, the content and availability of iron varies considerably among the different inorganic sources, with availability values ranging between 10 and 100% (Ammerman *et al.*, 1995). Recent studies have shown that providing organic sources in the diet can improve animal performance. For example, the addition of organic iron (600 g Bioplex Fe per tonne, Alltech Inc.) to a normal lactation diet fed some 7 days before farrowing and throughout a 26-day lactation, improved feed intake of the sow, as well as weaning weight of the piglets (Table 2). In a separate farm trial, again adding 600 g Bioplex Fe per tonne to a normal lactation diet (Brown, unpublished), there was a reduction in pre-weaning mortality from 11.2 to 9.4% and an overall trend toward increased weaning weight, with fewer lightweight piglets. The suggestion is that more iron may cross the placenta and is transferred into the foetuses which then have higher blood haemoglobin and immunoglobulin levels at birth. This higher immune status and viability results in a stronger piglet, consuming more milk and performing better. As a consequence of the higher milk yield, the feed intake of the sow must increase (Figure 1).

**Table 2.** The effect of organic iron (Bioplex Fe) on sow and piglet performance[1].

| Diet | Control | Organic iron (600 g/t) |
|---|---|---|
| No. of sows | 43 | 41 |
| Mean feed intake, kg/day | 4.69 | 4.83 |
| No. of piglets weaned | 10.5 | 10.4 |
| Mean weaning weight, kg | 7.86 | 8.15 |
| Average piglet growth, g/day (Day 7 to weaning) | 250 | 278 |

[1]Smyth, 1998 (personal communication).

Other studies have shown improved reproductive performance in sows, probably through the actions of the iron-dependent uterine protein, uteroferrin, which is secreted in early pregnancy and which enhances embryo survival (see Figure 3).

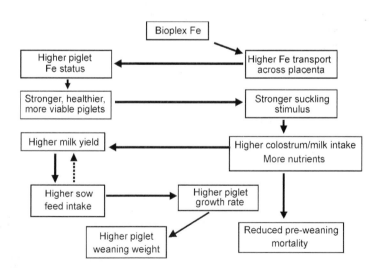

**Figure 1.** Suggested actions of organic iron in sows.

## Copper

Copper (Cu) is required for the proper function of the central nervous, immune and cardiovascular systems and in pigmentation of the skin. Although the minimum requirement is only 5–10 ppm, higher levels stimulate growth. Copper, and copper sulphate in particular, has therefore been added to pig diets as a growth enhancer. However, recent studies suggest that organic sources of copper may be more effective in promoting growth than copper sulphate. A 5.0% improvement in daily feed intake and a 4.8% improvement in growth rate were observed in piglets when organic copper was given at the same level as the traditional copper sulphate (Figure 2). Other field studies support these findings, such as those presented in Table 3. One interesting feature of this trial was the considerably reduced coefficient of variation (CV) of the growth rate of the piglets on Treatment 2. This suggests more uniform and less variable piglets, which makes for easier management and husbandry as well as a quicker throughput of piglets with fewer 'stragglers'. This has important practical and economic implications.

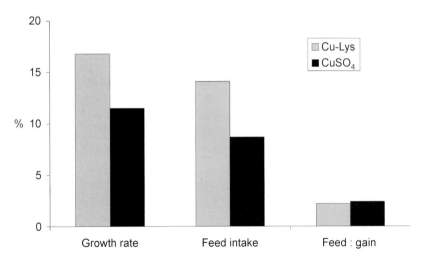

**Figure 2.** Improvement (%) in performance of piglets fed copper relative to controls with no added copper. (Coffey *et al.*, 1994).

Work in rats has also shown a considerably higher utilisation of copper from organic sources compared with copper sulphate, resulting in significantly higher levels in body tissue (Du *et al.*, 1996). Cell mitogenic activity is also increased and this leads to higher hormonal and therefore metabolic status, resulting in improved performance. This may have considerable significance if copper levels are reduced by legislation to non-growth-promoting levels, as is currently being suggested within Europe. It is possible that providing organic copper at these lower levels may exert the same growth promoting effects as the higher levels of inorganic copper.

**Table 3.** The effect of Bioplex Cu on piglet performance (10-30 kg body weight).

|  | Treatment 1 | Treatment 2 | Treatment 3 | SED* |
|---|---|---|---|---|
| Total Cu, ppm | 160 | 160 | 160 | |
| Copper sulphate, mg/kg | 160 | 60 | 60 | |
| Bioplex Cu, mg/kg | – | 100 | 100 | |
| Tylosin, mg/kg | 40 | – | 40 | |
| Feed intake, kg/day | 1.27 | 1.34 | 1.24 | 0.076 |
| Growth rate, g/day | 592 | 656 | 597 | 30.2 |
| Feed:gain, g/g | 2.15 | 2.04 | 2.08 | 0.102 |

* The standard error of difference between 2 mean values is based on the variation between pens of piglets within treatments.

# Zinc

Zinc (Zn) is a component of many metabolic functions and plays a vital role in hormone secretion, especially those relating to growth, reproduction, immunocompetence and stress response. Zinc is involved in the process of keratin generation and in collagen and skin nucleic acid synthesis. Zinc also has specific relevance to the boar, since it is essential for sexual development and spermatogenesis.

In terms of immunocompetence, zinc has a positive effect on both the immune response to pathogens and the prevention of disease by maintaining healthy epithelial tissue. In this respect, zinc oxide is usually added at high inclusion levels (3 kg/ton) to piglet diets because of its known pharmacological effects, increasing growth rate and reducing the incidence of scouring. However, the availability of zinc oxide, compared with zinc sulphate and organic zinc, is low. In one study, providing 250 ppm of zinc methionine or 160 ppm zinc sulphate gave equal performance to 2000 ppm of zinc oxide; however the health status of the piglets is unknown. This may also have environmental implications, since less zinc will be excreted with the lower level of the organic zinc included in the diet.

Cheng *et al.* (1998) compared the response of piglets fed zinc sulphate and zinc lysine in lysine-deficient (0.8% lysine) and lysine-adequate (1.1% lysine) diets. As expected, performance was higher for the piglets fed the 1.1% lysine diet compared with the 0.8% lysine diet. There was little difference in performance between the two sources of zinc but for the piglets fed the lysine-adequate diet, the feed:gain ratio was lower on the zinc lysine complex compared with the zinc sulphate diets, but not significantly so (P<0.05) (Table 4).

More recently, Spears *et al.* (1999a) fed piglets from 3 weeks to 10 weeks of age diets containing either 50 or 150 ppm supplemental zinc provided as either 100% zinc sulphate, 75% zinc sulphate ($ZnSO_4$) and 25% zinc proteinate, or 50% $ZnSO_4$ and 50% zinc proteinate (Bioplex Zn, Alltech Inc.). Zinc levels did not affect feed intake, growth rate or feed:gain ratio over the period of the study (Table 5). However, during the first two weeks

**Table 4.   The effect of zinc source on piglet performance (1.1% lysine diet; pooled results)[1].**

| Zn source | Basal | Zn sulphate | Zn lysine |
|---|---|---|---|
| Zinc, mg/kg | 0 | 100 | 100 |
| Feed intake, g/day | 517 | 541 | 509 |
| Growth rate, g/day | 294 | 303 | 305 |
| Feed:gain, g/g | 1.76 | 1.78 | 1.67 |

[1]Cheng *et al.*, 1998.

of the study, in piglets fed 50 ppm zinc, replacing a portion of the $ZnSO_4$ with Bioplex Zn tended to improve both feed intake and growth rate. In the 150 ppm zinc treatments, piglets that received 50% of supplemental zinc from zinc proteinate had a higher (P<0.05) gain and feed:gain ratio than those fed 25% of added zinc in proteinated form over the entire study period. Interestingly, there were no major effects of zinc source on plasma zinc or on cellular immune response but piglets receiving organic zinc tended to have a greater skinfold thickness response to PHA administration than those receiving only $ZnSO_4$.

**Table 5.   Effect of zinc source on piglet performance[1].**

| | 50 ppm Zn | | | 150 ppm Zn | | |
|---|---|---|---|---|---|---|
| Zn sulphate, mg/kg | 100 | 75 | 50 | 100 | 75 | 50 |
| Organic Zn, %[2] | – | 25 | 50 | – | 25 | 50 |
| Feed intake, g/day | 697[a] | 775[b] | 756[ab] | 716[ab] | 711[a] | 725[ab] |
| Growth rate, g/day | 408[ab] | 437[a] | 416[ab] | 411[ab] | 385[b] | 429[a] |
| Feed:gain, g/g | 1.71[ab] | 1.77[ab] | 1.82[ab] | 1.74[ab] | 1.85[a] | 1.69[b] |

[1]Spears *et al.*, 1999a.
[2]Bioplex Zn, Alltech Inc.
[ab]Means in a row without a common superscript differ (P<0.05).

In a separate study, Spears *et al.* (1999b) showed that the levels of zinc and copper normally added to pig diets can be greatly reduced without affecting performance of gilts from weaning to slaughter. However, replacing a proportion of the normal inorganic trace elements in the reduced trace mineral diet with organic minerals resulted in lower concentration of zinc and copper in faeces than pigs fed the reduced inorganic diets.

# Selenium

Selenium (Se) deficiency symptoms in pigs include mulberry heart disease, reduced immune function, lower reproductive performance, white muscle disease, MMA (mastitis, metritis and agalactia) and reduced glutathione peroxidase activity. Selenium is particularly important in the diet of the sow. Inadequate selenium will result in problems at farrowing. Low milk selenium content leads to higher piglet mortality and lethargic and weak piglets as well as mulberry heart disease. Indeed, the role of selenium is similar to that of vitamin E, as both are antioxidants.

The normal source of selenium is sodium selenite, but recent trials conducted by Professor Don Mahan at the University of Ohio have shown that when 'organic' selenium (Sel-Plex, Alltech Inc.) was provided in the diet of sows at the same level as the normal inorganic sodium selenite, the selenium content of the milk increased 3-fold (Mahan and Kim, 1996). Similar results were also obtained by Janyk *et al.* (1998) at the Irene Animal Science Centre in South Africa; and when piglet performance was recorded, piglet growth rate was 10 g/day higher and piglet mortality during lactation was considerably reduced when sows were given Sel-Plex compared with the sodium selenite.

When organic selenium was fed to growing/finishing pigs and the selenium content measured in loin muscle, there was a 20-fold increase in the selenium content of freeze-dried samples of loin (Soo-Han, 1998, personal communication). There were also improvements in the colour of the pork. Since selenium intake has been found helpful in the prevention of cancer, then the production and consumption of selenium-enriched pork may be a valuable way not only of meeting the daily selenium requirements of the human, but also of improving human health. This brings us to the concept of 'functional foods' and indicates the role that pig meat could play in this important concept.

More detailed accounts of the role of selenium in animal nutrition, and organic selenium in particular, are discussed elswhere in these proceedings.

## Chromium

Chromium (Cr) is now regarded by many as an essential mineral for pigs since it is involved in many processes within the body. Chromium is especially important through its role in the 'glucose tolerance factor' in insulin action and sensitivity and in the reduction of stress. As a consequence, in several trials, chromium inclusion has shown to improve both litter size and farrowing rate in sows and growth rate and carcass composition in grow/finish animals (Lindemann, 1996; 1998; Campbell, 1998). The higher number of piglets born alive, as observed in several trials, probably results from the action of insulin which influences follicular development, LH and FSH secretion and hence, ovulation rate. Progesterone concentration in the plasma is also changed and this affects the action of uterine secretory proteins such as uteroferrin (iron-dependent) and retinol-binding protein (vitamin A-dependent) which control embryo survival. Information on the actions of chromium in enhancing embryo survival was recently provided by Bortolozzo *et al.* (1998) (Table 6). A possible role for several of the elements in influencing sow productivity is suggested in Figure 3.

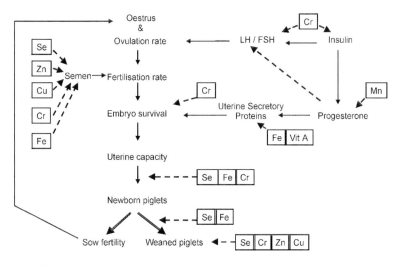

**Figure 3.** The potential role of trace elements in sow reproduction.

**Table 6.   Effect of chromium yeast on sow reproduction[1].**

|  | Control | Chromium[2] |
| --- | --- | --- |
| No. of sows | 41 | 41 |
| Average no. of ovulations | 16.5 | 17.1 |
| Embryo survival rate, % | 77.0 | 78.9 |
| No. of viable embryos | 12.7 | 14.0 |

[1] Bortolozzo *et al.* (1998).
[2] 200 ppm.

Chromium is also known to reduce stress and this probably has a positive effect on both the well-being of the sow and boar, as well as the piglet at weaning (Bontempo *et al.*, 1998).

In the grow/finish pigs, the effects of chromium are probably mediated through the action of the growth-promoting hormones which repartition nutrients in favour of lean rather than fat deposition. This has resulted in larger loin eye muscle area and more carcass lean.

## Conclusions

Trace mineral nutrition has been a particularly neglected area of pig science. Modern genotypes, with higher levels of productivity, may require higher levels than are currently recommended. However, mineral status is not just a question of quantity, but very much a question of mineral source and bioavailability. The benefits of including trace minerals at the level required by the modern animal and in the most readily absorbed form are measurable in increased performance, better health and welfare. In this respect it is likely that organic minerals will play an increasing role in pig nutrition, not only for meeting the true requirements of the animal for optimal performance, but also for providing healthy meat for the consumer.

# References

Ammerman, C.B., D.B. Baker and A.J. Lewis. 1995. Bioavailability of nutrients for animals. Academy Press, San Diego.

Bontempo, V., A. Baldi, V. Dell'Orto, F. Cheli, F. Fantuz, C. Ferrari and G. Savoini. 1998. Use of chromium yeast in weaned piglets' diets. In: Proceedings of the 15th International Pig Veterinary Society Congress, 2:18. (S. Done, J. Thomson and M. Varley, eds.). Nottingham University Press, Nottingham. UK.

Bortolozzo, I. I. Pinheiro Machado, R. Wentz, R. Nague and A.M. Perez, Jr. 1998. Effect of chromium piccolinate on swine reproduction. In: Proceedings of the 15th International Pig Veterinary Society Congress, 3:79. (S. Done, J. Thomson and M. Varley, eds.). Nottingham University Press, Nottingham.

Campbell, R.G. 1998. Chromium and its role in pig production. In: Biotechnology in the Feed Industry, Proceedings of the 14th Annual Symposium (T.P. Lyons and K.A. Jacques, eds.) Nottingham University Press. Nottingham, UK. Page 229.

Cheng, J., E.T. Kornegay and T. Schell. 1998. Influence of dietary lysine on the utilisation of zinc from zinc sulfate and zinc-lysine complex by young pigs. J. Anim. Sci. 76:1064.

Close W.H. 1998. The role of trace mineral proteinates in pig nutrition. In: Biotechnology in the Feed Industry, Proceedings of the 14th Annual Symposium (T.P. Lyons and K.A. Jacques, eds.) Nottingham University Press. Nottingham, UK. Page 469.

Coffey, R.D., G.L. Cromwell and H.J. Monegue. 1994. Efficacy of copper-lysine complex as a growth promotant for weanling pigs. J. Anim. Sci. 72:2880.

Du, Z., R.W. Hemken, J.A. Jackson and D.S. Trammell. 1996. Utilisation of copper in copper proteinate, copper lysine and cupric sulfate using the rat as an experimental model. J. Anim. Sci. 74:1657.

Janyk, W.S., D.J. Opperman, C.C. Rall, P.L. Opperman and A.T. Browne, 1998. Effect of organic or inorganic selenium and vitamin E supplementation on sow reproductive performance. Asia-Pacific Animal Science Meetings, July 1998.

Lindemann, M.D. 1996. Organic chromium – the missing link in farm animal nutrition. In: Biotechnology in the Feed Industry, Proceedings of the 14th Annual Symposium (T.P. Lyons and K.A. Jacques, eds.) Nottingham University Press. Nottingham, UK. Page 229.

Lindemann, M.D. 1998. Organic chromium – an exciting beginning, a promising future. In: Biotechnology in the Feed Industry, Proceedings of the 14th Annual Symposium ( T.P. Lyons and K.A. Jacques (eds.) Nottingham University Press. Nottingham, UK

Mahan, D.C. and Y.Y. Kim. 1994. Effect of inorganic or organic selenium at two dietary levels on reproductive performance and tissue selenium concentrations in first parity gilts and their progeny. J. Anim. Sci. 74:2711.

Mahan D. and C.A. Newton. 1995. Effect of initial breeding weight on macro- and micro-mineral composition over a three-parity period using a high-producing sow genotype. J. Anim. Sci. 73:151.

Spears, J.W., J. A. Armstrong and E. van Heugten. 1999a. Effect of dietary zinc source and level on performance, zinc status and immune response of nursery pigs. In: Proceedings of the North Carolina Waste Management Symposium. North Carolina State University, Raleigh. Page 376.

Spears, J. W., B.A. Creech and W.L. Flowers. 1999b. Reducing copper and zinc in swine waste through dietary manipulation. In: Proceedings of the North Carolina Waste Management Symposium. North Carolina State University, Raleigh. Page 179.

# Effects of Eggshell 49, dietary calcium level and hen age on performance and egg shell quality

NECMETTIN CEYLAN[1] AND SHEILA E. SCHEIDELER[2]

[1] Ankara University, Faculty of Agriculture, Department of Animal Science, Ankara, Turkey
[2] University of Nebraska, Department of Animal Science, Lincoln, Nebraska, USA

## Introduction

Egg shell quality has always been a problem in the layer industry. Economic losses because of poor shell quality are estimated to be greater than $250 million per year (Bell, 1998). Numerous studies have been conducted to solve poor shell quality problems. Many of these studies have focused on macro minerals, especially calcium (Ca) and phosphorus (P) (Keshavarz, 1988; Roush et al.,1986). A study on different levels of calcium (2.5, 3.5 and 4.5%) has shown that both 3.5 and 4.5% Ca decreased egg deformation and 4.5% Ca also increased shell weight ($P<0.05$) (Clunies et al., 1992). Wallner-Pendleton and Scheideler (1996) reported improved egg weight, egg production and bone ash when dietary calcium was increased from 3.5 to 5.5% in the diet of older (60+ weeks) laying hens. No significant effects on shell quality were measured. Trace minerals such as manganese (Mn) and zinc (Zn) play an important role in egg shell and shell membrane formation due to the fact that these are co-factor and/or structural components of enzyme systems responsible for carbonate formation and mucopolysaccharide synthesis, respectively (Gomez-Basuri, 1998). Recent studies by Keshavarz at Cornell (cited by Gomez-Basuri, 1998) and Miles at the University of Florida (1998) on this subject have illustrated that replacement of inorganic manganese and zinc with different levels of zinc and manganese proteinate from Eggshell 49 improved egg shell quality ($P<0.05$).

One can ask why use organic minerals instead of inorganic? Gill (1997) reported that chelated trace mineral (organic) sources are more biologically available in an animal digestive system than inorganic minerals, perhaps resulting in less mineral pollution of the environment. In a field study conducted by Miles (1998) with 52–61 week old layers, there was an improvement in egg grading when Eggshell 49 was added at a rate of 1 kg/ton. Others have emphasized that the shell to organic membrane relationship is critical to good shell quality. Another factor influencing egg shell quality is hen age; calcium uptake decreases as hens get older

(Al-Batshan *et al.*, 1994). Eggshell 49 has been recommended as a supplement, particularly after week 49 (Klecker *et al.,* 1997).

The mixed results of the studies mentioned indicate that macro and trace mineral form as well as hen age can all have significant effects on egg shell quality. The question asked in the following study was 'What are the combined effects of organic trace minerals (from Eggshell 49), calcium level and age on egg shell quality?'

## Materials and methods

DIETS, MANAGEMENT AND TREATMENTS

During 1997–1998 the University of Nebraska layer nutrition program conducted a long term trial testing effects of supplemental manganese and zinc from Eggshell 49 (Alltech Inc.) and dietary calcium level on egg shell quality and metabolic measurements. Eight diets were assigned to Hy-Line W-36 laying hens beginning at 20 weeks of age and were fed until 60 weeks of age. Two levels of calcium (3.5 and 4.0%) and two levels of Eggshell 49 (0 or 2 lb/ton) were tested. In order to answer questions about the best time to begin feeding Eggshell 49, the product was offered either not at all, during weeks 20–40 only, during weeks 40–60 only or throughout the experiment (weeks 20–60). This yielded a factorial treatment arrangement. Each treatment was replicated six times with six hens per replicate pen for a total of 48 pens. The research was conducted at the University of Nebraska (Lincoln) in industry-type caging and stocking densities. Diets were formulated according to the National Research Council (1994) recommendations. After 44 weeks of age diets were reformulated to decrease the diet density as per the Hy-Line Management Guide (1995). Nutrients and ingredient composition of experimental diets are given in Table 1. The diets were presented in mash form and feed and water were consumed *ad libitum*. Egg production, feed intake and cracked eggs were recorded daily. Egg weights, egg specific gravity, albumen height (Haugh units), dry shell percent and shell strength were measured bi-weekly. Hens were weighed at the start of experiment and at three-week intervals thereafter.

SHELL GLAND CARBONIC ANHYDRASE ACTIVITY

To ascertain potential effects of zinc supplementation on carbonic anhydrase activity, an *in vitro* assay was conducted with shell gland tissue obtained at 40 and 60 weeks of age. The shell gland was immediately rinsed with ice-cold glass-distilled water and kept in an ice bath. After being blotted dry, the shell gland was cut into two portions longitudinally. One portion was minced finely with scissors into a weighing tube kept on ice and homogenized with ice-cold distilled water. The homogenate was centrifuged at 1500 x g at 4 °C for 10 minutes.

**Table 1. Ingredient and nutrient composition of the diets.**

| | 20–40 weeks | | | | 40–60 weeks | | | |
|---|---|---|---|---|---|---|---|---|
| | 3.5 Ca% | | 4% Ca% | | 3.5% Ca% | | 4% Ca | |
| | Control | Eggshell 49 | Control | Eggshell 49 | Control | Eggshell 49 | Control | Eggshell 49 |
| Corn | 62.30 | 62.30 | 59.80 | 59.80 | 65.78 | 65.78 | 63.08 | 63.08 |
| Soybean meal | 24.12 | 24.12 | 24.59 | 24.59 | 22.07 | 22.07 | 22.44 | 22.44 |
| Corn oil | 0.065 | 0.065 | 0.79 | 0.79 | — | — | — | — |
| Tallow | 3.0 | 3.0 | 3.0 | 3.0 | 1.8 | 1.8 | 2.8 | 2.8 |
| Calcium carbonate | 6.54 | 6.54 | 7.86 | 7.86 | 6.70 | 6.70 | 8.05 | 8.05 |
| Oyster shell | 1.50 | 1.50 | 1.50 | 1.50 | 1.50 | 1.50 | 1.45 | 1.45 |
| Dicalcium phosphate | 1.76 | 1.76 | 1.76 | 1.76 | 1.50 | 1.50 | 1.50 | 1.50 |
| DL-methionine | 0.12 | 0.12 | 0.12 | 0.12 | 0.08 | 0.08 | 0.08 | 0.08 |
| Salt | 0.40 | 0.40 | 0.40 | 0.40 | 0.40 | 0.40 | 0.40 | 0.40 |
| Lysine | 0.04 | 0.04 | 0.03 | 0.03 | — | — | — | — |
| Vitamin premix[2] | 0.04 | 0.04 | 0.04 | 0.04 | 0.04 | 0.04 | 0.04 | 0.04 |
| Mineral premix[2] | 0.10 | 0.10 | 0.10 | 0.10 | 0.10 | 0.10 | 0.10 | 0.10 |
| Eggshell 49[1] | No | Yes | No | Yes | No | Yes | No | Yes |
| **Nutrient composition:** | | | | | | | | |
| ME, kcal/kg | 2891 | 2891 | 2889 | 2889 | 2860 | 860 | 2859 | 2859 |
| Crude protein, % | 17.0 | 17.0 | 17.0 | 17.0 | 16.0 | 16.0 | 16.0 | 16.0 |
| Calcium, % (calculated) | 3.5 | 3.5 | 4.0 | 4.0 | 3.5 | 3.5 | 4.0 | 4.0 |
| Calcium, % (analyzed) | 3.6 | 3.5 | 4.1 | 4.0 | 3.5 | 3.6 | 4.0 | 4.1 |
| Available phosphorus, % | 0.4 | 0.4 | 0.4 | 0.4 | 0.4 | 0.4 | 0.4 | 0.4 |
| Methionine + cystine, % | 0.7 | 0.7 | 0.7 | 0.7 | 0.6 | 0.6 | 0.6 | 0.6 |
| Lysine, % | 0.9 | 0.9 | 0.9 | 0.9 | 0.8 | 0.8 | 0.8 | 0.8 |
| Mn, ppm (calculated) | 169.5 | 174.0 | 171.5 | 176.0 | 169.0 | 173.5 | 170.0 | 174.5 |
| Mn, ppm (analyzed) | 173.0 | 180.0 | 176.0 | 183.0 | 172.0 | 180.0 | 174.0 | 180.0 |
| Zn, ppm (calculated) | 164.5 | 172.0 | 164.5 | 172.0 | 163.5 | 171.0 | 163.5 | 171.0 |
| Zn, ppm (analyzed) | 168.0 | 184.0 | 169.0 | 185.0 | 167.0 | 179.0 | 170.0 | 181.0 |

[1]Eggshell 49, added at 2 lb/ton, contains 4,500 ppm manganese and 7,500 ppm zinc in organic form (manganese and zinc proteinate).

[2]Vitamin mineral premix provided per kg: Mn, 88 mg; Cu, 6.6 mg; Fe, 8.5 mg; Zn, 88 mg; Se, 0.30 mg; vitamin A, 6,600 IU; cholecalciferol, 280 units; vitamin E, 10 IU; vitamin K, 2.0 mg; riboflavin, 4.4 mg; pantothenic acid, 6.6 mg; niacin, 24.2 mg; choline, 110 mg; vitamin $B_{12}$, 8.8 ethoxyquin, 1.1 mg/kg.

Enzyme activity was determined on the supernatant using modifications (Worthington Enzymes Manual, 1998) of the electrometric method of Wilbur and Anderson (1948) in which the time required for a saturated $CO_2$ solution to lower the pH of 0.02 M tris buffer from 8.3 to 6.3 in the presence of the enzyme was measured at 2°C.

INTESTINAL CALCIUM UPTAKE

To test effects of dietary calcium and Eggshell 49 effects on *in vitro* calcium utilization, calcium uptake was determined in the duodenum of hens at 40 and 60 weeks of age by a modification of the method of Al-Batshan *et al.* (1994). Tissues from the same birds killed for shell gland sampling were used to determine calcium uptake in the duodenum. Birds which had a fully calcified egg in the shell gland were selected for the calcium uptake analysis.

# Results

20–40 WEEKS OF AGE

### Performance and albumen height

Table 2 shows the dietary effects on average hen weights, egg production, feed intake, feed conversion, egg mass, egg weight and Haugh unit for the 20–40 weeks period. Main effect means and interaction (treatment) means are given. In this period four of the eight diets are the same since Eggshell 49 supplementation did not begin until after 40 weeks of age for two of the treatments. Neither Eggshell 49 nor calcium level affected hen weight, egg mass, feed conversion, egg weight or albumen height (Haugh units) during the first period (Table 2). A significant interaction between calcium level and Eggshell 49 occurred with respect to egg production and egg mass such that when hens were fed 4.0% Ca treatments, Eggshell 49 supplementation decreased egg production by nearly 2%. However, in diets containing 3.5% Ca, Eggshell 49 had a more positive effect on egg production and egg mass. Hens given 4% Ca diets tended to have higher feed intake (P<0.06). Eggshell 49 calcium level treatments resulted in a significant interaction for feed conversion ratio (FCR) in that Eggshell 49 tended to improve feed conversion in birds given 3.5% Ca and have a negative impact on this parameter in birds given 4% Ca.

### Egg shell quality, serum calcium, calcium uptake and carbonic anhydrase activity

Average specific gravity, dry shell percent, shell strength, cracked eggs, serum calcium, shell gland carbonic anhydrase activity and calcium uptake results from 20–40 weeks are presented in Table 3. Shell specific gravity was unaffected by treatment (Table 3). Eggshell 49 had a positive impact on dry shell percent, shell strength and percent cracked eggs. These results

**Table 2.** Effects of dietary calcium level, Eggshell 49 and hen age on hen weight, egg production, egg weight, egg mass, Haugh units, feed intake, and feed conversion ratio during 20–40 weeks of age.

| Calcium (%) | Eggshell 49 | Hen weight | | Egg production (%) | Egg weight (g) | Egg mass (g) | Haugh units | Feed intake (g) | FCR Feed:gain |
|---|---|---|---|---|---|---|---|---|---|
| | | 20 weeks (g) | 40 weeks (g) | | | | | | |
| 4 | No Eggshell 49 | 1278.7 | 1488.3 | 89.27 | 54.07 | 48.28 | 84.22 | 91.92 | 1.905 |
| 4 | Eggshell 49 weeks 20–40 | 1283.6 | 1482.6 | 87.47 | 53.26 | 46.59 | 84.76 | 92.04 | 1.976 |
| 4 | Eggshell 49 weeks 40–60 | 1279.1 | 1521.9 | 89.24 | 53.03 | 47.35 | 85.33 | 93.29 | 1.973 |
| 4 | Eggshell 49 weeks 20–60 | 1280.6 | 1531.6 | 87.94 | 53.92 | 47.43 | 85.83 | 91.69 | 1.933 |
| 3.5 | No Eggshell 49 | 1284.0 | 1493.9 | 86.73 | 53.46 | 46.36 | 86.92 | 92.02 | 1.985 |
| 3.5 | Eggshell 49 weeks 20–40 | 1285.8 | 1502.4 | 89.93 | 53.69 | 48.30 | 85.52 | 91.04 | 1.886 |
| 3.5 | Eggshell 49 weeks 40–60 | 1286.9 | 1507.7 | 88.07 | 53.12 | 46.83 | 85.32 | 91.56 | 1.959 |
| 3.5 | Eggshell 49 weeks 20–0 | 1278.2 | 1450.8 | 88.35 | 54.08 | 47.80 | 85.52 | 91.80 | 1.923 |
| SEM | | 14.4 | 23.7 | 0.88 | 1.33 | 0.026 | 0.58 | 0.89 | 0.77 |
| Significance | | NS | NS | 0.01 | NS | NS | NS | NS | NS |
| **Eggshell 49** | | | | | | | | | |
| Without | | 1282.2 | 1502.7 | 88.33 | 53.42 | 47.21 | 85.45 | 92.20 | 1.955 |
| With | | 1282.1 | 1491.9 | 88.42 | 53.74 | 47.53 | 85.41 | 91.64 | 1.929 |
| Significance | | NS | NS | NS | NS | NS | NS | NS | NS |
| **Ca Level** | | | | | | | | | |
| 3.5% | | 1283.7 | 1488.2 | 88.27 | 53.58 | 47.32 | 85.81 | 91.60 | 1.938 |
| 4.0% | | 1280.5 | 1506.4 | 88.48 | 53.57 | 47.42 | 85.03 | 92.23 | 1.946 |
| Significance | | NS | NS | NS | NS | NS | NS | NS | NS |
| Eggshell 49 × Ca level interaction | | NS | NS | 0.001 | NS | 0.01 | NS | 0.06 | 0.05 |

**Table 3.** Effects of dietary calcium level, Eggshell 49 and hen age on specific gravity, dry shell percent, shell strength, cracked eggs, serum calcium, calcium uptake and carbonic anhydrase activity from 20–40 weeks of age.

| Dietary calcium | Eggshell 49 | Egg shell specific gravity | Shell | Egg shell strength | Cracked eggs | Serum Ca | Duodenal Ca uptake (4 minutes) | Duodenal Ca uptake (9 minutes) | Carbonic anhydrase activity |
|---|---|---|---|---|---|---|---|---|---|
| (%) | | (g/ml) | (%) | (Newtons) | (%) | (mg/100ml) | (nM Ca/mg) | (nM Ca/mg) | (Units/g tissue) |
| 4 | No Eggshell 49 | 1.085 | 8.89 | 30.13 | 0.815 | 31.78 | 408.9 | 565.6 | 217.7 |
| 4 | Eggshell 49 weeks 20–40 | 1.086 | 9.07 | 31.46 | 0.701 | 30.05 | 451.8 | 518.9 | 221.4 |
| 4 | Eggshell 49 weeks 40–60 | 1.085 | 8.94 | 30.25 | 1.190 | 29.96 | 411.9 | 574.0 | 219.4 |
| 4 | Eggshell 49 weeks 20–60 | 1.085 | 8.83 | 31.26 | 0.623 | 30.52 | 308.5 | 526.2 | 239.2 |
| 3.5 | No Eggshell 49 | 1.085 | 8.74 | 29.26 | 0.973 | 28.40 | 347.7 | 464.5 | 194.5 |
| 3.5 | Eggshell 49 weeks 20–40 | 1.085 | 8.91 | 30.26 | 0.651 | 31.10 | 353.7 | 434.0 | 227.1 |
| 3.5 | Eggshell 49 weeks 40–60 | 1.085 | 8.82 | 29.49 | 0.849 | 29.24 | 381.2 | 431.8 | 187.3 |
| 3.5 | Eggshell 49 weeks 20–60 | 1.085 | 8.99 | 32.33 | 0.856 | 29.56 | 291.8 | 445.2 | 204.2 |
| **SEM** | | 0.0007 | 0.09 | 0.81 | 0.125 | 1.28 | 44.7 | 55.9 | 20.2 |
| Significance | | NS | NS | NS | NS | NS | NS | NS | 0.05 |
| **Eggshell 49** | | | | | | | | | |
| Without | | 1.085 | 8.85 | 29.79 | 0.957 | 29.85 | 387.4 | 521.5 | 204.7 |
| With | | 1.085 | 8.95 | 31.33 | 0.708 | 30.31 | 351.5 | 481.1 | 222.9 |
| Significance | | NS | 0.07 | 0.01 | 0.05 | NS | NS | NS | 0.03 |
| **Calcium level** | | | | | | | | | |
| 3.5% | | 1.085 | 8.86 | 30.33 | 0.832 | 29.58 | 343.6 | 456.4 | 203.3 |
| 4.0% | | 1.085 | 8.93 | 30.78 | 0.832 | 30.58 | 395.3 | 546.2 | 224.4 |
| Significance | | NS | NS | NS | NS | NS | NS | 0.04 | 0.01 |
| Eggshell 49 × Ca level interaction | | NS | NS | NS | NS | NS | NS | NS | NS |

are in agreement with those reported in the Keshavarz study as well as Miles (1998). Eggshell 49 supplementation markedly increased activity of shell gland carbonic anhydrase, an enzyme with a potential relationship to shell quality. Increasing calcium level also increased the enzyme activity significantly (P<0.01). Wang *et al.* (1996) reported carbonic anhydrase activity in hens with high quality eggs to be greater (P<0.01) than activity in hens producing low quality eggs. In this study a positive relationship between enzyme activity and shell quality criteria was evident (Figure 1). Calcium uptake in the duodenum increased with dietary calcium level (P<0.05) but was unaffected by Eggshell 49 at both 4 and 9 minute measurements. Serum calcium levels were unaffected by treatments. In summary, Eggshell 49 supplementation had a positive impact on most shell criteria during the 20–40 week period.

OVERALL RESPONSE: 20–60 WEEKS

### Performance and albumen height

The hens receiving Eggshell 49 in both the 20–40 and 40–60 week periods had the lowest weight (Table 4). This can be attributed in part to egg production because these hens, along with those given Eggshell 49 weeks 40–60, had higher egg production. Feed intake was unaffected by treatment for the entire experiment. Significant interaction effects on egg production for the entire period were similar to those noted in the 20–40 week period. Egg production, feed intake, feed conversion and egg mass were unaffected by treatments. Egg weight, Haugh units, and specific gravity were also unaffected. These results are in agreement with Keshavarz (cited by Gomez-Basauri, 1998). Although the difference was not significant,

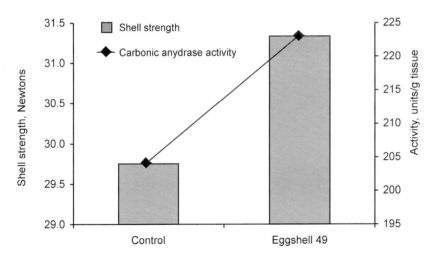

**Figure 1.** Effects of Eggshell 49 on shell strength and carbonic anhydrase activity at 20–40 weeks of age.

**Table 4.** Effects of dietary calcium level, Eggshell 49 and hen age on hen weight, egg production, feed intake, egg weight, egg mass, feed conversion ratio, Haugh unit, and specific gravity.

| Dietary calcium (%) | Eggshell 49 | Hen weight (g) | Feed intake (g) | Egg production (%) | Egg weight (g) | Egg mass (g) | FCR Feed:gain | Haugh units | Specific gravity (g/ml) |
|---|---|---|---|---|---|---|---|---|---|
| 4 | No Eggshell 49 | 1393.1 | 91.00 | 81.08 | 56.69 | 45.98 | 1.98 | 79.78 | 1.081 |
| 4 | Eggshell 49 weeks 20–40 | 1431.3 | 92.00 | 79.51 | 56.54 | 44.97 | 2.05 | 80.96 | 1.082 |
| 4 | Eggshell 49 weeks 40–60 | 1451.2 | 93.26 | 81.83 | 56.21 | 46.03 | 2.03 | 80.56 | 1.081 |
| 4 | Eggshell 49 weeks 20–60 | 1405.7 | 90.97 | 81.00 | 56.70 | 45.93 | 1.98 | 80.96 | 1.081 |
| 3.5 | No Eggshell 49 | 1443.9 | 91.95 | 79.77 | 56.32 | 44.94 | 2.05 | 81.46 | 1.080 |
| 3.5 | Eggshell 49 weeks 20–40 | 1418.5 | 90.90 | 82.17 | 56.00 | 46.04 | 1.98 | 80.69 | 1.081 |
| 3.5 | Eggshell 49 weeks 40–60 | 1425.7 | 91.25 | 80.28 | 56.07 | 45.05 | 2.03 | 80.41 | 1.081 |
| 3.5 | Eggshell 49 weeks 20–60 | 1406.8 | 92.62 | 80.99 | 57.00 | 46.19 | 2.00 | 80.80 | 1.081 |
| SEM | | | 1.46 | 0.78 | 0.69 | 0.89 | 0.04 | 0.94 | 0.005 |
| P-value | | 0.001 | NS | 0.012 | NS | NS | NS | NS | NS |
| **Eggshell 49** | | | | | | | | | |
| | Control | 1418.5 | 80.43 | 80.43 | 56.51 | 45.46 | 1.48 | 80.62 | 1.081 |
| | Weeks 20–40 only | 1424.9 | 91.45 | 80.84 | 56.27 | 45.50 | 2.01 | 80.82 | 1.081 |
| | Weeks 40–60 only | 1438.5 | 92.25 | 81.05 | 56.15 | 45.54 | 2.03 | 80.48 | 1.081 |
| | Eggshell 49 weeks 20–60 | 1406.3 | 91.80 | 81.00 | 56.85 | 46.06 | 1.99 | 80.88 | 1.081 |
| | Significance | 0.002 | NS | NS | NS | NS | NS | NS | NS |
| **Calcium level** | | | | | | | | | |
| | 3.5% | 1423.7 | 91.68 | 80.81 | 56.35 | 45.55 | 2.015 | 80.84 | 1.081 |
| | 4.0% | 1420.3 | 91.81 | 80.86 | 56.54 | 45.73 | 2.010 | 80.56 | 1.081 |
| | Significance | NS | NS | 0.001 | NS | NS | NS | NS | NS |
| Eggshell 49 × Ca level interaction | | 0.0001 | NS | NS | NS | NS | NS | NS | NS |

the heaviest egg weight and highest albumen quality was found in the groups receiving Eggshell 49 in both the 20–40 and 40–60 week periods.

***Egg shell quality, serum calcium, calcium uptake and carbonic anhydrase***
Dry shell percent, shell strength, and percent cracked eggs were influenced significantly by Eggshell 49 supplementation (Table 5). Dry shell percent was highest in hens given diets which had contained Eggshell 49 during the 20–40 week period and 4% Ca and next highest in hens given Eggshell 49 during both periods (Table 5, Figure 2). The lowest percent shell was found in the 3.5% Ca diet without Eggshell 49 during the entire experiment.

Increasing dietary calcium from 3.5 to 4% also improved percent dry shell. These results are in agreement with those reported by Clunies *et al.* (1992) who reported that 4.5% dietary calcium increased shell weight. Interaction between Eggshell 49 and dietary calcium was also significant (P<0.012). Eggshell 49 had a positive effect on shell strength when given throughout the 20–60 trial period. Eggshell 49 from 20–40 or 40–60 weeks provided intermediary positive effects on shell strength. Both 3.5 and 4.0% Ca without Eggshell 49 for the entire experiment had the poorest shell strength. Klecker *et al.* (1997) reported that Eggshell 49 improved shell strength, shell weight and shell thickness, in agreement with results of this study. The percentage of cracked eggs was significantly reduced when Eggshell 49 was included from 20–60 weeks of age. Increasing dietary calcium from 3.5 to 4% also tended to decrease (P<0.08) percent cracked eggs.

Shell gland carbonic anhydrase activity was affected by both calcium level and Eggshell 49 (Figure 3). Hens receiving Eggshell 49 in both the

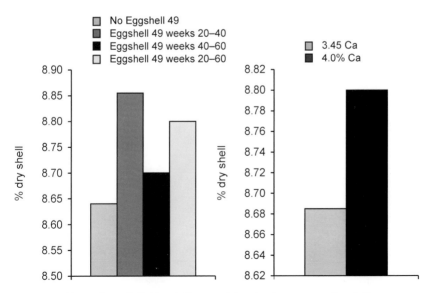

**Figure 2.** Effects of Eggshell 49 and dietary calcium level on percent dry shell.

**Table 5.** Effects of dietary calcium level, Eggshell 49 and hen age on dry shell percent, shell strength, cracked eggs, serum calcium, calcium uptake and carbonic anhydrase activity.

| Dietary calcium | Eggshell 49 | Dry shell | Shell strength | Cracked eggs | Serum Ca | Duodenal Ca uptake (4 minutes) | Duodenal Ca uptake (9 minutes) | Carbonic anhydrase activity |
|---|---|---|---|---|---|---|---|---|
| (%) | | (%) | (Newton) | (%) | (mg/100ml) | (nMCa/mg) | (nMCa/mg) | (Unit/g tissue) |
| 4 | No Eggshell 49 | 8.77 | 28.48 | 0.695 | 31.80 | 317.0 | 445.5 | 145.5 |
| 4 | Eggshell 49 weeks 20–40 | 8.97 | 29.41 | 0.899 | 29.89 | 366.4 | 488.3 | 155.4 |
| 4 | Eggshell 49 weeks 40–60 | 8.76 | 28.41 | 1.229 | 29.09 | 331.3 | 517.0 | 178.1 |
| 4 | Eggshell 49 weeks 20–60 | 8.72 | 29.47 | 0.607 | 30.20 | 333.4 | 436.0 | 200.1 |
| 3.5 | No Eggshell 49 | 8.50 | 27.22 | 1.268 | 28.56 | 361.6 | 536.0 | 158.1 |
| 3.5 | Eggshell 49 weeks 20–40 | 8.77 | 28.43 | 1.048 | 31.41 | 411.9 | 377.2 | 188.9 |
| 3.5 | Eggshell 49 weeks 40–60 | 8.64 | 28.15 | 1.356 | 28.54 | 386.1 | 508.4 | 214.9 |
| 3.5 | Eggshell 49 weeks 20–60 | 8.86 | 29.52 | 0.715 | 28.14 | 452.8 | 522.6 | 195.3 |
| **SEM** | | 0.08 | 0.58 | 0.162 | 1.57 | 49.9 | 74.4 | 13.9 |
| Significance | | 0.001 | 0.07 | 0.05 | 0.05 | 0.067 | NS | 0.01 |
| **Eggshell 49** | | | | | | | | |
| Control | No Eggshell 49 | 8.64 | 27.85 | 0.982 | 30.18 | 339.3 | 490.8 | 151.8 |
| Eggshell 49 | Weeks 20–40 only | 8.87 | 28.92 | 0.974 | 30.65 | 389.2 | 432.8 | 172.2 |
| Eggshell 49 | Weeks 40–60 only | 8.70 | 28.27 | 1.293 | 28.82 | 358.7 | 512.5 | 196.5 |
| Eggshell 49 | weeks 20–60 | 8.79 | 29.50 | 0.661 | 29.17 | 393.1 | 479.3 | 197.7 |
| Significance | | 0.002 | 0.028 | 0.02 | NS | NS | NS | 0.01 |
| **Calcium level** | | | | | | | | |
| 3.5% | | 8.69 | 28.33 | 1.098 | 29.16 | 402.7 | 486.1 | 169.77 |
| 4.0% | | 8.80 | 28.95 | 0.857 | 30.25 | 336.0 | 471.6 | 189.32 |
| Significance | | 0.01 | NS | 0.08 | 0.09 | 0.005 | NS | 0.01 |
| Eggshell 49 × Ca level interaction | | 0.01 | NS | NS | 0.06 | NS | NS | 0.01 |

20–40 and 40–60 week periods had the greatest enzyme activity while the hens receiving no Eggshell 49 had the lowest value. Hens receiving 4% Ca tended to have higher carbonic anhydrase activity than those receiving 3.5% Ca. Increasing dietary calcium level from 3.5 to 4% decreased duodenal calcium uptake. The highest calcium uptake was found in the 3.5% Ca diet containing Eggshell 49 from 20–60 weeks.

Calcium uptake tended to increase in response to Eggshell 49 (Table 5). These results are contrary to the 40 week results (Table 3) at which time the 4.0% Ca treatment had greater uptake than 3.5% Ca. We may attribute this change to age as younger layers produce smaller eggs than older hens. As a result, 3.5% Ca is sufficient for young hens, but as hens get older the efficiency of calcium absorption would need to increase in order to meet calcium requirements. Al-Batshan *et al.* (1994) has reported a decline in egg shell quality as the hen ages which may be attributed in part to reduced intestinal calcium uptake as well as to increased egg size. There was also a decrease in carbonic anhydrase activity and calcium uptake (Tables 3 and 5) as hens become older. Comparing the 40 week and 60 week results it is evident that egg shell quality is declining. Hence we can postulate that the decline in enzyme activity and calcium uptake as hens age is related to decreased shell quality.

Serum calcium tended to be lower in hens given 3.5% Ca (Table 5). This may explain the increased efficiency of calcium absorption in response to calcium demand. Wang *et al.* (1996) also noted that serum calcium tended to decrease as egg shell quality decreased. They suggested that serum calcium was lower in birds laying eggs with high quality shells than in hens producing low quality egg shells.

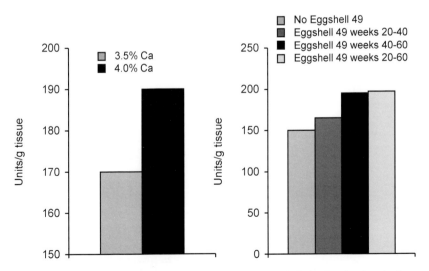

**Figure 3.** Effects of dietary calcium level and Eggshell 49 on shell gland carbonic anhydrase activity.

## Summary

From these results we can conclude that Eggshell 49 starting at 20 weeks till 60 weeks of age had a positive impact on all shell quality criteria. Further, although 3.5% Ca in the diet was found to be adequate for 20–40 weeks, 4.0% Ca should be recommended after 40 weeks.

## Acknowledgments

Appreciation is expressed to Alltech, Inc. for support of the study, to Curtis Novak, Lyle Robeson, Tommi Jones, and Minnie Stephens for their help.

## References

Al-Batshan, H.L., S.E. Scheideler, B.L. Black, J.D. Garlich and K.E. Anderson. 1994. Duodenal calcium uptake, femur ash, and egg shell quality decline with age and increase following molt. Poultry Sci. 73:1590–1596.

Bell, D. 1998. Egg shell quality: Its impact on production, processing and marketing economics. *In*: Biotechnology in the Feed Industry, Proceedings of the 14th Annual Symposium (T.P. Lyons and K.A. Jacques, eds). Nottingham University Press, Nottingham, UK. p. 447–466.

Clunies, M., D. Parks and S. Leeson. 1992. Calcium and phosphorus metabolism and egg shell formation of hens fed different amounts of calcium. Poultry Sci. 71:482–489.

Gill, C. 1997. Organic Trace Metal Assays. Feed International. 18(10):18–22.

Gomez-Basauri, J. 1998. Egg shell quality: Overcoming production losses with a novel enzyme activator. *In*: Biotechnology in the Feed Industry, Proceedings of the 14th Annual Symposium (T.P. Lyons and K.A. Jacques, eds). Nottingham University Press, Nottingham, UK. p. 437–445.

Keshavarz, K. 1988. Calcium nutrition can directly influence shell quality. Feedstuffs. Febr. 20, 1988. p. 23–24.

Klecker, D., L. Zemar, V. Viske, J. Gomez Basauri. 1997. Influence of trace mineral proteinate supplementation on egg shell quality. Poultry Sci. 76(Suppl. 1)131.

Miles, R.D. 1998. The influence of Eggshell 49 on shell quality of hens grouped by their shell quality. Poultry Sci. 77(Suppl. 1):43.

National Research Council. 1994. Nutrient Requirements of Poultry (9th Ed.). National Academy Press, Washington, DC.

Roush, W.B., M. Mylet, J.L. Rosenberger and J. Derr. 1986. Investigation of calcium and available phosphorus requirements for laying hens by response surface methodology. Poultry Sci. 65:964–970.

Wallner-Pendleton, E. and S.E. Scheideler. 1996. The influence of varying levels of calcium and vitamin $D_3$ in the mature laying hen's diet: effects on egg production, shell quality, bone ash and urolithiasis. The Nebraska Poultry Report, University of Nebr. Coop. Ext. E.C. 96–259A.

Wang, C.W., K. T. Nam, O. E. Olsen and C.W. Carlson. 1996. Relationship between egg shell quality and biochemical parameters of calcium metabolism. AJAS 9(6):715–722.

Wilbur, K., and N. G. Anderson. 1948. Electrometric and calorimetric determination of carbonic anhydrase. J. Biol. Chem. 176:147–154.

Worthington Enzymes Manual. 1998. Carbonic Anhydrase. Worthington-biochem.com/C/CA.

# The 100-day contract with the dairy cow: 30 days prepartum to 70 days postpartum

JAMES N. SPAIN

*University of Missouri, Columbia, Missouri, USA*

## Introduction

The concept of setting goals and time constraints is not new in business management. But how does it apply to dairy farm management? In evaluating the production cycle of the dairy herd, a 100-day period of critical importance exists. The '100 day contract' with the dairy cow begins 30 days before calving and runs through first breeding to 70 days postpartum. The terms of the contract include birth of a live calf with the cow remaining healthy during the transition period; high peak milk production; controlled loss of body condition and high fertility at first breeding. The momentum toward successful achievement begins in the close-up dry cow group and builds through calving to first breeding. Getting the cow off the track at any point disrupts the momentum and can lead to 'wrecks'. Wrecks include metabolic disorders during the periparturient period that can have a long-term impact on production and reproduction. This paper will focus on a phase by phase look at the negotiations required to successfully fulfill the 'contract' as well as the long-term consequences of cows getting off track.

## The dry cow

The contract begins with the care and preparation of the prepartum dry cow. The concept of preparing the dry cow is different from the traditional view of the dry period as a 'rest' phase (Gerloff, 1988). The cow must be prepared for calving and initiation of lactation. Goff and Horst (1997) concluded that the periparturient period should adapt the rumen while maintaining normal calcium metabolism and a strong immune system. Although not producing milk, the pregnant, prepartum cow is undergoing metabolic changes involving reproduction and new mammary growth. Bell *et al.* (1995) measured energy and protein deposition in the uterus and fetus. Their research clearly illustrated the increased nutrient requirements during the final 30 days of gestation (Table 1). In short, there is a significant increase in metabolism of the cow during the final 30 days of gestation and therefore a need to maintain intake and proper plane of nutrition.

Table 1.   Rates of energy and protein deposition in uterus and fetus during pregnancy in Holsteins[1].

| | Energy (kcal/d) | | Protein (g/d) | |
|---|---|---|---|---|
| Gestation (d) | Uterus | Fetus | Uterus | Fetus |
| 210 | 631 | 500 | 76 | 54 |
| 230 | 694 | 601 | 90 | 73 |
| 250 | 757 | 703 | 103 | 91 |
| 270 | 821 | 805 | 117 | 110 |

[1]Adapted from Bell *et al.* (1995).

ENDOCRINE CHANGES AFFECT INTAKE

With the approach of parturition, the animal undergoes a significant shift in endocrine balance and profile. Goff and Horst (1997) reported that cows experienced an increase in circulating levels of estrogen and cortisol. Dry matter intake is affected by endocrine shifts and feed intake decreases during the last two weeks of gestation. Dry matter intake has been shown to decline by as much as 30 to 40%, from 2% to less that 1.5% of the animal's body weight. Lower feed intake results in a negative energy status and mobilization of fat and protein. Severe decreases in feed intake put the animal at risk for a number of metabolic disorders.

PARTURITION DISEASE COMPLEX

Severe losses of body stores or a more general lack of properly balanced nutrients increase the risk of the animal experiencing a number of metabolic diseases. Markusfeld (1993) describes these as a parturition disease complex. It is important to understand that these disorders are not independent but are related. A cow suffering from milk fever is at increased risk for retained placenta, left displaced abomasum, and/or ketosis. A number of other interactions exist among periparturient diseases.

Grohn *et al.* (1995) recently reported the incidence of these diseases for Holstein cows in New York (Table 2). As the median day of occurrence indicates, these diseases are most likely to occur during the period immediately after calving. However, these disorders have an impact on production and reproduction during the entire lactation. Cows experiencing any one of these disorders are at much greater risk of suffering from a number of the other periparturient dysfunctions. Furthermore, these periparturient disorders disrupt the cow's metabolic momentum toward high peak milk yields and also have negative carryover effects on reproductive performance.

Table 2. Lactational incidence risks and median days postpartum of disorders in 8070 multiparous Holstein cows in New York state[1].

| Disorder | Lactational incidence | |
|---|---|---|
| | Risk (%) | Median day of occurrence |
| Retained placenta | 7.4 | 1 |
| Metritis | 7.6 | 11 |
| Ovarian cyst | 9.1 | 97 |
| Milk fever | 1.6 | 1 |
| Ketosis | 4.6 | 8 |
| Displaced abomasum | 6.3 | 11 |
| Mastitis | 9.7 | 59 |

[1]Grohn *et al.*, 1995.

## Calving and subsequent reproduction

The culmination of periparturient disorders is lost production and income. Markusfeld (1993) reported significant decreases in milk production and reproductive performance of cows suffering from postparturient uterine (PPU) disease (Table 3). The decreases in milk production and reduced reproduction efficiency associated with the periparturient diseases mean that incidence of these diseases must be closely monitored. Retained placenta and related reproductive tract infections are often assumed to be caused by nutritional deficiencies. More specifically, since researchers reported the relationship between vitamin E, selenium and retained placenta, many producers first react to cows calving with retained placenta by increasing vitamin and mineral supplementation of the dry cow diet. Correct vitamin and mineral supplementation is certainly a goal of properly managing the transition cow. French researchers, however, more completely described retained placenta as an under-nutrition disease. Chassagne and Chacornac (1994) reported that cows that retained the placenta were on a lower plane of nutrition. Blood metabolite measurements showed higher fat mobilization and lower blood glucose, as well as lower blood calcium and amino acids (Table 4). In addition, cows with retained placenta had lower circulating monocytes.

Table 3. Losses due to postparturient uterine diseases[1].

| | Milk, lb/305d | Days open |
|---|---|---|
| With PPU disease | 19,677 | 125 |
| Without PPU disease | 21,978 | 99 |
| Difference | + 2,121 | −26 |

[1]Adapted from Markusfeld, 1993.

**Table 4.** Measurements of blood metabolites and nutrients between normal cows and cows with retained placenta[1].

| Item | Retained | Normal |
|---|---|---|
| Glucose, ng/dl | 59.6 | 61.8 |
| NEFA, meq/dl | 0.494 | 0.340** |
| Amino acids, moles/dl | 2.34 | 2.48 ** |
| Calcium, mg/dl | 96.3 | 98.5 ** |
| Monocytes, $10^3$/ml | 225 | 310 ** |

[1]Adapted from Chassagne and Chacornac (1994).
**P<0.05.

## NUTRITION AND PERIPARTURIENT DISEASES

These results emphasize the importance of the overall plane of nutrition. A common limitation is the forage quality selected for feeding the dry cow herd. In addition, the feeding management system fails to promote feed intake in dry cows. Lower plane of nutrition results in excessive body weight losses and can disrupt energy metabolism.

Grohn and others determined ketosis was an important metabolic disorder compared to other diseases. Ketosis is related to disrupted energy metabolism. Simensen *et al.* (1990) reported peak levels of ketones in milk at 17 to 31 days after calving. There was a significant relationship between milk yields and increasing acetoacetate (a ketone) in the milk. As acetoacetate increased to levels >0.1 nmol per liter of milk, there was a significant decrease in milk production. Therefore, it has been established that early lactation cows suffering from ketosis have lower milk production.

Although not reported as often as other calving disorders, milk fever is a significant risk factor for several other disorders including retained placenta and displaced abomasum. Subclinical milk fever, ketosis, or a combination of the two can directly affect the chances of successfully accomplishing the '100 day contract'. Cornell researchers reported increased incidence of milk fever as lactation number and genetic potential increased. These same researchers cited studies that showed decreased productive life by 3.4 years. Given that older, higher producing cows are most susceptible to these disorders, the economic impact of parturient paresis can be significant in lost production but also loss due to premature culling.

The concern of disrupted metabolism caused by ketosis and milk fever is the increased risk of other periparturient diseases. Curtis *et al.* (1983) reported that milk fever resulted in significant increases in the incidence of other transition cow problems. As illustrated in Table 5, milk fever led to increased risk of dystocia, retained placenta, left displaced abomasum, ketosis and mastitis.

Based on review of the literature, Coppock (1974) concluded that factors causing loss of muscle tone (atony) increased risk of displaced abomasum. These results were supported by a more current report by Massey *et al.*

Table 5.  Influence of hypocalcemia on risk of other periparturient disorders[1].

| Disease | Odds ratio | P value |
|---|---|---|
| Dystocia | 2.8 | |
| Retained placenta | 6.5 | |
| Left displaced abomasum | 3.4 | |
| Ketosis | 8.9 | 0.0001 |
| Mastitis | 8.1 | 0.0001 |

[1]Adapted from Curtis *et al.*, 1983.

(1993) who found that milk fever increased the risk of a displaced abomasum 4.8 times.

The often-overlooked aspect of displaced abomasum was the increased risk with the heightened stress of parturition. Other factors that Coppock identified as risk factors included toxemia due to metritis and mastitis. Although the displaced abomasum can be repaired surgically, milk production is reduced by 8 to 10% compared to normal cows in the same herd.

NUTRITION AND IMMUNE FUNCTION

One key variable associated with transition cow health is the immune function. Cai *et al.* (1994) reported that cows suffering from metritis or mastitis during early lactation had reduced immune cell function before calving. Cows with retained fetal membranes had lower immune cell function for the first week postpartum. Immune cell function was also lower during the summer months of June, July, and August. These researchers concluded that neutrophil function could predispose the animals to periparturient disorders. Kehrli *et al.* (1989) found normal primiparous Holsteins suffered immunosuppression associated with impaired immune cell function. More recently, Kimura *et al.* (1999) reported that lower immune function could be associated with a shift in the phenotype of circulating immune cells.

Nutrients that influence immune function range from energy and protein balance to the micronutrients including vitamins and trace minerals. Considerable effort has been invested in an effort to describe antioxidant balance in cattle during the periparturient period. Pryor (1976) reported that plasma zinc decreased more than 30% on the day of calving and first day of lactation. As lactation progressed, cows reached prepartum levels by seven days postpartum.

More recently, Goff and Stabel (1990) reported a much more severe decline in plasma zinc during the periparturient transition phase. Plasma zinc declined 67% with the nadir occurring at one day postpartum. Plasma retinol and $\alpha$-tocopherol declined 38% and 47%, respectively. After calving, zinc, vitamin E, and retinol returned to near normal levels by 3, 10, and 14 days postpartum, respectively. The change in circulating antioxidants might be associated with secretion of these nutrients in colostrum. Kincaid and Cronrath (1992) reported that zinc concentrations in mammary gland secretions increased more than two times in colostrum compared to milk.

This transfer of nutrients into colostrum could be partially responsible for the reduction in circulating antioxidant nutrients.

Hogan *et al.* (1992) reported that supplemental vitamin E administered via parenteral injection increased circulating tocopherol. Cows injected with vitamin E had immune cells with a greater intracellular cytocide compared to cows receiving the placebo (80.1 *vs* 70.8, respectively). These results revealed that as circulating tocopherol increased, the intracellular kill of pathogenic bacteria also increased. The use of dietary supplements or injectable nutrient precursors may allow for the enhancement of immune function during the transition phase.

## ANIMAL HOUSING, ANIMAL STRESS, AND THE PERIPARTURIENT COW

A growing list of research publications can now be summarized in stating that nutrition management is a key to successful completion of the 100-day contract. One factor critical to a successful transition cow contract that affects the success of the nutrition management program is the housing environment of the transition cow. The dry cow experiences a significant stress associated with the aforementioned transition. The housing system is key to minimizing exposure to environmental stress. The following description can and should be applied to all animal housing systems, but is especially important for the transition cow. The housing system should protect the animal from injury and disease. This is especially important for the dry cow during late gestation. Harmon and Crist (1994) reported that the incidence of environmental mastitis is highest the first two weeks and the last two weeks of the dry period. Voermans (1997) recommended evaluating the housing system in terms of ability to reduce exposure of the animals to pathogens. Furthermore, Voermans concluded that the important benefits of good housing in minimizing animal stress were manifested in improved immune function and increased resistance to challenge by pathogenic microorganisms. Clean, dry bedding is essential to improved animal health, especially in the periparturient transition phase.

The environment in which cows are fed is also important when evaluating the transition program and ability to successfully achieve the 100-day contract. Much has been written pertaining to the feeding environment of lactating cows; but comparatively little information is available relative to the periparurient cow. Adequate bunk space to allow all cows equal access at feeding time is important, as is the availability of water relative to distance from feed (<50 feet) and the number of animal spaces, In managing the transition cow group, there can be large fluctuations in the number of cows on a day to day basis. The amount of feed delivered must be carefully monitored as group size changes when fresh cows are moved out after calving and late gestation cows are added. Age and body weight of the cows entering and leaving the production group will also affect the amount fed. These details of where and how feed is offered to the transition cow group can determine the success or failure of the early lactation cow.

# Early postpartum cows

Prevention of metabolic disorders and diseases is critical to successfully reaching the 100-day contract. The second phase is to achieve peak milk and good fertility at first service. Miettinen (1990) reported that cows with higher levels of ketone bodies (acetoacetate and ß-hydroxybutyrate) had increased days to first service and decreased pregnancy rate and, as a result, longer days open with higher services per conception (Table 6). The results of this study from Finland illustrate the importance of minimizing metabolic disorders on reproductive efficiency.

Table 6.   The effects of early postpartum energy status on reproductive performance[1].

|  | Days to first service | Days open | Services per conception | First service conception rate (%) |
|---|---|---|---|---|
| Normal | 70.5 | 80 | 1.2 | 75 |
| Subclinical ketosis | 75.8 | 102 | 2.0 | 44 |
| Ketotic | 78.0 | 100 | 1.9 | 40 |

[1]Adapted from Miettinen, 1990.

## NUTRITION IN THE POSTPARTUM COW: IMPACT ON REPRODUCTION

A common denominator among periparturient diseases is a reduced plane of nutrition. This poor level of nutrition is directly related to intake and energy balance. Energy balance during the periparturient period has a large impact on reproduction. Butler *et al.* (1981) reported that energy balance during the first 20 days was inversely related to days required to reach normal ovulation. These researchers also noted that normal ovarian function was observed 10 days after energy balance reached its lowest point and began to return to a positive balance. Lucy *et al.* (1991) reported similar results with an increased number of larger follicles present as estimated energy balance increased. Another concern is the carryover effect of negative energy balance on fertility. Britt, from North Carolina State, has proposed that a period of negative energy balance influences the development and quality of pre-ovulatory follicles. In this case, cows experiencing severe body condition loss in the last weeks of gestation and/or early lactation will have reduced conception rates. Poor fertility would be due to an 'imprinting' of ovulatory follicles during development and recruitment of these oocytes.

### *Protein nutrition and reproduction*
While the relationship between energy balance and reproduction has become better understood, the effect of protein nutrition on reproductive efficiency is less clear. During the last several years, the Degradable

Protein System has been adopted for diet formulation for growing and lactating dairy cattle. The objective of this system is to provide sufficient soluble/degradable protein to maximize rumen microbial fermentation and growth, with undegraded intake protein supplying amino acids to the small intestine above microbial supply. This balance of protein types would prevent excess ammonia production in the rumen leading to elevated blood urea nitrogen (BUN) levels. Several reports suggest that increased BUN levels cause increased levels of urea/ammonia in reproductive tract secretions. These nitrogen compounds could result in decreased viability of the sperm cells, ovulated egg cells and the embryo itself. Decreased fertility would result, with increased services per conception and days open. Serum urea levels in excess of 20 mg/dl have been reported as a means of evaluating the balance between degradable and undegradable in lactating cows. This figure must be used with caution as undegradable intake protein supplied in excess of the animal's requirements will ultimately be converted to urea.

Research evaluating protein nutrition and reproductive performance is confounded with energy status of the animal. Higher protein diets will generally elicit a milk production response resulting in a more negative energy balance. Conversion of ammonia to urea by liver tissue also requires energy. In a number of research trials diets were reformulated by removing cereal grains and increasing degradable protein. This change in itself could influence energy balance of the cow.

### Managing protein balance

Guidelines for the proper balance of protein types are determined by the types of feedstuffs and forages used. In general, 60–65% of the dietary crude protein should be in the form of degradable crude protein. Of the degradable protein, 40–60% should be soluble crude protein. Undegradable intake protein should make up 35–40% of diet protein. Although it is unclear if imbalances will adversely affect reproductive efficiency of dairy cows, properly balanced protein components of the diet will enhance production, improve efficiency and minimize incidence of increased blood urea nitrogen levels.

### Minerals, vitamins and reproduction

Balancing energy and protein are critical in achieving maximum production. Micronutrients, i.e., minerals and vitamins, are also important in achieving efficient and profitable levels of production. Several minerals and the fat-soluble vitamins have been associated with reproductive performance. Of the macrominerals, calcium:phosphorus ratios and total intake of the minerals are extremely important in preventing milk fever at calving. Cows suffering from milk fever are more prone to retained fetal membranes, a prolapsed uterus and metritis. Therefore, dry cow nutrition management is important in prevention of these disorders and problems. Should a herd develop milk fever problems, calcium intake should be evaluated. Calcium intake should be limited to less than 75 g per cow per day. Phosphorus intake should be kept at a ratio of 1.5:1 relative to calcium. In the event milk fever problems continue, anionic salts can be used as an additional aid for its prevention. Anionic salt packs should only be used if correcting calcium intake fails to control milk fever.

Two microminerals associated with enhancing reproductive performance are zinc and selenium. The specific role of zinc in reproduction is not well defined but may indirectly result from the many functions of zinc in metabolism and immunity. Zinc supports tissue healing and restructuring that may be important in postpartum uterine healing. Zinc is also a component of enzyme systems that could influence hormonal profiles during pregnancy. Selenium's role in reproduction has been more closely evaluated. A number of published reports indicate that supplementation of selenium and vitamin E decrease the incidence of retained placenta, metritis and increase the rate of uterine involution. Vitamin E and selenium reduce tissue damage and function to maintain tissue integrity. This role of the micronutrients could enhance the uterine environment and support increased fertility.

### Managing minerals and vitamins

Minerals and vitamins are added in small quantities, but it is essential that they be provided in adequate amounts to meet the animals needs. Calcium and phosphorus intake should be closely controlled in the prepartum transition diet to supply less than 75 g of calcium, with phosphorus maintained at 1.5:1 ratio to calcium. Zinc, selenium, vitamin E and all other micronutrients should be balanced to meet but not exceed recommended levels. In some cases, additional vitamin E and selenium have been used in problem herds. However, extreme care must be exercised relative to intake.

### Feeding system considerations

In addition, nutritional management is critical to achieving peak milk production to genetic potential. In doing this, many nutrition programs are designed to 'lead feed' or 'challenge feed' the fresh cow immediately after calving. In fact, many producers begin to accelerate grain feeding during the prepartum period. While the concept of this approach is correct, the implementation must be accomplished carefully. Excessive grain feeding can lead to ruminal acidosis, which can result in decreased dry matter intake and can predispose cows to other periparturient diseases. Acidosis can also result in laminitis in cattle (Vermunt and Greenough, 1994). These scientists report that systemic infections can contribute to laminitis. For example, cows with severe metritis can develop laminitis in response to the systemic disease. Poor locomotion due to sore feet can result in significantly lower milk production. The largest incidence of lameness reportedly occurs during the first 50 to 70 days after calving, the period of peak milk production (Collick *et al.,* 1989). Lameness also resulted in a significant increase in days to first service, days open and services per conception. The result of over-compensating with grain can actually be higher cull rates due to lowered milk yield and poor reproductive performance due to sore feet.

## Summary

The '100 day contract' is a series of delicate negotiations for the dairy farm manager. Unsuccessful negotiations at any point increases the risk of overall failure. The stress of calving must be intensively managed to reduce the odds of periparturient disease and increase the odds of success. Getting the details right and ensuring adequate intake of all nutrients are the key elements of the '100 day contract'.

## References

Bell, A.W., R. Slepetio and R.A. Ehrhardt. 1995. Growth and accretion of energy and protein in the gravid uterus during late pregnancy in Holstein cows. J. Dairy Sci. 78:1954.

Butler, W.R., R.W. Everett and C.E. Coppock. 1981. The relationship between energy balance, milk production and ovulation in postpartum Holstein cows. J. Anim. Sci. 53:742.

Chassagne, M. and J.P. Chacornac 1994. Blood metabolites as indicators of nutritional risk factors for retained placenta in the dairy cow. Veterinary Research 25:2.

Cai, Tian-Quan, P.G. Weston, L.A. Lund, B. Brodie, D.J. McKenna and W.C. Wagner. 1994. Association between neutrophil functions and periparturient disorders in cows. Am. J. Vet. Res. 55(7):934.

Collick, D.W., W.R. Ward and H. Dobson. 1989. Associations between types of lameness and fertility. Vet. Record 125:103.

Coppock, C.E. 1974. Displaced abomasum in dairy cattle: Etiological factors. J. Dairy Sci. 57:926.

Curtis, C.R., H.N. Erb, C.J. Sniffen and R.D. Smith. 1984. Epidemiology of parturient paresis: predisposing factors with emphasis on dry cow feeding and management. J. Dairy Sci. 67:817.

Curtis, C.R., H. Erb, C. Sniffen, R. Smith, P. Powers, M. Smith, M. White, R. Hillman and E. Pearson. 1983. Association of parturient hypocalcemia with eight periparturient disorders in Holstein cows. J. Am. Vet. Med. Assoc. 5:559.

Gerloff, B.J. 1988. Feeding the dry cow to avoid metabolic disease. Vet. Clinics of N. America: Food An. Pract. 4(2):379.

Goff, J.P. and R.L. Horst. 1997. Physiological changes at parturition and their relationship to metabolic disorders. J. Dairy Sci. 80:1260–1268.

Goff, J.P. and J.R. Stabel. 1990. Decreased plasma retinol, α-tocopherol, and zinc concentration during the periparturient period: effect of milk fever. J. Dairy Sci. 73:3195–3199.

Grohn, Y.T., S.W. Eicken and J.A. Herth. 1995. The association between previous 305 day milk yield and disease in New York state dairy cows. J. Dairy Science 78:1693.

Harmon, R.J. and W.L. Crist. 1994. Environmental mastitis in lactating and dry cows and prepartum heifers. Proceedings, National Mastitis Council. pp. 241–249.

Hogan, J.S., W.P. Weiss, D.A. Todhunter, K.L. Smith and P.S. Schoenberger. 1992. Bovine neutrophil responses to parenteral vitamin E. J. Dairy Sci. 75:399–405.

Kehrli, Marcus E., B.J. Nonnecke and J.A. Roth. 1989. Alterations in bovine neutrophil function during the periparturient period. Am. J. Vet. Res. 50(2):207.

Kimura, K., J.P. Goff, M.E. Kehrli and J.A. Harp. 1999. Phenotype analysis of peripheral blood mononuclear cells in periparturient dairy cows. J. Dairy Sci. 82:315–319.

Kincaid, R.L. and J.D. Cronrath. 1992. Zinc concentration and distribution in mammary secretions of peripartum cows. J. Dairy Sci. 75:481–484.

Lucy, M.C., C.R. Styples, F.M. Michel and W.W. Thatcher. 1991. Energy balance and size and number of ovarian follicles detected by ultrasonography in early postpartum dairy cows. J. Dairy Sci. 74:473.

Markusfeld, O. 1993. Parturition disease complex of the high-yielding dairy cow. Acta Vet. Scand. Suppl. 89:9.

Massey, C.D., C. Wong, G.A. Donovon and D.K. Beade. 1993. Hypocalcemia at parturition as a risk factor for left displacement of the abomasum in dairy cows. J. Am. Vet. Med. Assoc. 6:852.

Miettinen, P.V.A. 1990. Metabolic balance and reproductive performance in Finnish dairy cows. J. Vet. Med. A37:417.

Pryor, W.J. 1976. Plasma zinc status of dairy cattle in the periparturient period. New Zealand Vet. Journal. 24:57–58.

Simensen, E., K. Halse, P. Gillund and P. Lutnaes. 1990. Ketosis treatment and milk yield in dairy cows related to milk acetoacetate levels. Acta Vet. Scand. 31:443.

Vermunt, J.J. and P.R. Greenough. 1994. Predisposing factors of laminitis in cattle. Br. Vet. J. 150:151.

Voermans, J.A.M. 1997. Health and disease perspectives. Proceedings of the 5th international symposium on livestock environment.

# MEAT QUALITY – THE CONSUMER'S ULTIMATE CONCERN

# The role of nutrition in maintaining quality of poultry products

*Department of Animal and Poultry Science, University of Guelph, Guelph, Ontario, Canada*

## Introduction

One reason for the success of the poultry meat industry has been the consumer perception of a healthy product. Certainly poultry meat contains less fat than do comparable beef or pork products; and in most situations such fat is predominantly unsaturated. Eggs, on the other hand, have suffered more negative consumer attitudes related to health, most of which stemmed from the issue of cholesterol metabolism as perpetuated by the medical profession in North America. While issues of the relationship between diet and plasma cholesterol in humans are now far from clear, it is obvious that overwhelming "negative press" takes many years to correct in terms of regaining market share of any food product. Consequently, today the poultry meat and egg industries are acutely aware of quality and composition of their products as they relate to positioning relative to competing products, and also in relation to consumer attitudes and choice. Quality, therefore, is emerging as an important issue in the poultry industry, and in a number of situations poultry nutrition can play a significant role. While it is realized that quality encompasses a number of important issues (size, conformation, microbial load, etc.), this review deals essentially in the transport of nutrients from the feed to the bird and how this influences composition relative to current consumer needs and perceptions.

## Normal product composition

Both meat and eggs are excellent sources of protein and amino acids and can provide significant portions of the recommended daily intake for consumers. Nutritionally speaking, poultry meat and eggs both provide a rich source of essential amino acids, so just 100 g of poultry meat or one large egg virtually meet the adult's requirement for amino acids (Table 1). There seems little potential to further increasing the amino acid

89

profile of poultry products, especially in view of the lack of knowledge shown by most consumers about the need or biological role of amino acids in human nutrition. However, both poultry meat and eggs are deficient in most minerals and vitamins. The fatty acid profile of poultry products tends to reflect that found in the diet, and this situation can be capitalized upon to manipulate fat composition of both eggs and meat.

**Table 1.   Content of selected nutrients in poultry meat and eggs in relation to human daily requirements.[1]**

| Nutrient | Adult daily requirement | Supplied by: | |
|---|---|---|---|
| | | 100 g cooked meat | 1 large egg |
| Protein, g | 52 | 27 | 8 |
| Energy, kcal | 2350 | 239 | 100 |
| Calcium, mg | 750 | 15 | 36 |
| Phosphorus, mg | 925 | 182 | 141 |
| Iron, mg | 11 | 1.30 | 1.40 |
| Zinc, mg | 11 | 1.90 | 0.90 |
| Lysine, g | 0.80 | 2.20 | 0.60 |
| Meth + Cys, g | 0.90 | 1.10 | 0.50 |
| Tryptophan, g | 0.20 | 0.30 | 0.10 |
| Threonine, g | 0.50 | 1.10 | 0.40 |
| Vitamin $B_{12}$, µg | 2.00 | 0.30 | 0.46 |
| Thiamin, mg | 0.95 | 0.06 | 0.11 |
| Niacin, mg | 15 | 8.50 | 12.40 |

[1]Leeson, 1993.

## PROTEIN AND AMINO ACID COMPOSITION

Virtually all the protein and amino acids in meat birds are found in the muscles, while in eggs about 50% is found in yolk and the remainder in the albumen. As a generalization, the quality and especially the composition of proteins are virtually immune to dietary manipulation. Feeding diets deficient in amino acids can lead to reduced muscle growth or smaller egg size, yet the amino acid profile of these proteins remains intact. Even within the carcass of the chicken, the different muscles are virtually identical in amino acid composition (Table 2). The fact that muscles as diverse as the breast and wing are so similar in composition brings into question the industry practice of trying to preferentially influence breast development via manipulation of dietary amino acid profile.

## FAT COMPOSITION

Both the quantity and composition (quality) of carcass fat and eggs can be influenced by nutrition. For meat birds there is a direct relationship between diet energy level and fatness and also diet protein and fatness.

**Table 2.** Amino acid profile of muscles in the broiler chicken (g/100 g protein).[1]

|  | Breast | Thigh | Drum | Wing |
|---|---|---|---|---|
| Lysine | 8.48 | 8.50 | 8.50 | 8.51 |
| Methionine | 2.77 | 2.75 | 2.77 | 2.78 |
| Tryptophan | 1.17 | 1.17 | 1.17 | 1.18 |

[1]Leeson, 1993

Quality parameters today usually dictate as little fat as possible and this can be achieved by feeding high protein and/or low energy (Table 3).

**Table 3.** Effect of dietary protein or energy on carcass composition of broilers at 49 days.[1]

| Dietary protein | Carcass fat | | Carcass protein | |
|---|---|---|---|---|
| (%) | (%) | (g) | (%) | (g) |
| 16 | 50.0[d] | 252[d] | 40.7[a] | 202[a] |
| 20 | 46.2[c] | 237[c] | 44.9[b] | 227[b] |
| 24 | 42.4[b] | 210[b] | 47.7[c] | 233[b] |
| 28 | 39.4[a] | 189[a] | 49.9[cd] | 233[b] |
| 32 | 39.2[a] | 185[a] | 50.3[d] | 233[b] |
| 36 | 38.3[a] | 179[a] | 50.7[d] | 234[b] |
| Dietary metabolizable energy (kcal/kg) | | | | |
| 2600 | 37.5[a] | 161[a] | 51.9[e] | 221 |
| 2800 | 39.3[b] | 178[b] | 50.0[d] | 225 |
| 3000 | 42.4[c] | 208[c] | 47.1[c] | 229 |
| 3200 | 42.6[c] | 211[c] | 46.9[c] | 230 |
| 3400 | 45.6[d] | 236[a] | 44.7[b] | 229 |
| 3600 | 47.9[c] | 258[e] | 42.9[a] | 229 |

[1]adapted from Jackson *et al.* (1982).
[a-e]P<0.01.

### Omega-3 fatty acids

There has been considerable interest in the enrichment of poultry products with omega-3 fatty acids. Increased intake of these nutrients by humans has been shown to offer some potential in reducing the risk of coronary heart disease (Kinsella *et al.*, 1990; Kromhout, 1992). Other studies reported that consumption of eicosapentaenoic acid (EPA) and decosahexaenoic acid (DHA) reduced serum triglyceride levels and increased platelet n-3 fatty acid content (Sanders and Roshanai, 1983; Holub *et al.*, 1987; Harris, 1989). In addition, DHA is physiologically essential in the membrane phospholipids of the brain and retina for mental performance and visual acuity, respectively (Health and Welfare Canada, 1990).

Fish oils are rich sources of EPA and DHA and poultry meat and eggs can be enriched by simply adding these oils to layer diets. Table 4 shows results of some recent studies where we added menhaden oil to diets of broilers during the finisher period.

**Table 4.    Effect of dietary fish oils on egg yolk composition (%).[1]**

| Fish oil (%) | Linolenic acid (18:3ω3) | EPA (20:5ω3) | DHA (22:6ω3) |
|---|---|---|---|
| 0 | 0.5 | 0.0 | 0.5 |
| 2 | 0.5 | 0.3 | 1.7 |
| 4 | 0.8 | 0.6 | 2.5 |
| 6 | 1.2 | 1.2 | 3.9 |

[1]Gonzalez and Leeson (1998, unpublished data).

A major limitation to this type of enrichment is the fishy 'taint' associated with EPA and DHA. In North America 2% fish oil is likely to be the maximum inclusion level for layer diets and even at this level our preliminary results suggest some problems in consumer taste panels. The inclusion of fish oils containing EPA and DHA in the diets of laying hens also results in the enrichment of eggs with these fatty acids. Diets containing 3% menhaden oil fed to laying hens results in decreased yolk content of arachidonic acid, while EPA, DHA and linolenic acid contents increased. None of the egg production parameters measured was affected by the dietary inclusion of menhaden oil.

Other studies have involved dietary plant feedstuffs rich in n-3 fatty acids that are less likely to impart undesirable organoleptic characteristics in such enriched eggs. Caston and Leeson (1990) fed laying hens diets containing flax seed which is a source of linolenic acid (18:3 n-3) at levels of 0, 10, 20 and 30%. Fatty acid profile of the eggs showed large increases in n-3 and some n-6 fatty acids at all levels of dietary flax seed addition (Table 5).

**Table 5.    Effect of feeding flax on egg composition.[1]**

|  | Dietary flax (%) | | | |
|---|---|---|---|---|
| Fatty acid | 0 | 10 | 20 | 30 |
| Linoleic, % | 14.1 | 14.6 | 15.4 | 17.1 |
| Linolenic, % | 0.4 | 4.6 | 8.9 | 11.5 |
| Linoleic:linolenic | 5.3:1 | 3.2:1 | 1.7:1 | 1.5:1 |
| Cholesterol, mg/egg | 200.8 | 202.7 | 202.6 | 198.0 |

[1]Adapted from Caston and Leeson, 1990.

Eggs from hens fed a 30% flax seed diet had a linoleic acid:linolenic acid ratio of 1.5:1 versus 35.3:1 for the unsupplemented diet. In a similar study Cherian and Sim (1991) investigated the effects of both dietary flax seed and canola seed on yolk fatty acid composition. Sixteen percent dietary canola meal resulted in 2.4% linolenic acid in the yolk compared to 8.8% in the flax seed treatment. However, both canola meal and flax seed increased EPA and DHA in the egg yolk to about the same level. Consistent with the results of earlier reports by Caston and Leeson (1990), these findings illustrate the possibility for enrichment of eggs with n-3 fatty acids by the use of normal dietary components. These changes in egg fatty acid profile provide an alternative or additional source of linolenic acid to the human diet.

Consumption of n-3 enriched eggs has produced changes in serum and platelet lipid composition of human subjects similar to those produced by the use of other dietary sources of n-3 fatty acids. Ferrier *et al.* (1992) studied the changes in serum lipids and platelet fatty acid composition in human subjects following consumption of linolenic acid enriched eggs. Consumption of linolenic acid enriched eggs, but not regular eggs, for one or two weeks resulted in a marked decline (35%) in serum triglyceride levels with no change in total or high density lipoprotein (HDL) cholesterol. There was an even more dramatic change in platelet phospholipid n-3 fatty acid level, where DHA content increased by some 60% in subjects consuming n-3 enriched eggs.

There are differences in the composition of n-3 fatty acids obtained as a result of using fish *versus* vegetable feedstuffs in the hen's diet. Low levels of fish oil (3.0%) resulted in higher increases in the levels of DHA (3.5%) and EPA (0.52%) compared to relatively lower increases brought about by the use of much higher levels of seed meals (Hargis and Van Elswyk, 1991). The differences in the egg contents of the 20-carbon family of n-3 fatty acids is an indication of poor efficiency of conversion of linolenic acid to DHA and EPA by poultry.

### Cholesterol

Cholesterol is mainly an issue with eggs, although it is interesting that consumers have little knowledge or concern about consumption of other cholesterol-rich foods such as shellfish. Eggs have been forever linked with the cholesterol issue, and in reality the only positive marketing approach is related to lowered cholesterol in any product. Unfortunately, the egg is very resistant to manipulation of its cholesterol content via layer nutrition or any other means.

Eggs are high in cholesterol because of its role in sustaining the developing embryo. Cholesterol has many and varied uses in the developing embryo including its role as a structural component of cell membranes, and as a precursor for sex and adrenal hormones, vitamin D, and the bile acids (Griffin, 1992). Young chicks do not have the enzymes necessary for cholesterol synthesis, which emphasizes the importance of cholesterol being deposited in the egg. An egg contains about 200-250 mg cholesterol, and most of this is transferred from the yolk to the embryo during the final week of incubation (Griffin, 1992). Cholesterol content of the egg can be influenced to some extent by intakes of energy and fat (Leeson, 1993). Diet fat *per se* does not seem to be a factor, although in most instances high-fat diets imply that high energy diets are used. Sutton *et al.* (1984) reported that restricting the energy intake of laying hens to 75% of *ad libitum* intake resulted in decreased total amount of cholesterol excreted via the egg, although this was associated with reduction in egg production. The influence of dietary energy and body weight of the hen on egg cholesterol is mediated through their effects on egg size. Reducing energy intake in order to achieve a measurable reduction in egg cholesterol concentration has the disadvantage of adversely affecting egg production.

One percent cholesterol added to the diet of laying hens increased egg cholesterol by about 25% compared to an unsupplemented group that had no change in plasma cholesterol concentration (Sutton *et al.*, 1984). Dietary fibre influences cholesterol metabolism by a possible combination of different processes. These include lowered cholesterol absorption, binding with bile salts in the intestinal tract, shortening the intestinal transit time, and increasing fecal sterol excretion (Hargis, 1988). Turk and Barnett (1972) tested the effects of different fibre sources added to corn/soya diets fed laying hens on egg yolk cholesterol level. Alfalfa was the most effective of all the fibre sources tested that concomitantly had the least harmful effects on egg size, egg production and feed efficiency. In a similar study comparing the effects of different fibres, Story and Kritchevsky (1976) found that cellulose bound about 1.4% of all the bile acids tested, whereas alfalfa bound up to 15.9%. Nakaue *et al.* (1980) reported that the superior cholesterol lowering effect of alfalfa is not related to its saponin content. Reduction in egg cholesterol achieved by such dietary manipulations are, however, only marginal, with little evidence to suggest a commercially significant reduction.

The reasons behind the lack of success in attempts to lower egg cholesterol content have been described by Griffin (1992) in a recent review article. It was proposed that egg cholesterol is determined by the cholesterol content of individual yolk lipoprotein moieties, rather than by the bird's plasma cholesterol concentration. Given that most cholesterol in lipoproteins is associated with the surface layers, reduction in egg cholesterol content can therefore occur only when the lipoprotein particle size is increased. Such a scenario will reduce the contribution of surface cholesterol molecules relative to total fat. Unfortunately, an increase in lipoprotein particle size will tend to reduce the efficiency of the critical transport of bigger sized "molecules" through the follicle wall. It seems, therefore, that meaningful reduction in egg cholesterol content will likely accrue only through the genetic manipulation of processes involved in lipoprotein synthesis and transport to the developing follicle.

### Fat stability

With a trend toward replacement of saturated with unsaturated fats in poultry products there is increased concern over long term stability of both meat and eggs. In poultry nutrition this situation is accentuated due to the trend for increasing fat usage in various diets together with the fact that most fat sources today are tending towards products with high unsaturated fatty acid content (eg., poultry grease *vs* tallows). Of even greater concern is the use of so-called restaurant greases, where fatty acid profile and stability are more questionable (see next section on trans fatty acids). Unstabilized fat will eventually oxidize, where the characteristic rancid taste and smell produced are due to accumulation of products such as aldehydes, ketones and hydroxy acids. Such oxidation is inevitable but can be managed by judicious use of antioxidants and cold-temperature storage.

As previously indicated, the fat composition of both eggs and meat is influenced by diet fat profile. Therefore feeding unsaturated oils (e.g., soybean oil) is likely to cause more problems than feeding palm or coconut oils. Oxidative degeneration of fats and oils begins at the CH bond next to the unsaturated C=C bond. Problems occur when so-called free radicals are generated, which have an unpaired electron resulting in instability and reactivity. The process therefore becomes autocatalytic and once started the process of 'rancidity' occurs quickly and is virtually irreversible. This oxidation can occur in the feed, in the chicken and/or in the egg or meat in storage. The role of antioxidants is to become oxidized themselves by reacting with the free electron. However, unlike other fatty acids, the 'reacted' antioxidant is stable and so the chain reaction stops. It is obvious therefore that antioxidants must be added to fats as soon after manufacture as possible.

Vitamin E has long been known for its antioxidant properties. Vitamin E scavenges peroxyl free radicals that lead to further chain reactions and there is a correlation between vitamin E content of membranes and their susceptibility to oxidation. Vitamin C also plays some role as an antioxidant and complements vitamin E in being most active in the aqueous phase. In studies with broiler chickens, Bartov and Bornstein (1978) showed that vitamin E was effective in stabilizing abdominal fat, while stability of thigh meat was only protected by synthetic antioxidants. While vitamin E still plays an important role as an antioxidant, use of new types of processed fats and oils often dictates the need to select more effective synthetic antioxidants.

Our recent studies outline the problem encountered when using oxidized fat in diets for young birds (Table 6). Young broilers digested the oxidized fat very poorly and consequently there was reduced diet apparent metabolizable energy (corrected for nitrogen) (AMEn) and slower early growth. There was also a significant increase in liver size, suggestive of abnormal metabolism. Of more direct interest in terms of meat quality is the effect of rancid fat on the accumulation of peroxide type products in meat or eggs. Lin *et al* (1989) show significant accumulation of oxidation products in thigh meat of broilers even during storage at –20°C (Table 7). Oxidized oil obviously caused a substantial rise in thigh meat thiobarbituric acid (TBA) indicative of oxidative rancidity. The levels achieved after two months storage at –20°C were of sufficient magnitude to cause potential organoleptic problems.

As previously discussed, a more recent concern with fat quality is the trend to incorporation of longer chain fatty acids ($\omega$-3, $\omega$-6) etc. where rate and susceptibility to rancidity may be greater. To some extent this situation can be counteracted by judicious use of antioxidants. Table 8 shows oxidative rancidity of high $\omega$-3 eggs stored at 4 or 25°C for up to five weeks.

**Table 6.    Effect of fat oxidation on early broiler growth and development.**

| Fat | 0–2 weeks weight gain (g) | Feed:gain | Diet AMEn (kcal/kg) | Fat digestion (%) | Liver weight (g/100g BW ). |
|---|---|---|---|---|---|
| Fresh | 265 | 1.63 | 3044 | 86.0 | 3.1 |
| Oxidized | 251 | 1.64 | 2905 | 79.5 | 4.1 |
| Significance | * | NS | ** | * | * |

[1]Namkung and Leeson (unpublished data).

**Table 7.    Effect of feeding regular or oxidized fat with or without antioxidants on thigh meat TBA values.[1]**

| Meat storage (-20°C) | Regular oil | Oxidized oil | + Vit. E 200 mg/kg | + Antioxidant |
|---|---|---|---|---|
| 1 day | 0.3 | 0.5 | 0.2 | 0.2 |
| 2 months | 0.8 | 4.4 | 0.4 | 0.4 |
| 6 months | 1.8 | 5.1 | 0.6 | 0.6 |

[1]Adapted from Lin *et al.* (1989).

**Table 8.    Effect of storage time and temperature on malondialdehyde accumulation in regular or high omega-3 eggs (µg/g egg yolk).[1]**

| Egg type | Temp,°C | Weeks storage 1 | 2 | 3 | 4 | 5 |
|---|---|---|---|---|---|---|
| Control | 4 | 0.5 | 0.5 | 0.5 | 0.6 | 0.7 |
|  | 25 | 0.5 | 0.5 | 0.5 | 1.0 | 1.6 |
| ω-3 | 4 | 0.5 | 0.4 | 0.3 | 0.5 | 0.6 |
|  | 25 | 0.5 | 0.5 | 0.5 | 2.0 | 2.5 |

[1]Leeson and Squires (unpublished data).

At 4°C, which is the recommended temperature for egg storage, there is minimal rancidity of the ω-3 eggs, and accumulation of malondialdehyde is comparable to that occurring in conventional eggs. At 25°C, which is obviously an unusual storage condition, there is greater rancidity of the ω-3 eggs, but not until after three weeks storage.

### Trans fatty acids

There is current concern about the trans fatty acid content of poultry products, which develop as a result of feeding hydrogenated restaurant fats and oils. Deep-fat frying now represents a major use of edible oils in North America; and the trend in recent years has been for these restaurants to replace tallows and lards with vegetable oils. This change has been undertaken on the basis of consumer concerns about saturated fats. However, vegetable oils are notoriously unstable, and so they are often hydrogenated as a means of ensuring greater stability for repeated or continuous cooking procedures. During hydrogenation the level of polyunsaturates is reduced, but concomitantly there is increased formation of so called trans fatty acids. Trans fatty acids are isomers of the naturally occurring cis fatty acids. Trans fatty acids have been associated with impaired lipid metabolism in general and especially in an animal's ability to synthesize essential fatty acids and prostaglandins (Kinsella *et al.*, 1980). In assaying a number of commercial grade feed fats, Al-Athari and Watkins (1988a) found trans acids of 18:1 to range from 0-11.7% while levels of trans 18:2 were much lower and rarely exceeded 1%. Emken (1984) suggests that hydrogenated soybean oil will usually contain around 12% trans 18:1 and about 9% other trans fatty acids. Al-Athari and Watkins (1988b) showed that chicks fed trans fatty acids in the form of hydrogenated soybean oil had poorer performance and transfatty acids accumulated in the abdominal fat and liver. These workers concluded that trans fatty acids impaired essential fatty acid metabolism in the chick. There seems little doubt that dietary trans fatty acids are deposited in the tissue of most animals (Bonaga *et al.*, 1980; Elson *et al.*, 1981) and so this becomes a quality issue for the poultry industry.

The uptake of trans fatty acids by humans eating poultry meat or eggs, even from birds fed quite high levels of trans fatty acids, will be quite small. In relation to consumption of margarines, etc., the contribution of poultry products is minimal. Even cows' milk naturally contains 5-10 times the levels of trans fatty acids (due to hydrogenation action of rumen microbes) as found in poultry products. Our main concern should perhaps be bird health and performance, but with today's impressionable consumer, even trace amounts of potentially hazardous nutrients can become a marketing nightmare.

Although there are only likely to be relatively low amounts of trans fatty acids accumulated in broilers or turkeys fed hydrogenated restaurant greases, there is long-term concern about accumulation caused by continual recycling of poultry fats within integrated operations. There is no work currently available on the effect of continually (eg., 4–6 cycles) recycling poultry fat that initially contains moderate levels of trans fatty acids. In this same context there is concern about accumulation of non-volatile breakdown products from cooking fats that are known to be toxic and will be present to some degree in restaurant greases. Unfortunately, use of restaurant greases *per se* is difficult to rationalize in attempting to optimize the quality of poultry products.

### Vitamin composition

Consumers are aware of vitamin content of foods as a quality issue. The cereal industry has labeled their products for vitamins for many years, even though their contribution of certain vitamins is quite low. Consumer surveys have shown that vitamin enriched cereals are selected over non-enriched products when price is comparable. Recent analysis of eggs from different sources shows high variability in their vitamin contents (Naber and Squires, 1993). The results show a greater range in egg content of vitamins A and $B_{12}$ but a lower range for riboflavin. This variability in egg vitamin content is of concern when consistency of food composition is desired, and particularly when one considers the nutrient labeling of foods (Naber, 1993). There is potential to increase the vitamin content of both meat and eggs although to date most attention has centred on eggs. Layer nutrition is a major factor influencing egg vitamin content. However, the influence of dietary vitamin intake on vitamin enrichment of eggs is very variable among different vitamins. Squires and Naber (1993a) reported that egg riboflavin level in yolk and albumen responded rapidly to the dietary level of this vitamin. Similarly, the egg content of vitamin $B_{12}$ was almost exactly proportional to diet content over one to four times the NRC (1984) requirement for the hen (Squires and Naber, 1992). There did not seem to be a ceiling on vitamin $B_{12}$ transfer to the eggs even when up to four times the NRC requirement were given to the hens (Naber, 1993). There is, however, a ceiling on the amount of riboflavin that the laying hens can transfer to the egg when fed diets containing between two and four times their require-ment as established by NRC (1984). On the other hand, when laying hens were fed vitamin A at four times their requirement, the egg content of vitamin A responded only partially (Squires and Naber, 1993b). This was attributed to the modulating effect and storage capacity of vitamin A in the liver.

Naber (1993), in a review of factors influencing egg vitamin content, concluded that feed vitamin content has the greatest and most widespread influence on egg vitamin content. Using data from studies that reported diet vitamin level and feed intake on the one hand and egg output, i.e., egg weight and production on the other, Naber (1993) calculated the efficiency of vitamin transfer into eggs as a function of intake (Table 9).

Table 9.    Classification of vitamins by relative transfer efficiency from diet to egg.[1]

| Transfer efficiency[2] | Vitamin |
| --- | --- |
| Very high (60 to 80%) | Vitamin A |
| High (40 to 50%) | Riboflavin<br>Pantothenic acid<br>Biotin<br>Vitamin $B_{12}$ |
| Medium (15 to 25%) | Vitamin $D_3$<br>Vitamin E |
| Low (5 to 10%) | Vitamin $K_1$<br>Thiamin<br>Folacin |

[1]Adapted from Naber, 1993.
[2]When the vitamin is fed at one or two times the NRC dietary requirement.

The transfer efficiency of vitamin A at dietary levels equivalent to one or two times the NRC requirement was very high (up to 80%), but this dropped markedly when the dietary level was raised to four times requirement (Squires and Naber, 1993b). The increase in egg yolk vitamin A content of some 67% in response to dietary increase from one to two times the requirement is consistent with results of similar studies reported earlier by Reddy *et al.* (1978). This is an indication of the possibility of egg enrichment with vitamin A, even though this trend declines at high levels of diet vitamin enrichment. The transfer of dietary vitamin $B_{12}$ into eggs was as efficient as for riboflavin, pantothenic acid and biotin, i.e., about 50% with dietary levels at one to two times requirement. Unlike riboflavin, however, this level of transfer efficiency continued in the case of vitamin $B_{12}$ even at very high dietary levels of up to 40 times requirement. Clearly, extensive enrichment of eggs with vitamin $B_{12}$ is possible (Naber, 1993).

## Conclusions

While egg and poultry meat products are well positioned relative to other animal proteins in terms of "marketable" nutrient profile, there is potential for improvement in perceived quality. Such quality issues are enrichment of fatty acids now deemed useful in human nutrition together with limitation of undesirable products such as lipid peroxides and trans fatty acids. Once thought of as only valid for the insignificant 'health-store' market, designer poultry products are now entering mainstream marketing.

## References

Al-Athari, A.K. and B.A. Watkins. 1988a. Chromatographic analysis of 18:1 isomers in blended feed-grade fats used in poultry diets. Poultry Sci. 67: 307–312.

Al-Athari, A.K. and B.A. Watkins. 1988b. Distribution of trans and cis 18:1 fatty acid isomers in chicks fed different fats. Poultry Sci. 67: 778–786.

Bartov, I. and S. Bornstein. 1978. Stability of abdominal fat and meat of broilers: Effect of duration of feeding antioxidants. Br. Poultry Sci. 19: 129–135.

Bonaga, C., M.G. Trizzino, M.A. Pasquariello and P.L. Biagi. 1980. Nutritional aspects of trans fatty acids. Note I. Their accumulation in tissue lipids of rats with normolipidic diets containing margarine. Biochem. Exp. Biol. 16: 51–4.

Caston, L. and S. Leeson. 1990. Dietary flax and egg composition. Poultry Sci. 69: 1617–20.

Cherian, G. and J.S. Sim. 1991. Effect of feeding full fat flax and canola seeds to laying hens on the fatty acid composition of eggs, embryos and newly hatched chicks. Poultry Sci. 70: 917–22.

Elson, C.E., N.J. Benevenga, D.J. Canty, R.H. Grummer, J.J. Lalich, J.W. Porter and A.E. Johnson. 1981. The influence of dietary unsaturated cis and trans and saturated fatty acids on tissue lipids of swine. Atherosclerosis 40: 115–37.

Emken, E.A., 1984. Nutrition and biochemistry of trans and positional fatty acid isomers in hydrogenated oils. Annu. Rev. Nutr. 4:339–376.

Ferrier, L.K., L. Caston, S. Leeson, E.J. Squires, B. Celi, L. Thomas and B.J. Holub. 1992. Changes in serum lipids and platelet fatty acid composition following consumption of eggs enriched in alpha-linolenic acid (LnA). Food Res. Intern. 25: 263.

Griffin, H.D. 1992. Manipulation of egg yolk cholesterol: A physiologist's view. World's Poultry Sci. J. 48: 101–112.

Hargis, P.S., 1988. Modifying egg yolk cholesterol in the domestic fowl - a review. World's Poultry Sci. 44:17–29. Hargis, P.S. and M.E. Van Elswyk, 1991. Modifying yolk fatty acid composition to improve health quality of eggs. Pages 249–260 in C. Haberston and C.E. Morris, eds. Fat and cholesterol reduced foods: technologies and strategies. Gulf Publishing Co., Houston, U.S.A. Harris, W.S., 1989. Fish oils and plasma lipid and lipoprotein metabolism in humans: a critical review. J. Lipid Res. 30:785–807.

Health and Welfare Canada, 1990. Nutrition recommendations. Minister of Supply and Services, Ottawa, ON. Holub, B.J., D.J. Bakker and C.M. Skeaff, 1987. Alterations in molecular species of cholesterol esters formed via plasma lecithin-cholesterol acyltransferase in human subjects consuming fish oil. Atherosci. 66:11–18. Jackson, S., J.D. Summers and S. Leeson. 1982. Effect of dietary protein and energy on broiler carcass composition and efficiency of nutrient utilization. Poultry Sci. 61: 2224–2231.

Kinsella, J.E., G. Bruckner, J. Mai and J. Shimp. 1980. Metabolism of trans fatty acids with emphasis on the effects of trans, trans-octadecadienoate on lipid composition, essential fatty acid, and prostaglandins: an overview. Am. J. Clin. Nutr. 34: 2307–18.

Kinsella, J.E., B. Lokesh and R.A. Stone. 1990. Dietary n-3 polyunsaturated fatty acids and amelioration of cardiovascular disease: possible mechanism. Am. J. Clin. Nutr. 52:1–28.

Kromhout, D., 1992. Dietary fats: Long-term implications for health. Nutr. Rev. 50:49–53.

Leeson, S. 1993. Potential of modifying poultry products. J. Appl. Poultry Res. 2: 380–384.

Lin, C.F., A. Ashgar, J.I. Gray, D.J. Buckley, A.M. Booren, R.L. Crackel and C.J. Flegal. 1989. Effects of oxidized dietary oil and antioxidant supplementation on broiler growth and meat stability. Br. Poultry Sci. 30: 855–864.

Naber, E.C. 1993. Modifying vitamin composition of eggs: A review. J. Appl. Poultry Res. 2: 385–393.

Naber, E.C. and M.W. Squires. 1993. Vitamin profiles as indicators of nutritional status in the laying hen: Diet to egg transfer and commercial flock survey. Poultry Sci. 72: 1046–1053.

Nakaue, N.S., R.R. Lowry, P.R. Sheeke, and G.H. Arscott, 1980. The effect of dietary alfalfa of varying saponin cotent on yolk cholesterol level and layer performance. Poutlry Sci. 59:2744–2748. National Research Council, 1984. Nutrient requirements of Poultry. 8th rev. ed. National Academy Press, Washington, DC. Reddy, V.R., B. Panda and V.R. Sadagopan. 1978. Relation of different levels of dietary vitamin A of laying hens to vitamin A content of egg yolk and newly hatched chicks. Ind. Vet. J. 55: 554–558.

Sanders, T.A. and F. Roshanai. 1983. The influence of different types of omega-3 polyunsaturated fatty acids on blood lipids and platelet function in healthy volunteers. Clin. Sci. 64: 91–99.

Squires, M.W. and E.C. Naber. 1992. Vitamin profiles of eggs as indicators of nutritional status in the laying hen: Vitamin B12 study. Poultry Sci. 71: 2075–2082.

Squires, M.W. and E.C. Naber. 1993a. Vitamin profiles of eggs as indicators of nutritional status in the laying hen: Riboflavin study. Poultry Sci. 72: 483–484.

Squires, M.W. and E.C. Naber. 1993b. Vitamin profiles of eggs as indicators of nutritional status in the laying hen: Vitamin A study. Poultry Sci. 72: 154–164.

Story, J.A. and D. Kritchevsky. 1976. Comparison of the binding of various bile acids and bile salts *in vitro* by several types of fibre. J. Nutr. 106: 1292–1294.

Sutton, C.C., W.M. Muir and G.E. Mitchell. 1984. Cholesterol metabolism in the laying as influenced by cholesterol, caloric intake and genotype. Poultry Sci. 63: 972–980.

Turk, D.E. and B.D. Bernett. 1972. Diet and egg cholesterol content. Poultry Sci. 51(Suppl. 1): 1881 (Abstr.)

# Effects of organic chromium (Bio-Chrome) on growth, efficiency and carcass characteristics of feedlot steers

GREGORY V. POLLARD AND C. REED RICHARDSON

*Texas Tech University, Lubbock, Texas*

## Summary

Two levels of chromium (Cr) yeast, 0.2 ppm and 0.4 ppm, were fed in a typical feedlot ration to supply approximately 1.8 and 3.1 mg Cr per head per day to feedlot steers in a university research feedlot on the southern High Plains of Texas for 196 days. Average daily gain, dry matter intake and feed efficiency were not affected by the 0.2 ppm treatment; however, the 0.4 ppm treatment reduced average daily gain and dry matter intake while increasing the feed:gain ratio. Cattle supplemented with 0.4 ppm chromium had larger longissimus muscle areas and decreased final yield grades, hot carcass weights and marbling scores. Organic chromium improved carcass traits while not adversely affecting performance when fed at 0.2 ppm of feedlot diets. No effects of treatment on cortisol levels were seen, except on day 196 when steers receiving 0.2 ppm Cr had elevated serum cortisol compared to the other treatments.

## Introduction

Rate of growth and feed conversion by feedlot cattle are highly influenced by feed intake and energetic efficiency (NRC, 1996). Chromium is an important trace element in the regulation of blood glucose and immune response in humans and laboratory species (NRC, 1997). Chromium is known to be a structural component of a glucose tolerance factor, which potentiates the action of insulin and is an essential trace mineral for normal metabolism of carbohydrates and lipids (NRC, 1989; Mertz, 1993). Recently, chromium has been shown to improve reproduction, growth and carcass characteristics of pigs fed organic sources of chromium (Boleman *et al.*, 1995; Lindemann *et al.*, 1995; Kornegay *et al.*, 1997; Mooney and Cromwell, 1997). Research regarding the use of chromium on immune response in cattle has shown that benefits from supplemental chromium include enhanced cell-mediated immunity, reduced blood cortisol levels and increased antibody titers (Chang and Mowat, 1992; Kegley *et al.*, 1996; Mallard and Borgs, 1997). Moonsie-Shageer and Mowat (1993) demonstrated the effectiveness of supplemental chromium on reducing morbidity in stressed feeder calves. However, research pertaining to chromium in the diets of beef cattle has been less consistent in its effect on performance and growth parameters.

The effect of chromium as a potential carcass modifier has been well documented in research with swine (Page *et al.*, 1993; Gebert and Wenk, 1994; Boleman *et al.*, 1995). Recent research by Kornegay *et al.* (1997) found that chromium increased longissimus muscle area, and when pigs were fed chromium at lighter weights for a longer period of time the increase in longissimus muscle area was greater compared to shorter feeding periods. Similar results were found by Mooney and Cromwell (1997) who, in addition to increased longissimus muscle area, found that chromium improved carcass protein deposition rate and decreased fat percentage. Hasten *et al.* (1997a; 1997b) found similar results in work with rats in regard to reduced fat accretion when supplemental chromium was fed. The present experiment examined the effects of Bio-Chrome (Alltech Inc.), organic chromium derived from yeast, on performance and carcass characteristics of feedlot steers.

## Materials and methods

The objectives of this research were to determine the effects of organic chromium on dry matter intake, average daily gain, feed: gain ratio, blood cortisol levels and carcass characteristics of feedlot steers.

ANIMALS AND DIETS

The 196 day trial was conducted at the Texas Tech University Burnett Center research feedlot on the southern High Plains of Texas during the winter of 1997 and spring of 1998. One-hundred and five crossbred steers (283 kg) composed of primarily Angus, Hereford, Charolais and Simmental breeding were kept outdoors in pens of seven animals over a partially slotted concrete floor and equipped with an automated feed delivery system. Feed for each pen was individually batched and delivered at approximately 09:00 each morning. Prior to feeding, feed remaining in bunks was visually estimated and used to adjust intake. Treatments consisted of basal diet (control), basal diet plus 0.2 ppm chromium from Bio-Chrome (0.2 ppm Cr), and basal diet plus 0.4 ppm chromium from Bio-Chrome (0.4 ppm Cr).

Diets fed daily to the steers were typical feedlot diets consisting of a steam-flaked grain sorghum and cottonseed hull base (Table 1). Upon arrival steers were immediately processed, which included anti-clostridial vaccination (Ultrabac/Somubac™, SmithKline Beecham), deworming (Ivomec™, Meriel) and antibiotic (Micotil™, Elanco Animal Health).

Steers were implanted with Synovex-S™ (Fort Dodge Animal Health), individually ear tagged, tail bobbed, weighed and placed on a step-up receiving diet containing chlortetracycline and sulfamethiazine (AS 700, Roche Animal Health). The following day animals were sorted by weight and randomly assigned by weight to five pens of seven steers per pen for a total of 35 steers per treatment. The Bio-Chrome treatments were started immediately after sorting and fed while steers were moved up to the high concentrate diet (28 days), and were fed for the remainder of the study.

Table 1.   Composition of experimental diets.

| Ingredients | Control | 0.2 ppm Cr | 0.4 ppm Cr |
|---|---|---|---|
| Grain sorghum, steam flaked | 80.00 | 79.75 | 79.50 |
| Cottonseed hulls | 7.85 | 7.85 | 7.85 |
| Cottonseed meal | 1.90 | 1.90 | 1.90 |
| Molasses, liquid | 4.30 | 4.30 | 4.30 |
| Fat, yellow grease | 2.30 | 2.30 | 2.30 |
| Urea | 0.50 | 0.50 | 0.50 |
| Limestone, ground | 1.04 | 1.04 | 1.04 |
| Salt | 0.12 | 0.12 | 0.12 |
| Potassium chloride | 0.39 | 0.39 | 0.39 |
| Trace mineral premix[a] | 0.23 | 0.23 | 0.23 |
| Vitamin A premix[b] | 0.30 | 0.30 | 0.30 |
| Vitamin E premix[c] | 0.16 | 0.16 | 0.16 |
| Rumensin/Tylan premix[d] | 0.91 | 0.91 | 0.91 |
| Chromium premix[e] | – | 0.25 | 0.50 |
| Total | 100.00 | 100.00 | 100.00 |

[a]Trace mineral premix contains (ppm) I, 559; Mn, 3815; Zn, 3815; Cu, 375; Co, 23; Fe, 1840.
[b]Vitamin A premix provides 300,000 IU of Vitamin A acetate per kg.
[c]Vitamin E premix provides 1765 IU of $\alpha$-tocopherol per kg.
[d]Rumensin/Tylan premix provides 360 mg/hd/d of Monensin and 66.64 mg/hd/d of Tylosin
[e]Chromium premix contains 80 ppm Cr.

The 0.2 ppm Cr treatment group received a premix (0.25% of the diet) consisting of ground grain sorghum and Bio-Chrome (80 ppm Cr). The 0.4 ppm Cr treatment group received the same premix at 0.50% of the diet. The chromium premix in each treatment group replaced steam-flaked grain sorghum in the basal diet to ensure that diets were isonitrogenous and isocaloric for each treatment group.

MEASUREMENTS

Individual steer weights were recorded at 28-day intervals during the experiment. Average daily gain, feed:gain ratio and dry matter intake were calculated for each period. Blood samples were collected from each steer in the morning on days 0, 14, 28, 56 and 196 via jugular venipuncture for cortisol determination. Immediately upon collection blood samples were placed on ice for transport back to the laboratory where serum was separated and stored at -20°C until cortisol analysis was conducted using

105

a cortisol specific radioimmunoassay kit (Coat-A-Count, Diagnostic Products Corporation). At the conclusion of the study steers were transported by truck to a commercial packing plant where liver abscess scores, final yield grade, marbling scores, dressing percentage, longissimus muscle area, and quality grade were measured by trained personnel.

This completely randomized experiment was analyzed using GLM procedure of SAS (1995). Pen was the experimental unit and means were separated using Fischer's Protected Least Significant Difference Test.

# Results and Discussion

PERFORMANCE EFFECTS

### Effects on average daily gain, dry matter intake and feed efficiency
No differences were detected for average daily gain, feed:gain ratio or dry matter intake during the first 56 days of the study (Table 2). These data are consistent with previous studies conducted by Chang *et al.* (1992) and Kegley *et al.* (1996) who also found these parameters unaffected by chromium supplementation. However, steers receiving the 0.4 ppm Cr treatment tended (P = 0.17) to eat less feed during the first two periods. During these two periods a seasonal effect may have been present which suppressed performance because of temperature fluctuations in excess of 17°C per day for the majority of the 56 day interval.

Table 2.   Effect of Bio-Chrome on average daily gain, dry matter intake and feed efficiency of steers days 0-56.

|                          | Control | 0.2 ppm Cr | 0.4 ppm Cr |
| ------------------------ | ------- | ---------- | ---------- |
| Initial weight, kg       | 282.28  | 287.24     | 280.32     |
| Dry matter intake, kg/d  | 8.26    | 8.30       | 7.66       |
| Average daily gain, kg/d | 0.78    | 0.78       | 0.75       |
| Feed:gain ratio          | 10.59   | 10.64      | 10.17      |

During the final 140 days of the study (Table 3) no differences in dry matter intake among treatments were detected (Tables 3 and 4). However, steers receiving 0.4 ppm Cr had lower average daily gain (P <0.05) and increased feed:gain (P< 0.05) which is consistent with results obtained by Chang and Mowat (1992) who found that supplemental chromium at 0.2 ppm did not improve performance compared to control cattle. In contrast, Moonsie-Shageer and Mowat (1993) found that chromium improved intake and daily gain when fed at 0.2 ppm. Average daily gain and dry matter intake increased for all treatments during the final 140 days when compared to performance during the initial 56 days of the study, which further suggests an environmental effect on performance during the first 56 days of the study.

Overall, cattle receiving 0.2 ppm Cr were not different (P <0.05) from control steers in the performance variables measured (Table 4). However, 0.4 ppm Cr (treated cattle) weighed less (P<0.05) at the completion of the study, had lower average daily gain (P<0.05) and higher feed:gain (P<0.05) than both the control and 0.2 ppm Cr treatments.

**Table 3.  Effect of Bio-Chrome on average daily gain, dry matter intake and feed efficiency of steers days 57-196.**

|  | Control | 0.2 ppm Cr | 0.4 ppm Cr |
| --- | --- | --- | --- |
| Initial weight, kg | 360.00[a] | 349.27[a] | 343.85[b] |
| Dry matter intake, kg/d | 8.40 | 9.37 | 8.04 |
| Average daily gain, kg/d | 1.24[a] | 1.31[a] | 0.99[b] |
| Feed:gain ratio | 6.76[a] | 7.17[a] | 8.09[b] |

[a,b]Means in the same row with different superscripts differ (P<0.05).

**Table 4.  Effect of Bio-Chrome on overall average daily gain, dry matter intake and feed efficiency of steers days 0-196.**

|  | Control | 0.2 ppm Cr | 0.4 ppm Cr |
| --- | --- | --- | --- |
| Initial weight, kg | 282.28 | 287.24 | 280.32 |
| Final weight, kg | 506.73[a] | 512.12[a] | 461.16[b] |
| Dry matter intake, kg/d | 8.22 | 8.96 | 7.80 |
| Average daily gain, kg/d | 1.11[a] | 1.16[a] | 0.93[b] |
| Feed:gain ratio | 7.40[a] | 7.75[ab] | 8.43[b] |

[a,b]Means in the same row with different superscripts differ (P<0.05).

## EFFECTS OF BIO-CHROME ON CARCASS CHARACTERISTICS AND SERUM CORTISOL

The 0.2 ppm Cr treatment increased (P <0.05) hot carcass weight over 0.4 ppm Cr treatment with control steers being intermediate (Table 5). Dressing percent, marbling score and final yield grade were reduced (P <0.05) compared to control and 0.2 ppm Cr treatments when the 0.4 ppm Cr treatment was fed. Longissimus muscle area was increased (P <0.08) with increasing level of Cr supplementation. Kornegay *et al.* (1997) and Mooney and Cromwell (1997) both reported a similar effect in pigs supplemented with 0.2 ppm Cr. No effects of treatment on serum cortisol were seen on days 0, 14, 28 and 56; however on day 196 steers on the 0.2 ppm Cr treatment had an increased (P<0.05) serum cortisol.

Table 5.   Effects of Bio-Chrome level on carcass characteristics.

|  | Control | 0.2 ppm Cr | 0.4 ppm Cr |
|---|---|---|---|
| Hot carcass weight, lb | 302.18[a] | 315.44[b] | 275.78[c] |
| Dressing percentage, % | 63.37[a] | 63.65[a] | 62.16[b] |
| Longissimus muscle area, cm². | 77.94[x] | 81.35[y] | 81.55[z] |
| Marbling score[1] | 472.09[a] | 445.62[a] | 394.57[b] |
| Final yield grade | 2.53[a] | 2.32[a] | 1.56[b] |

[1]Marbling scores: 300=traces, 400=slight, 500=small.
[a,b,c]Means in the same row with different superscripts differ (P≤0.05).
[x,y,z]Means in the same row with different superscripts differ (P=0.08).

## Conclusions

Feedlot cattle supplemented with Bio-Chrome had significantly larger longissimus (ribeye) muscle areas than those on the control diet. Hot carcass weight was also increased by 0.2 ppm Cr supplementation. Average daily gain and dry matter intake were decreased, and feed:gain was increased in cattle supplemented with 0.4 ppm Cr. These data indicate that Bio-Chrome when supplemented at 0.2 ppm improves two economically important carcass traits, hot carcass weight and longissimus muscle area. In addition, when Cr is supplemented at 0.4 ppm, longissimus muscle area is increased to an even greater extent than seen with 0.2 ppm Cr.

## References

Boleman, S.L., S.J. Boleman, T.D. Bidner, L.L. Southern, T.L. Ward, J.E. Pontif and M.M. Pike. 1995. Effect of chromium picolinate on growth, body composition, and tissue accretion in pigs. J. Anim. Sci. 73:2033.

Chang, X. and D.N. Mowat. 1992. Supplemental chromium for stressed and growing feeder calves. J. Anim. Sci. 70:559.

Chang, X., D.N. Mowat and G.A. Spiers. 1992. Carcass characteristics and tissue-mineral contents of steers fed supplemental chromium. Can. J. Anim. Sci. 72:663.

Gebert, S. and C. Wenk. 1994. Effect of chromium and manganese supplementation form on performance, digestion, carcass characteristics and blood parameters of finishing gilts. Bio-Chrome (Co-Factor III) Alltech, Inc. Swiss Federal Institute for Technology, Zurich, Switzerland.

Hasten, D.L., M. Hegsted, M.J. Keenan and G.S. Morris. 1997a. Effects of various forms of dietary chromium on growth and body composition in the rat. Nutr. Res. 17:283.

Hasten, D.L., M. Hegsted, M.J. Keenan, and G.S. Morris. 1997b. Dosage effects of chromium picolinate on growth and body composition in the rat. Nutr. Res. 17:1175.

Kegley, E.B., J.W. Spears and T.T. Brown. 1996. Immune response and disease resistance of calves fed chromium nicotinic acid complex or chromium chloride. J. Dairy Sci. 79:1278.

Kornegay, E.T., Z. Wang, C.M. Wood and M.D. Lindemann. 1997. Supplemental chromium picolinate influences nitrogen balance, dry matter digestibility, and carcass traits in growing-finishing pigs. J. Anim. Sci. 75:1319.

Lindemann, M.D., C.M. Wood, A.F. Harper, E.T. Kornegay and R.A. Anderson. 1995. Dietary chromium picolinate additions improve gain:feed, and carcass characteristics in growing-finishing pigs and increase litter size in reproducing sows. J. Anim. Sci. 73:457.

Mallard, B.A. and P. Borgs. 1997. Effects of supplemental trivalent chromium on hormone and immune responses of cattle. In: Biotechnology in the Feed Industry Proc. 13th Alltech Annual Symposium. (T.P. Lyons and K.A. Jacques, eds.), Nottingham Univ. Press, U.K.

Mertz, W. 1993. Chromium in human nutrition: a review. J. Nutr. 123:626.

Mooney, K.W. and G.L. Cromwell. 1997. Efficacy of chromium picolinate and chromium chloride as potential carcass modifiers in swine. J. Anim. Sci. 75:2661.

Moonsie-Shageer, S. and D.N. Mowat. 1993. Effect of level of supplemental chromium on performance, serum constituents and immune status of stressed feeder calves. J. Anim. Sci. 71:232.

National Research Council. 1989. Recommended dietary allowance, 10th edition. Washington, D.C.: National Academy of Sciences, National Academy Press.

National Research Council. 1996. Nutrient requirements of beef cattle, 7th edition. Washington, D.C: National Academy of Sciences, National Academy Press.

National Research Council. 1997. The role of chromium in animal nutrition. Washington, D.C. National Academy of Sciences, National Academy Press.

Page, T.G., L.L. Southern, T.L. Ward and D.L. Thompson. 1993. Effect of chromium picolinate on growth and serum and carcass traits of growing-finishing pigs. J. Anim. Sci. 71:656.

SAS Institute. 1995. SAS procedures guide version 6, 3rd edition. SAS Institute Inc. Cary, NC.

# Liquid feeding of pigs: potential for reducing environmental impact and for improving productivity and food safety

PETER H. BROOKS, COLM MORAN and JANE D. BEAL

*University of Plymouth, Newton Abbot, Devon, UK*

## Introduction

Liquid feed delivery systems for pigs have tended to be more common in areas where liquid by-products are readily available and where the size of the production unit can justify the capital expenditure involved. Although historically the availability of liquid by-products may have been the main incentive for installing a liquid feed system, there are now additional compelling reasons why liquid feeding should be considered. This review considers some of the environmental, production and food safety benefits that may be available to producers who adopt liquid feeding.

Before discussing our ideas and research on liquid feeding it is important to define exactly what we are talking about. Liquid feeding involves the use of a diet prepared either from a mixture of liquid food industry residues and conventional dry raw materials, or from dry components mixed with water. Generally, the mixing will be undertaken at a central point and the liquid feed will be transferred to the pig by a pipeline delivery system. A liquid diet will typically contain 200–300 g dry matter per kg. This feeding system should not be confused with wet/dry feeder systems where water and feed are kept separate up to the point of delivery to the pig. A key difference between these two feeding systems is the length of time that the dry matter fraction of the diet is in a liquid medium before it is consumed by the pig. This has important implications for the microbiology and nutrient availability of the food which is discussed in this paper.

## Potential advantages of liquid feeding

Traditionally producers have perceived a number of advantages in using liquid feeding. These include:

- reduction of food loss as dust during handling and feeding

- improvement in the pig's environment and health due to the reduction of dust in the atmosphere
- improved pig performance and feed conversion rate (FCR)
- flexibility in raw material use (opportunity to utilise more economic food sources and reduce cost per kg gain)
- improved materials handling (system can act as both a feed mixing and distribution system)
- increased accuracy of rationing (computer control brings a degree of accuracy to the system that it is difficult to emulate with dry feeding systems)
- improved dry matter intake in problem groups (e.g. weaners and lactating sows)

Liquid feeding of growing finishing pigs is generally associated with improved daily liveweight gain and improved feed conversion. Jensen and Mikkelsen (1998) reviewed nine recent studies in which the performance of pigs fed dry or liquid diets were compared. A summary of these trials is given in Table 1.

Table 1.  Improvement (%) in growth rate and feed conversion ratio in nine experiments conducted to compare liquid and dry feeding for grow-finish pigs[1].

| Improved daily weight gain | | Improved feed conversion ratio | |
| Mean  (SD) | Range | Mean  (SD) | Range |
| --- | --- | --- | --- |
| 4.4 ±(5.4) | −2.6–15.0 | 6.9±(3.5) | 1.9–12.7 |

[1]Jensen and Mikkelsen, 1998.

To these advantages must now be added benefits which can accrue to the environment through:

- the utilisation of co-products from the human food industry which would otherwise incur a cost for environmentally acceptable disposal
- reduction in potential environmental loading with protein through the easy adoption of 'phase feeding'
- reduction in potential environmental loading with minerals (particularly phosphorus) through the activation of endogenous phytase in cereal grains.

## Utilisation of liquid co-products from the human food industry

Although liquid co-products of many sorts are used for pig feeding in a number of countries around the world, it is the feed and farming industry in the Netherlands which furnishes the best example of co-product utilisation.

In the Netherlands it has been estimated that a total quantity of about 6.5 million tonnes of co-products are used directly on the farm (de Haas,

1998). It is notable that the quantity of material has increased dramatically in recent years and is predicted to increase still further. Of the 6.5 million tonne total, approximately 35% (2.3 million tonnes) is fed to pigs (Table 2), and of this 70% is carbohydrate rich (Scholten *et al.*, 1998).

**Table 2.** Amount of liquid co-products (tonnes) from the food industry delivered directly to pig farms in the Netherlands[1].

| Product | 1993 | 1996 |
|---|---|---|
| Wheat starch industry | 650,000 | 885,000 |
| Potato processing industry | 350,000 | 525,000 |
| Dairy industry | 300,000 | 300,000 |
| Fermentation industry | 80,000 | 120,000 |
| Beer industry | 80,000 | 100,000 |
| Sugar industry | 25,000 | 50,000 |
| Other | 170,000 | 360,000 |
| Total amount (tonnes) | 1,655,000 | 2,340,000 |

[1]Scholten *et al.*, 1998.

The importance of these co-products to pig production is put into perspective when it is remembered that the net production of pork in the Netherlands in 1996 was 1.6 million tonnes (Meat and Livestock Commission, 1998). The co-product materials vary considerably in dry matter content both between and within product; an important point which needs to be taken into account when formulating diets using them. An indication of dry matter content and normal inclusion rates are given in Table 3.

**Table 3.** Dry matter content and inclusion rates of co-products used in pig feeds[1].

| Ingredient | Tonnage | Dry matter (%) | Inclusion rate (%) |
|---|---|---|---|
| Wheat starch | 885,000 | 15–25 | 30 |
| Sugar molasses | 150,000 | 15–20 | 5 |
| Brewer's spent grains | 625,000 | 21 | 5 |
| Fresh maize gluten | 95,000 | 44 | 5 |
| Brewer's yeast | 70,000 | 15 | 12 max |
| Steamed potato peel | 500,000 | 14 | 15–20 |
| Whey/milk products | 300,000 | 5 | 15 |
| Mycelium and yeast washes | 78,000 | 17 | 5 |
| Oils and fats | 55,000 | 35 | 7 |
| Bakery and waffle products | 80,000 | 65 | 25–30 |
| Onion juice | 50,000 | 10 | 7 |

[1]Fraser, 1998.

With correct formulation these products can be used without detriment to pig performance. For example Scholten *et al.* (1997) used combinations of liquid wheat starch, potato steam peel and cheese whey to replace

35% of the dry matter in growing pig diets and 55% in finishing diets at a water to feed ratio of 2.6:1. The results of their study (Table 4) show that when the diet is properly balanced there is no loss in performance as a result of feeding co-products.

Table 4. Performance of growing-finishing pigs fed a liquid diet with or without liquid co-products[1].

| | Control diet (meal + water) | Co-product diet | SEM |
|---|---|---|---|
| Number of pigs | 296 | 296 | |
| Initial weight, kg | 25.1 | 25.1 | |
| Final weight, kg | 111.3 | 113.4 | |
| Daily gain, g/day | 740[a] | 768[b] | 4.7 |
| Feed intake, kg/day | 1.99[a] | 1.98[b] | 0.01 |
| Feed conversion ratio | 2.69[a] | 2.58[b] | 0.02 |
| Lean meat percentage | 55.3[c] | 54.8[d] | 0.16 |

[1]Scholten *et al.*, 1997.
[abcd]Means in a row differ ([a,b] $P<0.001$; [c,d] $P<0.05$).

It is also important to the livestock industry that in solving an environmental problem for the human food industry it does not merely move the problem from factory to farm. Once again studies from the Netherlands provide us with some valuable information on this topic. Ronald Scholten and his co-workers have looked at the effect of using co-products on the environmental characteristics of growing/finishing pigs (Table 5). Their studies showed that ammonia emission was similar for liquid-fed pigs fed conventional diets and those fed diets including co-products. Manure production of pigs fed co-products was 2.4% higher when expressed on the basis of manure produced per kg growth (Table 6).

Table 5. Environmental characteristics of growing-finishing pigs fed a liquid diet with or without liquid co-products[1].

| | Control diet (meal + water) | Co-product diet |
|---|---|---|
| Ammonia emission, kg/place/year | 1.9 | 2.0 |
| Manure production, litres/place/year | 1,092 | 1,156 |
| Manure production, litres/kg of growth | 4.1 | 4.2 |
| Dry matter content of the manure, % | 8.3 | 6.8 |
| pH of the manure | 7.3 | 7.5 |

[1]Scholten *et al.*, 1997.

Our studies with young pigs (7-25 kg) show that effluent volume is increased when pigs are fed on liquid diets rather than dry pelleted diets (Table 6). However, this does not imply an increased environmental loading as the increased biological efficiency of the pig means that the amount of nitrogen and mineral voided per kilogram of growth is actually reduced.

Table 6.  Effluent production by weaner pigs fed dry and liquid diets[1].

| | Trial 1 | | | Trial 2 | | |
|---|---|---|---|---|---|---|
| | Dry | Liquid | $SE_D$ | Dry | Liquid | $SE_D$ |
| Daily gain, g | 343 | 428 | 21*** | 397 | 454 | 14*** |
| Total water use, ml/pig/day | 1306 | 2298 | 64*** | 1499 | 2028 | 84** |
| Effluent production, ml/pig/day | 754 | 1058 | 46** | 982 | 1189 | 31* |
| Effluent production, litres/kg gain | 2.20 | 2.47 | +12.3% | 2.47 | 2.62 | +6.1% |

[1]Russell *et al.*, 1996.
Means differ: * $P<0.05$; ** $P<0.01$; ***$P<0.001$.

Some of the co-products which are used in liquid form could be dried and incorporated into conventional dry compounded feed. However, feeding them in liquid form removes the cost of drying and reduces dependence on non-renewable energy sources. On the debit side, the use of liquid co-products increases transportation costs as more water is shipped with the dry matter. Consequently, there is an increased demand for non-renewable energy for transportation. As a result some products can only be used efficiently when the pig production unit is situated close to the source of supply. However, in Europe many products are transported considerable distances as 'back loads' in tankers that would otherwise be travelling empty. Thus in real terms there is only a marginal increase in fuel cost to set against the material (i.e., the difference between running the tanker empty and full).

Drying and subsequent incorporation into dry diets would not be a viable economic option for co-products with very low dry matter content. These materials would still have to be disposed of in an environmentally acceptable manner. The alternative routes for disposal of these materials would be through a sewerage system (either public or privately owned) or through addition to landfill sites. In developed economies both the economic and the environmental cost of such disposal continues to increase.

Therefore, when deciding whether to utilise co-products as feed stocks or make them environmentally non-damaging through waste treatment it is important to audit the alternative processes to ensure that they are ultimately beneficial to the environment.

## Liquid feeding: improving nutritional management, reducing environmental impact

It is beyond the scope of this paper to consider all the environmental benefits which can be obtained through the adoption of liquid feeding.

However, two opportunities for improved nutritional management should be noted, namely reduced nitrogen output in effluent through the adoption of 'phase feeding' and reduced phosphorus output in effluent through the action of endogenous phytase in cereal grains.

PHASE FEEDING

The pork industry naturally wishes to maximise lean growth and as a consequence diets are designed to maximise it in those animals capable of making a response. The rate of lean growth relative to voluntary energy intake declines continuously with increasing liveweight of the animal. Thus the requirement for protein and energy can only be matched by a continuous adjustment of the lysine (ideal protein) to digestible energy intake (Gill, 1998). Thus in order to maximise protein utilisation and minimise the nitrogen content of the effluent the energy:lysine ratio should be changing continuously to reflect the animal's requirement (Figure 1a). The environmental consequences of failing to match animal requirements are considerable. For example, if the pig in Figure 1a were fed a single diet throughout the growing period it would excrete 0.5 kg more nitrogen than a pig fed diets which fitted the requirement curve. In practice, few units use more than two diets throughout the growing-finishing period (see example in Figure 1b). As a result, finishing pigs on most production units are still supplied with an excess of protein for much of their growth period. Large 'all in, all out' finishing piggeries provide an opportunity to feed a series of diets which more closely match the pig's requirement (Figure 1c). However, on units which house different weights of pig in the same house, matching the diet to the requirement of individual pens of pigs is much more difficult. Modern computerised liquid feeding facilities make this possible. Dual pipeline systems make it possible to mix two diets of different energy:lysine ratios in order to match the nutrient requirement of individual pens of pigs precisely.

STEEPING: ACTIVATING PLANT ENZYMES

Another benefit of liquid feeding is that it provides the opportunity for steeping raw materials prior to feeding. Phytases which occur naturally in the pericarp of some cereal grains and seeds are activated if the raw materials are soaked. Thus soaking wheat and barley increased phytate hydrolysis whereas rapeseed and soyabean were little affected (Figure 2). The addition of exogenous phytase to the material being steeped is much more beneficial in the case of soyabean than in the case of wheat (Figure 3); but even with wheat there is some increase in phosphorus availability. Steeping increases the bioavailability of other minerals as well (Table 7). However, the increases in bioavailability tend to reach significance only when an exogenous phytase source is added.

Recent work in our laboratory (Beal *et al.*, 1998) has shown that steeping soyabean meal with protease increases the *in vitro* digestibility of protein (Table 8).

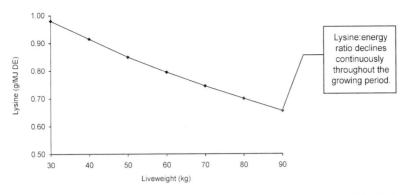

(a) Relationship between liveweight and required lysine: energy ratio (after Gill, 1998).

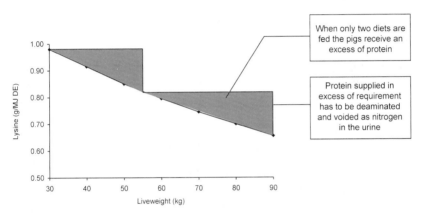

(b) Excess protein provided by a two diet system in the grow-finish period.

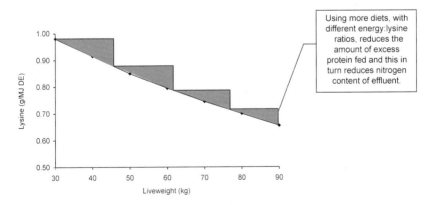

(c) Excess protein provided by a four diet system in the grow-finish period.

**Figure 1.** phase feeding reduces the wastage of protein and reduces the nitrogen content of effluent.

117

An interesting aspect of this study was the difference in the protein digestibility of soyabean depending upon the processing treatment to which it had been subjected.

**Table 7.  Effect of soaking and phytase addition to a wheat (75%) based diet on mineral bioavailability (%) in the pig.[1]**

| Mineral | Control | Feed soaked in water for 12 hrs | Feed soaked in water + phytase for 12 hrs |
|---|---|---|---|
| Phosphorus (total) | 52[a] | 56 | 63[a] |
| Phosphorus (plant origin) | 37[a] | 41 | 50[b] |
| Calcium | 66 | 69 | 76 |
| Magnesium | 13[a] | 24[b] | 45[ab] |
| Copper | 15[ab] | 25[ac] | 39[bc] |
| Zinc | 92 | 94 | 94 |

[1]Seguier and Orr, unpublished data.
[abc] Means with the same superscript differ, P<0.05.

In growth studies (Beal *et al.*, 1999) steeping raw or micronized soya with a protease enzyme for 24 hrs prior to feeding significantly improved daily gain and FCR for pigs fed raw soya diets (Table 9). Although there was no significant improvement in performance due to protease pretreatment for pigs fed micronized soya diets, the time taken to reach slaughter weight was significantly reduced (P<0.05) by $4 \pm 1.86$ days.

These results suggest that liquid feeding presents an opportunity for the use of exogenous enzymes which can be targeted on specific raw materials. By this means the nutritional value of ingredients can be increased. When this improved availability of nutrients is reflected in changes in diet formulation, the pollutant potential of effluent can be reduced.

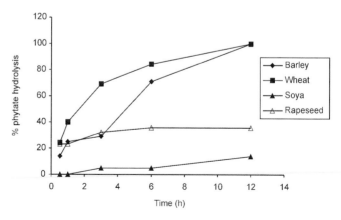

**Figure 2.** Effect of soaking raw materials in water on phytate hydrolysis (Seguier and Orr, unpublished data).

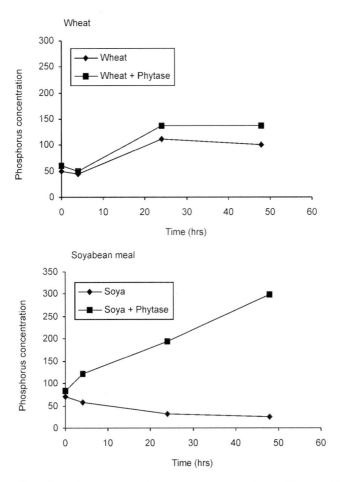

**Figure 3.** Effect of steeping raw materials in water or water + phytase (Geary and Brooks, unpublished data).

**Table 8.** *In vitro* nitrogen digestibility (%) of soyabean meals steeped for 24 hrs with three different proteases[3].

|  | Control | Protease 2 | Protease 3 | Protease 4 |
|---|---|---|---|---|
| Raw soyabean | 75.8 | 85.8[a1] | 88.9[a] | 85.8[a1] |
| Steam pressure cooked | 80.3 | 84.0[a1] | 84.9[a1] | 87.8[a1] |
| Micronised | 74.7 | 79.1[a2] | 82.7[1] | 77.8[a] |
| Toasted and milled | 67.8[1] | 73.5[a] | 74.4[a] | 74.8[a] |
| Autoclaved | 70.1[1] | 81.1[a2] | 78.1 | 82.3[a] |

[a] Values in a row differ from control, P<0.05.
[1,2] Values in a column differ, P<0.05.
[3]Beal *et al.*, 1998.

Table 9. Performance of pigs in the finisher period fed raw or micronized soya with or without protease pretreatment[1].

| | Raw soya | | Micronized soya | |
|---|---|---|---|---|
| Enzyme addition | – | + | – | + |
| Feed intake, kg/pig | 1.78 | 1.77 | 1.90 | 1.94 |
| Daily gain, g | 515* | 606* | 828 | 886 |
| FCR | 3.52* | 3.04* | 2.31 | 2.12 |

[1]Beal *et al.*, 1999.
*Means in a row differ, P<0.05.

# Fermented liquid feed: an alternative to antibiotic growth promoters?

A new development in liquid feeding is the deliberate fermentation of the feed before presentation of the food to the pig. This approach is creating great interest in Europe as producers strive to find alternatives to the antibiotic growth promoters which are being removed from the market.

## EFFECT OF DRY, LIQUID AND FERMENTED FEED ON GROWTH PERFORMANCE OF PIGLETS

The effect of presenting pigs with their feed dry (DF), liquid (freshly prepared) (LF) or as fermented liquid feed (FLF) has been reviewed recently (Jensen and Mikkelsen, 1998). The results of their review are summarised in Table 10.

Table 10. Improvement (%) in growth rate and food conversion ratio in experiments in which the performance of pigs fed dry feed (DF), liquid feed (LF) or fermented liquid feed (FLF) was compared[1].

| | No. of trials | Improved daily weight gain | | Improved food conversion ratio | |
|---|---|---|---|---|---|
| | | Mean (SD) | Range | Mean (SD) | Range |
| LF *v.* DF | 10 | 12.3 (9.4) | −7.5–34.2 | −4.1 (11.8) | −32.6–10.1 |
| FLF *v.* DF | 4 | 22.3 (13.2) | 9.2–43.8 | −10.9 (19.7) | −44.3–5.8 |
| FLF *v.* LF | 3 | 13.4 (7.1) | 5.7–22.9 | −1.4 (2.4) | −4.8–0.6 |

[1]After Jensen and Mikkelsen, 1998.

In weaner pigs daily liveweight gain is improved by on average 12.3% by presenting the feed in liquid form compared with dry and by a further 13.4% if the liquid feed is fermented (Table 10). However, FCR is generally somewhat poorer on LF and FLF compared with dry feed. This is in contrast to the results obtained from slaughter pigs (Table 1) and probably reflects differences in feeding behaviour between older and newly-weaned pigs. Our data (Table 6) show how FCR may be improved by altering trough design. Furthermore, recent work by our group has shown that in addition to trough design the position of the troughs in the pen and the pig to feeding space ratio all have an impact on FCR and individual pig growth rate. This is an area of study in which we are actively engaged at the present time.

### *Ad libitum* fermented liquid feed for weaners

Feeding weaner pigs on liquid diets has been attempted on a number of occasions in the past. The major problem has been to devise suitable feeding equipment and maintain the feed in a hygienic and palatable state. The approach that we have taken is to ferment the diets with *Lactobacillus* spp. before feeding. Our studies (Russell *et al.*, 1996) have shown significant differences in the growth rate of pigs fed dry or liquid diets, particularly in the first three weeks following weaning (Table 11). In these studies high quality commercial dry diets were used which had a very high digestibility and palatability and included lactose (from dry milk by-products) or added glucose. These fermented diets are very well accepted by weaners and there was no evidence of post-weaning scours. Growth rate was also improved by feeding fermented liquid feed rather than dry pelleted feed (Table 12).

Table 11.   Dry matter intake of piglets fed dry pelleted feed or fermented liquid feed[1].

| Week post weaning | Trial 1 | | | Trial 2 | | |
|---|---|---|---|---|---|---|
| | Dry pelleted feed | Fermented liquid feed | $SE_D$ | Dry pelleted feed | Fermented liquid feed | $SE_D$ |
| 1 | 130 | 416 | 11*** | 199 | 271 | 9* |
| 2 | 354 | 741 | 19*** | 418 | 560 | 16** |
| 3 | 636 | 1068 | 16*** | 686 | 819 | 12*** |
| 4 | 889 | 1204 | 35 | 877 | 954 | 9** |
| Overall | 443 | 807 | 11*** | 545 | 654 | 10*** |

[1]Russell *et al.*, 1996.
Means differ: * P<0.05; ** P<0.01; ***P<0.001.

It is notable in this study that the improved growth rate of pigs fed fermented liquid feed rather than dry pelleted feed appears to decline in the later weeks. Subsequent re-analysis of this and other studies indicates that this is because diets formulated on the basis of anticipated dry matter intake as dry pelleted feed provide excess protein to piglets on fermented liquid feed where intakes may be 20% greater. Under these circumstances feed utilisation is reduced, water consumption (and hence effluent production) is increased and ultimately dry matter intake is affected. This implies that when constructing diets for weaners which are going to be fed fermented liquid feed, care must be taken to formulate diets on the basis

121

Table 12. Growth rate (g/day) of piglets fed dry pelleted diets or fermented liquid feed[1].

| Week post-weaning | Trial 1 | | | Trial 2 | | |
|---|---|---|---|---|---|---|
| | Dry pelleted feed | Fermented liquid feed | SE$_D$ | Dry pelleted feed | Fermented liquid feed | SE$_D$ |
| 1 | 162 | 123 | 23** | 140 | 178 | 21 |
| 2 | 264 | 426 | 37*** | 340 | 425 | 18** |
| 3 | 529 | 635 | 38** | 511 | 602 | 21*** |
| 4 | 674 | 630 | 44 | 594 | 610 | 22 |
| Overall | 343 | 428 | 21*** | 397 | 454 | 14*** |

[1]Russell *et al.*, 1996.
Means differ: * P<0.05; ** P<0.01; ***P<0.001.

of nutrient intake per pig per day, using a realistic estimate of dry matter intake.

A subsequent study investigated the effect of dry matter concentration of the diet on performance (Geary *et al.*, 1996). We found that young pigs were capable of high dry matter intakes even on diets with a very low dry matter content. However, in order to avoid excess effluent production we would recommend that the dry matter content of the diet should not fall below 200 g/kg. Our data suggest that performance might be improved further by feeding a higher dry matter concentration ( 250 g/kg) following weaning and reducing the dry matter concentration (to around 200 g/kg) by four weeks post-weaning.

### Controlling fermentation

A major problem in the use of fermented liquid feed is maintaining control over the fermentation. Jensen and Mikkelsen (1998) have demonstrated the importance of temperature in controlling the fermentation and lowering the pH of the feed. Using a 0.5 residue and 8 hr replenishment of the tank, they found that a steady state was reached in 50 hrs when the tank was maintained at 25°C whilst around 100 hrs were required when the tank was maintained at 15°C. Their studies also suggest that approximately 3% of the dry matter and energy content of the feed is lost during the fermentation process (Table 13).

However, some caution should be exercised in interpreting data where energy values are derived from equations developed to predict energy value in dry feed. In liquid feed it is possible to get a reduction in gross energy while at the same time getting an increase in net energy. This is because some oligosaccharides and sugars present in the diet are being turned into volatile fatty acids which have a higher digestible energy (DE) value. Also, changes in the gut architecture produced by feeding fermented liquid feed may increase the pig's absorptive capacity. Thus even though fermentation is an energy demanding process, the positive benefits may make the effect on energy supply to the pig neutral.

Table 13.   Effect of fermentation temperature on the chemical composition of liquid feed[1].

| Treatment | Dry matter (%) | Energy (MJ/kg) | Starch (g/kg) | Total N (g/kg) |
|-----------|----------------|----------------|---------------|----------------|
| Non-fermented | 24.1a | 4.77a | 97.5 | 9.8 |
| 15 (C) | 23.4b | 4.62b | 97.6 | 9.4 |
| 20 (C) | 23.4b | 4.65b | 95.9 | 9.3 |
| 25 (C) | 23.2b | 4.58b | 96.5 | 9.4 |
| 30 (C) | 23.4b | 4.63b | 97.5 | 9.8 |
| Loss, % | 3.1 | 3.1 | | |

[1]Jensen and Mikkelsen, 1998.

In the early studies at our centre, we relied upon naturally occurring lactic acid bacteria to ferment the diets. Although this produced satisfactory results, we were concerned by the uncontrolled nature of this system. In particular, we were concerned that pig producers would not be able to exercise the same levels of control that could be achieved in experimental facilities. Therefore, our current work is investigating the use of specific lactic acid bacteria inoculants to control fermentation. In one study (Geary *et al.*, 1999) we acidified the diet either with lactic acid or through fermentation with *Pediococcus acidilactici*. Performance of the pigs did not differ between treatments and was better than that obtained in previous experiments where uncontrolled lactic acid bacteria fermentation was used (Table 14).

Table 14.   Performance of pigs fed liquid feed acidified with either lactic acid (control) or as a result of fermentation of the diet with *Pediococcus acidilactici*[1].

| Parameter | Control Lactic acid | *Pediococcus acidilactici* | SED |
|-----------|---------------------|---------------------------|-----|
| Dry matter feed intake, g/day | 536 | 563 | 71 |
| Daily gain, g/day | 474 | 496 | 25 |
| Dry matter FCR | 1.15 | 1.11 | 0.09 |
| Total water intake, ml/pig/day | 2078 | 2283 | 252 |
| Average water intake from drinkers, ml/pig/day | 511 | 638 | 133 |
| Average effluent production, ml/pig/day | 1118 | 1359 | 185 |

[1]Geary *et al.*, 1999.

It is worth noting that even when the diet was acidified with lactic acid, a population of lactic acid bacteria still developed. Over time as many lactic acid bacteria were present in the lactic acid treatment as in the treatment which had been fermented with *Pediococcus acidilactici* (Figure 4).

### The dangers of uncontrolled fermentations
It is important to recognise that uncontrolled fermentation always occurs to some extent in liquid feeding systems. Smith (1976) showed that lactic acid bacteria which occur naturally on cereal grains will proliferate in a wet feed system and reduce the pH (increase the acidity) of the diet. In Smith's study, adding water to the meal at feeding time produced a diet

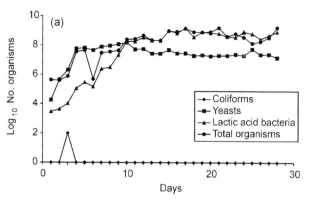

(a) Acidified with lactic acid.

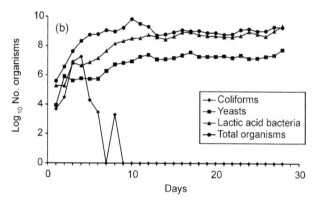

(b) Acidified with *Pediococus acidilactici.*

**Figure 4.** Effect on the microbial flora of acidifying feed to circa pH 4 either by addition of lactic acid or by fermentation with *Pediococcus acidilactici.* (Geary *et al.,* 1999).

with a pH of 5.8. Soaking the mixture for 24 hrs resulted in a massive proliferation of lactic acid bacteria which produced a beneficial increase in the acidity of the diet.

Because pipeline liquid feeding systems are not normally sterilised between feeds they are generally microbiologically active and the feed system acts as a microbiological fermenter. In 1989 a Danish survey revealed that it took 3–5 days for the lactobacilli levels to elevate and stabilise in pipeline feeding systems (Hansen and Mortensen, 1989). The survey also found that it could be detrimental to sterilise pipeline feeding systems as this removed the lactobacilli and reduced the acidity of the system. This in turn allowed coliform bacteria to proliferate for a period of 1–5 days until lactobacilli re-established themselves and lowered the pH again. The coliform 'bloom' which followed the sterilisation of pipeline systems was often associated with outbreaks of diarrhoea which resolved themselves as the acidity of the system was restored.

It should be noted that recent developments in liquid feeding equipment and feeding practice may have undesirable effects. There has been a move to feeding weaner pigs, lactating sows and even grow-finish pigs *ad libitum* on liquid diets. Liquid feed equipment manufacturers have started to market systems which mix small quantities of feed at regular intervals and deliver this into short troughs which always contain some feed. When components used to construct the diet are sufficiently acid, or have been deliberately acidified in order to eliminate bacteria and yeasts (pH<2.5), fermentation in the trough is usually inhibited and the feed in the trough retains its palatability. (Note that in these circumstances the final diet fed the pig will still be around pH 4.0). However, when the pH of the diet is above 4.5, undesirable fermentations take place and enteropathogens such as coliforms and salmonellae can proliferate.

In addition to the potential growth of pathogens other undesirable fermentations can occur in the diets. Uncontrolled yeast fermentations are a particular problem as they can either produce excessive alcohol or make the diet unpalatable. When short troughs (intended for *ad libitum* feeding) are used and the feed is unpalatable, behavioural problems may occur. In these circumstances pigs compete to eat fresh feed when it is delivered to the trough rather than feeding throughout the 24 hrs as intended. This can lead to aggression and the subsequent development of vices.

On units where these problems are occurring, producers are not attempting to produce fermented liquid feed. Fermentation is unwanted and uncontrolled. Studies that we have conducted in our laboratories suggest that it will be extremely difficult to devise procedures to prevent these unwanted fermentations. To date we have been unable to find any sterilant material that we can add to liquid diets which is both economically viable and maintains the palatability of the feed.

### Beneficial effects of fermented liquid feed

There are a number of reasons why the use of fermented liquid feed may benefit the weaner pig:

- Improved feed intake may maintain the growth of the gut epithelium.
- Acidity of the diet may help control pathogens both in the feed and in the pig's gut.
- Lactic acid bacteria may have a beneficial effect on the lower gut microflora.

The fastest growing tissue in the pig's body is the epithelial lining of the small intestine. Many of the nutrients needed for growth are directly absorbed from the gut lumen. Even transient starvation will result in a rapid reduction in villus height and thus reduce the absorptive capacity of the gut (Pluske *et al.*, 1996a; 1996b). Conversely, a diet which is palatable and well accepted by the newly-weaned pig will ensure an adequate supply of nutrients to the brush border.

The weaned pig lacks stomach acid which is the first line of defence against bacterial invasion. Mikkelson and Jensen (1997) found that fermented liquid feed results in a significant increase in stomach acidity. Our recent studies (Moran and Brooks unpublished data) confirm this and suggest that stomach pH may be lowered by as much as 2 units. Because of the buffering capacity of the gut the pH is not much altered in other parts of the tract. However, the relative proportions of the different short chain fatty acids are affected (Table 15).

Table 15.  Concentration of short chain fatty acids in the gastrointestinal tract of piglets fed unfermented liquid (control) feed or fermented liquid feed[1].

| | Acetic acid | | Lactic acid | |
|---|---|---|---|---|
| | unfermented liquid feed | fermented liquid feed | unfermented liquid feed | fermented liquid feed |
| Stomach | 16.6 | 16.5 | 37.3 | 81.7** |
| Small intestine 1 | 10.6 | 8.8 | 7.7 | 26.3** |
| Small intestine 2 | 10.2 | 9.1 | 13.7 | 24.5 |
| Small intestine 3 | 11.7 | 9.8 | 38.0 | 32.7 |
| Small intestine 4 | 12.8 | 13.3 | 47.6 | 40.2 |
| Caecum | 73.8 | 93.0*** | 2.3 | 2.9 |
| Colon 1 | 61.0 | 87.3*** | 0.5 | 0.0 |
| Colon 2 | 55.6 | 72.8** | 0.7 | 0.0 |
| Colon 3 | 60.1 | 69.9 | 1.0 | 0.0 |

[1]After Mikkelson and Jensen, 1997.
*Means differ: * $P<0.05$; **$P<0.01$; ***$P<0.001$.

The alteration of pH has a marked effect on the microbial population in both the feed and the pig. In a survey of 320 farms in Holland the incidence of subclinical salmonella infection was ten times lower on farms with liquid feeding and was particularly low on farms that fed acidified cheese whey (Tielen *et al.*, 1997). In other studies (van Winsen *et al.*, 1997) it was found that pig feed fermented with *L. plantarum* had a bacteriostatic effect during the first two hours and a bacteriocidal effect thereafter. After six hours *S. typhimurium* could not be detected. In non-fermented feed *S. typhimurium* survived and multiplied during the first 10 hrs of storage.

Feeding fermented liquid feed does not appear to produce any significant effect on the number of lactic acid bacteria throughout the gut but it does dramatically reduce the number of coliforms in the lower small intestine, caecum and colon (Jensen *et al.*, 1998; Moran and Brooks, unpublished data).

## Conclusions

Liquid feeding has the potential to make a significant contribution to the environment both through recycling human food residues and through more efficient utilisation of conventional feed ingredients. In this context the opportunities presented for more effective, targeted use of exogenous enzymes is of particular interest.

The use of fermented liquid feed has great promise both as a means of overcoming the post-weaning growth lag and as a way of increasing feed safety by salmonella exclusion. Studies to date have already shown that fermented liquid feed can result in improved performance of the weaner pig. The identification and use of specific lactic acid bacteria to ferment the feed may enable pathogen exclusion both from the diet and from the pig. In addition, the system may provide a replacement for antibiotic growth promoters without loss of productivity.

However, there are a number of problems still to be solved before this can be regarded as a commercial feeding system which can be generally adopted on commercial units. Thus the objectives of our ongoing research programme are:

- to select appropriate lactic acid bacteria for use as inoculants to produce fermented liquid feed
- to identify nutrient and raw material constraints to be used in the formulation of diets which will be fermented
- to define Standard Operating Procedures for farmers which will ensure that suitable and safe fermented liquid feed can be produced
- to specify and develop feeding equipment capable of producing/maintaining fermented liquid feed.

## References

Beal, J. D., P. H. Brooks and H. Schultze. 1998. The effect of pre-treatment with different proteases on the *in vitro* digestibility of nitrogen in raw soyabean and four differently processed full fat soyabean meals. *In:* Book of Abstracts of the 49th Meeting of the European Association of Animal Production. Warsaw 24th–29th August. Wageningen Pers, Wageningen. 264 (abs).

Beal, J. D., P. H. Brooks and H. Schulze. 1999. The effect of protease pre-treatment of raw or micronized soyabean meal on the growth performance and carcass composition in liquid fed grower and finisher pigs. BSAS Winter Meeting, Scarborough.

de Haas, T. C. M. 1998. Home mix farming with food industry co-products: experience in the Netherlands and its worldwide possibilities. In: Biotechnolgy in the feed industry, proceedings of the 14th Annual Symposium (T.P. Lyons and K.A. Jacques) Nottingham University Press, Nottingham. pp. 613–618.

Fraser, S. 1998. Liquid assets. Feed Milling. 192:(2)45–49.

Geary, T. M., J. D. Beal, P. H. Brooks and A. Campbell. 1999. Effect on weaner performance and diet microbiology of feeding a liquid diet acidified to pH 4 with either lactic acid or through fermentation with *Pediococcus acidilactici*. Journal of the Science of Food and Agriculture (In press).

Geary, T. M., P. H. Brooks, D. T. Morgan, A. Campbell and P. J. Russell. 1996. Performance of weaner pigs fed *ad libitum* with liquid feed at different dry matter concentrations. Journal of Science of Food and Agriculture. 72:17–24.

Gill, B. P. 1998. Phase feeding: effects on production efficiency and meat quality. Meat and Livestock Commission, Milton Keynes. pp. 56.

Hansen, I. D. and B. Mortensen. 1989. Pipe-cleaners beware. Pig International. 19:(11)9–10.

Jensen, B. B. and L. L. Mikkelsen. 1998. Feeding liquid diets to pigs. In: Recent advances in animal nutrition 1998 (P.C. Garnsworthy and J. Wiseman, eds). Nottingham University Press, Thrumpton, Nottingham. 107–126.

Meat and Livestock Commission. 1998. Pig Yearbook 1998. Meat and Livestock Commission, Milton Keynes.

Mikkelson, L.L. and B. B. Jensen. 1997. Effect of fermented liquid feed (FLF) on growth performance and microbial activity in the gastrointestinal tract of weaned piglets. In: Digestive Physiology in Pigs. (J.P. Laplace, C. Fevrier and Barbeau, eds). EAAP Publication No.88, INRA, Paris. 639–642.

Pluske, J. R., M. J. Thompson, C. S. Atwood, P. H. Bird, I. H. Williams and P. E. Hartman. 1996a. Maintenance of villus height and crypt depth, and enhancement of disaccharide digestion and monsaccharide absorption, in piglets fed on cows' whole milk after weaning. British Journal of Nutrition. 76:409–422.

Pluske, J. R., I. H. Williams and F. X. Aherne. 1996b. Maintenance of villous height and crypt depth in piglets by providing continous nutrition after weaning. Journal of Animal Science 62:131–144.

Russell, P. J., T. M. Geary, P. H. Brooks and A. Campbell. 1996. Performance, water use and effluent output of weaner pigs fed *ad libitum* with either dry pellets of liquid feed and the role of microbial activity in the liquid feed. Journal of Science of Food and Agriculture. 72:8–16.

Scholten, R.H.J., A.I.J. Hoofs and M.P. Beurskens-Voermans. 1997. Bijproductenrantsoen voor vleesvarkens: invloed van voerniveau en aminozurengehalte (in Dutch). Praktijknoderzoek Varkenshouderij, pp. 1–12.

Scholten, R. H. J., V. D. Peet-Schwering, L.A. den Hartog, P.C. Vesseur and M.W.A. Verstegen. 1998. Effect of liquid by-products on performance and health of pigs. 49th Annual Meeting of the European Association for Animal Production, Warsaw, Poland. 1–12.

Smith, P. 1976. A comparison of dry, wet and soaked meal for fattening bacon pigs. Experimental Husbandry. 30:87–94.

Tielen, M.J.M., F.W. van Schie, P. J. van der Wolf, A. R. W. Elbers, J. M. C. C. Koppens and W. B. Wolbers. 1997. Risk factors and control measures for subclinical salmonella infection in pig herds. In: Proceedings of the second international symposium on epidemiology and control of salmonella in pork. (S. Bech-Nielsen and J.P. Nielsen, eds)

Copenhagen, Denmark, August 20–22. Federation of Danish Pig Producers and Slaughterhouses, Copenhagen. 32–35.

van Winsen, R. L., H.A.P. Urlings and J.M.A. Snijders. 1997. Feed as a vehiculum of salmonella in pigs. In: Proceedings of the second international symposium on epidemiology and control of salmonella in pork. (S. Bech-Nielsen and J.P. Nielsen, eds.) Federation of Danish Pig Producers and Slaughterhouses, Copenhagen, Denmark. 157–159.

# Control of foodborne pathogens in pigs

NOEL T. KAVANAGH

*Oldcastle Laboratories, Cogan Street, Oldcastle, Co. Meath, Ireland*

## Introduction

A zoonosis is an infectious disease naturally transmissible between vertebrates and man. At first sight the list of potential zoonoses is quite imposing; however when the exotic and rare zoonoses are removed from the list it is easier to focus on a relatively short list of important pathogens. Whilst the threat of zoonoses from pig meat is significantly lower than that from other species, it is vitally important that all parties involved in the pig industry focus on reducing the risk of zoonoses to an insignificant level in view of the fact that food safety has assumed a role of increased importance in pig meat. Control programmes designed to reduce the prevalence of foodborne pathogens in pig meat must commence on the farm with the objective of reducing the prevalence of the organisms in pigs at slaughter. Butchering and processing procedures should be designed to prevent cross-contamination of carcasses.

The main foodborne zoonotic pathogens in pigs are probably salmonella, yersinia, campylobacter and toxoplasma, with salmonella being by far the most important (Table 1). There are two primary species of campylobacter, *coli* and *jejuni*. Pigs primarily carry *C. coli,* but can also carry *C. jejuni.* Food poisoning in humans is more often associated with *C. jejuni,* which is mainly sourced from poultry, other meats, unpasteurised milk, contaminated water and contact with other animals such as dogs. The pig is the primary source of *Yersinia enterocolitica.* The organism is harboured in the pig's tonsils and intestine so carcass contamination may occur in the slaughterhouse. *Toxoplasma gondii* is spread from cats to pigs. It is not host-specific and can also be associated with abortions in sheep. It can cause abortions in women. Davies *et al.* (1998b) reported that management practices in modern production systems in North Carolina in the US appear to virtually eliminate the risk of infecting finishing pigs with either *T. gondii* and *Trichinella spiralis.* Food poisoning caused by other organisms such as *Listeria monocytogenes* and clostridia species can be associated with incorrect food storage procedures. The Erysipelas bacterium *Erysipelothrix rhusiopathiae* can infect sheep, turkeys and fish as well as pigs. It is also commonly found in soil. Erysipeloid in humans is primarily an occupational hazard to slaughterhouse and fish factory workers. Abscesses, associated with *Staphylococcus aureus*, are rarely associated with food poisoning in humans. *S. aureus* food poisoning in humans is more commonly associated with poor storage conditions and post processing contamination. In general, the strains found in red meat differ from human strains of *S. aureus* (Roberts, 1982). *Staphylococcus aureus* associated abscesses are, however, aesthetically unacceptable and therefore strict hygiene procedures must be followed so that lesions are detected, removed, and prevented from entering the food chain. Influenza viruses may be transmitted from humans to pigs and *vice versa*. It is important that the pig veterinarian have a sound working knowledge of pig zoonoses such that the relatively rare and exotic ones be identified, thus allowing him to focus on the important ones such as salmonella and in particular multi-antibiotic resistant phage types of *Salmonella typhimurium*. Salmonella control must commence at farm level with a view to reducing the exposure rate of pigs to salmonella on the farm. This should be supported by sound butchering, transporter and lairage hygiene procedures in order to prevent pig exposure to salmonella at slaughter and contamination of carcasses during the butchering process. The importance of good hygiene procedures in the kitchen cannot be over emphasised, since salmonella can be killed by exposure to a temperature of 71.5°C for a period of only 15 seconds. As salmonella control progresses, it is important that an intensive control programme be introduced in those herds containing multi-antibiotic resistant salmonellae.

Table 1. A comparison of pig zoonoses among Ireland, the European mainland and the rest of the world[1].

|  | Ireland | Mainland EU | Rest of world |
| --- | --- | --- | --- |
| Salmonella | + | + | + |
| Yersinia | + | + | + |
| Campylobacter | + | + | + |
| Toxoplasma | −[1] | + | + |
| Influenza | + | + | + |
| *Streptococcus suis* | + | + | + |
| *Leptospira pomona* | − | + | + |
| *Brucella suis* | − | + | + |
| Japanese B- encephalitis | − | − | + |
| Trichinella | − | + | + |
| Anthrax | − | + | + |

[1]Limited serological survey (Kavanagh 1998).

## Sources of foodborne pathogens

The route of infection of the most important food pathogens listed in Table 2 is the oral route. Therefore the prevalence of the organism in sows and finishing pigs at slaughter will be influenced by the rate of exposure of pigs to contaminated faeces of mainly pigs, birds, mice and cats. The identification and characterisation of the main foodborne pathogens in pigs are also documented. The methods of dissemination of foodborne pathogens are listed in Table 3 where the period of survival in the environment varies from three weeks to 18 months. Because the primary route of infection of the most important food pathogens is oral, the prevalence of the organism at slaughter will be influenced by exposure to contaminated faeces.

Table 2.  Identification and characterisation of the main foodborne microbial hazards of pig origin.[1]

| Organism | Route of infection | At-risk group | Severity of disease | How common is the disease | Sporadic or outbreak |
|---|---|---|---|---|---|
| *Salmonella* spp. | Oral | Consumer | +++ | ++++ | Sporadic |
| *Y. enterocolytica* | Oral | Consumer | +/++ | ++ | Sporadic |
| *C. jejuni/coli* | Oral | Consumer | ++ | ++++ | Outbreak |
| *T. gondii* | Oral | Consumer | +/++ | + | Sporadic |

[1]All are of animal origin and cause disease in humans.

Table 3.  Methods of dissemination of foodborne pathogens.

| Organism | Environmental survival | Incubation period | Period of shedding | Route |
|---|---|---|---|---|
| *C. jejuni/coli* | Slurry: 24 days at 8°C | 1–3 days | Several months | Faeces |
| *Y. enterocolitica* | 3 weeks | 2–3 weeks | 30 weeks | Faeces |
| *T. gondii* | 1 year Infectivity via cat faeces: 3 days | | Viable in tissues 2 years | Cat faeces |
| *Salmonella* | Farm buildings 18 months, Cattle slurry and pasture 11–12 weeks | | 28 weeks | Faeces (commonly) Aerosol (occasionally) |

# CAMPYLOBACTER

In the United Kingdom the reported number of cases of human campylobacter infection exceeds that of salmonella and is still rising. Most epidemiological studies have indicated that poultry meat is the major risk factor for campylobacter (Kapperud *et al.*, 1992). The majority (over 90%) of campylobacter isolates from pig faeces are *C. coli* (Madden *et al.*, 1996) while most (about 90%) human clinical isolates are *C. jejunii* (Newell, 1997). Nevertheless, *C. jejunii* can be isolated from pig carcasses (Stern *et al.*, 1985). Surveys of pigs at slaughter indicate that 50–100% of normal pigs are colonised with thermophilic campylobacters before and at the time of slaughter (Rosef *et al.*, 1983). The organism can survive in pig slurry for 24 days and infected pigs can shed the organism in the faeces for several months. Transmission from pig to pig is via faecal contamination of the pens, feed or water.

## ARCOBACTER

Evidence is now accumulating that *Arcobacter spp.*, in particular *A. butzleri*, are pathogenic in man where they induce diarrhoea (Marinescu *et al.*, 1996) and abdominal cramps (Vandamme and Goosens, 1992). These organisms can also be isolated from poultry and cattle. In the pig they have been associated with late term abortions and vaginal discharges, and in cattle with abortions. Being closely related to campylobacter these organisms colonise the pig's intestine and pig exposure is primarily by the faecal/oral route.

## YERSINIA ENTEROCOLITICA

*Yersinia enterocolitica*, the cause of human yersiniosis, is harboured by healthy pigs. Studies of the dissemination of infection in pig facilities indicate that infection is transmitted in contaminated pens where the organism can persist on the floors for three to 12 weeks (Fukushima *et al.*, 1983). Transmission from pig to pig is via faecal contamination of the accommodation, water or feed. Following exposure of pigs to *Y. enterocolitica*, the organism is shed in the faeces within two to three weeks and shedding continues for approximately 30 weeks so pigs are capable of spreading disease for approximately 32 weeks following exposure to the organism (Fukushima *et al.*, 1984). *Y. enterocolitica* is more frequently isolated in finishing pigs than in sows. Following exposure to contaminated pens shortly after weaning, the prevalence of yersinia-positive pigs reaches a peak at 12–21 weeks of age and then gradually decreases, such that the organisms are not commonly isolated from pigs over 30 weeks of age. The cessation of yersinia excretion in faeces at greater than 30 weeks of age may be associated with the establishment of local immunity in the gut, and this could explain why the rate of excretion from older sows is relatively low as compared with finishers. *Y. enterocolitica* is best known for its cross reaction with Brucella which gives false positives on Brucella serological tests.

## TOXOPLASMA GONDII

Humans usually become infected with *Toxoplasma gondii* by ingesting oocysts in food and water contaminated by cat faeces or by consuming tissue cysts in under-cooked meat (Dubey and Beattie, 1988).

Toxoplasmosis occurs worldwide, and the prevalence in finisher pigs varies in different parts of the world. *T. gondii* is a coccidian parasite, of which the cat is the definitive host. The oocysts are shed in cat faeces and may contaminate feed, water and soil that could be ingested by pigs. The oocysts become infective in less than seven days. Ingestion of oocysts by the pig results in the production of tissue cysts which cause a human health risk if consumed. Exposure of women to *T. gondii* for the first time during pregnancy can result in perinatal mortality and birth defects. Infection of immuno-compromised humans, eg., HIV patients, can result in encephalitis, blindness and death.

Management factors can influence the level of toxoplasma in pigs. Lubroth *et al.*, (1983) demonstrated that the prevalence of *T. gondii* in pigs raised in total confinement was low since they rarely had contact with wildlife which can have a high carrier rate of *T. gondii*. Assadi-Rad *et al.* (1995) studied the risk factors associated with the transmission of *T. gondii* to sows kept in different management systems and demonstrated that sows kept outdoors at any time were 23 times more likely to be seropositive than sows kept indoors. Sows on farms known to have cats were 2.6 times more likely to be seropositive than those on farms without cats. They concluded that the high risk of toxoplasmosis in outdoor sows was due to environmental contamination in addition to known exposure to cats which are the definitive host for *T. gondii*. Efficient rodent control also plays a role, since previously toxoplasma-free cats can become seropositive due to consumption of infected rodents. Smith *et al.* (1992) also demonstrated that the prevalence of *T. gondii* antibodies in pigs increased with age and that the prevalence could be reduced through total confinement.

## SALMONELLA

The epidemiology of salmonella infection in pigs is complex and involves two-way transmission between man and pigs, the environment, animal feedstuffs, rodents, birds and flies.

Whilst a high percentage of sows in a herd may be serologically positive for salmonella, where hygiene procedures are satisfactory and the farrowing area is operated on an all in/all out system, the rate of transmission of salmonella from sows to piglets may be relatively low, particularly where early weaning (<21 days) is practised. However, if pigs are weaned at more than 28 days of age, the rate of salmonella transmission from sows to piglets may increase due to loss of maternal antibodies in the pigs. A minimum weaning age of 21 days is set by EU regulations.

Rodents (mice and rats) can infect pigs with salmonella and be infected by pigs. Flies can mechanically transmit salmonella between groups of pigs. Birds, particularly pigeons, seagulls and sparrows can introduce salmonella to pigs by direct contamination of troughs or pens where they have access to pig feed (Wray and Davies, 1996). They can also contaminate cereals which are grown and subsequently fed to pigs. Carrier pigs can shed the organism in passageways, loading ramps, pig transporters and in lairages such that the organism can be spread to other pigs if hygiene procedures in these areas are inadequate. The majority of pigs are infected with salmonella by the oral/fecal route; however the organism can also be spread by aerosol transmission (Fedorka-Cray *et al.*, 1995). Power-washing and disinfection of partly depopulated pig houses could enhance the spread of salmonella to the remaining pigs in a house through aerosol contamination created by the power-washer. As a result it is imperative that rooms be operated strictly on an all-in all-out basis.

Salmonellae are almost ubiquitous and can be found in the environment of many animal species. Given that complete eradication is unrealistic, the objective is to reduce pig exposure to a level that constitutes a minimal human health risk. Human cases of foodborne salmonella infection are less commonly associated with pigs than with other animal products, particularly eggs and poultry.

## MYCOBACTERIUM AVIUM-INTRACELLULARE

*Mycobacterium avium-intracellulare* sometimes occurs in pigs, causing lesions in cervical and occasionally mesenteric lymph nodes. These lesions are readily detected by meat inspectors and the affected head or offal condemned. Similar lesions can also be caused by yersinia and *Mycobacterium bovis,* however, *M. bovis* is not a significant disease of pigs in Ireland. *M. avium* infections of humans are rarely derived from infected pigs and are more commonly associated with infections which humans derive from the environment. As a result *M. avium* infected pig carcasses pose no risk to humans (Brown and Tollison, 1979).

## STAPHYLOCOCCUS AUREUS

Abscesses associated with *Staphylococcus aureus,* are rarely associated with food poisoning in humans. *S. aureus* food poisoning in humans is more commonly associated with poor storage conditions and post-processing contamination. In general, the strains found in red meat differ from strains of found in humans (Roberts, 1982). *S. aureus* abscesses are, however, aesthetically unacceptable. Therefore strict hygiene procedures should be followed so that lesions are detected, removed and prevented from entering the food chain.

## HELICOBACTER PYLORI

*Helicobacter pylori* is associated with gastritis, peptic ulcers and gastric cancer in humans (Marshall, 1994). Many domestic species including the pig can harbour the organism; however there is no evidence that occupational exposure to domestic animals increases the risk of human infection (Thomas *et al.*, 1994).

# Types of salmonella isolated from pigs in Ireland

During the period 1995–1997 approximately two thirds of the salmonella strains isolated from Irish pigs were *Salmonella typhimurium* (Figure 1) and the balance made up of *S. derby, choleraesuis, bredeny, goldcoast, london, mbandaka, panama*, and *infantis*. (Table 4). These findings are broadly similar to those reported from Great Britain where *S. typhimurium* and *derby* are ranked 1 and 2; however *choleraesuis* is more prevalent in Ireland, making up 9% of isolates compared with 2.5% in Britain.

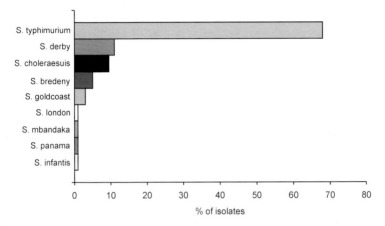

**Figure 1. The isolation rate of *Salmonella typhimurium* from Irish pigs (1995-1997)**

Table 4.   The type of Salmonella isolated from pigs in Ireland during 1995 – 97.

|  | Number of isolates | Percentage of isolates |
| --- | --- | --- |
| *Salmonella typhimurium* | 47 | 67.14 |
| *Salmonella derby* | 8 | 11.42 |
| *Salmonella cholerasuis* | 6 | 8.57 |
| *Salmonella bredeny* | 3 | 4.29 |
| *Salmonella goldcoast* | 2 | 2.86 |
| *Salmonella london* | 1 | 1.43 |
| *Salmonella mbandaka* | 1 | 1.43 |
| *Salmonella panama* | 1 | 1.43 |
| *Salmonella infantis* | 1 | 1.43 |
| Total | 70 | 100 |

ANTIBIOTIC RESISTANCE PATTERNS OF SALMONELLA ISOLATES FROM PIGS IN IRELAND

Isolates were classified as multi-resistant if resistance to ampicillin, chloramphenicol and tetracylines was demonstrated. Of the *S. typhimurium* isolates, 44.6% were classified as multi-resistant (Table 5). In Britain approximately 95% of salmonella DT104 isolates were multiresistant in 1996 (Threfall *et al.*, 1997). None of the remaining salmonella serovars demonstrated multi resistance.

**Table 5.** **Multi-antibiotic resistance patterns of salmonella isolates from pigs in Ireland during 1995–1997.**

| | Number of isolates | Number of resistant isolates | Percentage of multi-resistant isolates |
|---|---|---|---|
| *S. typhimurium* | 47 | 21 | 44.6 |
| *S. derby* | 8 | 0 | 0 |
| *S. cholerasuis* | 6 | 0 | 0 |
| *S. bredeny* | 3 | 0 | 0 |
| *S. goldcoast* | 2 | 0 | 0 |
| *S. london* | 1 | 0 | 0 |
| *S. mbandaka* | 1 | 0 | 0 |
| *S. panama* | 1 | 0 | 0 |
| *S. infantis* | 1 | 0 | 0 |

# Methods of identifying carrier pigs and pigs previously exposed to salmonella

Kazboher *et al.* (1997) compared the results of salmonella cultures from faecal samples, mesenteric lymph nodes and carcass surface swabs and found a salmonella prevalence rate of 3.7, 3.3 and 4.7%, respectively. The results suggest that faecal samples are a reliable indicator of salmonella carrier rates as are mesenteric lymph nodes and, by extension, caecal contents. They also found that serological tests using polymerase chain reaction (PCR) technology identified a similar prevalence rate to that of bacteriological tests using culture procedures. While test results on individual animals gave poor correlation between the tests, as a screening procedure good correlation between test procedures was recorded. They concluded that the serological method was a suitable technique for use in the context of a continuous monitoring programme. The serological method has the further advantages in that it can detect herds with a history of salmonella infection, it is inexpensive and sample handling procedures are convenient.

In Denmark the Danish Mix ELISA (enzyme-linked immunosorbent assay) test is used on either meat juice or serum as a method of establishing the exposure rate to salmonella during production. They have also established a correlation between positive ELISA test results (the presence of salmonella antibodies in serum or meat juice) and the salmonella carrier rate.

SALMONELLA CONTROL IN IRELAND

The traditional method of identifying carrier pigs involved specialised culture techniques using pre-enrichment procedures in order to enhance the isolation rate. A range of procedures have been documented for isolation of salmonella (Bager and Peterson, 1991). The method of choice, and the one which is approved for use in accredited laboratories in Ireland, is the Rappaport and Vassiliadis (RV) procedure with pre-enrichment. This procedure produces the highest sensitivity and therefore the greatest chance of isolating salmonella organisms if present. However, enrichment culture procedures are expensive and for this reason ELISA tests were developed, initially in Denmark, and later in other countries. The ELISA test can be applied to meat juice and serum and offers the most sensitive and economic method of monitoring the incidence of exposure of pigs to salmonella. With this system the rate of exposure of pigs to salmonella can be monitored at the slaughter house and also at various stages during the production cycle. Thus it is possible to establish the point of exposure and then to facilitate the introduction of control procedures designed to reduce the exposure rate. For example, pigs could be exposed to salmonella in one house at a particular stage of the production cycle and therefore all pigs going through that house could experience a high exposure rate. At the same time pigs in other houses could remain unexposed. Identification of the area of exposure facilitates tailoring the control programme to focus on the area of exposure.

Meat samples are identified, collected and frozen at the slaughterhouse. All samples are forwarded to the laboratory and the meat juice is obtained when the frozen samples are thawed. All the meat juice samples are examined by an indirect ELISA based on a combination of the lipopolysaccharide (LPS) antigens 0:1, 4, 5, 6, 7 and 12 (Table 6). The Mix ELISA detects about 95% of all salmonella serotypes occurring in Irish pigs (Kavanagh, 1998b). Herds are categorised on the basis of the prevalence of seropositives using a rolling average of three tests (24 samples per test) conducted at four-monthly intervals (Table 7).

Table 6. **Lipopolysaccharide (LPS) O antigens of common salmonella serotypes.**

| Serovar | LPS |
|---|---|
| *Salmonella typhimurium* | 1, 4, 5, 12 |
| *Salmonella cholerasuis* | 6, 7 |
| *Salmonella infantis* | 6, 7 |
| *Salmonella london* | 3, 10 |
| *Salmonella derby* | 1, 4, 5, 12 |
| *Salmonella bredeney* | 1, 4, 12, 27 |
| *Salmonella enteritidis* | 1, 9, 12 |
| *Salmonella dublin* | 1, 9, 12 |
| *Salmonella panama* | 1, 9, 12 |

**Table 7.** Herd categorisation based on prevalence of seropositive meat samples.

| Category | Seroprevalence |
|---|---|
| Level 1 herds | low, ≤10% |
| Level 2 herds | moderate, 11 – 50% |
| Level 3 herds | high, 50% |

# Sources of salmonella infection in pigs

## RODENTS AND BIRDS AS SALMONELLA CARRIERS

Davies and Wray (1995) reported that 35% of mice carried *Salmonella enteritidis* in the liver, 46% in the intestine and 10% in droppings. This confirms that mice can be a major source of salmonella to pigs. In a further study with mice artificially infected with *S. enteritidis* they found that mice shed 1,000–10,000 salmonella per 100 droppings for 3–4 weeks following exposure. Salmonella shedding in the droppings continued for a further five months but at a lower rate. As $10^4$ colony forming units (CFU) of *S. typhimurium* is sufficient to infect one pig this highlights the importance of good rodent control at farm level, since mice can shed up to 100 faecal pellets per day and one faecal pellet is sufficient to infect a pig. It is therefore conceivable that one mouse could infect up to 100 pigs per day. In addition, seagulls, sparrows and pigeons can contaminate feed mills and pig farms with *Salmonella typhimurium* (Wray and Davies, 1996).

## SALMONELLA IN PIG FEEDS

*Salmonella typhimurium* is occasionally isolated from raw materials from finished feed in the UK (MAFF, 1995). *S. typhimurium* is not, however, amongst the top five pig feed salmonella isolates (MAFF, 1995) (Table 8). *Salmonella kedouga* and *senftenberg* isolates are common to both UK pig feed and pigs, suggesting that these two salmonella serotypes may be transmitted by pig feed (MAFF, 1995) (Table 9).

### The influence of feed type on salmonella prevalence
In Denmark, the prevalence of salmonella seropositives is three times higher when finishers are fed purchased, heat treated, pelleted feed instead of home-mixed meal. (Dahl and Wingstrand, 1997; Bager, 1994). This does not suggest that the pelleted feed is a source of *S. typhimurium*, since *S. typhimurium* has never been isolated in Danish feedstuffs. It has been suggested that the larger particle size of the home-mixed feed (rolled grain) compared to that of the purchased heat treated pelleted feed may partly explain the difference in seropositivity between pigs fed pelleted and home-mixed feed.

**Table 8.**   Top 5 salmonella serotypes isolated from pig feed in the UK in 1994 and 1995[1].

| Serotype | 1994 | 1995 |
|---|---|---|
| | Number of isolates | |
| *S. senftenberg* | 25 | 31 |
| *S. mbandaka* | 20 | 24 |
| *S. tennessee* | 20 | 13 |
| *S. binza* | 15 | |
| *S. kedougou* | 10 | |
| *S. liverpool* | | 13 |
| *S. cubana* | | 10 |
| *S. taksony* | | 8 |

[1]MAFF, 1995.

**Table 9.**   Top 12 salmonella serotypes isolated from pigs in the UK in 1995.[1]

| | Number of isolates |
|---|---|
| *S. typhimurium* | 218 |
| *S. derby* | 57 |
| *S. kedouga* | 9 |
| *S. goldcoast* | 8 |
| *S. give* | 5 |
| *S. panama* | 5 |
| *S. cholerasuis* | 4 |
| *S. anatum* | 3 |
| *S. infantis* | 3 |
| *S. livingstone* | 3 |
| *S. senftenberg* | 3 |
| *S. 412* | 1 |

[1]MAFF, 1995.

The relative risk of salmonella seropositivity at pig level is 2.7 times higher when finishers are fed dry pelleted feed in contrast to fermented wet feed (Dahl and Wingstrand, 1997; Bager 1994). This may be associated with an altered gut fermentation process due to the feeding of fermented wet feeds or feeds of larger particle size providing an unsuitable environment for salmonella proliferation in the gut. Salmonella favour a pH higher than 4. In most wet feeding systems, where the product is allowed to ferment, a natural fermentation process results in the growth of lactic acid-producing bacteria and yeast. The protective effect of feeding fermented wet feed may be underestimated. The Danish results to date would suggest that more specific research should be carried out on the influence of particle size and fermented wet feed on salmonella seropositivity in finishers. The influence of enzymes, organic acids and dietary raw materials on the salmonella carrier rate deserves further research.

Kavanagh and Spillane (unpublished) established in a survey of pigs at slaughter that the prevalence of salmonella antibodies in pigs fed a

141

diet containing whey was less than one third that of pigs fed a liquid diet without whey (Table 10 and 11). Meat juice samples were tested by the Mix ELISA test.

**Table 10.** **The prevalence of positive meat juice ELISA test results in pigs fed a diet containing whey.**

| Farm | % positive | Herd size | Number of samples |
|------|-----------|-----------|-------------------|
| A | 39 | 430 sow unit[1] | 108 |
| B | 8 | 1500 sow unit[1] | 144 |
| C | 7 | 600 sow unit1 | 84 |
| D | 12 | 1100 sow unit[1] | 79 |
| E | 2 | 6500 finisher | 30 |
| F | 0 | 750 sow unit | 60 |
| G | 11 | 7000 finisher | 123 |
| Mean | 11.3 | | 105 |

[1]Integrated breeding herd, selling finishers.

**Table 11.** **The prevalence of positive meat juice ELISA test results in pigs fed on wet feed without whey.**

| Farm | % positive | Herd Size | No. of samples |
|------|-----------|-----------|----------------|
| H | 9 | 400 sow unit[1] | 48 |
| I | 95 | 5000 finishers | 90 |
| J | 42 | 4200 finishers | 60 |
| K | 21 | 2700 finishers | 53 |
| L | 0 | 1400 sow unit[1] | 54 |
| M | 41 | 450 sow unit[1] | 48 |
| Mean | 34.7 | | 59 |

[1]Integrated breeding herd, selling finishers.

## THE INFLUENCE OF FLOOR TYPE ON PREVALENCE OF *SALMONELLA* IN FAECAL SAMPLES

Davies *et al.* (1997) reported that the prevalence of salmonella in faecal samples was lowest in pigs housed on fully slatted floors compared with all other floor types and was highest in pigs raised on dirt lots. Unfortunately, many slatted floors are of poor quality and design in which circumstances the welfare requirements of the pig might not be satisfied. However, good quality, well designed slatted floors can increase pig comfort, and by reducing pig faecal contact reduce the rate of pig exposure to potential foodborne pathogens. The actual choice of slat design will vary, depending on the type and age of pigs.

Sow housing type could also influence the prevalence of foodborne pathogens in sows at slaughter. It has been demonstrated that outdoor sows can have a significantly higher carrier rate of *Toxoplasma gondii* than sows housed indoors. As efficient salmonella control progresses at farm level, the role of the sow in transmission may assume greater importance than at present. Housing systems that minimise the sow's contact with contaminated faeces may be needed, especially when piglets are weaned at more than four weeks of age. Davies *et al.* (1998a) identified a high prevalence of Salmonella shedding in breeding animals and suggested food products derived from culled breeding pigs may be an important source of foodborne disease.

## SALMONELLA CARRIERS

The results of recent investigations have indicated that following oral exposure of pigs to *S. typhimurium*, the bacterium may be isolated from caecal contents within 4–6 hrs (Fedorka-Cray *et al.*, 1995). Consequently, pigs could become carriers as a result of exposure to dirty loading ramps, dirty transporters and contaminated lairages.

### Influence of herd size on the prevalence of salmonella carriers

A survey in the USA revealed that the percent of farms with at least one salmonella positive sample increased as herd size increased, from 32% of farms selling <2,000 pigs annually to 57% selling >10,000 pigs (Bush and Fedorka-Cray, 1997). This trend has been observed in Ireland by Kavanagh (1997) where the mean herd size from which *S. typhimurium* was isolated was 910 sows compared with a mean herd of 410 sows without an isolation. A similar trend was observed in Denmark (Baggesen *et al.*, 1996). The conclusion is that the highest prevalence of salmonella is most likely to be found in the larger pig farms. In the Danish studies *S. typhimurium* was isolated in 23.1% of large herds (producing >2,600 pigs per year) compared with 14.7% of small herds (annual production 500–550 slaughter pigs per year). Carstensen and Christensen (1998) reported that whilst herd size was positively associated with the seroprevalence of *S. enteriticia*, it was of little significance because the within-herd and between-herd variations were relatively larger in comparison.

# Production of salmonella-free pigs

## EARLY WEANING, ALL IN/ALL OUT MANAGEMENT

Early weaning has been practised in the US to produce salmonella-free pigs in conjunction with multi-site production systems. A survey of nine farms by Fedorka-Cray *et al.* (1994b) found that all pigs, with the exception of one, when tested at 142 days post-weaning were negative on culture for salmonella. With multi-site production systems each unit is operated on an all in/all out production system. This highlights the importance of all in/all out management and demonstrates quite clearly that piglets are generally free or have a low carrier rate at weaning. If combined with good hygiene procedures, all in/all out production and elimination of cross-contamination, this negative salmonella status can be maintained through to slaughter.

## SURVIVAL OF SALMONELLA IN THE ENVIRONMENT

Salmonellae are ubiquitous organisms. It is unlikely that the eradication of salmonella in domestic animals is possible in the foreseeable future. In the circumstances a sustained effort should be made to reduce and control the incidence of infection in animals and the prevalence of carriers. Not only can salmonellae from animals be a direct source of contamination in humans, but the recycling of salmonellae from man to animals occurs through direct transmission or environment pollution with sewage effluent and sewage sludge. Effluent can be a source of environmental contamination of pastures and crops which subsequently act as a source of salmonella to other animal species consuming the crops produced on the contaminated area.

Salmonellae can grow either aerobically or anaerobically at temperatures between about 7 and 48°C (optimum 37°C). They prefer a pH of between 4 and 8. They are readily killed by heat (e.g. 71.7°C for 15 seconds) and by acid (e.g. <pH 4). They are resistant to both freezing and drying. Salmonellae may persist for up to 18 months in farm buildings (Table 12). They can also survive for long periods in infected faeces, depending on climatic conditions.

Table 12.   Survival of salmonella in the environment[1].

| Farm building | 18 months |
|---|---|
| Poultry litter | 2-20 weeks |
| Treated sewage (final effluent) | 68% infected |
| Cattle slurry on pasture | 11-12 weeks |

[1]Wray and Davies, 1996.

# Reducing carcass contamination at slaughter

## TRANSPORT AND LAIRAGE

Withdraw feed at least 12 hours before slaughter in order to reduce the risk of stomach rupture during evisceration. Transport pigs in clean, previously disinfected transporters and ensure that pigs are as clean as possible. Keep transportation and lairage stress to a minimum, since stress increases the risk of cross-contamination due to shedding of salmonella. Therefore, stress of transport and lairage time should be kept to a minimum. Research has shown (Morgan *et al.*, 1987) that as lairage time increases the *Salmonella* carrier rate increases. Lairage water supply should be checked regularly in order to ensure that it is of suitable quality. Protected nipple drinkers should be used rather than drinking bowls or troughs.

ORGAN RUPTURE

The primary source of cross-contamination at slaughter is associated with contamination by the rectum, rupture of the gallbladder or viscera and contamination from the tongue and tonsils during butchering procedures. The application of rectal seals as the rectum is removed reduces the risk of cross contamination during butchering (Nielsen *et al.*, 1997). Great care should be taken during butchering to avoid the gallbladder when the midline incision is made. The gallbladder should be removed intact before brisket splitting. Avoid rupturing the viscera during evisceration. For this reason it is important that the stomach be empty and feed be withdrawn from pigs at least 12 hours before slaughter.

Instrument hygiene should be such that cross-contamination by contaminated instruments is avoided. This is particularly important when the viscera, gallbladder or stomach have been ruptured and the instruments contaminated.

Ideally the head, heart, liver, esophagus and lungs should be removed without exposing the tonsils in order to eliminate the risk of cross-contamination by exposure to the tongue and tonsils. This, however, contravenes current EU regulations. The primary organisms associated with cross-contamination occurring during this procedure are salmonella, *Yersinia enterocolitica* and campylobacter.

MEAT INSPECTION

Cross-contamination can also occur during meat inspection. *S. typhimurium* could be isolated from 70% of tonsils 22 weeks after pigs had been exposed to the organism (Wood *et al.*, 1989). Next to the tonsils, the mucosa of the caecum, ileum and colon yielded *S. typhimurium* most consistently at necropsy. *S. typhimurium* was isolated from 55% of submandibular lymph nodes on necropsy. The submandibular lymph node drains the tonsils. These lymph nodes are incised during meat inspection and as a result there is a high risk of cross-contamination of carcasses in association with routine meat hygiene procedures. For this reason it is imperative that the meat inspector and butcher sterilise their instruments after incising the lymph nodes. In contrast, salmonella was not isolated from the liver, heart or spleen of pigs more than two weeks after exposure to *S. typhimurium*. This suggests that the primary source of cross-contamination is likely to be the rectum, the tonsil and the submandibular lymph nodes in pigs that had been exposed to *S. typhimurium* more than two weeks before slaughter, providing the viscera and gallbladder were removed intact.

*Trends in meat inspection systems*

In early 1996 the EC veterinary committee recommended that visual postmortem inspection of pig meat be accepted for pigs coming from pig units in which antemortem inspection is conducted within a HACCP-based quality system (EU Directive (Fresh Meat) 91/497/EEC). This is based on the following rationale:

- Pigs with lesions would be identified; and identification of sick pigs likely to be shedding organisms of foodborne significance is best conducted prior to slaughter of normal pigs.
- While non-detection rates for some lesions are higher in the absence of palpation and incision, these are insignificant as very few visible lesions are a threat to consumer health.
- A slight increase in non detection rate is insignificant when compared with the threat presented by the hidden "hazards" such as salmonella, yersinia and campylobacter.
- Pigs without lesions, as identified by on farm antemortem inspection, are more likely not to have residues.
- Producers are more effective in detecting suspect pigs than antemortem inspection at the abbattoir as they are aware of medication and health status. Furthermore inspection of pigs is facilitated by examining them in their normal unstressed state (Habours *et al.*, 1991; Berends *et al.*, 1993).

This is an innovative approach to meat hygiene procedures which reduces the emphasis on palpation and incision of glands in the slaughterhouse, provided satisfactory guidelines are followed from farm to slaughterhouse. Where tuberculosis is not a problem there is little benefit in palpation and incision of submandibular glands in the slaughterhouse and indeed this can create a risk of cross-contamination by salmonella from contaminated instruments. The directive requires that a HACCP plan be in place on the supplying farms for a period of at least 12 months. Further, the farms must carry out a pre-delivery inspection of pigs and identify those needing special attention on the slaughter line. Normal pigs are pre-selected on the farm before delivery and subjected to a visual inspection only. Abnormals are then inspected using traditional meat inspection procedures.

This system has the advantage of reducing the risk of cross-contamination associated with palpation. Staff are released for visual examinations which are designed to reduce the number of carcasses containing aesthetic lesions. It also releases staff and funds to carry out more technical investigations using techniques designed to identify the presence of organisms which could pose a food safety risk (Mousing *et al.*, 1997).

The disadvantage of the above system is that it places greater emphasis on quality control procedures on supplying farms; and the experience in Denmark would suggest that there is a risk that more aesthetic defects may go undetected. This could, in part, be overcome by requiring meat inspectors to keep a log of normal carcasses, as distinct from only logging carcasses with visual defects.

# Summary

Food safety will occupy a prime position in the eyes of the consumer over the next 10 years and programmes designed to improve food safety will require close liason among veterinarians, government agencies, producers, meat processors, supermarket chains, consumer associations, transporters and pharmaceutical companies. As the food safety directorate in the EU is now responsible for agriculture-related decisions and is controlled by the Commissioner for Consumer Affairs, the commission may be even more influenced than previously by political rather than scientific considerations with regard to agricultural policy.

The ability of a pig to reach its genetic potential is influenced by its health status. There will be a requirement to reduce the quantity of routine antibiotics administered on farms in order to satisfy quality assurance and residue avoidance programmes. As a result, the emphasis on improving herd health status will increase with the objective of maximising the economic efficiency of pig production whilst satisfying food safety standards. Improvements in herd health status could be achieved by depopulation and restocking programmes, age segregated weaning, segregated early weaning, vaccination, all in/all out systems of pig production, improved environment and management.

There is potential to develop new systems of meat inspection revolving around farm-based HACCP systems. Such systems would release expensive veterinarians and technicians from routine inspection and make funds available for more modern and sophisticated techniques for monitoring of zoonotic organisms.

Both feed type and housing affect salmonella seroprevalence of pigs. Seroprevalence of pigs fed a diet containing wet fermented meal or whey and meal is approximately one third that of pigs receiving a pelleted diet. A pig house designed to reduce the prevalence of foodborne pathogens at slaughter should allow all in/all out operation of rooms, minimise pig contact with faeces, birds, flies, cats and rodents. Therefore small modules using all in/all out systems are crucial to the success of the control programme. The actual module size can vary depending on herd size, the maximum size being that of one week's pig production.

The long-term success of farm-based programmes designed to meet food safety guidelines (Kavanaugh, 1997) will be dependent to a great extent on the design of pig housing and the quality of management. The success of such programmes favours fully or semi-slatted systems which minimise pig contact with contaminated faeces, water or feed. Great difficulty will be experienced in satisfying the basic guidelines to prevent cross-contamination in semi-intensive or extensive systems based on straw bedding, continuous throughput and inefficient effluent control, with the possible exception of multi-site all-in-all-out systems. However, with current planning restrictions there is little potential for the development of multi-site pig production systems in Ireland.

As food safety issues assume greater importance in pig production, more research will be required to establish the influence of house type and management on the prevalence of foodborne pathogens in pigs at slaughter. With the exception of toxoplasma there is little reference in the literature as to the effects of housing and production system on the prevalence of pig foodborne pathogens such as yersinia, campylobacter, salmonella and arcobacter. There is a requirement for research programmes to target such topics in the future. The ultimate objective should be to develop systems and procedures that enhance food safety and satisfy the welfare requirements of the pig without compromising the economy of pig production.

# References

Assadi-Rad, A. M., J. C. New and S. Patton. 1995. Risk factors associated with the transmission of *Toxoplasma gondii* to sows kept in different management systems in Tennessee. Veterinary Parasitology 57:289–297.

Bager, F. 1994. Salmonella in Danish pig herds. Risk factors and sources of infection. Proc. XVII Nordic Veterinary Congress, 26–29 July 1994, Reykjavik, pp. 79–82.

Bager, F. and J. Peterson. 1991. Sensitivity and specificity of different methods for the isolation of *Salmonella* from Pigs. Acta vet. Scandinavia 32:473–481.

Baggesen, D.L., H.C. Wegener, F. Bager, H. Stege and J. Christensen. 1996. Herd prevalence of *Salmonella enterica* infections in Danish slaughter pigs determined by microbiological testing. Preventative Veterinary Medicine 26:201–213.

Berends, B.R., J.M.A. Snijders and J.G. van Logtestijn. 1993. Efficacy of current EC meat inspection procedures and some proposed revisions with respect to microbiological safety: a critical review. Veterinary record 133:411–415.

Brown, J. and J. W. Tollison. 1979. Influence of pork consumption on human infection with *Mycobacterium avian-intracellulare*. Applied Environmental Microbiology 38:1144–1146.

Bush, E.J. and P.J. Fedorka-Cray. 1997. Risk factors associated with shedding of *salmonella* by US finishing herds. American Association of Swine Practitioners. pp. 433–436.

Carstensen, B. and J. Christensen. 1998. Herd size and seroprevalence of *Salmonella enterica* in Danish swine herds: a random-effects model for registering data. Preventive Veterinary Medicine 34(2/3):191–203.

Dahl, J. and A. Wingstrand. 1997. Reduction of subclinical salmonella-infection in Danish pigs herds. Salmonella and Salmonellosis. pp. 631–635.

Davies, P.R., W.E.M. Morrow, F.T. Jones, J. Deen, P.J. Fedorka-Cray and I.T. Harris. 1997. Prevalence of salmonella in finishing swine raised in different production systems in North Carolina, USA. Epidemiology and Infection 119:237–244.

Davies, P.R., F.G.E.M. Bovee, J.A. Funk, W.E.M. Morrow, F.T. Jones and J. Deen. 1998a. Isolation of *Salmonella* serotypes from faeces of pigs raised in a multiple-site production system. Journal of the American Veterinary Medical Association 212(12):1925–1928.

Davies, P.R., W.E.M. Morrow, J. Deen, H. Gamble and S. Patton. 1998b. Seroprevalence of *Toxoplasma gondii* and *Trichinella spiralis* in finishing swine raised in different production systems in North Carolina, USA. Preventive Veterinary Medicine 36(1):67–76.

Davies, R.H. and C. Wray. 1995. Mice as carriers of *Salmonella enteritidis* on persistently infected poultry units. Veterinary Record September 30:337–341.

Dubey, J. P. and C. P. Beattie. 1988. Toxoplasmosis of animals and man. CRC Press Inc., Boca Raton, Florida. 220P.

Fedorka-Cray, P.J., S.C. Whipp, R.E. Isaacson, N. Nord and K. Lager. 1994b. Transmission of *Salmonella typhimurium* to swine. Veterinary Microbiology 41:333–344.

Fedorka-Cray, P.J., L.C. Kelley, T.J. Stabel, J.T. Gray and J.A. Laufer. 1995. Alternate routes of invasion may affect pathogenesis of *Salmonella typhimurium* in swine. Infection and Immunity 63(7):2658–2664.

Fukushima, H., R. Nakamura, Y. Ito, K. Saito, M. Tsubokura and K. Otsuki. 1983. Ecological studies of *Yersinia enterocolitica* in pigs. I. Dissemination of *Yersinia enterocolitica* in pigs. Veterinary Microbiology 8:469–483.

Fukushima, H., R. Nakamura, Y. Ito and K. Saito. 1984. Ecological studies of *Yersinia enterocolitica*. II. Experimental infection with *Yersinia enterocolitica* in pigs. Veterinary Microbiology 9:375–389.

Habours, A.H.M., J.F.M. Smeets and J.M.A. Snijders. 1991. Predictability of postmortem abnormalities in shipments of slaughter pigs as an aid for meat inspection. The Veterinary Quarterly 13:74–80.

Kapperud, G., E. Skjerve, N.H. Bean, S.M. Ostroff and J. Lassen. 1992. Risk factors for sporadic *Campylobacter* infections: Results of a case-control study in southeastern Norway. Journal of Clinical Microbiology 30:3117–3121.

Kazboher, A.M., L. Geue, C.H. Staak, G. Steinbach, W. Rabsch, R. Helmuth, T.H. Blaha and D. Protz. 1997. Prevalence of Salmonellae in German slaughter pigs as detected by cultural, serological and PCR techniques. Salmonella and Salmonellosis. pp. 315–320.

Kavanagh, N. T. 1997. *Salmonella* and Food Safety report. Irish Association of Pig Meat Processors and Irish Farmers Association Industry Report. pp. 1–21.

Kavanagh, N. T. 1998. Antibiotic resistance patterns of *Salmonella* isolates from pigs in Ireland. Proceedings of the 15th International Pig Veterinary Society Congress, Birmingham, UK, pg. 282.

Lubroth, J. S., D. W. Dreeson and R. A. Ridenhour. 1983. The role of rodents and other wildlife in the epidemiology of swine toxoplasmosis. Preventive Veterinary Medicine 1:169–178.

Madden, R. H., L. Moran and P. Scates. 1996. Sub-typing of porcine and human *Campylobacter* spp. using RAPD. In: Campylobacters, Helicobacters and Related Organisms (D.G. Newell, R.A. Felman and J. Ketley, eds.) Plenum Press, New York. pp. 213–216.

Marinescu, M., A. Collignon, F. Squinazi, R. Derimany, D. Woodward and H. Lior. 1996. Two cases of persistent diarrhoea associated with *Arcobacter* spp. In: *Campylobacter, Helicobacters* and related organisms. (D.G. Newell, R.A. Felman and J. Ketley, eds.) Plenum Press, New York, pp. 521–523.

Marshall, B.J. 1994. *Helicobacter pylori*. American Journal of Gastro-enterology 89:116–128.

Ministry of Agriculture, Fisheries and Food. 1995.

Morgan, I.R., F.L. Krautil and J.A. Craven. 1987. Effect of time in lairage on caecal and carcass salmonella contamination of slaughter pigs. Epidem. Inf. 98:323–30.

Mousing, J., J. Kyrval, T.K. Jensen, B. Aalbaek, J. Buttenschon, B. Svensmark and P. Willeberg. 1997. Meat safety consequences of implementing visual postmortem meat inspection procedures in Danish slaughter pigs. The Veterinary Record, May 3, 472–477.

Nielsen, B., L.L. Sorensen and H.D. Emborge. 1997. The Danish Salmonella surveillance programme for pork. Salmonella and Salmonellosis 619–625.

Newell, D.G. 1997. Campylobacters, Helicobacters and related organisms: disease associations in pigs. The Pig Journal. 39:63–73.

Roberts, D. 1982. Bacteria of Public health Significance. In: Meat Microbiology. (M.H. Brown, ed.) Applied Science Publishers Ltd, London, 319–386.

Rosef, O., B. Gondrosen, U. Kapperud and B. Underdal. 1983. Applied and Environmental Microbiology 64:855–859.

Smith, K.E., J. Jeffrey, A. Zimmerman, S. Patton, G.W. Beran and H.T. Hill. 1992. The epidemiology of toxoplasmosis on Iowa swine farms with an emphasis on the roles of free living mammals. Veterinary Parasitology 42:199–211.

Stern, N. J., M.P. Hernandez, L. Blankenship, K.E. Deibel, S. Doores, M.P. Doyle, C.S. Ng, J.N. Sofo, W.H. Sveum and D.C. Westhoff. 1985. Journal of Food Production 48:595–599.

Thomas, D.R., R.L. Salmon, S.M. Kench, D. Meadows, T.J. Coleman, P. Morgan-Capner and K.L. Morgan. 1994. Zoonotic illness, determining the risks and measuring exposure and a history of illnesses in a well characterised rural population in the UK. Journal Epidemiology Community Health 48:151–155.

Threfall, E.J., L.R. Ward and B. Rowe. 1997. Increasing incidence of resistance to trimethoprim and ciprofloxacin in epidemic *Salmonella typhimurium* DT104 in England and Wales. European communicable disease bulletin 2(11)81–84.

Vandamme, P. and H. Goosens. 1992. Zentracblatt fur Bacteriologie 276:447–472.

Wood, R.L., A. Pospischil and R. Rose. 1989. Distribution of persistent *Salmonella typhimurium* infection in internal organs of swine. Am. J. Vet. Res. 50(7):1015–1021.

Wray, C. and R. H. Davies. 1996. A veterinary view of *Salmonella* in farm animals. PHLS Microbiology Digest 13(1):44–48.

# MANNAN OLIGOSACCHARIDE APPLICATION IN PIG AND POULTRY DIETS

# Agricultural use of antibiotics and antibiotic resistance in human pathogens: is there a link?

ABIGAIL A. SALYERS

*Department of Microbiology, University of Illinois, Urbana, Illinois, USA*

## Introduction: antibiotic resistance in agricultural settings

There is general agreement that the use of antibiotics in agriculture leads to increases in the incidence of resistant bacteria in the intestines of animals exposed to antibiotics (Endtz *et al.*, 1991; Helmuth and Protz, 1997; WHO Report, 1997; Witte, 1998). One of the clearest examples of a cause and effect relationship between antibiotic use in agriculture and increasing resistance in animal commensals is the impact of the use of noursethricin, an aminoglycoside, in East Germany (Witte, 1998). Within two years of the initiation of use in 1983, resistance to noursethricin appeared and continued to increase in incidence until 1990 when its use was discontinued. We can be reasonably sure that the resistance arose from agricultural use because noursethricin has not been used in human medicine and resistance to aminoglycosides is generally restricted to one or two types of aminoglycoside in contrast to the wide cross-resistance seen in the case of other antibiotics.

In recent years, more and more reports documenting antibiotic resistance in bacteria isolated from farm animals have begun to appear (Aaerstrup *et al.*, 1998; Bates *et al.*, 1994; DANMAP, 1997; Welton *et al.*, 1998; Witte, 1998; Wray *et al.*, 1993). A few recent examples of such reports will serve to illustrate some important features of resistance in animal isolates. Van den Braak *et al.* (1998) found that 79% of poultry carcasses taken from supermarkets or local meat markets contained vancomycin-resistant enterococci. Aaerstrup *et al.* (1998) found that 59% of *Enterococcus faecium* isolated from live chickens were resistant to vancomycin. The drug avoparcin, a vancomycin analog, was used in Europe as a growth promoter until 1997 when approval of its use was suspended. Not all investigators find such high levels of resistant strains. Klein *et al.* (1998) found no vancomycin-resistant enterococci, in fact few enterococci of any kind, in samples of minced beef and pork from supermarkets in Germany. Aaerestrup *et al.* (1998) also found no vancomycin-resistant enterococci in the intestines of cattle in Denmark, but they did find that

155

29% of enterococci from live pigs were resistant. In general, a Danish surveillance program (DANMAP, 1997) found less antibiotic resistance in bacteria from the intestines of cattle than in those isolated from pigs or chickens.

These differences may reflect differences in the way antibiotics are used in cattle farming as opposed to pig farming or chicken farming or differences in crowding. Another possible explanation is suggested by a careful perusal of Aarestrup *et al.* (1998), the only paper to provide a detailed breakdown of the data on levels of resistance in the strains they tested. The breakpoint between resistance and susceptibility for vancomycin was 8 µg/ml in this study. Klein *et al.* (1998) did not provide MIC values or indicate the breakpoint they used. Van den Braak *et al.* (1998) used 6 µg/ml as the definition of resistance. In the study of Aarestrup *et al.* (1998), 29% of the strains were listed as resistant to avoparcin, but 55% of the strains had MICs of 2-8 µg/ml - still technically susceptible but getting close to resistant. Similarly, none of the *E. faecalis* strains from pigs were scored resistant, but over half had an MIC value of 2 or more and 20% had MIC values of 4-8 µg/ml, right below the breakpoint. Thus, a slight adjustment in the breakpoint could have had significant effects on the number of strains classified as resistant. Clinical microbiologists have learned this lesson from seeing 'sensitive' species become largely 'resistant', apparently almost overnight. But in reality, the distribution within the 'sensitive' category had been inching toward the breakpoint for a long time. It is better to think of susceptibility as a population distribution. As the population becomes less susceptible and moves toward the breakpoint, resistance levels can go rather rapidly from low to high, making it seem as if resistance arose within a very short time when in fact susceptibility had been decreasing for some time.

## Antibiotic use patterns – an important parameter

How antibiotics are used, i.e., the amount administered and the time frame of administration, would be expected to have an effect on the frequency with which resistant strains will be selected in a particular setting (Lipsitch and Levin, 1997). When antibiotic use is transient, bacteria resistant to the antibiotic are selected initially, but may then be unable to complete with susceptible bacteria when antibiotic selection is removed. This may be the reason why drastically reducing the use of a previously overused antibiotic in human medicine is usually followed by a decrease in the incidence of resistant strains (see, for example, Westh, 1995). If antibiotic selection is continuous over long periods of time, however, bacteria have the chance to accumulate mutations that allow them to retain their resistance phenotype without losing fitness in the absence of selection. This has been shown in laboratory experiments using *E. coli* (Bottger *et al.*, 1998; Lenski *et al.*, 1994; Schrag *et al.*, 1997). We do not know the extent to which this type of adaptation occurs in nature or how long selection must be maintained for the adaptation to occur. In fact, the answer is likely to be different for different bacterial species and for different animals.

There are reasons to believe that the way antibiotics are used in agriculture makes the emergence of resistant strains even more likely than the way antibiotics are used in human medicine. Only about 20% of the antibiotics used in agriculture are used to treat sick animals. As with the treatment of human infections, high doses of antibiotics are administered over a short period of time. These are conditions least likely to select for stable resistant bacteria. Antibiotics are also administered prophylactically to prevent infections in animals living in crowded conditions. Antibiotics are used prophylactically in human medicine too, but there is an important difference. In human medicine, prophylaxis, like treatment, is administered to individual patients with risk factors that make them likely to acquire an infection. Also, since surgery or some other temporary intervention is the factor that dictates prophylaxis, prophylactic use of antibiotics in humans is usually of limited duration. In agriculture, whole herds or flocks are involved and the administration of antibiotic may occur for prolonged periods.

An agricultural use of antibiotics that has no parallel in human medicine is the use of antibiotics as growth promoters. Addition of low concentrations of antibiotics to animal feed can add 4-5% to the weight of an animal without increasing the amount of food consumed (WHO report, 1997). In some cases this weight gain may be due to the prevention of disease. In others, it may be due to some physiological effect on the animal. Whatever the reason for the efficacy of antibiotics as growth promoters, farmers believe in it and use large amounts of antibiotics for this purpose. At least half of the antibiotics used in agriculture are used as growth promoters. Growth promoters are supplied in very low concentrations, less than 200 gm of active substance per ton of feed. This amounts to an antibiotic concentration of <0.1µg/ml. Concentrations in this range have been called subtherapeutic because they are assumed to be too low to have any effect on the growth of the bacteria. This assumption may be correct in some cases, but there are many species of bacteria that are hypersusceptible to antibiotics and have a minimal inhibitory concentration in this range. The fact that the breakpoint that separates resistant strains from sensitive strains is 4–8 µg/ml for many antibiotics should alert us to the fact that a concentration of 0.1 µg/ml is not so low after all. Moreover, concentrations of an antibiotic high enough to have a marginal effect on a bacterium's competitiveness but low enough to allow the bacterium to grow may be precisely the conditions most likely to foster resistance. The antibiotic exerts a slight selective pressure, but the bacterium can still grow well enough to accumulate mutations or acquire new DNA that increase its resistance to the antibiotic.

Since agricultural antibiotics are used in large quantities and must be cheap enough to be economical for the farmer, pharmaceutical companies that sell antibiotics for use on the farm market antibiotic preparations that are much less pure than those intended for human consumption. One of the contaminants of these preparations is DNA from the antibiotic-producing microbe. Antibiotic-producing bacteria have resistance genes to protect them from the antibiotic they produce. Webb and Davies (1993) showed that agricultural antibiotic preparations contained levels of resistance genes from the producer that were high enough to be easily detectable by PCR. Thus, resistance genes are being fed along with the antibiotics that select for strains that acquire them. Of course, the resistance gene would have to enter intestinal bacteria, integrate into the chromosome and be expressed in their new host. This series of steps would occur at low frequency because most intestinal bacteria are not naturally transformable and would thus not take up the DNA, and DNA would have to integrate by illegitimate recombination, an inefficient process. If the gene were not expressed at first, gene expression would have to be activated by mutations in the promoter or insertion of an insertion sequence in the promoter region to provide a new promoter. Although this series of steps is extremely unlikely, the constant presence of the antibiotic would quickly select for a bacterium that acquired the resistance gene. Recently, the vancomycin resistance genes in the bacterium that produces vancomycin have been cloned and sequenced (Marshall *et al.*, 1998). Their sequences are only about 60% identical to vancomycin resistance genes currently being found in vancomycin-resistant strains. This is strong proof that the vancomycin resistance genes that are turning up in animal isolates in Europe did not arise as a result of uptake of DNA from the antibiotic preparations being fed to animals.

## Farmers and their animals: the first victims of resistance?

Discussions of the impact of agricultural use of antibiotics tend to focus on the impact of such use on humans. Yet, overuse and abuse of antibiotics on the farm is most likely to affect animals first. Given the crowded conditions that characterize most animal production facilities today, an antibiotic resistant animal pathogen could wreak havoc. A recent episode in the US provides a sobering picture of the threat to farmers posed by increasingly resistant animal pathogens. In spring of 1998 on a calf farm outside Tuscon, Arizona, calves began dying within a few days of being brought to the facility. The pathogen responsible for these deaths proved to be *Salmonella typhimurium*. This particular strain was resistant to all the antibiotics available to the veterinarian. The end result was that the calf farm went out of business (Don Guiney, personal communication). Similar antibiotic treatment failures have been experienced by Southeast Asian shrimp farmers, who today can no longer use antibiotics to prevent bacterial infections of shrimp larvae because resistance to available antibiotics has rendered antibiotics ineffective.

The first reason to reevaluate antibiotic use patterns in agriculture is the protection of animals and their owners. Farm workers and their families are exposed to antibiotics while caring for their animals. There is little information about the effect of antibiotic use on their normal microflora.

A person who goes to the hospital for surgery has a 4-5% chance of contracting a post-surgical infection. Many of these infections are caused by the patient's own microflora. Being colonized with antibiotic-resistant bacteria, especially multiple resistant ones, is not good for your health.

## Impact on human health outside the farm

Many veterinarians and agriculture industry representatives seem to think that the only potential hazard to the general public arising from antibiotic use in agriculture is selection of antibiotic-resistant salmonella and campylobacter strains, which could be spread through the food supply to humans. This potential hazard is often dismissed as unimportant because antibiotics are generally not used to treat human gastroenteritis. In fact, in the case of *E. coli* O157:H7, antibiotics seem to make the disease worse, probably because antibiotics trigger the entry into lytic phase of a lysogenic bacteriophage that carries the Shiga toxin genes. The argument that antibiotic-resistant salmonella and campylobacter species are not a particular problem overlooks an important point: a fraction of people with gastroenteritis go on to develop the systemic form of the disease. Systemic disease is life-threatening and must be treated with antibiotics. The Center for Disease Control (CDC) has estimated that there are thousands of cases of systemic salmonella and campylobacter infections each year in the US – not exactly a negligible problem. Moreover, since campylobacter infections have now been linked to Guillain-Barre syndrome, physicians may decide that treatment is worthwhile after all.

The main risk to human health comes from the movement of antibiotic-resistance genes from bacteria in food to bacteria that cause human disease. The bacterial pathogens clinicians and the public really worry about are bacteria such as *Streptococcus pneumoniae* and *Staphylococcus aureus* that killed many people in the pre-antibiotic era and are still taking a heavy toll even though they are still susceptible to some antibiotics. Bacterial pneumonia, of which *S. pneumoniae* is the leading cause, is currently the most common cause of infectious disease death in the US. Opportunistic pathogens such as *Enterococcus* spp. are also cause for concern because they are common causes of life-threatening hospital-acquired infections. A person who enters a hospital colonized with multi-drug resistant *S. pneumoniae, S. aureus* or *Enterococcus* spp. has an increased risk of dying from a post-surgical infection caused by members of his or her own bacterial flora. Such patients also bring into the hospital antibiotic-resistant bacteria that can spread to other patients on the hands of hospital staff members. *S. pneumoniae* and *S. aureus* are primarily human pathogens. Enterococci are colonizers of many animals as well as humans.

One way these major human pathogens could be affected by agricultural use of antibiotics is through exposure of farm workers to antibiotics. Many people are transiently colonized with *Streptococcus pneumoniae* or other potentially pathogenic bacterial species at various times in their lives.

Continuous exposure to antibiotic dusts could encourage the development of resistant strains of these species, which could later cause serious disease. Resistant strains could also be passed to family members and other contacts. Such events would probably have a relatively localized effect, although the increasing tendency of people to travel widely might increase the impact of multi-drug resistant strains. A second, and potentially more serious, way human-specific pathogens could be affected by antibiotic-resistant animal bacteria is through the transfer of antibiotic-resistance genes from the animal strain to human strains during transient colonization of the human intestine. That is, resistant strains could be transmitted through the food supply to the human intestine where horizontal gene transfer would move the resistance genes into human strains. There have been a number of reports, including some of those already mentioned, documenting the presence of antibiotic-resistant enterococci in human foods. One limitation of these studies is that they have focused exclusively on meat and animal products such as milk and cheese.

Water could also serve as a vehicle for the transfer of antibiotic resistant bacteria to humans. Manure management remains a large and largely unsolved problem in agriculture. Antibiotic-resistant bacteria are being found in water supplies (McKeon *et al.*, 1995). Antibiotics themselves, especially the fluoroquinolones, are also being detected at fairly high levels in wastewater (Raloff, 1998). The unanswered question is where do the antibiotic resistant bacteria and the antibiotic residues come from - agricultural sources or human fecal pollution or a combination of the two? The use of untreated or partially treated water for irrigation or for washing vegetables, or the use of manure as fertilizer for vegetables and fruits could both contaminate food plants with antibiotic-resistant bacteria. To what extent this actually occurs in the case of fruits and vegetables is unknown. Few studies have been done of resistance patterns in the intestinal microflora of vegetarians, but one study by Elder *et al.* (1993) found higher levels of multi-drug resistant bacteria in the intestines of vegetarians than in the bacteria of meat eaters.

Antibiotic-resistant enterococci and other members of the normal flora of animals, which are carried into human food could colonize humans or even cause extraintestinal disease. Kluytmans *et al.* (1995) analyzed a 1994 outbreak of methicillin-resistant *Staphylococcus aureus*, in which the bacteria appeared to have been spread on food. The source of this outbreak was almost certainly one of the health care workers who contaminated the food, and not a case involving contamination on the farm or during processing, but it shows that the hospital food supply can serve as a vector for pathogens that cause extraintestinal disease. The patients fed the contaminated food developed sepsis and post-operative infections and a number of hospital staff members were colonized with the strain, making them a possible new source of methicillin-resistant *Staphylococcus aureus* for critically ill patients. This is the only food-initiated outbreak of its type to be reported so far, but such events may be more common than we think since food is not commonly considered as a likely vector for extraintestinal infections.

Transmission events of this type would be limited to hospitals or nursing homes, where large numbers of people with impaired immune systems are housed, and is unlikely to be a problem in other institutions such as schools and military installations.

## Assessing resistance gene transfer between bacteria that colonize humans

Once an antibiotic-resistant bacterium has been ingested by someone, the bacterium can transfer its resistance genes to another bacterium. At first glance, this might appear to be a very infrequent event, but new studies suggest that this sort of horizontal transfer event is unexpectedly common. So far, the main evidence supporting the hypothesis that horizontal gene transfer events occur in the intestine comes from finding the same resistance genes in very different hosts. If copies of a resistance gene in these different hosts have virtually identical DNA sequences, horizontal transfer of some sort is the most likely explanation. An alternative explanation of such events is that selection pressures to keep the amino acid sequence of the protein constant also keep the DNA sequence constant. Thus, two genes could arise independently in two different bacterial species but end having very similar sequences. This is called convergent evolution. Since, however, the third base in many codons can vary without changing the amino acid sequence, two genes with identical amino acid sequences could differ by as much as 20% at the DNA sequence level. For this reason, copies of the same gene in different bacterial species that are 95-100% identical at the DNA sequence level are virtually guaranteed to have been acquired by horizontal gene transfer. The best examples are those where the DNA sequence identity is 99-100%. Such events are likely to have been recent. An obvious limitation of this type of analysis is that, although one can say with some certainty that the gene has been transferred horizontally, it is usually not possible to deduce the direction of transfer simply from sequence identity, unless the resistance gene has a %G+C or codon usage that differs substantially from the host chromosome. Moreover, it is not possible to deduce whether the transfer occurred directly between the two species or indirectly by means of a third or fourth participant. Nonetheless, this type of analysis gives some indication of the extent to which gene transfer actually occurs in nature.

Over the past few years, a number of examples have been found that support the hypothesis that horizontal gene transfer events do occur in nature between very distantly related species and may, moreover, occur rather frequently (McDonald *et al.*, 1997; Teuber *et al.*, 1996; Van den Bogaard *et al.*, 1997; Van den Braak *et al.*, 1998). No one has yet measured the frequency of transfer directly in a farm animal or human, but the fact that it was easy to find such examples suggests that they are not rare events. Some examples are provided in Table 1. These show that gene transfer occurs within the human colon and within the intestines of farm animals. Often the genes are associated with known transmissible elements but in other cases either the conditions needed to promote transfer in the laboratory were not achieved or the gene had been transferred in but was no longer transferred out.

Table 1. Some of the cases in which virtually identical resistance genes have been found in distantly related species of bacteria, suggesting that gene transfer has occurred between these species in nature[1].

| Resistance gene | Bacterial species | Site of isolation |
|---|---|---|
| *tetQ* | *Bacteroides* spp. | Human colon |
| | *Porphyromonas* spp. | Human mouth |
| | *Prevotella ruminicola* | Bovine rumen |
| *ermG* | *Bacteroides* spp. | Human colon |
| | *Bacillus sphaericus* | Soil |
| *tetK* | *Staphylococcus xylosus* | Cheese |
| | *Staphylococcus aureus* | Human body, infections |
| *tetS* | *Lactococcus lactis* | Cheese |
| | *Listeria monocytogenes* | Human infection |
| *cat* | *Enterococcus faecalis* | Sausage |
| | *Staphylococcus aureus* | Human infection |

[1]Salyers and Shoemaker, 1996; Teuber *et al.*, 1996.

Some surprising conclusions emerge from the evidence summarized in Table 1. First, transfer of antibiotic resistance genes can occur between bacteria normally found in the intestines of animals and bacteria normally found in the intestines of humans. Nikolich *et al.* (1994) found alleles of *tetQ* in animal species of *Prevotella ruminicola* and in human colonic *Bacteroides* spp. that shared more than 95% DNA sequence identity. By contrast, the chromosomes of *P. ruminicola* and *Bacteroides* spp. share less than 5% DNA-DNA homology. In this case, on the basis of DNA sequences upstream and downstream of *tetQ*, the authors deduced that the direction of transfer had probably been from human to animal bacteria (Nikolich *et al.*, 1994). In the case of a *vanA* gene found in animal and human strains of *Enterococcus faecium*, the transfer may have been from animal to human bacteria (Van den Braak *et al.*, 1998; Werner *et al.*, 1997). The evidence for this was that the *vanA* gene cluster in animals had one signature, and some of the human strain *vanA* clusters had a different signature, but the human strains also carried *vanA* clusters with the animal signature. Copies of virtually identical alleles of *tetQ* and *tetM* have been found in human oral and intestinal bacteria, another indication that bacteria normally found in different sites can exchange genes. Perhaps the most troubling evidence comes from examples where the same resistance gene was found in bacteria isolated from unpasteurized cheese or uncooked meat and in bacteria isolated from human patients (Teuber *et al.*, 1996). Most of the human clinical isolates were species that are normally found in the human colon, such as *Enterococcus* spp. These examples support the hypothesis that bacteria carried on human foods are exchanging antibiotic resistance genes with bacteria in the human intestine during their brief passage through the human intestine.

Most of the examples given in Table 1 were found by accident and not by design. In such cases, the design of the experiment and control of parameters was not optimal and the results should be interpreted with caution. What emerges from these examples, however, is the growing conviction that well-designed real time experiments should be conducted to determine how rapidly genes from bacteria in food are transferred to human or animal intestinal bacteria. Such experiments are expensive enough that some justification for undertaking them is necessary. Table 1 contains enough evidence to justify moving to the next step. The examples given in Table 1 all came from retrospective studies, where the results of gene transfer events are seen in the present and scientists try to guess how they came to pass. Until prospective experiments are done, where the parameters are more carefully controlled and the direction of transfer is more easily deduced, many people will remain unconvinced that such events as the transfer of genes from foodborne bacteria to human intestinal bacteria occur with appreciable frequency.

Clearly, the ideal way to determine gene transfer rates would be to seed humans or animals with a resistant strain of bacteria and monitor the spread of the resistance gene. This has been done with laboratory rodents in a few cases (see for example, Doucet-Populaire *et al.,* 1992), and transfer rates were detectable over fairly short periods of time. The East German experience with noursthricin use also supports the possibility of gene transfer: the noursthricin resistance gene turned up in shigella strains (Witte, 1998). Shigella is a human-specific pathogen. An advantage of this prospective type of study is that the direction of transfer is known and rates of transfer can be deduced, at least approximately. This approach has some disadvantages, however. First, it is very expensive to do such experiments with farm animals or humans rather than laboratory rodents, and these are the experiments that will be most convincing. Second, gene transfer elements vary considerably in frequency of transfer. Some have regulated transfer and will only transfer if the inducing conditions pertain. The nature of the recipient also affects transfer frequencies. So unless a single species is targeted and only transfers within this species are monitored, interpretation becomes complex and problematic. These are not arguments against this type of study, but rather indicate the need to develop an adequate framework for interpretation in which to analyze the outcome.

Antibiotic use patterns can differ from one country to another and such differences will have an effect on the ecology of resistant strains. In Europe, avoparcin was used heavily on farms from 1995 to 1997, when approval was suspended, whereas avoparcin was never approved for use in the United States. Vancomycin has been used much less extensively in European hospitals than in US hospitals. Thus, in Europe, the principal use of glycopeptides is in agriculture whereas in the US the principal use is to treat human infections. Accordingly, patterns of resistance development would be expected to be different in Europe and the US. In fact, this proves to be the case. Coque *et al.* (1996) surveyed hospital, community and animal isolates obtained in the US state of Texas. They found vancomycin-resistant enterococci in hospitals but not in the intestines of members of the community, in the intestines of animals or on meat products. Studies carried out in Europe, by contrast, find few if any vancomycin-resistant enterococci in hospitals but Van den Bogaard and Stobberingh (1999) have found vancomycin-resistant *Enterococcus faecium* in the fecal microflora of urban adults and on chicken carcasses offered for sale in meat markets. Defending the use of avoparcin on farms in Europe by arguing that US experience has shown that hospital use, not farm use, is the important selective pressure is inappropriate because use patterns differ so much.

Not only are antibiotic use patterns different in different countries but some antibiotics used in agriculture are a greater threat to human therapy than others. Avoparcin has been mentioned. Other antibiotics of primary concern are the fluoroquinolones, another class of frontline human antibiotics; virginiamycin, a streptogramin that can elicit cross-resistance to streptogramins, and macrolide antibiotics currently used to treat human infections. Avilomycin has been reported to elicit cross-resistance to a new human use antibiotic everninomycin (Aaerstrup, 1998). Streptogramins have not been used previously for the treatment of human infections, but some of the new antibiotics currently being considered for approval for treatment of human infections are streptogramins (e.g., Synercid). Since these antibiotics are needed badly for treatment of patients with multiple antibiotic-resistant infections, it seems prudent to make sure that these new drugs are not compromised before the first vial destined for treatment of human disease is opened. Focusing on future uses of antibiotics to treat human disease rather than current use has become more important than ever, given new developments in the understanding of human disease. This is well-illustrated by a recent clinical trial, which demonstrated that administration of the macrolide erythromycin to pregnant women significantly reduced the risk of premature births, presumably because it controlled cases of bacterial vaginosis (Hauth *et al.*, 1995). Currently, another macrolide, azythromycin, is being tested for its ability to prevent heart disease. Mounting evidence supports a role for the bacterium *Chlamydia pneumoniae* in at least some cases of atherosclerosis. If this hypothesis proves to be correct, timely antibiotic therapy could prevent atheroslerosis and heart attacks. These potential new uses of macrolides could make the macrolides even more important in human medicine than they are today. Thus, in deciding what antibiotics are to be avoided or more strictly controlled with respect to agricultural use, it is important to consider future use as well as present use. Another consideration that should be taken into account is genetic linkage of resistance genes. If two types of resistance gene are generally found together on the same transmissible element, either antibiotic could select for both of them. For example, in *Bacteroides* species, erythromycin resistance is often accompanied by tetracycline resistance (Salyers *et al.*, 1997). This type of linkage has also been seen, although not universally, in Gram-positive cocci. Examples of more than one type of resistance gene on a plasmid have also been reported in many studies. In fact, there are special elements in the Enterobacteriaciae that recruit resistance genes of various sorts to create gene clusters (Hall and Collis, 1995).

There are some agriculturally used antibiotics that can be ranked as least likely to cause problems in human medicine, at least for the present. For example, monensin, an antibiotic that forms channels in bacterial membranes and collapses the proton motive force, is used exclusively in agriculture. It has never been proposed as a human use antibiotic and does not cross-select for resistance to any antibiotic being used to treat humans. Bacitracin might be included in this category. It is used in some topical ointments designed for human use but it is by no means a frontline human drug. Even here, however, caution is in order because there have been reports that bacitracin can eliminate carriage of vancomycin-resistant enterococci or even treating patients with this disease (O'Donnovan *et al.* 1994). If this is borne out by subsequent studies, the view of bacitracin's importance in human medicine may change dramatically. As the infectious disease picture continues to change, today's irrelevant-to-human-medicine antibiotic could easily become tomorrow's frontline human therapy. This fact of life is going to make it increasingly difficult for scientists in regulatory agencies to make choices about what antibiotics are approved for agricultural use.

Another fact of life is that the timing of resistance development varies widely from species to species and from antibiotic to antibiotic. Some antibiotics seem to generate resistant strains more readily than others. It is important to understand this to avoid a fallacy that is often committed: the fallacy of assuming that since resistance has not arisen after years of use of an antibiotic means that resistance will never develop. An instructive example is provided by penicillin resistance in streptococci. *E. coli* and many other Gram-negative species began to develop resistance to ampicillin and penicillin almost immediately after these antibiotics began to be used in human medicine. Since this did not happen with *S. pneumoniae*, which remained sensitive to penicillin for decades, physicians lulled themselves into believing that *S. pneumoniae* would never become resistant to penicillin. When penicillin-resistant strains finally arrived, they were not prepared either medically or intellectually to see *S. pneumoniae* go from an easily treated pathogen to a multiple-resistant one. During the long period of penicillin sensitivity, *S. pneumoniae* strains were picking up resistances to other antibiotics such as tetracycline, erythromycin and aminoglycosides, but clinicians did not pay attention to this trend because they assumed that penicillin would always be effective. This example illustrates the fact that there is usually some warning about the imminent emergence of multi-drug resistant strains if the surveillance apparatus is in place and scientists in the area understand how to look for emerging resistance trends.

## Conclusions

The oft-expressed view that the main resistance problem arising from agricultural use of antibiotics is transmission of antibiotic-resistant zoonotic pathogens to humans far underestimates the complexity, magnitude and potential impact of antibiotic use in agriculture. A far greater danger is that antibiotic resistant bacteria from animals, whether pathogen or commensal, will be transmitted to humans through the food supply and will transfer resistance genes to human intestinal bacteria and through them to serious human pathogens. That is, the spread of genes is the problem, not just the spread of bacteria. Evidence is mounting that transfer of antibiotic resistance genes between bacteria normally found in the animal intestinal tract or in food and bacteria found in the human intestine occurs far more frequently than would have been expected from laboratory experiments. The direction of transfer is uncertain in most cases, but the fact that a genetic conduit of some sort is open between animal and human bacteria increases the possibility of resistance gene flow from animal bacteria to human bacteria via the food supply. The possibility of gene transfer should be considered seriously in any deliberations over safety issues. Another factor that has received insufficient attention is the stability of resistance genes in most hosts. Contrary to earlier beliefs, antibiotic resistance genes do not take a fitness toll in most cases. This is probably the case because under selective pressure, bacteria make genetic changes that improve the fit between a newly acquired resistance gene and its bacterial host. Resistance genes are not only easy to get, but also hard to lose (Salyers and Amabile-Cuevas, 1997). Thus, the spread of a particular type of resistance gene may be difficult or impossible to reverse. It is of primary importance to prevent the spread of resistance genes in the first place, by prudent use of antibiotics.

Debates on antibiotic resistance have centered on livestock animals such as pigs, chickens and cattle. Yet, antibiotics are also used by vegetable and fruit growers and in aquaculture. Use in these areas may have as great an impact on human health and the environment as antibiotic use in animal production. Another area deserving more attention is the antibiotic resistant bacteria in the intestines of companion animals (Devriese *et al.*, 1996). Antibiotic-resistant bacteria in dog or cat food could be spread to companion animals and through them to humans. No one disputes the important contribution to the spread of antibiotic-resistant bacteria made by the abuse and overuse of antibiotics in human medicine. The fact that this is probably the main cause of the rise in antibiotic resistance, however, is not an argument for ignoring antibiotic overuse and abuse in agriculture.

The public view the use of antibiotics to treat human infections as necessary and desirable. By contrast, most agricultural uses other than treatment of sick animals, appears to those who know little about it to be optional and in some cases frivolous. Thus, the public may support an end to use of antibiotics as growth promoters or as plant protection agents despite the fact that these uses probably do not make as great a contribution to resistance in human pathogens as human clinical use. Moreover, it is important to realize that the extent of the contribution agricultural use of antibiotics makes to resistance in human pathogens has not been established. It may be greater than we think.

Perhaps the most serious difficulty in trying to define safe and prudent use of antibiotics in agriculture is that antibiotics may not be the only selective pressure maintaining antibiotic-resistance genes in the environment. Antibiotic resistance genes can be genetically linked to other genes such as different antibiotic resistance genes (see, e.g., Woodford *et al.*, 1995) or metal resistance genes (Hall and Collis, 1995; Salyers and Amabile-Cuevas, 1997). In such cases, a different class of antibiotic or even metal pollution could select for the particular antibiotic resistance gene linked to it.

Studies of the effects of antibiotic use in human medicine or agriculture seldom establish a resistance baseline in the surrounding area of the site being tested. Nor do they establish whether the resistances they detect are linked to some other trait that could be the actual target for local selective pressure. Langlois *et al.* (1988) reported that age and housing location could affect the number of antibiotic resistant bacteria in the intestines of pigs that had not been exposed to antibiotics. What is the selective pressure in cases such as this? There are many such observations that cannot be easily explained simply by invoking antibiotic exposure. The debate over agricultural use of antibiotics is never going to be settled scientifically without more information on the likelihood of resistance genes moving through the food chain to human bacteria and what are the most important selection pressures that select and maintain resistant bacteria in the environment. In the past, the agriculture industry has been able to counter challenges of its use of antibiotics by exerting political and economic pressure to avoid unwelcome regulations. So far, the American public has accepted this or ignored the issue completely. If, however, there are some cases of human treatment failures that can be traced to agricultural use of antibiotics, public opinion could change dramatically. It is time for the industry and the public to take a careful and critical look at the way it uses antibiotics and how this use might influence human health.

Most of the surveillance efforts to track resistant bacteria are focusing on hospitals. This is understandable because hospitals are already collecting data on resistant bacteria, although for legal reasons they may be reluctant to release it to a central data-collecting organization. Also, hospitals are clearly a breeding ground for antibiotic-resistant bacteria. Nonetheless, many regulatory issues and safety concerns, including those related to agricultural use of antibiotics, focus on bacteria found in the community or on the farm, especially the commensals. To gather information about antibiotic resistant commensal bacteria of humans and animals, the author and Stuart Levy have created an NIH-financed web site devoted to this issue. The web site is called ROAR for Reservoirs Of Antibiotic Resistance. It can be reached at www.roar.antibiotic.org. There is also an informal communications network being organized, where issues important to scientists in industry, academia and governmental agencies will be discussed. If you would like to become a member of this network, contact the author at abigails@uiuc.edu. The purpose of the network is to share information and to find common grounds of agreement on contentious resistance issues involving commensal bacteria.

## Acknowledgments

Some of the work mentioned in this paper was supported by grant AI/GM 22383 from the U.S. National Institutes of Health.

## References

Aarestrup, F.M. 1998. Association between decreased susceptibility to a new antibiotic for treatment of human diseases, everinomicin (SCH 27899), and resistance to an antibiotic used for growth promotion in animals, avilamycin. Microbial Drug Resistance 4:137–141.

Aaerstrup, F.M., F. Bager, N.E. Jensen, M. Madsen, A. Meyling and H.C. Wegener. 1998. Surveillance of antimicrobial resistance in bacteria isolated from food animals to antimicrobial growth promoters and related therapeutic agents in Denmark. APMIS 106: 606–622.

Bates, J., J.Z. Jordens and D.T. Griffiths. 1994. Farm animals as a putative reservoir for vancomycin-resistant enterococcal infection in man. J. Antimicrob. Chemother. 34, 507–514.

Bottger, E.C., B. Springer, M. Pletschette and P. Sander. 1998. Fitness of antibiotic-resistant microorganisms and compensatory mutations. Nature Med. 12:1343–1344.

Coque, T.M., J.F. Tomayko, S.C. Ricke, P.C. Okhyusen and B. E. Murray. 1996. Vancomycin-resistant enterococci from nosocomial, community and animal sources in the United States. Antimicrob. Agents Chemother 40, 2605–2609.

DANMAP. 1997. Consumption of antimicrobial agents and occurrence of antimicrobial resistance in bacteria from food animals, food and humans in Denmark. No. 1, 1997, Danish Zoonosis Centre, Danish Veterinary Laboratory, Bulowsvej 27. D-1790 Copenhagen V.

Devriese, L.A., M. Ieven, H. Goossens, P. Vandamme, B. Pot, J. Hommez and F. Haesebrouck. 1996. Presence of vancomycin-resistant enterococci in farm and pet animals. Antimicrob. Agents Chemother.40:2285–2287.

Doucet-Populaire, F., P. Trieu-Cuot, A. Andremont, and P. Courvalin. 1992. Conjugal transfer of plasmid DNA from *Enterococcus faecalis* to *Escherichia coli* in the digestive tracts of gnotobiotic mice. Antimicrob. Agents Chemother. 36:502–504.

Elder, H.A., I. Roy, S. Lehman, R.L. Phillips and E.H. Kass. 1993. Human studies to measure the effect of antibiotic residues. Vet. Human Toxicol. 35(Suppl 1):31–36.

Endtz, H.P., G. J. Ruijsvan, B. Klingeren, W.H. Jansen, T. van der Reyden and R.P. Mouton. 1991. Quinolone resistance in campylobacter isolated from man and poultry following the introduction of fluoroquinolones in veterinary medicine. J. Antimocrob. Chemother. 27:199–208.

Hall, R.M. and C.M. Collis. 1995. Mobile gene cassettes and integrons: capture and spread of genes by site-specific recombination. Mol. Microbiol. 15:593–600.

Hauth, J.C., R.L. Goldenberg, W.M. Andrews, M.B. DuBard and R.L. Copper. 1995. Reduced incidence of preterm delivery with metronidazole and erythromycin in women with bacterial vaginosis. New Engl. J. Med. 333:1732–1736.

Helmuth, R. and D. Protz. 1997. How to modify conditions limiting resistance in bacteria in animals and other reservoirs. Clin. Infect. Dis. 24(Suppl.):S136–139.

Klein, G., A. Pack and G. Reuter. 1998. Antibiotic resistance patterns of enterococci and occurrence of vancomycin-resistant enterococci in raw minced beef and pork in Germany. Appl. Environ. Microbiol. 64:1825–1830.

Kluytmans, J. *et al.* 1995. Food initiated outbreak of methicillin-resistant *Staphylococcus aureus* analyzed by pheno- and genotyping. J. Clin. Microbiol. 33:1121–1128.

Langlois, B. E., K.A. Dawson, I. Leak and D.K. Aaron. 1988. Effect of age and housing location on antibiotic resistance of fecal coliforms from pigs in a non-antibiotic-exposed herd. Appl. Environ. Microbiol. 54:1341–1344.

Lenski, R.E., S.C. Simpson and T.T. Nguyen. 1994. Genetic analysis of a plasmid-encoded, host genotype-specific enhancement of bacterial fitness. J. Bacteriol. 176:3140–3147.

Lipsitch, M. and B.R. Levin. 1997. The population dynamics of antibiotic therapy. Antimicrob. Agents Chemother. 41:363–373.

Marshall, C.G., I.A.D. Lessard, I.-S. Park and G.D. Wright. 1998. Glycopeptide antibiotic resistance genes in glycopeptide-producing organisms. Antimicrob. Agents Chemother. 42:2215–2220.

McDonald, L.C., M.J. Kuehnert, F.C. Tenover and W.R. Jarvis. 1997. Vancomycin-resistant enterococci outside the health care setting: Prevalence, sources and public health implications. Emerging Inf. Dis. 3:311–317.

McKeon, D. M., J. P. Calabrese and G. K. Bissonnette. 1995. Antibiotic resistant Gram-negative bacteria in rural groundwater supplies. Water Res. 29:1902–1908.

Nikolich, M., G. Hong, N. Shoemaker and A.A. Salyers. 1994. Evidence that conjugal transfer of a tetracycline resistance gene *(tetQ)* has occurred very recently between the normal microflora of animals and the normal microflora of animals. Appl. Environ. Microbiol. 60:3255–3260.

O'Donovan, C.A., P. Fan-Harvard, F.T. Tecson-Tumang, S.M. Smith and R.H. Eng. 1994. Enteric eradication of vancomycin-resistant *Enterococcus faecium* with oral bacitracin. Diagn. Microbiol. Infect. Dis. 18:105–109.

Raloff, J. 1998. Drugged waters. Science News 153:187–189.

Salyers, A.A. and C.F. Amabile-Cuevas. 1997. Why are antibiotic resistance gene so resistant to elimination? Antimicrob. Agents Chemother.

Salyers, A. A. and N. B. Shoemaker. 1996. Resistance gene transfer in anaerobes: New insights, new problems. Clin. Infect. Dis. 23 (Suppl.):S36–43.

Schrag, S.J., V. Perrot and B.R. Levin. 1997. Adaptation to the fitness costs of antibiotic resistance in *Escherichia coli*. Proc. R. Soc. Lond. B. Biol. Sci. 264:1287–1291.

Teuber, M. V. Perreten and F. Wirsching. 1996. Antibiotikumresistente bakterien: eine neue dimension in der lebensmittel-mikrobiologie. Lebensmittle-technologie 29:182–199.

Van Belkun, A., N. van den Braak, R. Thomassen, H. Verbrugh and H. Endtz. 1996. Vancomycin-resistant enterococci in cats and dogs [letter]. Lancet 348, 1038–1039.

Van den Bogaard, A.E., L.B. van den Jensen and E.E. Stobberingh. 1997. An identical VRE isolated from a turkey and a farmer. New Engl. J. Med., in press.

Van den Bogaard, A. E. and E. E. Stobberingh. 1999. Antibiotics in animal feeds and emergence and dissemination of bacterial resistance in man. (Submitted for publication).

Van den Braak, N., A. Van Belkum, M. Van Keulen, J. Vliegenthart, H.S. Verbrugh and H.P. Endtz. 1998. Molecular characterization of vancomycin-resistant enterococci from hospitalized patients and poultry products in the Netherlands. J. Clin. Microbiol. 36, 1927–1932.

Webb V, and J. Davies. 1993. Antibiotic preparations contain DNA: a source of drug resistance genes? Antimicrob Agents Chemother 37:2379–2384.

Welton, L. A. *et al.* 1998. Antimicrobial resistance in enterococci isolated from turkey flocks fed virginiamycin. Antimicrob. Agents Chemother. 42:705–708.

Werner, G., I. Klare and W. Witte. 1997. Arrangement of the vanA gene cluster in enterococci of different ecological origin. FEMS Microbiol. Lett. 155, 55–61.

Westh, H. Influence of erythromycin consumption on erythromycin resistance in *Staphylococcus aureus* in Denmark. APUA Newsletter 13(1):1–4.

WHO Report. 1997. The medical impact of the use of antimicrobials in food animals. WHO/EMC/ZOO/97.4

Witte, W. 1998. Medical consequences of antibiotic use in agriculture. Science 279: 996–997.

Woodford, N., A-M. Adebiyi, M-F. Palepou and B. D. Cookson. 1998. Diversity of VanA glycopeptide resistance elements in enterococci from humans and nonhuman sources. Antimicrob. Agents Chemother. 42: 502–508.

Woodford, N., B. L. Jones, Z. Baccus, H.A. Ludlam and D. F. Brown. 1995. Linkage of vancomycin and high-level gentamicin resistance genes on the same plasmid in a clincal isolate of *Enterococcus faecalis*. J. Antimicrob. Chemother. 35:179–184.

Wray, C., I. M. McLare, and P. J. Carroll. 1993. *Escherichia coli* isolated from farm animals in England and Wales between 1986 and 1991. Vet. Rec. 133:439–442.

# The move away from antibiotic growth promoters in Europe

PETER SPRING

*Swiss College of Agriculture, Zollikofen, Switzerland*

## Introduction: antibiotic response, antibiotic resistance and the European ban

The growth-promoting effects of subtherapeutic dietary levels of antibiotics were discovered in the late 1940s when a fermentation extract of *Streptomyces aureofaciens* was included in chicken diets. The performance responses were beyond what could be explained by the nutritive value of the extract. Analysis of the extract revealed low levels of chlortetracycline, and follow-up studies confirmed the antibiotic to be the performance-enhancing compound. Improved animal performance was soon demonstrated in other animal species and with other dietary antibiotics. A very strong body of data on the use of antimicrobial growth promoters has since accumulated. A recent review of the literature indicates that in 12,153 trials, the addition of antimicrobial growth promoters to animal diets increased production 72 % of the time (Rosen, 1996). Due to this impressive amount of positive trial data the inclusion of subtherapeutic levels of antibiotics to monogastric diets has been a standard practice for many years. In 1997 the use of antibiotics as growth promoters in the EU amounted to 1,600 tons of active ingredients or 15% of the total antibiotic usage of 10,500 tons according to a survey by the European Health Industry Association. European consumption of antibiotics for therapeutic use in animals was 3,500 tons or 33 %, while for human health it was 5,400 tons or 52 %.

ANTIBIOTIC RESISTANCE: UNDERSTOOD FROM THE BEGINNING

The existence of antibiotic resistance in bacteria has been known for almost as long as antibiotics themselves. Alexander Fleming, who discovered penicillin in 1928, warned that bacterial resistance to antibiotics can develop. He based his warning on observations he made in laboratory cultures. In the early years of antibiotic use resistance problems were rare and not of major concern. However, the discovery by Watanabe (1963) that antibiotic resistance can be transferred from one bacteria to another via transfer of resistance encoding plasmids (conjugations), and the increasingly frequent occurrence of resistant bacteria in the field made it clear that resistance could develop and spread much faster than initially expected. The problem needed to be addressed scientifically.

In the late 1960s antibiotic resistant *Salmonella typhimurium* were isolated from several calf herds in England. The same resistant bacteria could also be isolated from people in close contact with those animals. The English government asked a scientific committee to evaluate (Schwan Committee) whether resistant bacteria from animals could be transferred to humans and pose a health threat by rendering therapeutic antibiotic treatments less effective. The Schwan committee assessed the risk as low, but stated that a transfer of resistant bacteria to humans could not be excluded (Schwan, 1969). Therefore the committee recommended that antibiotics be grouped according to their use in feed or therapeutic products. Antibiotics used in medicine could no longer be fed at subtherapeutic levels as growth promoters.

## BANNING OF ANTIMICROBIAL GROWTH PROMOTERS IN EUROPE

The discussion about risks associated with antibiotics used as feed additives continued in Europe despite the actions taken as recommended by the Swann committee. In Sweden veterinarians tried to protect their business by pointing out risks involved in using subtherapeutical levels of antibiotics in animal diets. The discussion made the daily news and farmers and the feed industry were pressured to take action. The Swedish farmers' organization declared that they recognized the need for restrictive and controlled use of antibiotics. In 1986 the Swedish Parliament imposed a ban on antibacterial growth promoters.

The ban had a drastic effect on the total use of antibiotics in animal production in Sweden. Prior to the ban, nutritional and therapeutic applications each used about 20,000 kg of antibiotic products. When the ban was imposed therapeutic use increased temporarily but regressed to its pre-ban level. Overall the ban led to a 50% reduction in antibiotics used by the Swedish animal industry. The largest effects of the ban were felt in the broiler, and in particular the pig sectors. In the first year after the ban piglet mortality increased by 1.6 % and the occurrence of piglet diarrhea quadrupled (Best, 1996). However, changes in management practices have allowed the industry to partially reverse those losses (Figure 1).

The Swedish antibiotic-free approach was given little notice throughout Europe in the first few years after implementation. However, growing 'consumerism' and extended media coverage about multi-resistant strains of staphylococci infections in humans have rekindled doubt about the safety of growth promoters in the 1990s.

The EU ban of avoparcin in 1997 was a clear signal of the fast-changing situation. Avoparcin along with vancomycin, two glycopeptide

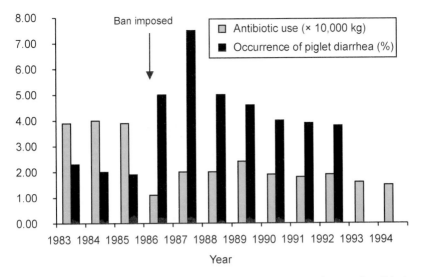

**Figure 1.** Effect of the ban of antimicrobial growth promoters on the use of antibiotics and the occurrence of piglet diarrhea in Sweden.

antibiotics, are the last known effective therapeutic agents against certain multi-resistant enterococci and staphylococci infections in humans. *In vitro* studies suggested that cross-resistance can develop against the two antibiotics; however, the connection between the use of avoparcin in the feed industry and the development of vancomycin-resistant bacteria in humans was considered very vague by the scientific community (SCAN, 1996). However, the scientific discussion showed the complexity of development and spread of resistant bacteria in the field and indicated that it would be difficult to assess the risks involved. The political committee of the EU did not want to take any chances and banned avoparcin in 1997.

The ban was extended by the EU in 1998 to include tylosin phosphate, zinc bacitracin, spiramycin and virginiamycin, four compounds related to antibiotic use in human medicine. Tylosin and spiramycin are part of the macrolide group of antibiotics. Erythromycin, an antibiotic widely used in humans, is part of the same group and shares common resistance mechanisms. The suspension of these four compounds will be reconsidered by the Council of European Agricultural Ministers before December 2000. However, it is questionable whether enough convincing data can be accumulated by then to rule out the possibility of cross-resistance. In addition, carbadox and olaquindox were banned due to a possible health threat posed to mill operators. The adjustment period for those products was set at August 31, 1999 and this decision is final.

This leaves the four antimicrobial growth promoters, monensin, avilamycin, salinomycin and flavomycin flavophospholipol which can be used nowadays in Europe. Those compounds are not related to therapeutic antibiotics in current use in humans and therefore no immediate risk has been associated with their use in animal feeds.

Several countries are taking a proactive approach and are pushing for a comprehensive ban. While the Swiss government has implemented a complete ban of antimicrobial growth promoters, the Danish animal production industry has imposed a voluntary ban. The Danish are also leading the push for an EU-wide legislative ban. Antibiotic-free production is helping the Danish animal industry to improve its reputation both within the country and in the export markets. The impact on animal performance and health has been less than expected (Petersen and Calleson, personal communication). It is possible that the high management standards on Danish farms alleviate the impact. It is also possible that the gap in animal performance between well-managed and poorly-managed farms will widen, since poor management can no longer be countered by disease-preventing feed antibiotics. This will clearly enhance the need for alternative products. The Danish farmer-owned research institutes have taken a leading role in Europe in re-evaluating response to various additives and nutrient sources in diets without antibiotic supplements.

# Mannan oligosaccharide: response in non-antibiotic diets

DANISH EXPERIENCE WITH BIO-MOS IN BROILERS

## *Experimental procedures*

As a means of providing information for the Danish farmers, the Danish Poultry Advisory Office tested the effects of three products against a negative control on broiler performance (Petersen *et al.*, 1999). The products were a killed lactobacillus preparation, mannan oligosaccharide (Bio-Mos, Alltech Inc.) and an organic acid mixture. A total of 960 Ross broilers were randomly assigned to 12 groups (3 replicates) of 80 birds each. Chicks were housed on shavings and bird density was similar to Danish commercial standards. The trial was repeated. Trial 1 lasted 36 days and Trial 2 last for 38 days.

All broilers received starter feed from day 0–6 and a grow/finisher feed from day 7 till the end of the trial (Table 1). From day 7 to 36 whole wheat was added to the diet to account for the changing requirement of the energy:protein ratio of the growing bird (day 7–13, 5% wheat; day 14–17, 10%; day 18–20, 15%; day 21–25, 24%; day 26–29, 28%; day 30–33, 30%; day 34–38, 35%). Over the entire trial wheat addition averaged 22%. Feed and water were provided *ad libitum*. Dietary treatments were as follows:

- Negative control: no additive.
- Killed lactobacillus product: 1 kg/t in the starter diet and 0.4 kg/t in the grow/finisher diet.
- Bio-Mos: 2 kg/t in the starter diet, 1 kg/t in the grow/finisher diet.
- Organic acid mixture: 3 kg/t.

Table 1.   Nutrient composition of the grow/finisher diet used in Trials 1 and 2 (%).

|  | (%) |
|---|---|
| Energy, MJ/kg | 13.2 |
| Crude protein | 22.5 |
| Crude fat | 11.7 |
| Met + Cys | 0.95 |
| Lysine | 1.30 |
| Threonine | 0.81 |
| Calcium | 1.00 |
| Phosphorus | 0.78 |
| Sodium | 0.16 |
| Chloride | 0.23 |

All birds were weighed by pen on days 7, 21 and 36 (38). Feed consumption was recorded for each of those trial periods. Mortality was recorded daily.

## Results

*Starter phase (days 1–7).* In Trial 1 birds receiving either the lactobacillus product or Bio-Mos were significantly heavier than the controls (Table 2). Those two additives also tended to improve feed efficiency (FCR); however improvements were not significant. No significant differences between treatments were noted in Trial 2 at day 7 (Table 3). In both trials early mortality was low (<1%).

*Grower phase (days 7–21).* In Trial 1 there was a trend toward higher body weight (4.0 %) in the group that received Bio-Mos. Feed conversion with Bio-Mos was significantly better (3.8%) compared to the control group. The group that received the lactobacillus preparation tended to convert feed more efficiently (P <0.05). Feed intake was equal in all four groups. In Trial 2 Bio-Mos tended to improve weight gain; however differences were not significant.

*Overall performance (days 1–36(38)).* Bio-Mos improved bodyweight by about 100 g (5.4%) compared to the control (P <0.05) (Table 2). The lactobacillus product tended to improve bodyweight, though the difference was not statistically significant. There was no extra weight gain with addition of the organic acids. A considerable improvement in feed efficiency (5%) was achieved with Bio-Mos addition (P<0.05.)

In Trial 2 Bio-Mos improved weight gain significantly (4.5 %) and tended to improve feed conversion (2.3%) (Table 3). Mortality in Trial 2 was slightly higher than in Trial 1; however, birds receiving Bio-Mos had the lowest mortality in both trials.

Taking the addition of wheat to the diet into account, the improvements with Bio-Mos were achieved with an inclusion of approximately 800 ppm (based on total diet). Those improvements are in agreement with

Table 2.  Summary of treatment effects on broiler performance (Trial 1, 36 days).

|  | Control | Lactobacillus product | Bio-Mos | Organic acids |
|---|---|---|---|---|
| Weight at 36 days, g | 1724 | 1742 | 1818 | 1715 |
| Relative to control, % | 100.0 | 101.0 | 105.4 | 99.5 |
| FCR at 36 days, kg/kg | 1.64 | 1.63 | 1.56 | 1.64 |
| Relative to control, % | 100.0 | 99.0 | 95.0 | 100.0 |
| Intake to 36 days, g | 2835 | 2833 | 2838 | 2818 |
| Relative to control, % | 100.0 | 99.9 | 100.1 | 99.4 |
| Mortality, % (cumulative) | 3.3 | 2.9 | 2.5 | 4.6 |

Table 3.  Summary of treatment effects on broiler performance (Trial 2).

|  | Control | Lactobacillus product | Bio-Mos | Organic acids |
|---|---|---|---|---|
| Weight at 38 days, g | 1822 | 1868 | 1905 | 1850 |
| Relative to control, % | 100.0 | 102.5 | 104.5 | 101.6 |
| FCR at 38 days, kg/kg | 1.65 | 1.65 | 1.61 | 1.66 |
| Relative to control, % | 100.0 | 100.0 | 97.7 | 101.0 |
| Intake to 38 days, g | 3000 | 3076 | 3066 | 3078 |
| Relative to control, % | 100.0 | 102.5 | 102.2 | 102.6 |
| Mortality, % (cumulative) | 5.4 | 4.6 | 4.2 | 5.0 |

findings made by Sims *et al.* (1998) and Roch (1999, personal communication) who reported improved performance with Bio-Mos in broilers. In the Danish trials the addition of Bio-Mos increased the gross margin per bird by 42 øre in Trial 1, and by 25 øre in Trial 2 (1 øre = 0.15 cents). Economically this amounts to a return on extra outlay for Bio-Mos addition of 6.4:1 and 3.5:1, respectively for Trials 1 and 2.

# Dietary mannan oligosaccharide and intestinal function

INTERACTION WITH GUT MICROFLORA

The gastrointestinal tract provides an extensive surface area in which direct contact takes place between the host animal and a wide variety of dietary substances, microorganisms and exogenous toxins (Gaskins, 1996). Accordingly, the intestine must permit the exchange of dietary substances between the gut lumen and the systemic circulation, while at the same time prevent penetration of pathogenic agents. To maximize protection against invaders a dense array of mucosal defense mechanisms are operating in the intestine. The defense mechanisms can be either non-immunologic or immunologic in nature. Feed additives used to enhance animal performance such as antibiotics, organic acids and high levels of inorganic copper or zinc sources aim at promoting gut health by modulating the non-immunologic defense mechanisms in the gastrointestinal tract (Swedish Ministry of Agriculture, 1997). The endogenous microflora form a major component of the non-immunologic protection system in the gut. By covering the intestinal lining, beneficial bacteria keep pathogens from attaching to the gut wall. This can be a very effective control measure since adherence to animal mucosal tissues is a crucial step in the colonization and infection process of many pathogens.

Many enteric pathogens use type-1-fimbriae, which bind to D-mannose-bearing receptors, to attach to the intestinal lining. In a recent screening study looking at bacterial attachment mechanisms, 66% of the strains of *Escherichia coli* tested expressed mannose-sensitive fimbriae (Finucane *et al.*, 1999a). The percentages of *Salmonella typhimurium* and *Salmonella enteritidis* strains that attached to mannose receptors were 80 and 67%, respectively. Mannose-type sugars in the diet can block bacterial attachment and therefore reduce pathogen colonization. Dietary mannan oligosaccharide effects on the gastrointestinal microflora were investigated in a series of broiler and turkey experiments and significant reductions in both salmonella and pathogenic *E. coli* were reported (Spring *et al.*, 1999).

In a recent turkey trial a reduction in *Clostridium perfringens,* the causative agent of necrotic enteritis, was reported in response to including mannans in the diet (Figure 2, Finucane *et al.*, 1999b). Clostridia are not known to express type-1-fimbriae. However, it might be possible that these changes were brought about through other effects exerted by Bio-Mos on the gut flora or on immune response. The turkeys fed Bio-Mos also had a higher cecal concentration of anaerobic bacteria. Many of the anaerobic cecal microorganisms in the turkey would be part of the fiber-degrading microbial population. Up to this time the effect of Bio-Mos on fiber-degrading bacteria has not been investigated. However, studies conducted in broilers suggest an interaction of Bio-Mos with this bacterial population. In broilers Bio-Mos has been shown to enhance fiber digestion suggesting an effect of Bio-Mos on the concentration or the efficiency of the fiber-degrading bacteria present in the ceca and colon of the broiler (Kumprecht *et al.*, 1997).

INTERACTION WITH THE IMMUNE SYSTEM

Research to date indicates that in addition to interacting with gut microflora, including mannan oligosaccharides in the diet supports immune function. To protect the extensive surface area of the gut the animal devotes a large part of its immune defense to that organ. Approximately 75% of all immune cells in the body are located within the intestine as part of the gut-associated lymphoid tissue (GALT). The mucosal IgA antibodies are a key part of the intestinal immunological protection. They provide protection by preventing adherence of bacteria or toxins to intestinal epithelial cells. In addition, they can kill bacteria directly via antibody-dependent cell-mediated cytotoxicity. A study conducted at Oregon State

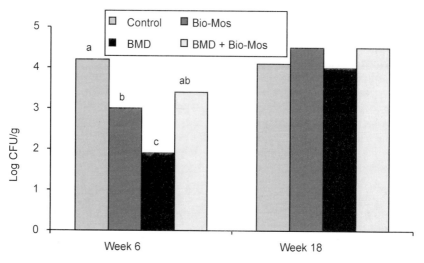

**Figure 2.** Effect of Bio-Mos and BMD on the intestinal concentrations of *Clostridium perfringens* in turkey poults (Finucane *et al.*, 1999b).

University reported increased concentrations of secretory IgA of about 25% with the addition of Bio-Mos (Savage *et al.*, 1996). Bio-Mos has also been shown to enhance macrophage response in different species (Spring and Pirvulesu, 1998). A variety of stimuli can activate macrophages. Phagocytosis of a particular antigen is an initial stimulus, but activity can be further enhanced by microbial cell wall products such as mannan oligosaccharides via the alternative pathway of the complement part of the immune system.

Vaccines have provided essential means to offset loses due to Marek's, Newcastle, and bronchitis diseases in poultry production. However, inadequate nutrition and stressors can reduce the response to a vaccine resulting in low antibody titers and insufficient protection, particularly in weaker birds. The development of better vaccines as well as dietary ingredients that are effective in supporting immune function can help to overcome some of those problems. Upendra (1999) tested the effects of adding Bio-Mos to broiler diets on vaccine titers of birds vaccinated against Newcastle disease using Lasota strain vaccine by intraoccular and intranasal routes. The birds receiving Bio-Mos had two- to four-fold increases in antibody titers (Figure 3). This enhancement in immune response via a nutritional route could play a major role in improving bird health and will require further investigation as the industry relies increasingly on preventative measures to protect intensively-reared food animals.

CHANGES IN INTESTINAL MORPHOLOGY

The structure of the intestinal mucosa can reveal information about gut health in response to diet. Stressors present in the digesta can lead relatively

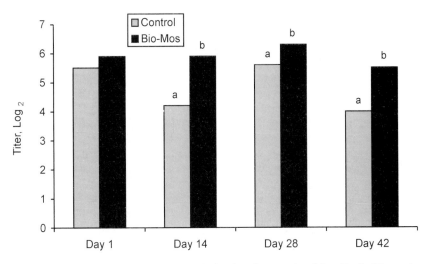

**Figure 3.** Effect of Bio-Mos on haemagglutination titers against New Castle Disease in broilers (Upenda, 1999).

quickly to changes in the intestinal mucosa due to the close proximity of the mucosal surface and the intestinal content (Nabuurs *et al.*, 1993). Changes in intestinal morphology such as shorter villi and deeper crypts have been associated with the presence of toxins. A shortening of the villi decreases the surface area for nutrient absorption. The crypt can be regarded as the villi factory and a large crypt indicates fast tissue turnover and a high demand for new tissue. Demand for energy and protein for gut maintenance is high compared to other organs. A fast growing broiler devotes about 12% of the newly synthesized protein to the digestive tract. Any additional tissue turnover will increase nutrient requirement for maintenance and will therefore lower the efficiency of the animal. Changes in intestinal morphology as described above can lead to poor nutrient absorption, increased secretion in the gut, diarrhea, reduced disease resistance and lower overall performance (Nabuurs *et al.*, 1993).

A study conducted at Oregon State University reported a reduction in crypt depth and an increase in villus length:crypt depth ratio in turkeys given dietary Bio-Mos (Savage *et al.*, 1997). The energy conserved by the reduced turnover rate of the epithelial cells might be utilized for lean tissue mass synthesis and can help to explain some of the improvements seen in body weight gain and feed conversion with Bio-Mos (Savage *et al.*, 1997).

## Summary

Mannan oligosaccharide derived from the cell wall of the yeast *Saccharomyces cerevisiae* offers a valuable nutritional tool to aid in supporting animal health and thereby optimize performance. In two broiler studies conducted by the Danish Poultry Advisory Office Bio-Mos improved weight gain by an average of 5.0 % and efficiency by 3.7%. These responses are similar to results in other commercial and controlled studies around the globe. Although much emphasis is placed upon 'growth promoter alternatives', it is clear that changing the way we look at dietary carbohydrates can improve performance and efficiency.

## References

Best, P. 1996. Production without antibiotics: The Swedish experience. Feed International. April 8.

Finucane, M, P. Spring and K.E. Newman. 1999. Incidence of mannose sensitive adhesins in enteric pathogens. Poster S179, Southern Poultry Science, Jan 18–21, Atlanta, GA.

Finucane, M, P. Spring, K.A. Dawson and M.D. Sims. 1999a. Effect of mannan oligosaccharide on intestinal microflora in turkey. Poult. Sci. (submitted).

Gaskins, H.R. 1996. Development and structure of mucosal defense in the pig intestine. In: Biotechnology in the Feed Industry, Proceedings of the 12th annual symposium (T.P. Lyons and K.A. Jacques, eds.) Nottingham University Press, Nottingham, UK. pp. 23–35.

Kumprecht, I., P. Zobac, V. Siske, A.E. Sefton and P. Spring. 1997. Effect of dietary mannanoligosaccharide level on liveweight and feed efficiency of broilers. In: Proceedings of the Int. Symp. on Non-digestible oligosaccharides. (R. Hartemink, ed.). Graduate School VLAG, Wageningen, NL. p.144.

Nabuurs, M.J.A., A. Hoogendoorn, E.J. Van der Molen and A.L.M. Van Osta. 1993. Villus height and crypt depth in weaned pigs reared under various circumstances in the Netherlands. Res. Vet. Sci. 55:78–84.

Petersen, C.B. 1999. British Society of Animal Production (submitted).

Rosen, G.D. 1996. Proceedings of the Worlds Poultry Science Society, Vol II, p.141. New Dehli.

Savage, T.F., P.F. Cotter and E.I. Zakrzewska. 1996. The effect of feeding a mannan oligosaccharide on immunoglobulins, plasma IgG and bile IgA of Wrolstad MW male turkeys. Poultry Sci. 75(Suppl. 1):143.

Savage, T.F., E.I. Zakrewska and J.R.Andreasen. 1997. The effects of feeding mannanoligosaccharide supplemented diets to poults on performance and the morphology of the small intestine. Poultry Sci. 76(Suppl. 1):139.

SCAN. 1996. Report of the scientific committee for animal nutrition (SCAN) on the possible risk for humans on the use of avoparcin as feed additive. VI/6474/96+cd.

Schwan, M. 1969. (Joint Committee on the use of antibiotics in animal husbandry and veterinary medicine): Report presented to Parliment Report Cmdn. 4190. Her Majesty's Stationery Office, London.

Sims, M.D., P. Spring and A.E. Sefton. 1998. Effect of mannan oligosaccharide on performance of commercial broiler chickens. Poult. Sci. 77(Suppl. 1):89.

Spring, P., C. Wenk, K.A. Dawson and K.E. Newman. 1999. Effect of mannanoligosaccharide on different cecal parameters and on cecal concentration on enteric bacteria in challenged broiler chicks. Poult. Sci. (submitted for publication).

Spring, P. and M. Pirvulescu. 1998. Mannanologosaccharide: Its logical role as a natural feed additive for piglets. In: Biotechnology in the Feed Industry, Proceedings of the 13th annual symposium (T.P. Lyons and K.A. Jacques, eds). Nottingham University Press, U.K. pp 553–62.

Swedish Ministry of Agriculture. 1997. Antimicrobial feed additives. Report from the Commission on Antimicrobial Feed Additives no. 132. Stockholm, Sweden.

Upendra, H.A. 1999. Studies on probiotics and mannan oligosaccharide: Their effect on performance, haematology, biochemistry and immunological aspects in broiler chicks. Dissertation. Univ. of Agri. Sci. Bangalore. India.

Watanabe, T. 1963. Infective heredity of multiple drug resistance in bacteria. Bacteriol. Rev. 27:87.

# Effect of hen age, Bio-Mos and Flavomycin on susceptibility of turkey poults to oral *Escherichia coli* challenge

A.S. FAIRCHILD[1], J.L. GRIMES[1], F.W. EDENS[1], M.J. WINELAND[1], F.T. JONES[2], AND A.E. SEFTON[3]

[1] *Department of Poultry Science, North Carolina State University, Raleigh, North Carolina,* [2] *Department of Poultry Science, University of Arkansas, Fayetteville, Arkansas and* [3] *Alltech Biotechnology Center, Nicholasville, Kentucky, USA*

## Abstract

The effects of *Escherichia coli*, hen age, and dietary Bio-Mos and Flavomycin were studied to determine their influence on poult performance from 1 to 21 days. Day-of-hatch male turkey poults (British United Turkeys) were orally gavaged (1 ml) with $10^8$ CFU/ml *E. coli* or sterile carrier broth. Within each *E. coli* treatment group, poults from two different hen ages (33 and 58 weeks of age) were fed diets containing Bio-Mos (2 lb/ton feed) and Flavomycin (2 g active ingredient/ton feed), alone and in combination, in a randomized complete block design. At week 1 and week 3, one bird per pen (n=128) was chosen for bacterial sampling. Aliquots from liver and intestinal tissue were spiral plated on the following media: Eosin Methylene Blue agar (EMB) for total coliforms, Tryptic Soy agar (TSA) for total aerobic bacteria, and lactobacillus selection agar (LBS) for *Lactobacillus* sp. Any sample yielding isolated *E. coli* colonies was subcultured and sent to the *E. coli* Reference Center, University Park, PA, for O serotyping. Individual body weight and feed consumption by pen were recorded on a weekly basis. Poult mortality was recorded on a daily basis. Feed conversion and body weight gains were calculated. Results indicate interactions of hen age with Bio-Mos and Flavomycin for bacterial counts for intestinal and liver tissues for both week 1 and week 3 (P≤0.05). Under *E. coli* challenge, Bio-Mos and Flavomycin (P<0.05) improved poult growth during week 2 while Flavomycin improved poult growth through week 3 (P≤0.05). Cumulative three week body weight gains for unchallenged poults were improved by both Bio-Mos and Flavomycin (P≤0.05). It may be concluded that dietary Bio-Mos and Flavomycin can improve the overall performance of poults especially when they are faced with an *E. coli* challenge during the first few weeks of life.

# Introduction

Antimicrobials have traditionally been used in the poultry industry to improve health and performance of birds by decreasing or altering the bacterial populations present in the digestive tract. This has been done during the grow-out period to protect the animal from pathogenic organisms and to increase weight gains and improve meat quality.

Antibiotics have come under increasing scrutiny by researchers and consumers alike because there are increasing percentages of antibiotic-resistant bacteria (including pathogenic strains) seen after the inclusion of antibiotics in the feed. Antibiotic resistance displayed by field *E. coli* isolates from North Carolina commercial turkey farms has been reported (Fairchild *et al.*, 1998), including resistance to enrofloxacin, one of the most recent antibiotics approved for use in poultry (Figures 1 and 2). Most of the antibiotics used as growth promoters have no significant approved claims to control disease (Gustafson and Bowen, 1997). Debate over resistance seen among Gram-negative bacteria such as *E. coli* and salmonella has generated the strongest objection to antibiotic use (Evagelisti *et al.*, 1975; Scioli *et al.*, 1983; Gustafson and Bowen, 1997). It has been reported that antibiotic resistance to indigenous *E. coli* in poultry has remained at a relatively high level since the 1950s (Gustafson and Bowen, 1997). Furthermore, claims have been made that the use of these antibiotics could disrupt normal gut microflora (Surawicz *et al.*, 1989).

Consequently, other approaches, such as competitive exclusion (CE) treatments, have been developed to counter the growth-depressing effects that certain strains of bacteria elicit in poultry. One type of CE aims at the development of a protective barrier bacteria population in the digestive tract that prevents the colonization of unfavorable (growth depressing and/or pathogenic) microorganisms. Some cultures have included *Lactobacillus* sp. (Francis *et al.*, 1978) or undefined normal avian gut flora (Nurmi and Rantala, 1973). Another CE type exploits the presence of mannose-specific fimbriae on unfavorable Gram negative bacteria such as strains of *E. coli* and salmonella. These bacteria use the fimbriae to attach to and then colonize the intestinal wall. Mannanoligosaccharides (MOS), derived from mannans on yeast cell surfaces, act as high affinity ligands (decoys), offering a competitive binding site for the bacteria (Ofek *et al.*, 1977). Pathogens with the mannose-specific fimbriae adsorb to the MOS (decoy) instead of attaching to intestinal epithelial cells, and therefore move through the intestine without colonization. Newman (1994) reported that the presence of dietary MOS in the intestinal tract removed pathogenic bacteria that could attach to the lumen of the intestine in this manner. This might provide a more favorable environment for nutrient utilization by the bird (Savage and Zakrzewska, 1996). The present study was designed to determine whether a MOS product, Bio-Mos, and an antibiotic used for growth enhancement, Flavomycin, alone or in combination would alter the numbers of intestinal tract and liver bacteria or improve perform-ance characteristics of poults from hens of two different ages chal-lenged with *E. coli* from 1-21 days of age.

# Materials and methods

### PREPARATION OF ORAL *E. COLI* CHALLENGE CULTURES

Five *E. coli* cultures (including one pathogenic culture), isolated from North Carolina commercial turkey farms, were chosen based on strong resist-ance to 8 different antibiotics available to the poultry industry and strong agglutination with Bio-Mos (Figures 1 and 2). A growth curve was performed to determine the point at which the cultures reached $10^8$ CFU/ml, which was the gavage dosage used in this study. Each was then grown independently overnight and mixed before administration. Serotypes used included O:2, O:19, O:88, and O:159. Additional cultures of the bacteria were grown throughout the study in order to provide supplemental oral challenge via water troughs on days 4, 8, 12, 16, and 20.

### EXPERIMENTAL BIRDS AND CHALLENGE PROTOCOL

Day-of-hatch male poults (British United Turkeys, Lewisburg, WV) (n=896) from both a young (33 weeks of age, WOA) and old (58 WOA) breeder flock were placed in four rooms with each room containing two batter-ies (Petersime Incubator Co., Gettysburg, OH ) with wire mesh floors. Sixteen pens were used in each battery with seven birds placed in each pen. At placement, poults were gavaged orally with either 1 ml of *E. coli* suspended in Veal Infusion broth (VI, Difco Laboratories, Detroit, MI) at a concentration of $10^8$ CFU/ml, or 1 ml of sterile VI broth. On days in which additional *E. coli* challenge was supplied, 0.1 ml of *E. coli* suspen-sion was added to the water troughs (2.0 liters) so that the final concentra-tion of *E. coli* in the troughs was $10^6$ CFU/ml. Water troughs were rinsed once per week and not disinfected to facilitate any bacterial growth. Two rooms each were used to house the challenged and unchallenged poults providing for a split plot arrangement of treatments. Control birds (without *E. coli* challenge) were gavaged first to lessen the likelihood of cross contamination.

### DIETARY TREATMENTS

The poults were fed a turkey starter ration (Table 1). The same ration was used for four dietary treatments: control, Bio-Mos (2 lb/ton feed, Alltech, Inc.), Flavomycin (2 g active ingredient/ton feed, Hoechst Roussel Vet) and Bio-Mos plus Flavomycin. De-ionized water and feed were provided *ad libitum*.

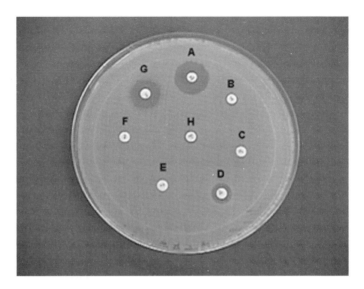

**Figure 1.** North Carolina field *Escherichia coli* isolate showing moderate and full resistance to eight antibiotics; none were categorized as susceptible using test guidelines. (A: Sulfadimethoxine 23.8 mcg /Ormetoprim 1.2 mcg; B: Chlortetracycline 30 mcg; C: Clindamycin 2 mcg; D: Gentamycin 10 mcg; E: Penicillin 10 units; F: Bacitracin 10 units; G: Neomycin 30 mcg; H: Enrofloxacin 5 mcg. All strengths listed as amount in each disk.)

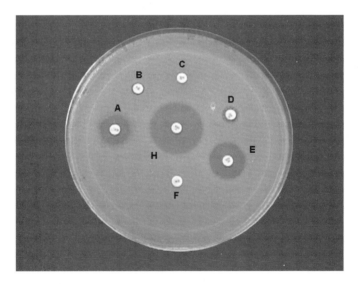

**Figure 2.** Second North Carolina field *Escherichia coli* isolate showing a more susceptible profile. A: Sulfadimethoxine/Ormetoprim; B: Chlortetracycline; C: Clindamycin; D: Gentamycin; E: Penicillin; F: Bacitracin; H: Enrofloxacin. Isolate is resistant to B, C, D, and F; susceptible to A, E, and H. All strengths are same for those used for Figure 1. 1

**Table 1.** Composition of the treatment diets.

| | | Diet | | |
|---|---|---|---|---|
| | Control | Flavomycin | Bio-Mos | Flavomycin+ Bio-Mos |
| Ingredient | | (%) | | |
| Corn | 43.0 | 43.0 | 42.9 | 42.9 |
| Soybean meal | 39.8 | 39.8 | 39.8 | 39.8 |
| Limestone | 1.5 | 1.5 | 1.5 | 1.5 |
| Poultry fat | 2.0 | 2.0 | 2.0 | 2.0 |
| Dical (18.5%) | 2.3 | 2.3 | 2.3 | 2.3 |
| Poultry meal | 8.0 | 8.0 | 8.0 | 8.0 |
| DL methionine | 2.2 | 2.2 | 2.2 | 2.2 |
| Lysine | 0.2 | 0.2 | 0.2 | 0.2 |
| Salt | 0.2 | 0.2 | 0.2 | 0.2 |
| Choline chloride | 0.2 | 0.2 | 0.2 | 0.2 |
| Minerals[a] | 0.2 | 0.2 | 0.2 | 0.2 |
| Vitamins[b] | 0.2 | 0.2 | 0.2 | 0.2 |
| Selenium[c] | 0.2 | 0.2 | 0.2 | 0.2 |
| Flavomycin-4 premix [d] | | 0.025 | | 0.025 |
| Bio-Mos[e] | | | 0.1 | 0.1 |
| Calculated analysis | | | | |
| Protein | 27.91 | 27.91 | 27.91 | 27.91 |
| ME (kcal/lb) | 1297.71 | 1297.71 | 1297.71 | 1297.71 |
| Fat | 5.22 | 5.22 | 5.22 | 5.22 |
| Methionine | 0.68 | 0.68 | 0.68 | 0.68 |
| Met + Cys | 1.13 | 1.13 | 1.13 | 1.13 |
| Lysine | 1.71 | 1.71 | 1.71 | 1.71 |
| Calcium | 1.44 | 1.44 | 1.44 | 1.44 |
| Available phosphorus | 0.73 | 0.73 | 0.73 | 0.73 |
| Sodium | 0.13 | 0.13 | 0.13 | 0.13 |

[a]Minerals mix supplied the following per kg of diet: 120 mg Zn as $ZnSO_4 \, H_2O$; 120 mg Mn as $MnSO_4 \, H_2O$; 80 mg Fe as $FeSO_4 \, H_2O$; 10 mg Cu as $CuSO_4$; 2.5 mg I as $Cu(IO_3)_2$; 1.0 mg Co as $CoSO_4$.

[b]Vitamin mix supplied the following per kg of diet when added at 0.2%: vitamin A, 6,600 IU; vitamin $D_3$, 2000 ICU; vitamin E, 33 IU; vitamin $B_{12}$, 19.8 µg; riboflavin , 6.6 mg; niacin, 55 mg; d-pantothenate, 11 mg; menadione, 2 mg; folic acid, 1.1 mg; thiamin, 2 mg; pyridoxine, 4 mg; d-biotin, 126 µg; ethoxyquin, 50 mg.

[c]Selenium premix supplied 0.21 mg Se, as $Na_2SeO_3$.

[d]Flavomycin added at 2 g active ingredient/ton of finished feed.

[e]Bio-Mos added at 2 lbs/ton of finished feed.

## SAMPLING, ENUMERATION, AND PERFORMANCE DATA

At weeks 1 and 3, one bird per pen (128 birds/week) was chosen at random for microbial analyses. The selected poults were weighed, euthanized, and liver and intestinal tract posterior to the duodenal loop were aseptically removed. The samples were then brought to a 1:10 dilution by weight in 0.85% saline and mechanically massaged (Stomacher® Model 80 Mark II Laboratory Blender, Tekmar-Dohrmann, Cincinnati, OH) for 1 minute. All samples were finally diluted to appropriate levels for plating. An aliquot from each sample (100 μl) was spiral plated (Model D, Spiral Systems Inc., Cincinnati, OH) on the following: Eosin Methylene Blue agar (EMB) for the isolation and enumeration of total coliforms, lactobacillus selection agar (LBS) for the enumeration of *Lactobacillus* sp. and Tryptic Soy agar (TSA) for the enumeration of total aerobic bacteria. Any EMB plate yielding isolated *Escherichia coli* colonies was subcultured and sent to the *E. coli* Reference Center, University Park, PA, for O serotyping to see if any serotypes retrieved matched those administered. Individual body weights and feed consumption by pen were measured on a weekly basis. Weekly and cumulative body weight gains, feed conversion ratios, and feed:gain ratios were calculated.

EXPERIMENTAL DESIGN AND STATISTICAL ANALYSIS

Within each gavage treatment group, birds were subjected to a randomized complete block arrangement of 2 hen ages x 2 levels of Bio-Mos x 2 levels of Flavomycin. All feed treatments were balanced on each side of each battery. Bacterial counts were transformed to their $Log_{10}$ values and mortality percentages were subjected to arc sine transformation before statistical analysis. All data were analyzed using the General Linear Models Procedures of SAS. The effects of *E. coli* challenge, hen age, Bio-Mos and Flavomycin were regressed on bacterial enumeration and poult performance. Treatment means were separated using the Least Significant Difference procedure of SAS. Any discussion of differences between treatment means in the following section are to be considered significant ($P \leq 0.05$) unless stated otherwise.

# Results and discussion

PERFORMANCE

Greater body weight gains were made during weeks one and two for poults challenged with *E. coli* when the poults were fed a diet supplemented with Bio-Mos or Flavomycin (Table 2). During week one, a diet supplemented with both Bio-Mos and Flavomycin in combination resulted in lower poult growth than for the control diet or diets with a single supplement. Poults fed the combination diet were intermediate in growth during week two and had equivalent growth during week three. Weekly body weight gains of poults without *E. coli* challenge were improved by both Bio-Mos and Flavomycin at the end of week two and by Flavomycin at the end of week three (Table 2). During week one, poults from old hens had significantly greater body weight gains than poults from young hens (70.5 *vs.* 58.9 g) when not challenged with *E. coli*. Under *E. coli* challenge during week one and for both challenge groups for weeks two and three, poults from old and young hens gained the same. Cumulative body weight gains (Table 3) following *E. coli* challenge were not significantly different at weeks

190

two or three but demonstrated a pattern similar to that observed for weekly gains (Table 2). Cumulative body weight gains of poults not challenged with *E. coli* were improved when the diet was supplemented with Bio-Mos or Flavomycin (Table 3).

Table 2. Effect of dietary Flavomycin (F) and Bio-Mos (B) on body weight gains (g) of poults from young (33 WOA) or old (58 WOA) turkey breeder hens with and without *E. coli* challenge.

| | With *E. coli* challenge | | | | | | | | |
|---|---|---|---|---|---|---|---|---|---|
| | Week 1 | | | Week 2 | | | Week 3 | | |
| Diet | Young | Old | Mean | Young | Old | Mean | Young | Old | Mean |
| Control | 58.6 | 58.2[b] | 58.4[b] | 156.7[b]* | 163.2* | 159.9[b] | 270.6 | 263.2 | 266.9 |
| F | 60.2 | 68.0[a] | 64.1[a] | 165.7[ab] | 174.3 | 170.0[a] | 261.1* | 280.2* | 270.7 |
| B | 66.6 | 67.5[a] | 67.1[a] | 173.7[a] | 163.7 | 168.7[a] | 273.8 | 266.3 | 270.0 |
| F+B | 52.6 | 52.7[b] | 52.7[c] | 167.5[ab] | 168.5 | 168.0[ab] | 273.4 | 282.4 | 277.9 |
| Mean | 59.5 | 61.6 | 61.9 | 165.9 | 167.4 | 167.6 | 269.7 | 273.0 | 271.9 |
| SEM | 1.5 | 1.5 | 2.1 | 2.5 | 2.6 | 3.5 | 4.5 | 4.6 | 6.4 |
| | Without *E. coli* challenge | | | | | | | | |
| Control | 54.1[b] * | 70.1* | 62.1[b] | 179.1[b] | 183.3[b] | 181.2[b] | 268.6[b] | 269.4[b] | 269.0[b] |
| F | 60.2[ab]* | 68.2* | 64.2[ab] | 195.7[a] | 199.9[a] | 197.8[a] | 296.5[a] | 307.2[a] | 301.9[a] |
| B | 59.6[ab]* | 71.6* | 65.6[ab] | 187.2[a] | 190.8[a] | 189.0[a] | 282.2[a] | 250.1[b] | 266.1[b] |
| F+B | 61.7[a] * | 72.1* | 66.9[a] | 189.8[a] | 197.9[a] | 193.9[a] | 280.5[ab] | 301.3[a] | 290.9[a] |
| Mean | 58.9* | 70.5* | 64.9 | 187.9 | 193.0 | 190.7 | 282.0 | 282.0 | 282.2 |
| SEM | 1.1 | 1.2 | 1.6 | 2.2 | 2.3 | 3.1 | 3.3 | 3.3 | 4.7 |

[a,b] Means within a column with no common superscript differ significantly (P≤0.05).
* Means within a row within a time period differ significantly (P≤0.05).

Weekly body weights of poults with and without *E. coli* challenge are summarized in Table 4. Following *E. coli* challenge, all poults had significantly higher body weights at day 7 when either Bio-Mos or Flavomycin was added to the diet, but not when the diet contained both additives. At day 14, poults fed Bio-Mos were heavier than poults fed no additive or both additives; while poults fed Flavomycin were intermediate in weight between Bio-Mos and control poults. At day 21, there were no significant differences in body weights of poults following *E. coli* challenge; although the numerical improvements for body weights in the presence of either feed treatment was greater than that observed at 14 days. For those poults not receiving an *E. coli* challenge, poults fed diets with Flavomycin or Bio-Mos plus Flavomycin were heavier at days 14 and 21, while those fed Bio-Mos were intermediate at day 14 but not different from controls at day 21 (Table 4). Poults from old hens weighed more than poults from young hens at day 7 for the control (125.1 *vs.* 112.7 g) and Bio-Mos (126.9 *vs.* 116.8 g) diets (Table 4). Poults from old hens weighed more than poults from young hens over all diets at day 7 (125.4 *vs.* 116.5 g) and day 14 (316.1 *vs.* 306.9 g). However, by day 21, there were

**Table 3.** Effect of dietary Flavomycin (F) and Bio-Mos (B) on cumulative body weight gains (g) of poults from young (33 WOA) or old (58 WOA) turkey breeder hens with and without *E. coli* challenge.

| | With *E. coli* challenge | | | | | | | | |
|---|---|---|---|---|---|---|---|---|---|
| | Week 1 | | | Week 2 | | | Week 3 | | |
| Diet | Young | Old | Mean | Young | Old | Mean | Young | Old | Mean |
| Control | 58.6 | 58.2[b] | 58.4[b] | 215.2 | 222.4 | 218.8 | 488.0 | 483.6 | 485.8 |
| F | 60.2 | 68.0[a] | 64.1[a] | 225.0 | 240.7 | 232.8 | 480.7 | 520.3 | 500.5 |
| B | 66.6 | 67.5[a] | 67.1[a] | 239.5 | 229.1 | 234.3 | 514.7 | 493.7 | 504.2 |
| F+B | 52.6 | 52.7[b] | 52.7[c] | 220.9 | 215.2 | 218.0 | 496.0 | 486.0 | 491.0 |
| Mean | 59.5 | 61.6 | 61.9 | 225.1 | 226.8 | 229.4 | 494.9 | 495.9 | 500.4 |
| SEM | 1.5 | 1.5 | 2.1 | 3.6 | 3.8 | 5.2 | 7.2 | 7.5 | 10.4 |
| | Without *E. coli* challenge | | | | | | | | |
| Control | 54.1[b*] | 70.1* | 62.1[b] | 234.9[b*] | 251.9[b*] | 243.4[b] | 503.4[b] | 523.0[c] | 513.2[c] |
| F | 60.2[ab*] | 68.2* | 64.2[ab] | 256.4[a] | 268.7[a] | 262.6[a] | 552.6[a] | 574.1[a] | 563.4[a] |
| B | 59.6[ab*] | 71.6* | 65.6[ab] | 246.4[ab*] | 264.0[ab*] | 255.2[ab] | 534.1[a] | 535.6[bc] | 534.8[b] |
| F+B | 61.7[a*] | 72.1* | 66.9[a] | 251.9[a] | 263.8[ab] | 257.9[a] | 534.6[a] | 558.6[ab] | 546.6[ab] |
| Mean | 58.9* | 70.5* | 64.9 | 247.4* | 262.1* | 255.7 | 531.2* | 547.8* | 541.4 |
| SEM | 1.1 | 1.2 | 1.6 | 3.0 | 3.1 | 4.3 | 5.5 | 5.6 | 7.8 |

[a,b] Means within a column with no common superscript differ significantly (P≤0.05).
* Means within a row within a time period differ significantly (P≤0.05).

no differences in body weights between poults from young and old hens (Table 4).

There were no differences in feed conversion between dietary or hen age treatments. Mean three week feed conversion for *E. coli* challenged poults was 1.42 (±0.03), and for unchallenged poults, 1.33 (±0.03). For poults receiving *E. coli* challenge, there was a significantly higher cumulative mortality (Table 5) in young poults fed the diet containing Bio-Mos and Flavomycin in combination, with mortality for the remaining treatments being intermediate between the control diet and the diet with both supplements. No other significant differences were observed.

The results of the performance data support previous findings in which feeding Bio-Mos or Flavomycin significantly improved body weight and weight gains of turkeys (Savage *et al.*, 1996; Savage *et al.*, 1997; Buresh *et al.*, 1986; Caston and Leeson, 1992), and extend those findings to improved body weights and weight gains of poults fed Bio-Mos with additional stress (Sims and Sefton, 1999). Sims and Sefton (1999) reared tom turkeys to 18 weeks of age on used turkey litter and fed diets with Bacitracin Methylene Disalycylate (BMD) and Bio-Mos alone and in combination along with a control diet. There were no significant differences in body weights at 6 or 12 weeks of age (Table 6). However, at both 15 and 18 weeks of age, turkeys fed BMD plus Bio-Mos were heavier (P≤0.05) than control fed birds while the birds fed either of the feed additives alone were intermediate in body weight (Table 6). Also, at 18 weeks

**Table 4.** Effect of dietary Flavomycin (F) and Bio-Mos (B) on body weights (g) of poults from young (33 WOA) or old (58 WOA) turkey breeder hens with and without *E. coli* challenge.

| | With *E. coli* challenge | | | | | | | | |
|---|---|---|---|---|---|---|---|---|---|
| | Day 7 | | | Day 14 | | | Day 21 | | |
| *Diet* | Young | Old | Mean | Young | Old | Mean | Young | Old | Mean |
| Control | 114.4[b] | 113.9[b] | 114.2[b] | 272.7[b] | 279.6[a] | 276.2[bc] | 545.2 | 542.9 | 544.1 |
| F | 115.7[ab] | 123.1[a] | 119.4[a] | 281.8[ab] | 295.9[a] | 288.8[ab] | 543.0 | 575.2 | 559.1 |
| B | 122.2[a] | 122.4[a] | 122.3[a] | 297.1[a] | 285.0[a] | 291.1[a] | 572.8 | 547.8 | 560.3 |
| F+B | 107.9[b] | 106.3[b] | 107.1[c] | 276.7[b] | 268.5[b] | 272.6[c] | 553.6 | 541.0 | 547.3 |
| Mean | 115.1 | 116.4 | 117.1 | 282.1 | 282.3 | 284.7 | 553.7 | 551.7 | 556.1 |
| SEM | 1.5 | 1.5 | 2.1 | 3.6 | 3.8 | 5.2 | 7.2 | 7.4 | 10.3 |
| | Without *E. coli* challenge | | | | | | | | |
| Control | 112.7[b]* | 125.1* | 118.9 | 296.6[b] | 305.7[b] | 301.1[b] | 567.5[b] | 575.0[b] | 571.3[b] |
| F | 117.8[a] | 123.1 | 120.4 | 315.3[a] | 322.0[a] | 318.6[a] | 594.0[ab] | 563.3[b] | 578.7[b] |
| B | 116.8[ab]* | 126.9* | 121.8 | 305.3[ab] | 314.8[ab] | 310.1[ab] | 594.0[ab] | 563.3[b] | 578.7[b] |
| F+B | 119.0[a] | 126.6 | 122.8 | 310.2[ab] | 321.9[a] | 316.1[a] | 594.1[ab] | 625.1[a] | 609.6[a] |
| Mean | 116.5* | 125.4* | 121.2 | 306.9* | 316.1* | 312.0 | 592.2 | 597.7 | 595.8 |
| SEM | 1.1 | 1.2 | 1.6 | 2.9 | 3.0 | 4.1 | 5.3 | 5.4 | 7.5 |

[a,b] Means within a column with no common superscript differ significantly (P≤0.05).
* Means within a row within a time period differ significantly (P≤0.05).

**Table 5.** Effect of dietary Flavomycin (F) and Bio-Mos (B) on mortality (%) of poults from young (33 WOA) or old (58 WOA) turkey breeder hens with and without *E. coli* challenge.

| | With *E. coli* challenge | | | | | | | | |
|---|---|---|---|---|---|---|---|---|---|
| | Week 1 | | | Week 2 | | | Week 3 | | |
| *Diet* | Young | Old | Mean | Young | Old | Mean | Young | Old | Mean |
| Control | 5.36 | 5.36 | 5.36 | 0.00 | 0.00 | 0.00 | 5.36[b] | 5.36 | 5.36 |
| F | 7.72 | 12.50 | 10.11 | 0.00 | 0.00 | 0.00 | 7.53[ab] | 12.50 | 10.01 |
| B | 9.32 | 7.97 | 8.64 | 1.97 | 0.00 | 0.90 | 11.29[ab] | 7.80 | 9.55 |
| F+B | 15.86 | 8.61 | 12.23 | 2.00 | 0.00 | 0.86 | 17.86[a] | 8.33 | 13.09 |
| Mean | 9.56 | 8.61 | 8.83 | 0.95 | 0.00 | 0.52 | 10.51 | 8.50 | 9.35 |
| SEM | 1.96 | 2.04 | 2.83 | 0.54 | 0.56 | 0.78 | 1.87 | 1.94 | 2.69 |
| | Without *E. coli* challenge | | | | | | | | |
| Control | 5.36 | 0.00 | 2.68 | 0.00 | 0.00 | 0.00 | 5.36 | 0.00 | 2.68 |
| F | 1.79 | 0.00 | 0.89 | 0.00 | 0.00 | 0.00 | 3.57 | 0.00 | 1.79 |
| B | 5.36 | 3.95 | 4.65 | 0.00 | 0.00 | 0.00 | 7.14 | 4.13 | 5.63 |
| F+B | 3.57 | 4.84 | 4.21 | 0.00 | 2.04 | 1.02 | 3.57 | 6.80 | 5.19 |
| Mean | 4.02 | 2.20 | 3.00 | 0.00 | 0.50 | 0.23 | 4.91 | 2.73 | 3.69 |
| SEM | 1.45 | 1.51 | 2.09 | 0.32 | 0.33 | 0.46 | 1.50 | 1.51 | 2.09 |

[a,b] Means within a column with no common superscript differ significantly (P≤0.05).

of age, birds fed Bio-Mos or BMD alone were heavier than control birds but were not as heavy as those fed Bio-Mos and BMD in combination (P≤0.05). In addition, feed conversion was improved (P≤0.05) at 18 weeks of age for those birds fed Bio-Mos plus BMD compared to control fed birds, while those fed either Bio-Mos or BMD alone were intermediate in feed conversion (Table 7). Even though the effects occurred at different age periods, the current study and that reported by Sims and Sefton (1999) agree in that poults challenged with a disease agent benefit when Bio-Mos is added to the diet and this benefit is comparable to antibiotic growth promotants such as Flavomycin or BMD. However, this study did not show significant improvements in feed efficiencies in poults not challenged with *E. coli* for any treatment diet, which agrees with previously reported studies (Savage *et al.*, 1996; Savage *et al.*, 1997; Buresh *et al.*, 1986; Caston and Leeson, 1992).

Table 6.   Effects of Bio-Mos and BMD on average liveweight (kg) of turkeys at 6, 12, 15 and 18 weeks[1].

|  | Week 6 | Week 12 | Week 15 | Week 18 |
|---|---|---|---|---|
| Control | 1.993[a] | 7.281[a] | 9.348[b] | 11.868[c] |
| Bio-Mos | 2.031[a] | 7.518[a] | 9.698[ab] | 12.563[b] |
| BMD | 2.127[a] | 7.545[a] | 9.716[ab] | 12.455[b] |
| Bio-Mos + BMD | 2.116[a] | 7.535[a] | 9.804[a] | 12.787[a] |

[ab]Means in a column with different superscripts differ (P≤0.05).
[1]Sims and Sefton, 1999.

Table 7.   Effects of Bio-Mos and BMD on average feed conversion of turkeys at 6, 12, 15 and 18 weeks[1].

|  | Week 6 | Week 12 | Week 15 | Week 18 |
|---|---|---|---|---|
| Control | 1.591[a] | 2.436[b] | 2.805[b] | 3.370[b] |
| Bio-Mos | 1.616[a] | 2.302[a] | 2.662[a] | 3.122[ab] |
| BMD | 1.556[a] | 2.341[ab] | 2.692[ab] | 3.154[ab] |
| Bio-Mos + BMD | 1.519[a] | 2.391[ab] | 2.739[ab] | 2.974[a] |

[ab]Means in a column with different superscripts differ (P≤0.05).
[1]Sims and Sefton, 1999.

Sims (1998) and Sims *et al.* (1998) reported similar findings with broiler chicks. Broiler chicks were reared in floor pens to 49 days of age using typical broiler diets with either Bio-Mos or BMD added to the diet and compared to a control diet. Bio-Mos was added at a rate of 2 lb/ton in the starter and 1 lb/ton in the grower and finisher. BMD was added at a rate of 50 g/ton to the starter and 25 g/ton in the grower and finisher. All diets contained Avatec (90 g/ton) as a coccidiostat. There were no significant differences in body weight or feed conversion of broilers fed the three treatment diets at 22 days of age. However, at 49 days of age, the broilers fed Bio-Mos or BMD (5.52 and 5.68 lb) were heavier than controls (5.27 lbs, P<0.05). Likewise, efficiencies were significantly improved by the treatment diets ( Bio-Mos, 1.83; BMD, 1.82; and control, 2.01). Mortality was not significantly different between treatments at either 22 (1.25%) or 49 (5.69%) days of age. Sims (1998) and Sims *et al.* (1998) also reported that the feed cost per lb of meat and feed cost per bird were reduced by Bio-Mos and BMD compared to controls. In addition, carcass market value and the return per bird less feed costs were increased by both additives. Sims and Sefton (1999) concluded that broilers fed Bio-Mos performed similarly to birds fed BMD, an observation supported by the current study.

BACTERIAL ENUMERATION

### With E. coli challenge
Based on serotyping results, two of the four serotypes administered were recovered in culture (O88 and O2), and one (O2) has been reported to be pathogenic to poultry (Heller and Drabkin, 1977). There were also a number of O serotypes recovered that were not administered. These could have been introduced in previous environments the poults were exposed to such as the breeder farm or hatchery, or during transport and handling by investigators.

At day 7, significantly less total aerobic bacteria were found in intestinal samples of poults from young hens if fed the Flavomycin diet (Table 8). Also at day 7, there were significantly fewer coliforms present in intestinal samples of poults from young hens if the poults were fed the Flavomycin diet compared to those fed Bio-Mos or Flavomycin plus Bio-Mos (Table 8). There were significantly fewer *Lactobacillus* sp. present at day 7 in intestinal samples of poults from young hens if the poults were fed the Flavomycin diet. Those fed the Bio-Mos diet were intermediate between those fed the Flavomycin diet and control and combination diets at day 7 and 21 (Table 8).

There were less total aerobic bacteria present in the liver samples of poults from old hens at day 7 if the poults were fed a diet supplemented with both Bio-Mos and Flavomycin (Table 8) with the Bio-Mos diet being intermediate to the control and Flavomycin diet means. Bio-Mos fed poults from young hens also had lower total aerobic counts at day 21 compared to Flavomycin or combination fed poults. Also, there were significantly fewer *Lactobacillus* sp. present in liver samples of poults from young hens fed a diet containing Bio-Mos or Bio-Mos plus Flavomycin at the end of week one and Bio-Mos at day 21.

### Without E. coli challenge
At day 7, there were fewer total aerobic bacteria in the intestines of poults from young hens if Bio-Mos and Flavomycin were both present in the diet (Table 9) with the Bio-Mos diet being intermediate to all

195

**Table 8.   Effect of dietary Flavomycin (F) and Bio-Mos (B) on $Log_{10}$ total aerobic, coliform and Lactobacillus sp. bacteria found in intestinal and liver tissue (CFU/g) of poults from young (33 WOA) and old (58 WOA) hens after oral *E. coli* challenge.**

| Diet | Day 7 | | | Day 21 | | |
|---|---|---|---|---|---|---|
| | Young | Old | Mean | Young | Old | Mean |
| *Control* | 7.37[a] | 6.89 | 7.13 | 6.00 | 5.56 | 5.78 |
| F | 6.57[b] | 7.17 | 6.87 | 6.05 | 5.12 | 5.58 |
| B | 7.23[a] | 6.85 | 7.04 | 6.06 | 6.35 | 6.20 |
| F+B | 7.61[a] | 7.04 | 7.33 | 6.27 | 6.07 | 6.17 |
| Mean | 7.20 | 6.99 | 7.08 | 6.10 | 5.77 | 5.93 |
| SEM | 0.11 | 0.12 | 0.16 | 0.23 | 0.23 | 0.33 |
| *Liver* | | | | | | |
| Control | 4.10 | 4.38[a] | 4.24 | 3.23[ab] | 3.42 | 3.32 |
| F | 3.82 | 4.38[a] | 4.10 | 3.73[a] | 3.41 | 3.57 |
| B | 4.03 | 3.96[ab] | 4.00 | 2.76[b] * | 3.61* | 3.18 |
| F+B | 4.19 | 3.54[b] | 3.86 | 3.93[a] | 3.39 | 3.66 |
| Mean | 4.04 | 4.06 | 4.07 | 3.41 | 3.46 | 3.41 |
| SEM | 0.13 | 0.14 | 0.19 | 0.13 | 0.14 | 0.19 |
| *Total coliform bacteria* | | | | | | |
| *Intestine* | | | | | | |
| Control | 5.18[ab] | 6.32 | 5.75 | 5.02 | 4.99 | 5.00 |
| F | 3.98[b] | 6.24 | 5.11 | 5.08 | 3.98 | 4.53 |
| B | 6.25[a] | 4.74 | 5.49 | 5.00 | 5.16 | 5.08 |
| F+B | 7.11[a] | 5.37 | 6.24 | 4.43 | 3.53 | 3.98 |
| Mean | 5.63 | 5.67 | 5.61 | 4.88 | 4.42 | 4.75 |
| SEM | 0.41 | 0.42 | 0.58 | 0.35 | 0.35 | 0.49 |
| *Liver* | | | | | | |
| Control | 3.45 | 3.67 | 3.56 | 3.03 | 2.44 | 2.74 |
| F | 2.78 | 3.16 | 2.97 | 3.09 | 2.61 | 2.85 |
| B | 3.19 | 3.12 | 3.15 | 2.38 | 3.32 | 2.85 |
| F+B | 3.17 | 3.23 | 3.20 | 3.38 | 3.23 | 3.30 |
| Mean | 3.15 | 3.29 | 3.21 | 2.97 | 2.90 | 2.89 |
| SEM | 0.22 | 0.23 | 0.32 | 0.20 | 0.20 | 0.29 |
| *Total Lactobacillus sp.* | | | | | | |
| *Intestine* | | | | | | |
| Control | 6.85[a] | 6.33 | 6.59[a] | 6.24 | 6.18[ab] | 6.21 |
| F | 5.21[b] | 6.23 | 5.72[b] | 6.18 | 5.67[b] | 5.92 |
| B | 5.78[ab] | 6.65 | 6.21[ab] | 6.31 | 6.46[a] | 6.38 |
| F+B | 6.65[a] | 6.95 | 6.80[a] | 5.98 | 6.43[a] | 6.20 |
| Mean | 6.12 | 6.54 | 6.30 | 6.18 | 6.18 | 6.16 |
| SEM | 0.20 | 0.21 | 0.29 | 0.12 | 0.13 | 0.18 |
| *Liver* | | | | | | |
| Control | 3.62[a] | 3.33 | 3.47[a] | 3.24 | 3.45 | 3.34 |
| F | 2.58[ab] | 3.00 | 2.79[ab] | 3.78 | 3.10 | 3.44 |
| B | 1.81[b] | 2.20 | 2.01[b] | 3.21 | 3.14 | 3.17 |
| F+B | 1.94[b] | 3.10 | 2.52[ab] | 3.69 | 2.83 | 3.26 |
| Mean | 2.49 | 2.91 | 2.69 | 3.48 | 3.13 | 3.29 |
| SEM | 0.27 | 0.28 | 0.38 | 0.18 | 0.18 | 0.25 |

[a,b] Means within a column with no common superscript differ significantly (P/H0.05).
* Means within a row within a day differ significantly (P/H0.05)

other treatment means. There were significantly fewer total aerobic bacteria in intestinal samples of poults from young hens at day 21 for the Bio-Mos diet compared to those fed Flavomycin, with levels for those fed the control and combination diets intermediate (Table 9). Also, at day 21, poults from young hens had significantly fewer total aerobic bacteria in intestinal samples than poults from old hens for the control diet (5.86 vs. 6.47, $Log_{10}$ values) (Table 9). There were also fewer coliforms present at day 7 in the intestine of poults from young hens where the poults were fed a diet with Bio-Mos and Flavomycin, compared to those fed Flavomycin alone. Levels in those fed the Bio-Mos and control diets were intermediate (Table 9). At day 21, there were fewer coliforms in intestinal samples from poults of old hens if the poults were fed a diet containing Flavomycin (Table 9) compared to those poults fed the combination diet, with levels of those fed the control and Bio-Mos diets intermediate. Also, poults from old hens had fewer coliforms present than poults from young hens if fed the Flavomycin diet (4.11 vs. 5.85, $Log_{10}$ values) (Table 9).

There were fewer total aerobic bacteria in liver samples at day 7 for the Bio-Mos and combination diets (Table 9) for poults from young hens. Across both hen ages, there were fewer total aerobic bacteria found in liver samples at day 7 for poults fed diets containing Bio-Mos and Bio-Mos plus Flavomycin, with levels of those fed the control diet intermediate (Table 9). There were fewer coliforms at day 7 in liver samples of poults from young hens if the poults were fed Bio-Mos. There were also fewer coliforms in liver samples for poults from young hens if fed a diet containing Bio-Mos, compared to those fed the control diet. The levels in those fed Flavomycin and combination diets were intermediate (Table 9). Also at day 7, there were lower levels of *Lactobacillus* sp. in livers of poults from young hens for the combination diet, with levels of those fed the Bio-Mos diet intermediate to other treatment means (Table 9).

### *Related research*

The tisue bacteria levels observed in this study are inconsistent with respect to treatment effects, which agrees with other reports. Stanley *et al.* (1996) previously reported that the inclusion of Bio-Mos in the diet of broiler chicks was unable to reduce the numbers of total coliforms in the ceca. The current study found that the inclusion of Bio-Mos had intermediate effects on total coliform bacteria found in the ceca plus intestines. The current study also demonstrated no gross changes in the composition of bacteria present due to inclusion of Flavomycin. This agrees with findings by Brenes *et al.* (1989) who demonstrated that Flavomycin did not influence the composition of intestinal microflora of chicks, which included coliforms, lactobacilli, enterococci and *Clostridia perfringens*.

**Table 9.** Effect of dietary Flavomycin (F) and Bio-Mos (B*)* on $Log_{10}$ total aerobic, coliform and *Lactobacillus* sp. bacteria found in intestinal and liver tissue (cfu/g) of poults from young (33 WOA) and old (58 WOA) hens without oral *Escherichia coli* challenge.

| | Day 7 | | | Day 21 | | |
|---|---|---|---|---|---|---|
| Diet | Young | Old | Mean | Young | Old | Mean |
| | Total aerobic bacteria | | | | | |
| *Intestines* | | | | | | |
| Control | 7.58[a] | 7.12 | 7.35 | 5.86[ab] * | 6.47* | 6.17 |
| F | 7.47[a] | 7.42 | 7.45 | 6.39[a] | 6.30 | 6.35 |
| B | 7.18[ab] | 7.29 | 7.23 | 5.80[b] | 6.28 | 6.04 |
| F+B | 6.78[b] | 7.20 | 6.99 | 6.08[ab] | 6.08 | 6.08 |
| Mean | 7.25 | 7.26 | 7.25 | 6.04 | 6.28 | 6.16 |
| SEM | 0.12 | 0.12 | 0.16 | 0.11 | 0.11 | 0.15 |
| *Liver* | | | | | | |
| Control | 4.52[a] | 4.08 | 4.30[ab] | 3.70 | 3.77 | 3.74 |
| F | 4.66[a] | 4.44 | 4.55[a] | 3.62 | 3.89 | 3.76 |
| B | 3.75[b] | 4.20 | 3.98[b] | 3.43 | 3.70 | 3.57 |
| F+B | 3.86[b] | 4.03 | 3.95[b] | 3.80 | 3.63 | 3.71 |
| Mean | 4.20 | 4.19 | 4.19 | 3.64 | 3.75 | 3.69 |
| SEM | 0.11 | 0.11 | 0.15 | 0.09 | 0.09 | 0.12 |
| | Total coliform bacteria | | | | | |
| *Intestine* | | | | | | |
| Control | 6.82[ab] | 6.73 | 6.77 | 5.86 | 4.48[ab] | 5.17 |
| F | 7.05[a] | 6.04 | 6.55 | 5.85* | 4.11[b] * | 4.98 |
| B | 5.72[b] | 6.63 | 6.17 | 5.51 | 4.98[ab] | 5.24 |
| F+B | 5.29[b] | 6.49 | 5.89 | 5.20 | 5.95[a] | 5.58 |
| Mean | 6.22 | 6.47 | 6.31 | 5.60 | 4.88 | 5.27 |
| SEM | 0.29 | 0.29 | 0.40 | 0.29 | 0.29 | 0.42 |
| *Liver* | | | | | | |
| Control | 4.15[a] | 3.44 | 3.80[a] | 2.85 | 3.34 | 3.10 |
| F | 3.32[ab] | 3.02 | 3.17[ab] | 2.88 | 2.88 | 2.88 |
| B | 2.46[b] * | 3.70* | 3.08b | 2.54 | 3.19 | 2.87 |
| F+B | 3.30[ab] | 3.38 | 3.34[ab] | 2.58 | 3.05 | 2.82 |
| Mean | 3.31 | 3.39 | 3.33 | 2.71 | 3.12 | 2.92 |
| SEM | 0.18 | 0.18 | 0.26 | 0.16 | 0.16 | 0.22 |
| | Total *Lactobacillus* sp. | | | | | |
| *Intestine* | | | | | | |
| Control | 6.02 | 6.17 | 6.09 | 5.57 | 6.45 | 6.01 |
| F | 6.36 | 6.83 | 6.60 | 5.89 | 5.86 | 5.87 |
| B | 5.70 | 5.88 | 5.79 | 5.79 | 5.91 | 5.85 |
| F+B | 6.36 | 6.33 | 6.34 | 5.64 | 5.57 | 5.60 |
| Mean | 6.11 | 6.30 | 6.22 | 5.72 | 5.95 | 5.83 |
| SEM | 0.22 | 0.22 | 0.31 | 0.22 | 0.22 | 0.31 |
| *Liver* | | | | | | |
| Control | 3.45[a] | 3.33 | 3.39 | 3.52 | 3.71 | 3.61 |
| F | 3.73[a] | 2.59 | 3.16 | 3.42 | 3.46 | 3.44 |
| B | 2.86[ab] | 2.81 | 2.83 | 3.52 | 3.49 | 3.51 |
| F+B | 2.23[b] | 3.07 | 2.65 | 3.54 | 3.43 | 3.48 |
| Mean | 3.06 | 2.95 | 3.00 | 3.50 | 3.52 | 3.51 |
| SEM | 0.21 | 0.21 | 0.30 | 0.13 | 0.13 | 0.18 |

[a,b] Means within a column with no common superscript differ significantly (P/H0.05).
* Means within a row within a day differ significantly (P/H0.05).

However, other reports suggest that Bio-Mos can alter the intestinal microflora. It was reported that pathogenic bacteria, which display mannose-specific fimbriae, can be removed from the gastrointestinal tract by introducing dietary MOS to the intestine (Newman, 1994). By decreasing the numbers of unfavorable bacteria in the intestinal lumen, the potential exists for improved animal performance since an environment suitable for the greatest nutrient utilization can be attained. In the current study, the inclusion of Bio-Mos and Flavomycin only altered intestinal and liver bacterial populations in a transient way. By day 21, there were no major differences in intestinal or liver bacteria numbers. However, liver total aerobic bacteria numbers in poults fed Bio-Mos tended to be lower than in poults fed the control diet for poults from young hens. Intestinal coliform numbers found in unchallenged poults from old hens tended to be lower in those poults fed Flavomycin.

## Conclusions

This trial has confirmed previous studies that have shown improved body weights and weight gains of poults when fed Bio-Mos or Flavomycin even in lieu of an *E. coli* challenge. Similar recently reported work (Sims, 1998; Sims *et al.*, 1998; Sims and Sefton, 1999) demonstrated that the inclusion of Bio-Mos and a growth promoting antibiotic (BMD) improved growth in turkeys at 18 weeks of age, and indicated additive effects on poult performance. In conclusion, Bio-Mos is an effective and viable alternative to dietary growth promotant antibiotics for the rearing of turkeys.

## References

Brenes, A., J. Trevino, C. Centeno and P. Yuste. 1989. Influence of peas (*Pisum sativum*) as a dietary ingredient and flavomycin supplementation on the performance and intestinal microflora of broiler chicks. Br. Poult. Sci. 30:81–89.

Buresh, R.E., R.H. Harms and R.D. Miles. 1986. A differential response in turkey poults to various antibiotics in diets designed to be deficient or adequate in certain essential nutrients. Poultry Sci. 65:2314–2317.

Caston, L.J. and S. Leeson. 1992. The response of broiler turkeys to Flavomycin. Can. J. Anim. Sci. 72:445–448.

Evangelisti, D.G., A.R. English, A.E. Girard, J.E. Lynch and I.A. Solomons. 1975. Influence of subtherapeutic levels of oxytetracycline on *Salmonella typhimurium* in swine, calves, and chickens. Antimicrobial Agents and Chemotherapy. 8:664–672.

Fairchild, A.S., J.L. Grimes, M.J. Wineland, and F.T. Jones, 1998. Disk diffusion antimicrobial susceptibility tests against avian *Escherichia coli* isolates. Poultry Sci. 77 (Supp. 1):94.

Francis, C., D.M. Janky, A.S. Arafa and R.H.Harms. 1978. Interrelationship of lactobacillus and zinc bacitracin in the diets of turkey poults. Poultry Sci. 57:1687–1689.

Gustafson, R.H. and R.E. Bowen. 1997. A review: antibiotic use in animal agriculture. J. of Appl. Bacteriol. 83:531–541.

Heller, E. D. and N. Drabkin. 1977. Some characteristics of pathogenic *E. coli* strains. Br. Vet. J. 133:572–578.

Newman, K., 1994. Mannan-oligosaccharides: Natural polymers with significant impact on the gastrointestinal microflora and the immune system. *In*: Biotechnology in the Feed Industry, Proceedings of the 10th Annual Symposium. (T.P. Lyons and K.A. Jacques, eds.). Nottingham University Press, Nottingham, UK, 167–174.

Nurmi, E. and M. Rantala. 1973. New aspects of *Salmonella* infection in broiler production. Nature (London) 241:210–211.

Ofek, I., D. Mirelman and N. Sharon. 1977. Adherence of *Escherichia coli* to human mucosal cells mediated by mannose receptors. Nature (London) 265:623–625.

Savage, T.F. and E.I. Zakrzewska. 1996. The performance of male turkeys fed a starter diet containing a mannanoligosaccharide (Bio-Mos) from day old to eight weeks of age. *In*: Biotechnology in the Feed Industry, Proceedings of the 12th Annual Symposium. (T.P. Lyons and K.A. Jacques, eds.). Nottingham University Press, Nottingham, UK, 47–54.

Savage, T.F., E.I. Zakrzewska and J.R. Andreasen, Jr. 1997. The effects of feeding mannan oligosaccharide supplemented diets to poults on performance and the morphology of the small intestine. Poultry Sci. 76 (Supp. 1):139.

Scioli, C., S. Esposito, G. Anzilotti, A. Pavone and C. Pennucci. 1983. Transferable drug resistance in *Escherichia coli* isolated from antibiotic-fed chickens. Poultry Sci. 62:382–384.

Sims, M.D., 1998. Evaluation of Bio-Mos vs. BMD and a negative control in diets fed to commercial broiler chickens. Resume of Investigator's Final Report. Virginia Scientific Research, Inc., Harrisonburg, VA.

Sims, M.D., P. Spring and A.E. Sefton. 1998. Effect of mannan oligosaccharide on performance of commercial broiler chickens. Poultry Sci. 77 (Supp. 1):89.

Sims, M. and A.E. Sefton. 1999. Comparative effects of a mannan oligosaccharide and an antibiotic growth promoter on performance of commercial tom turkeys. Poster presented at the 48th Western Poultry Disease Conference, Vancouver, British Columbia, Canada.

Stanley, V.G., H. Chukwu, C. Gray and D. Thompson. 1996. Effects of lactose and Bio-Mos in dietary application on growth and total coliform bacteria reduction in broiler chicks. Poultry Sci. 75 (Supp. 1):61.

Surawicz, C.M., G.W. Elmer, P. Speelman, L.V. McFarland, J. Chinn, and G. van Belle, 1989. Prevention of antibiotic-associated diarrhea by *Saccharomyces boulardii*: A prospective study. Gastroenterology 96:552–556.

# Nutrition and management of the early-weaned pig

CHARLES MAXWELL

*Animal Science Department, University of Arkansas, Fayetteville, Arkansas, USA*

## Introduction

The swine industry continues to move to earlier weaning. This trend is driven by economic factors such as improving the number of pigs per sow per year and the need to minimize the capital cost of farrowing facilities by moving more sows through the facilities. Tremendous strides have been made in improving performance in early-weaned pigs in the last decade. Several factors, including larger pigs at weaning, better nursery facilities and management as well as improved feeding programs, have contributed to the improved performance. These advances are the result of rapid development and implementation of advanced technologies. This paper will summarize three areas of technology development that have contributed to a better understanding of requirements for optimum performance of early-weaned pigs. These include the evolution of spray-dried plasma protein, the development of segregated early weaning (SEW) as a routine management tool and the potential of oligosaccharides derived from yeast cell wall for improving performance in young pigs.

## Spray-dried plasma protein

Weaning as early as three weeks of age has been accomplished for a number of years by the use of diets containing high levels of milk products (dried skim milk, dried whey, cheese by-product), fish meal and refined soybean protein as the primary protein source. More recently, weaning as early as two weeks of age, with an average weaning age of about 17 to 18 days, has become routine in large production complexes with three site production systems. The earlier pigs are weaned, the greater the need for a complex diet to minimize post-weaning lag. This was demonstrated by Okai *et al.* (1976). In this study, diets varying in complexity were fed to pigs weaned at three or five weeks of age. A more complex diet was required to minimize post-weaning lag in pigs weaned at three weeks of age than those weaned at five weeks.

In general, early-weaned pigs fed milk-based diets have out-performed those fed other protein sources (Fitzpatrick and Bayley, 1977; Wilson and Leibholz, 1981a,b,c; Walker *et al.*, 1986). Recent research has been directed toward attempts to identify other protein sources which can be efficiently substituted for milk proteins or which can be fed in combination with milk proteins to improve performance (Sohn and Maxwell, 1990a,b). Among the ingredients tested, spray-dried porcine plasma protein has been shown to consistently improve performance when included in starter diets (de Rodas *et al.*, 1995).

Spray-dried plasma protein (plasma protein), is the most exciting protein product to be tested in early weaning pig diets in recent years. Improved handling of the blood products and the utilization of the spray-drying process has dramatically improved the quality and subsequent use of blood protein products in nursery diets.

Several trials have been conducted to evaluate plasma protein for the young pig. Research at Oklahoma State University (de Rodas *et al.*, 1995) is typical of the responses observed. In this study, 144 pigs weaned at approximately 24 days of age and weighing 7.23 kg were fed one of three diets. Plasma protein (AP-820) or spray-dried blood meal (AP-300) was substituted on an equal lysine basis for dried skim milk in a complex prestarter diet essentially devoid of soybean proteins. Both plasma protein and blood meal improved gain and feed intake during week 1 and week 2 post-weaning (Table 1). Feed efficiency was not affected by treatment. It is interesting to note that feed intake and gain continued to be improved in pigs during a subsequent three week period when all pigs were fed a common corn-soybean meal starter diet.

A summary of studies evaluating plasma protein as a protein source is presented in Table 2. These studies indicate that plasma protein consistently improves feed intake and gain in young pigs. This effect is most evident in the first two weeks post-weaning. Effects of plasma protein also appear to be more evident in week 1 post-weaning than in week 2. Table 3 summarizes studies in which the week 1 and week 2 post-weaning data are presented. In four of the five studies, the gain response and the feed intake response to plasma proteins was greater in week 1 than in week 2. It is also interesting to note that scour score was reduced in pigs fed plasma protein in experiment 5 (Table 4).

Several trials have been conducted to determine the optimum level of spray-dried porcine plasma for weanling pigs. Gatnau *et al.* (1991) fed increasing levels of plasma protein (0 to 8%) to 28-day old pigs weighing 7.09 kg and fed a corn-soybean meal-whey diet. Lysine level was maintained at 1.2%. Gain and efficiency of gain in the first two weeks post-weaning improved with increasing plasma levels up to 6% of the diet. Similar results were reported in a larger study (96 pigs) with 25-day old pigs averaging 6.09 kg (Gatnau and Zimmerman, 1992). More recent studies at higher lysine levels, however, have shown that growth performance is enhanced in pigs fed up to 10% plasma protein (Kats *et al.*, 1994; Table 5). These researchers also

**Table 1.  The effect of plasma protein on performance of early weaned pigs[a].**

|  | DSM | Plasma protein | Blood meal |
|---|---|---|---|
| Dried skim milk, % | 10 | 0 | 0 |
| Plasma protein, % | 0 | 4.0 | 0 |
| Blood meal, % | 0 | 0 | 2.75 |
| Average daily gain, kg |  |  |  |
| Week 1 | 0.21[b] | 0.28[c] | 0.25[d] |
| Week 2 | 0.35[b] | 0.44[c] | 0.40[d] |
| Period 1 | 0.28[b] | 0.36[c] | 0.33[d] |
| Period 2 | 0.52[e] | 0.55[f] | 0.57[f] |
| Average daily feed intake, kg |  |  |  |
| Week 1 | 0.21[b] | 0.27[c] | 0.24[d] |
| Week 2 | 0.44[e] | 0.55[f] | 0.49[g] |
| Period 1 | 0.32[e] | 0.41[f] | 0.37[g] |
| Period 2 | 0.95[e] | 0.99[f] | 0.99[f] |
| Feed efficiency, F:G |  |  |  |
| Week 1 | 1.03 | 0.98 | 0.92 |
| Week 2 | 1.16 | 1.20 | 1.19 |
| Period 1 | 1.12 | 1.11 | 1.10 |
| Period 2 | 1.78 | 1.78 | 1.75 |

[a]de Rodas *et al.*, 1995 – Values are means of 8 pens with 6 pigs per pen (initially 7.23 kg).
[bcd]Means in the same row with different superscript differ (P<0.05).
[efg]Means in the same row with different superscript differ (P<0.01).

**Table 2.  A summary of recent experiments evaluating spray dried porcine plasma as a protein source for weanling pigs.**

|  |  |  | Percent improvement over pigs fed control diet | | |
|---|---|---|---|---|---|
| Experiment | Protein in control diet | Length of test post- weaning | Average daily gain | Average daily feed intake | Feed:gain |
| Hansen *et al.*, 1990 | Skim milk | 2 weeks | +42 | +37 | −3.6 |
| Gatnau *et al.*, 1991a | Soybean meal | 2 weeks | +102 | +76 | +12.0 |
| Kats *et al.*, 1994 | Skim milk | 2 weeks | +41 | +35 | +5.3 |
| deRodas *et al.*, 1995 | Skim milk | 2 weeks | +29 | +24 | +1.2 |
| Gatnau *et al*,. 1991b | Soybean meal | 2 weeks | +82 | +34 | +59.5 |
| Hansen *et al.*, 1993 |  |  |  |  |  |
| Exp. 1 | Skim milk | 2 weeks | +2 | 0 | +0.03 |
| Exp. 2 | Skim milk | 2 weeks | +27 | +27 | +0.01 |
| Gatnau *et al.* 1990 | Skim milk | 2 weeks | +50 | +54 | +29.3 |
| CS 1132[a] | Skim milk | 2 weeks | +22 | +19 | +3.1 |
| CS 1098[a] | Skim milk | 2 weeks | +12 | +9 | +3.6 |
| CS 1124[a] | Skim milk | 2 weeks | +15 | +19 | −1.9 |

[a]Central Soya Feed Research pig test.

observed improved performance with methionine supplementation in pigs fed diets containing high levels of spray-dried blood products.

The fraction of plasma protein responsible for producing the growth

Table 3.  **Summary of recent experiments evaluating spray dried porcine plasma as a protein source during week 1 and week 2 postweaning.**[1]

| | | Percent improvement over pigs fed control diet | | | | | |
| | | Average daily gain | | Average daily feed intake | | Feed efficiency | |
| Experiment | Protein in control diet | Week 1 | Week 2 | Week 1 | Week 2 | Week 1 | Week 2 |
|---|---|---|---|---|---|---|---|
| 1 | Skim milk | 33 | 26 | 28 | 25 | 4.8 | −3.3 |
| 2 | Casein | 18 | −2 | 24 | 18 | 2.9 | 16.9 |
| 3 | Skim milk | 119 | 28 | 85 | 39 | 35 | −6.8 |
| 4 | Skim milk | 14 | 18 | −6 | 2 | 20 | 23.9 |
| 5 | Skim milk | 22 | −9 | 24 | −11 | −0.02 | 12 |

[1] Experiment 1: Adapted from de Rodas et al., 1995.
  Experiment 2,3,4: Gatnau and Zimmerman, personal communication.
  Experiment 5: Hansen et al., 1994.

Table 4.  **Effect of plasma protein on scour score.**[1]

| | Scour index[2] | |
| Week | Control Soybean meal/whey | Spray-dried porcine plasma Whey |
|---|---|---|
| 1 | 2.57 | 1.85 |
| 2 | 3.14[a] | 2.00[b] |

[1] Gatnau and Zimmerman. (Personal communication)
[2] Index: 1=None, 2=Frequent, 3=Occasional, 4=Abundant, 5=Very severe.
[a,b]Means with different superscript differ (P<0.05).

Table 5.  **Effect of level of plasma protein on performance**[a].

| | | % Spray-dried porcine plasma | | | | | | |
| | Week | 0 | 2 | 4 | 6 | 8 | 10 | P<[b] |
|---|---|---|---|---|---|---|---|---|
| Daily gain, kg | 1+2 | 0.165 | 0.206 | 0.217 | 0.240 | 0.247 | 0.255 | L= 0.01 |
| | 1-4 | 0.295 | 0.327 | 0.312 | 0.334 | 0.326 | 0.331 | L=0.01 |
| Daily feed, kg | 1+2 | 0.206 | 0.244 | 0.256 | 0.290 | 0.302 | 0.300 | L= 0.01, Q=0.04 |
| | 1–4 | 0.624 | 0.668 | 0.612 | 0.653 | 0.617 | 0.623 | |
| Gain:feed | 1+2 | 0.79 | 0.84 | 0.85 | 0.82 | 0.81 | 0.84 | |
| | 1–4 | 0.71 | 0.72 | 0.72 | 0.71 | 0.71 | 0.72 | |

[a]Kats et al., 1994. Values are for a total of 534 weanling pigs (initially 6.4 kg and 21 d of age). Corn-soybean meal-dried whey diet with 1.5% lysine.
[b]L = linear, Q = quadratic.

response in phase 1 has been evaluated in three studies (Cain, 1995; Pierce *et al.*, 1995; Owen *et al.*, 1995). The major protein fractions of AP 920 include fibrin, high molecular weight (globulin), medium molecular weight (albumin) and low molecular weight (<10,000 mw) compounds. Data from the study of Cain (1995) are shown in Table 6.

Table 6. Effect of AP 920 fractions on growth of early-weaned pigs[a].

| | | | Molecular weight | | |
|---|---|---|---|---|---|
| Nutrient | Casein | AP920 | High | Medium | Low |
| Daily gain, g/d | 19[d] | 134[bc] | 158[b] | 78[cd] | 50[d] |
| Daily feed, g/d | 181[c] | 262[b] | 273[b] | 244[bc] | 191[c] |
| Feed/gain | 129[c] | 322[b] | 341[b] | 217[c] | 213[c] |

[a]Cain (1995). [a]Each mean represents data from three 15 d trials involving 135 pigs (45 pigs/trial) averaging 6.0 kg bodyweight and 19 days old.
[bcd]Means within a row with different superscripts differ (P<0.05).

Pigs fed the AP 920 diet grew faster and consumed more feed during the first two weeks post-weaning than those fed the negative control diet (P<0.05). Growth performance of pigs consuming the diet containing the high molecular weight fraction (globular proteins) was similar to that of pigs fed the AP 920 diet. Growth of pigs fed the medium molecular weight (albumin) or low molecular weight fractions was not different from that of the negative control. Increased small intestine villi surface area, enzyme activity and serum zinc were also associated with feeding the high molecular fraction. It seems likely to assume that either the immunoglobulins or other unknown factors in this fraction are responsible for the improved performance, intestinal function and zinc status. Results were similar in the other studies.

Also consistent with the concept that passive immunity via the globular fraction in plasma protein is involved in the improved performance in early-weaned pigs fed plasma protein are data showing that the greatest response to the addition of AP 920 occurs when pigs are fed in challenging environments. Coffey and Cromwell (1995) fed pigs weaned at 21 days either a dried skim milk or a plasma protein-based diet in two environments (clean and conventional). The clean environment consisted of an environmentally controlled room (temperature and humidity) previously free of pigs for six months, while the conventional environment consisted of the regularly-used nursery at the University Research Station. Pigs reared under segregated early weaning (SEW) conditions exhibited little response to spray-dried plasma protein whereas pigs reared in a conventional on-farm nursery exhibited a 32% improvement in gain when the diet was supplemented with spray-dried plasma protein (Table 7). Observations by Gatnau and Zimmerman (1991) were similar. This may be an indication that the improvement in immunocompetence of young

Table 7. Effect of protein source and environment on growth performance of early-weaned pigs[a].

| | Environment | | | |
|---|---|---|---|---|
| | Clean | | Conventional | |
| Diet | Dried skim milk[b] | Plasma protein[c] | Dried skim milk[b] | Plasma protein[c] |
| Daily gain, g/d[d,e,f] | 284 | 300 | 203 | 269 |
| Daily feed, g/d[g] | 411 | 483 | 260 | 376 |
| Feed/gain[h] | 1.46 | 1.62 | 1.31 | 1.41 |

[a]Adapted from Coffey and Cromwell, 1995. Each mean = 10 replicate pens; pigs weaned at 21 days; Data for weeks 1 and 2.
[b] Dried skim milk, (20% of diet).
[c]Plasma protein (8.3% of diet).
[d]Dried skim milk vs plasma protein (clean) NS.
[e]Dried skim milk vs plasma protein (conventional), protein source (P<0.01).
[f]Protein X Environment (P<0.01).
[g]Protein source x environment, P<0.05.
[h]Protein source (P<0.05); environment (P<0.01).

pigs mediated by immunoglobulins present in spray-dried plasma protein may not be as essential in an SEW environment and suggests that excellent performance can be obtained with SEW pigs fed less complex diets.

The above study suggests that other approaches may be used to obtain improved performance in pigs without the inclusion of plasma protein. The US swine industry is pursuing a program of earlier-weaning (as early as 14 days with an industry average of 17 to 18 days) with all-in, all-out placement of nursery pigs by site as a means of improving performance.

## Segregated early weaning

Early weaning at an age of less than 21 days and removal of pigs to a second isolated site, which is commonly referred to as segregated early weaning, has been shown to substantially reduce disease transfer from the dam (Fangman *et al.*, 1997). Weaning at an earlier age appears to enhance the success of eliminating pathogens (Wiseman *et al.*, 1994). This strategy has been successful in reducing the number of pathogens, but has not been successful in eliminating all pathogens. The premise is that pigs are removed from the sow while their immunity, as a consequence of maternal antibodies, is still high. This maternally derived passive immunity will prevent vertical transfer of indigenous pathogens. Pigs reared in isolation have been shown to have reduced immunological stress (Johnson, 1997) resulting in improved growth and efficiency of feed utilization. Harris (1993) has suggested weaning ages for a number of diseases (Table 8).

Williams *et al.* (1997a) observed that performance of pigs reared under a medicated early weaning scheme to minimize disease transition had improved average daily gain and feed efficiency when compared to pigs reared in a conventional system and exposed to older nursery pigs. This

Table 8.  Suggested weaning age to minimize disease transfer.[1]

| Organism | Weaning age |
|---|---|
| Pseudorabies virus | <21 days |
| *Actinobacillus pleuropneumoniae (APP)* | <21 days |
| *Mycoplasma hyopneumoniae* | <10 days |
| *Pasteurella multocida* | <10 days |
| *Haemophilus parasuis (HPS)* | <14 days |
| Porcine reproductive and respiratory syndrome virus (PRRS) | <10 days |
| *Salmonella cholerasuis* | <12 days |
| Transmissible gastroenteritis virus (TGE) | <21 days |

[1]Harris (1993).

is consistent with observations in our research at the University of Arkansas to determine if differences in immune stimulation can explain perform-ance differences in conventional *vs.* off-site reared pigs. A total 432 weanling barrows (19 ± 2 days of age) were obtained from a local commercial company from a single source. Half the barrows from litters were selected for the off-site nursery study (6 pigs/pen) with the remaining pigs staying in the conventional nursery facilities (approximately 18 pigs/pen). Pigs were weighed and serum samples obtained via venipuncture on day 0, 14 and 34 post-weaning from a total of 72 pre-selected pigs placed in the conventional facilities and an off-site nursery. A minimum of one pig/litter was sampled in the conventional facility and a minimum of two pigs in each of 36 pens were sampled in the off-site nursery. Serum $\alpha_1$-acid glycoprotein concentrations were determined using a commercial kit (porcine $\alpha_1$-acid glycoprotein plate, Development Technologies International, Inc., Frederick, MD) and a single radial immunodiffusion method. Pigs reared in the off-site nursery were 1.95 lb heavier (P <0.001) at day 14 post-weaning and 5.28 lb heavier (P<0.01) at 34 days post-weaning (Figure 1). In addition, serum $\alpha_1$-acid glycoprotein concentra-tion was elevated (P <0.01) in pigs reared in the conventional nursery. This suggests that reduced performance in a conventional nursery may be associated with the immunological stress associated with production under these conditions.

Patience *et al.* (1997) evaluated the impact of age and site of weaning on pig performance under high health conditions. Pigs were derived from a breeding herd free of infectious respiratory disease, internal and external parasites and most infectious gastrointestinal diseases. Sixteen litters were weaned at 12 ± 2 days and housed in an all-in, all-out nursery room at the swine center (Conventional SEW); 16 litters were weaned at 12 ± 2 days of age and moved to an off-site location (Off-site SEW) and 16 litters were weaned at 21 days and retained on-site (Control). At 21 days control pigs were heavier than off-site SEW or conventional SEW pigs. However, at 56 days of age the off-site SEW pigs were heavier than the convention SEW or control group (Table 9).

The response to SEW is not surprising and is consistent with expected performance in high health herds in animals not undergoing an acute phase

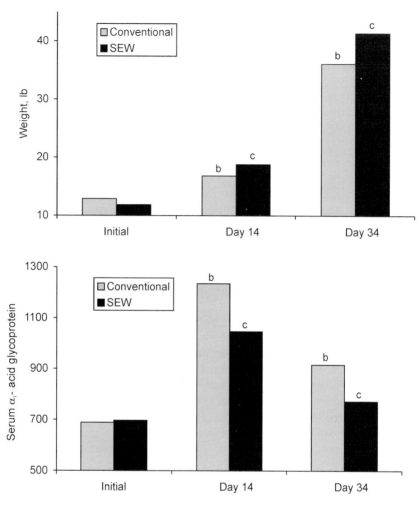

**Figure 1.** Effect of SEW on performance and acute phase protein levels (Maxwell. C.V., K.G. Friesen, D.H. Baird, M.E. Davis and D.C. Brown. University of Arkansas and The Pork Group, Inc. – unpublished data) ([b,c]Means with different superscripts differ, P<0.01).

**Table 9.    Impact of age and site of weaning on pig performance and health conditions.[1]**

| Item | Control (21 day wean) | Conventional SEW (12 day wean) | Off-site SEW (12 day wean) |
|---|---|---|---|
| Weight at 21 days, kg | 6.48[a] | 5.33[b] | 5.95[b] |
| Weight at 56 days, kg | 21.28[a] | 20.72[a] | 24.62[b] |

[a,b]Means with different superscript differ, P<0.05
[1]Patience *et al.* (1997).

response. Exposure of animals to antigens, however, has been shown to result in the release of cytokines that activate the immune system (Dinarello, 1984). This results in a major alteration of metabolic processes (Klasing, 1988) which depress protein synthesis (Jepson *et al.*, 1986) and stimulate protein degradation in skeletal muscle (Zamir *et al.*, 1994). Therefore, pigs which are undergoing exposure to antigens which activate the immune system would be expected to exhibit reduced feed intake and weight gain during the period of antigen exposure.

This is consistent with the concept described by Johnson (1997) who indicated that a dirty, less hygienic environment increases the level of immunological stress and depresses growth and performance of pigs. These effects are mediated by cytokines which affect feed intake and alter the utilization of protein. A second important feature of the inflammatory response is an increase in release of acute phase proteins by the liver. Synthesis of some acute phase proteins may increase several 100-fold. These acute phase proteins are synthesized at the expense of degradation of skeletal muscle protein. Reeds *et al.* (1994) estimated that to provide sufficient amounts of the limiting amino acid for acute phase protein synthesis (phenylalanine) would require more than a 2-fold increase in degradation of muscle protein. Thus, immunological stress is linked by cytokines to enhanced hepatic acute phase protein synthesis, and decreased muscle protein synthesis and/or increased muscle protein degradation.

This concept explains the impact that specific rearing regimes may have on pig performance. Numerous studies have shown that pigs kept under all-in, all-out management eat more, grow faster and are more efficient when compared to pigs under continuous flow management. Segregated early weaning is a management system which appears to have the potential to reduce immunological stress even further than that observed with all-in, all-out management.

Induction of immunological stress with lipopolysaccharide has demonstrated the relationship of this stressor with increased cytokine production (Johnson, 1997; Mandali *et al.*, 1997). In the Mandali *et al.* (1997) study, pigs injected with LPS polysaccharide exhibited elevated levels of $TNF_\alpha$ (Figure 2). IGF-1 concentrations were also substantially reduced (Figure 3).

A second study that demonstrates the impact of immunological stress on subsequent performance was reported by Ragland *et al.* (1997). In this study, SEW pigs were commingled with farm-reared pigs at approximately 60 days of age in a control test station. Average daily gain, feed efficiency, average daily lean gain and efficiency of lean gain were lower in SEW pigs when compared to conventional farm reared pigs (Table 10).

This suggests that the SEW reared pigs were undergoing increased immunological stress and reduced performance during the finishing period as a consequence of exposure to higher levels of pathogens during finishing. The best strategy for inhibiting the costly effects of increased immunological stress appears to be by avoiding contact with potential

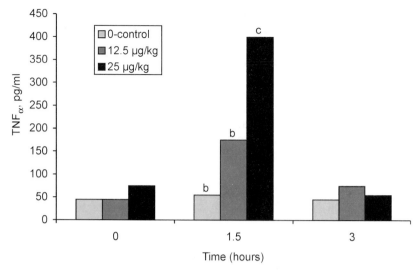

**Figure 2.** Effect of LPS (*E. coli* 0111:B4) on TNF$_\alpha$ ($^c$ means differ, P<0.01)..

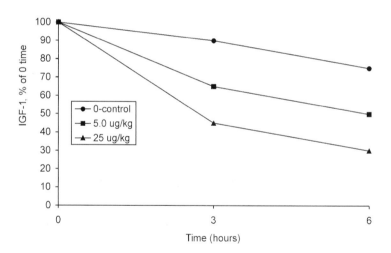

**Figure 3.** Effect of LPS (*E. coli* 0111:B4) on IGF-1 (time × treatment interaction, P<0.05).

**Table 10.    Performance traits of SEW and farm reared pigs.**[1]

|  | Farm-reared | SEW |
|---|---|---|
| Average daily gain, kg | 0.818 ± 0.009[a] | 0.751 ± 0.010[b] |
| Feed efficiency | 3.31 ± 0.07[a] | 3.53 ± 0.08[b] |
| Average daily lean gain, kg | 0.320 ± 0.005[a] | 0.288 ± 0.006[b] |
| Efficiency of lean gain | 8.47 ± 0.22[a] | 9.28 ± 0.25[b] |

[a,b] P<0.05.
[1]Ragland *et al.*, 1997.

bacterial and viral stressors from nursery to finishing. In fact, performance during finishing may be compromised by a strategy of commingling pigs from nurseries with varying levels of disease.

Pigs reared under isolated SEW conditions have not only been shown to exhibit improved performance, but carcass composition seems to be enhanced as well (Williams *et al.*, 1997b). Research by Frank *et al.* (1997), however, suggests that any effect of SEW on carcass composition is dependant upon genotype. These researchers compared performance and carcass composition of littermate barrows and gilts which were either segregated early-weaned at 13 days of age (4.8 kg) to an off-site nursery and finisher or conventionally weaned at 27 days of age (7.25 kg) to an on-site nursery and finisher. Genotypes were Landrace-Yorkshire cross (YL) or European Terminal Sire cross (ETS). The ETS pigs had larger loin eye area, higher percent lean and lower 10th rib backfat (Table 11).

**Table 11. Environmental effects of genetic potential for lean gain.[1]**

|  | Conventional | | SEW | |
| --- | --- | --- | --- | --- |
|  | ETS | YL | ETS | YL |
| Loin eye area, cm$^2$ [a,b] | 47.1 | 38.8 | 49.2 | 38.8 |
| % Lean[a,b] | 56.6 | 51.4 | 57.6 | 49.9 |
| Backfat, cm[a,c] | 1.69 | 2.24 | 1.64 | 2.62 |
| Death loss, %[c] | 18.5 | 5.6 | 3.6 | 2.8 |

[1]Adapted from Frank *et al.* (1997).
[a]Genotype, P<0.01.
[b]Environment x Genotype, P<0.05.
[c]Environment x Genotype, P<0.01.

However, the lower lean gain (YL) pigs had increased backfat and a lower percent lean in the SEW environment while the ETS pigs had no difference in backfat thickness and an improvement in percent lean in the SEW environment (environment x genotype interaction, P<0.05 and P<0.01, respectively). This study suggests that low lean gain pigs might get fatter and have lower lean yield under the faster growth SEW conditions whereas pigs with higher lean gain potential may have improved carcass composition.

It is also interesting to note that death loss was higher in pigs reared in the conventional environment than those reared in the SEW environment. This difference was primarily due to increased death losses in ETS pigs in the conventional environment suggesting that genetic differences exist for pig survival.

## Efficacy of Bio-Mos in improving gain and efficiency in early-weaned pigs

Oligosaccharides derived from yeast cell wall offer an additional technology with potential to improve health and performance in young pigs. Typically, pigs are commingled at weaning and reared in off-site nursery units before being transported for finishing in single source finishing systems. The stress of commingling pigs prior to the nursery phase of production and of long distance hauling to finishing locations is a concern for the swine industry. Polysaccharides derived from cell walls of yeast have been shown to improve performance and to enhance immune function. Researchers in aquaculture have found a yeast glucan which enhances the non-specific defense mechanism (Raa *et al.*, 1992; Engstad *et al.*, 1992) and survival in fish. Maintaining immunological integrity is particularly critical in the young pig since the trend to earlier weaning now commonly practiced in the swine industry has been associated with a decrease in cellular immunity (Blecha *et al.*, 1983). Similarly, performance has been improved in early-weaned pigs fed a glucan isolated from yeast (Schoenherr and Pollmann, 1994; Schoenherr *et al.*, 1994). Dvorak and Jacques (1997) reported that adding a mannan oligosaccharide (Bio-Mos) to the milk replacer improved gain and intake in young calves. Bio-Mos has also been shown to improve performance in nursery pigs (Spring and Privulescu, 1998). The following study was conducted to further assess the efficacy of Bio-Mos in improving performance in pigs fed two levels of inorganic copper (10 and 185 ppm) and reared in an off-site nursery unit.

EXPERIMENTAL PROCEDURES

A total of 216 weanling barrows [The Pork Group, Inc. terminal sire line X line I (commercial gilt); $21 \pm 2$ days of age] were obtained from The Pork Group, Inc. from a single source. Pigs were transported to the University of Arkansas off-site nursery facilities, sorted by weight, and divided into weight groups (blocks). Pigs within each weight group were allotted into equal subgroups (six pigs per pen). Treatments were then randomly assigned to pens (subgroups) within each of the weight groups. Four dietary treatments consisted of two levels of inorganic copper (Cu) (10 and 185 ppm) from copper sulfate with and without the addition of Bio-Mos (0 or 4.0 lb Bio-Mos /ton) in a $2 \times 2$ factorial arrangement of treatments. The specific diets during the first 10 days post-weaning (Phase 1) consisted of the following:

1. A negative control with Phase 1, 2, and 3 diets containing Cu as $CuSO_4$ at 10 ppm (Table 12).
2. The negative control Phase 1, 2, and 3 diets containing 10 ppm Cu plus 175 ppm Cu as $CuSO_4$ (1.4 lb/ton).
3. The negative control Phase 1, 2, and 3 diets containing 10 ppm Cu supplemented with 0.2% Bio-Mos (4.0 lb/ton).

4. The negative control Phase 1, 2, and 3 diets containing 10 ppm Cu plus 175 ppm Cu as $CuSO_4$ (1.4 lb/ton), and supplemented with 0.2% Bio-Mos (4.0 lb/ton).

Substitutions in all diets were made at the expense of corn. Phase 1 diets were formulated to contain 1.50% lysine, 0.90% methionine plus cystine, 0.90% calcium, 0.80% phosphorus, and 14.53% lactose and were fed for a period of 10 days. Upon completion of the Phase 1 diet, pigs were fed a Phase 2 diet (1.35% lysine) from day 10 to 24 and a Phase 3 diet (1.20% lysine) from day 24 to 38 post-weaning.

Table 12. Composition of basal diets[a].

| Item, % | Phase 1 | Phase 2 | Phase 3 |
|---|---|---|---|
| Yellow corn | 39.32 | 48.11 | 62.375 |
| Steam rolled oats | 5.00 | – | – |
| Deproteinized whey | 17.50 | 10.00 | – |
| Processed soy protein (Optipro) | 6.75 | – | – |
| Soybean meal, 48% CP | 10.00 | 28.30 | 30.00 |
| AP-301 | 2.00 | 2.00 | – |
| AP-920 | 3.75 | – | – |
| Select menhaden fish meal | 8.50 | 4.00 | – |
| Soybean oil | 4.00 | 4.00 | – |
| Fat | – | – | 4.00 |
| Ethoxyquin | 0.03 | 0.03 | 0.03 |
| Lysine HCl | – | – | 0.16 |
| Threonine | 0.05 | – | – |
| Methionine | 0.15 | 0.08 | 0.02 |
| Tylan-40 | – | – | 0.125 |
| Neoterromycin 10/5 | 1.00 | 1.00 | – |
| Mineral premix (NB-8557B)[b] | 0.10 | 0.15 | 0.15 |
| Vitamin premix (NB-6157B)[b] | 0.15 | 0.25 | 0.25 |
| Dicalcium phosphate | 1.30 | 1.40 | 1.88 |
| Calcium carbonate | 0.10 | 0.38 | 0.61 |
| Salt | 0.30 | 0.30 | 0.40 |
| *Calculated composition* | | | |
| Lysine | 1.50 | 1.35 | 1.20 |
| Threonine | 0.98 | 0.87 | 0.77 |
| Tryptophan | 0.27 | 0.26 | 0.24 |
| Met + Cys | 0.90 | 0.82 | 0.72 |
| Ca | 0.90 | 0.80 | 0.80 |
| P | 0.80 | 0.70 | 0.70 |
| Metabolizable energy | 1537 | 1542 | 1563 |
| Lactose | 14.53 | 8.30 | – |

[a]Basal diets were supplemented with 0.07% $CuSO_4$ or 0.2% Bio-Mos to provide four diets in each phase with and without Bio-Mos and with and without 175 ppm copper from $CuSO_4$. Copper and Bio-Mos were added at the expense of corn.
[b]Vitamins and minerals met or exceed NRC, 1998.

Pigs were housed in an off-site nursery facility in pens with two nipple waterers, a five-hole feeder, and Maxima nursery flooring. Pigs had *ad libitum* access to feed and water. For the first week of the trial the nursery was maintained at 85 °F and decreased 1 °F per week. Pig body weight and feed intake were determined at the initiation and termination of Phase 1, and weekly during Phases 2 and 3.

*In vitro* cellular response was measured using a lymphocyte blastogenesis assay (Blecha *et al.*, 1983). One blood sample was taken via venipuncture from two randomly selected pigs in each pen (total of 18 pigs per treatment, 72 pigs total). Samples were obtained on day 28, 30, 32, and 34 of the study with 25% of the pens sampled (18 pigs, 9 pens) on each of the four days. Approximately 15 ml of blood were collected in heparinized tubes by venipuncture for isolation of mononuclear cells. Blood mononuclear cells were isolated by gradient centrifugation and plated in 96-well round bottom plates (Corning, Corning NY) at a concentration of $2 \times 10^6$ cells/ml. Phytohemagglutinin (PHA) and pokeweed mitogen (PWM, Sigma Chemical) were used as mitogens at a concentration of 50 and 25 µg/ml, respectively. Incubation, labeling with [3]thymidine and cell harvesting followed procedures outlines by van Heugten and Spears (1997). Uptake of [3]thymidine served as the measure of cell proliferation.

Performance data were analyzed as a randomized complete block design with pen as the experimental unit and blocks based on initial body weight. Analysis of variance was performed using the GLM procedure of SAS (1988). The effects of block, $CuSO_4$, Bio-Mos, and $CuSO_4$ x Bio-Mos interaction effects were evaluated. Immune data were analyzed as a randomized complete block design with pen as the experimental unit. Analysis of variance was performed using the GLS procedure of SAS (1988). The effects of $CuSO_4$, Bio-Mos, and $CuSO_4$ x Bio-Mos interaction effects were evaluated.

RESULTS

A Bio-Mos x Cu level interaction was observed during Phase 1 (day 0 to 10) for average daily gain (P <0.01), average daily feed intake (P<0.10) and gain:feed (P<0.02). Average daily gain, feed intake and gain:feed increased with the addition of Bio-Mos at 0 ppm Cu, but either remained about the same or decreased with the addition of Bio-Mos at 185 ppmCu. Therefore, these data are presented as treatment means (Figure 4).

Performance data during Phase 2 and Phase 3, and results of the lymphocyte proliferation assay are presented as main effect means (Table 13) as no Bio-Mos x Cu level interaction was observed. Pigs fed diets supplemented with 185 ppm Cu during Phases 2 and 3 had greater daily gain (P <0.003 and P<0.01 for Phase 2 and 3, respectively and average daily feed intake (P<0.01 and P<0.04 for Phase 2 and 3, respectively) than those fed diets with 10 ppm Cu. Feed efficiency was similar among pigs fed both levels of copper. Additionally, pigs fed diets supplemented with Bio-Mos in Phase 3 had higher average daily gain (P <0.04) and gain:feed (P<0.09) than those fed diets without Bio-Mos. For the overall study, (days 0 to 38), pigs fed diets containing 185 ppm Cu had greater (P <0.01) average daily gain, average daily feed intake and gain:feed than those fed diets

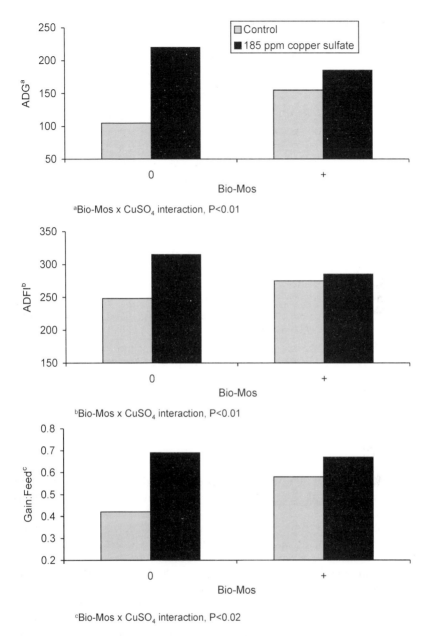

<sup>a</sup>Bio-Mos x CuSO₄ interaction, P<0.01

<sup>b</sup>Bio-Mos x CuSO₄ interaction, P<0.01

<sup>c</sup>Bio-Mos x CuSO₄ interaction, P<0.02

**Figure 4.** Effect of Bio-Mos and copper sulfate on average daily gain, g (ADG), average daily feed intake (ADFI), and gain:feed.

containing 10 ppm Cu. Pigs fed diets containing Bio-Mos had greater (P<0.04) average daily gain and gain:feed than those fed diets with no Bio-Mos. Dietary treatments did not affect lymphocyte proliferation from mitogen stimulation on samples taken on days 28, 30, 32, and 34 post-weaning.

**Table 13.** Main effects of Bio-Mos and copper sulfate addition to nursery pig diets.

|  | Bio-Mos | | Copper sulfate | | |
|---|---|---|---|---|---|
|  | – | + | – | + | Std error |
| Phase 2 (days 10 to 24) | | | | | |
| Average daily gain, g [a] | 400.26 | 417.52 | 375.00 | 442.78 | 11.60 |
| Average daily feed, g [b] | 497.69 | 506.36 | 467.38 | 536.66 | 17.36 |
| Gain:feed | 0.80 | 0.83 | 0.81 | 0.82 | 0.03 |
| Phase 3 (d 24 to 38) | | | | | |
| Average daily gain, g [b,c] | 523.57 | 564.04 | 518.10 | 569.51 | 12.96 |
| Average daily feed, g [d] | 890.82 | 897.27 | 852.40 | 935.68 | 26.88 |
| Gain:feed [e] | 0.59 | 0.63 | 0.61 | 0.61 | 0.01 |
| Overall trial (d 0 to 38) | | | | | |
| Average daily gain, g [a,c] | 401.94 | 427.16 | 383.62 | 445.49 | 8.16 |
| Average daily feed, g [a] | 611.47 | 616.60 | 579.74 | 648.33 | 14.64 |
| Gain:feed [b,c] | 0.67 | 0.71 | 0.67 | 0.71 | 0.01 |
| Lymphocyte proliferation, cpm[f] | | | | | |
| Unstimulated | 455.29 | 431.00 | 447.56 | 438.73 | 55.35 |
| PHA, 50 µg/ml | 45010.90 | 43129.36 | 44974.42 | 43165.85 | 5038.07 |
| PWM 25 µg/ml | 45180.86 | 49125.97 | 48589.46 | 45717.37 | 3913.91 |

[a] Copper sulfate effect; P<0.003.
[b] Copper sulfate effect; P<0.01.
[c] Bio-Mos effect; P<0.04.
[d] Copper sulfate; P<0.04.
[e] Bio-Mos effect; P<0.09.
[f] Data are means of 9 pens/treatment with 2 pigs/pen. One blood sample was collected from each pig on one of four days beginning on day 28 and ending on day 34 of the trial. Data are expressed as counts per minute.

The performance results of this study are consistent with previous results in young pigs and poultry. As in the present study, Schoenherr *et al.* (1994) and Van der Beke (1997) reported improved weight gain and feed efficiency in weanling pigs when oligosaccharides were added to the diet; and addition of Bio-Mos improved rate of gain (Stanley *et al.*, 1996) and efficiency (Kumprecht and Zoba, 1997) in broiler chicks. The improved performance may be explained by changes in intestinal morphology, such as greater crypt depth and increased villus width observed in a study by Savage *et al.* (1997). The addition of Bio-Mos to milk replacer improved gain and intake in young calves (Dvorak and Jacques, 1997). As in the young calf study, gain increased with the inclusion of Bio-Mos in the diet of young pigs. However, no significant increase in intake was observed in pigs fed diets containing Bio-Mos compared to those fed diets with no added Bio-Mos.

Previous research has reported that a yeast glucan enhances non-specific immunity in fish (Raa *et al.*, 1992; Engstad *et al.*, 1992). In the present study, the effect of Bio-Mos on the immunocompetence of weanling pigs was evaluated by mitogen-stimulated lymphocyte proliferation. Although response to mitogen was numerically greater in stimulated cell cultures from pigs fed Bio-Mos, neither Bio-Mos nor dietary copper had a significant effect on proliferation of lymphocytes from mitogen stimulation in the present experiment. This may be attributed to the high level of variability observed in the animals that were sampled.

This study indicates that the performance response to Bio-Mos in phase 1 varied with level of dietary Cu. However, in phases 2 and 3, diets containing either Bio-Mos or 185 ppm Cu resulted in improved performance.

## References

Blecha, F., D. S. Pollmann and D. A. Nichols. 1983. Weaning pigs at an early age decreases cellular immunity. J. Anim. Sci. 56:396.

Cain, C. 1995. Effect of AP 920 fractions on growth of early-weaned pigs. Proceedings of American Assoc. of Swine Practitioners, March, 1995.

Coffey, R. D. and G. L. Cromwell. 1995. The impact of environment and antimicrobial agents on the growth response of early-weaned pigs to spray-dried porcine plasma. J. Anim. Sci. 73:2532.

de Rodas, B.Z., K.S. Sohn, C.V. Maxwell and L.J. Spicer. 1995. Plasma protein for pigs weaned at 19 and 24 days of age: effect on performance and plasma insulin-like growth factor 1, growth hormone, insulin, and glucose concentrations. J. Anim. Sci. 73:3657.

Dinarello, C. A. 1984. Interleukin-1. Rev. Infect. 44:105.

Dvorak, R. A. and K. A. Jacques. 1997. Effect of adding mannan oligosaccharide (Bio-Mos) to the milk replacer for calves. J. Anim. Sci. 75(Suppl. 1):22.

Engstad, R. F., B. Robertson and E. Frivold. 1992. Yeast glucan induces increase in lysozyme and complement-mediated hemolytic activity in Atlantic salmon blood. Fish and Shellfish Immunology 2:287.

Fangman, T. J., M. S. Roderick and C. Tubbs. 1997. Segregated early weaning. Swine Health and Production. 5 (5):195.

Fitzpatrick, D.W. and H.S. Bayley. 1977. Evaluation of blood meal as protein source for young pigs. Can. J. Anim. Sci. 57:745.

Frank, J. W., B. T. Richert, A. P. Schinckel, B. A. Belstra and A. L. Grant. 1997. Environmental effects on genetic potential for lean gain. J. Anim. Sci. 75 (Suppl.1): 38.

Gatnau, R. and D.R. Zimmerman. 1991. Spray-dried porcine plasma (SDPP) as a source of protein for weanling pigs in two environments. J. Anim. Sci. 69(Suppl.1):103.

Gatnau, R. and D.R. Zimmerman. 1992. Determination of optimum levels of inclusion of spray-dried porcine plasma (SDPP) in diets for weanling pigs fed in practical conditions. J. Anim. Sci. 69(Suppl. 1):60.

Gatnau, R., P. Paul and D. Zimmerman. 1990. Spray-dried porcine plasma as a source of immunoglobulins for newborn pigs. Iowa State University Swine Research Report, p. 13.

Gatnau, R., D.R. Zimmerman, T.Diaz,and J. Johns. 1991. Determination of optimum levels of spray-dried porcine plasma (SDPP) in diets for weanling pigs. J. Anim. Sci. 69(Suppl. 1):369.

Hansen, J.A, R.D. Goodband, J.L. Nelssen and T.L. Weeden. 1990. Effect of substituting spray-dried plasma protein for milk products in starter pig diets. Kansas Swine Day Proceedings, p. 30.

Hansen, J.A., J.L. Nelssen, R.D. Goodband and T.L. Weeden. 1993. Evaluation of animal protein supplements in diets of early-weaned pigs. J. Anim. Sci. 71:1853.

Harris, D. L. 1993. Medicated early weaning. Proc. SE Swine Pract. Raleigh, North Carolina.

Jepson, M. M., J. M. Pell, P. C. Bates and D. J. Millward. 1986. The effects of endotoxemia on protein metabolism in skeletal muscle and liver of fed and fasted rats. Biochem. J. 235:329.

Johnson, R. W. 1997. Explanation for why sick pigs neither eat well nor grow well. Proc. Carolina Swine Nutr. Conf. P. 49.

Kats, L.J., J. L. Nelssen, M. D. Tokach, R. D. Goodband, J. A Hansen and J. L. Laurin. 1994. The effect of spray-dried porcine plasma on growth performance in the early-weaned pig. J. Anim. Sci. 72:2075.

Klasing, K. C. 1988. Nutritional aspects of leukocytic cytokines. J. Nutr. 124:906.

Kumprecht, I. and P. Zoba. 1997. Performance response of broilers to different levels of Bio-Mos in starter and grow/finish formulas. Poultry Sci. 76(Suppl. 1):132.

Mandali, S, B. Z. de Rodas, C. V. Maxwell, A. B. Arquitt and B. J. Stoker. 1997. Effect of endotoxin on trace minerals and immunological parameters in weanling pigs. J. Anim. Sci. 75(Suppl. 1):192.

Okai, D.B., F.X. Aherne and R.T. Hardin. 1976. Effects of creep feed and starter composition on feed intake and performance of young pigs. Can. J. Anim. Sci. 56:573.

Owen, K.Q., J.L. Nelssen, R.D. Goodband, M.D. Tobach, K.G. Friessen, B.T. Rickert, J.W. Smith and L.E. Russell. 1995. Effects of various fractions of spray-dried porcine plasma on performance of early-weaned pigs. J. Anim. Sci. 73:81(Abstr).

Patience, J. F., H. W. Gonyou, E. Beltranena, D. L. Whitington and C. S. Rhodes. 1997. The impact of age and site of weaning on pig performance under high health conditions. J. Anim. Sci. 75(Suppl. 1):246.

Pierce, J.L., G.L. Cromwell, M.D. Lindeman and R.D. Coffey. 1995. Assessment of three fractions of spray-dried porcine plasma on performance of early-weaned pigs. J. Anim. Sci. 73:81(Abstr).

Raa, J., G. Roerstad, R. Engstad and B. Robertson. 1992. The use of immunostimulants to increase resistance of aquatic organisms to microbial infections. In: Diseases in Asian Aquaculture (I. M. Shariff, R. P. Subasinghe and R. J. Author, eds.). Fish Health Section, Asian Fisheries Society, Manilla, Philippines. p 39–50.

Ragland, K. D., L. L. Christian, J. D. McKean and T. J. Baas. 1997. Performance carcass and muscle quality traits of centrally tested segregated early weaned and farm reared pigs. J. Anim. Sci. 75 (Suppl. 1):246.

Reeds, P. J., C. R. Fjeld and F. Jahoon. 1994. Do the differences between the amino acid composition of acute-phase and muscle proteins have a bearing on nitrogen loss in traumatic stress? J. Nutr. 124:906.

SAS. 1988. SAS Inst. Inc., Cary, NC.

Savage, T. F., E. I. Zakrzewska and J. R. Andreasen, Jr. 1997. The effects of feeding mannanoligosaccharide supplemented diets to poults on performance and morphology of the small intestine. Poultry Sci. 76(Suppl. 1):139.

Schoenherr, W. D. and D. S. Pollmann. 1994. New concept for feeding young pigs improves productivity. Feedstuffs 66:13.

Schoenherr, W. D., D. S. Pollmann and J. A. Coalson. 1994. Titration of MG on growth performance of nursery pigs. J. Anim. Sci. 72(Suppl. 1):57.

Sohn, K.S. and C.V. Maxwell. 1990a. Effect of source of dietary protein on performance of early weaned pigs. Okla. Exp. Sta. MP 129:288.

Sohn, K.S. and C.V. Maxwell. 1990b. Effect of dietary protein source on nutrient digestibility in early weaned pigs. Okla. Exp. Sta. MP 129:298.

Spring, P. and M. Privulescu. 1998. Mannanoligosaccharide: Its logical role as a natural feed additive for piglets. Pre-Conference Symposia, The 8TH World Conference on Animal Production, Seoul National University, Seoul, Korea.

Stanley, V. G., C. Gray and H. Chukwu. 1996. Effects of mannanoligosaccharide (Bio-Mos) on liver and egg cholesterol and tissue protein concentration in chickens. Poultry Sci. 75(Suppl. 1):61.

Van der Beke, N. 1997. The use of mannanoligosaccharides (Bio-Mos) and lactic acid bacteria (Lacto-Sacc) in piglet feed. Thesis, Department of Biotechnological Sciences, Landscape Management and Agriculture, Gent, Belgium.

Van Heugten, E. and J. W. Spears. 1997. Immune response and growth of stressed weanling pigs fed diets supplemented with organic and inorganic forms of chromium. J. Anim. Sci. 75:409.

Walker, W.R., C.V. Maxwell, F.N. Owens and D.S. Buchanan. 1986. Milk versus soybean protein sources for pigs. I. Effects on performance and digestibility. J. Anim. Sci. 63:505.

Williams, N. H., T. S. Stahly and D. R. Zimmerman. 1997a. Effect of chronic immune system activation on the rate, efficiency and composition of growth and lysine needs of pigs fed from 6 to 27 kg. J. Anim. Sci. 75:2463.

Williams, N. H., T. S. Stahly and D. R. Zimmerman. 1997b. Effect of chronic immune system activation on the growth and dietary lysine needs of pigs fed from 6 to 112 kg. J. Anim. Sci. 75:2481.

Wilson, R.H. and J. Leibholz. 1981a. Digestion in the pig between 7 and 35 days. 1. The performance of pigs given milk and soybean proteins. Br. J. Nutr. 34:301.

Wilson, R.H. and J. Leibholz. 1981b. Digestion in the pig between 7 and 35 days of age. 2. The digestion of dry matter and the pH of digesta in the pigs given milk and soybean proteins. Br. J. Nutr. 45:321.

Wilson, R.H. and J. Leibholz. 1981c. Digestion in the pig between 7 and 35 days of age. 3. The digestion of nitrogen in pigs given milk and soyabean proteins. Br. J. Nutr. 45:337.

Wiseman, B., T. Molitor, M. White, R. Morrison and G. Dial. 1994. Health and immunological aspects of early weaning. Proc. AASP Annual Meeting. P. 191.

Zamir, O., W. O'Brien, R. Thompson, D. C. Bloedow, J. E. Fischer and P. Hasselgren. 1994. Reduced muscle protein breakdown in septic rats following treatment with interleukin-1 receptor antagonist. Int. J. Biochem. 26:943.

# Feeding weaner pigs without in-feed antibiotics

G. BOLDUAN

*Institute for Applied Agricultural Ecology, University of Rostock, Germany*

## Introduction

With the EU ban on the use of four antibiotic feed supplements and the phasing out of the quinoxaline derivatives carbadox and olaquindox in 1999, a substitute for the so-called growth promoters must be found for the entire field of animal husbandry. The situation is made all the more important in Germany by the continuing decline in prices on the pig market. In part as a consequence of this, many commercial piggeries want to move to a shorter three-week suckling period in order to produce pigs more efficiently and more economically. This pressure favours the larger pig producers and requires a diet that enables smaller piglets to be reared in a healthy, efficient and economic way without the use of antibiotics. It must be stated that at present animal nutrition research is not prepared for this challenge and must now rapidly develop alternatives to antibiotic feed supplements.

Current wisdom holds that the usual weaning procedures are accompanied by a general weakening of the immune system. From this point of view, development of the segregated early weaning and medicated early weaning systems in the US are, therefore, both timely and extremely valuable. The positive effect of reducing outside stress on the immune system (especially stress arising from infection) is understood from developments in poultry farming over the last 40 years. Nevertheless, the improvement in performance that can be achieved in pigs remains highly impressive. These new methods of production are understandably of interest to the German pig breeders, and variations that are better suited to the smaller local production units are spreading rapidly. One could say that 'the battle is half won' if, in response to the discontinued use of antibiotics, breeders were to switch to this type of scheme.

Whatever happens, nutritional physiologists will remain concerned with the problem of how to supply nutrients to the intestine such that the natural flora predominate and that any possible 'derailing' of the major intestinal immune function is recognized and dealt with locally without burdening the general immune system. The weaner diet must protect the integrity of the intestinal wall as well as continuously inhibit the growth of possibly pathogenic microorganisms. Failure to do so can result in proliferation of pathogens. As local cases have demonstrated, endotoxins of pathogenic bacteria can penetrate the intestinal barrier causing 15% mortality rates in weaners; though these cases involved the particularly pathogenic O:139 strain of *E. coli* (oedematous form of colienterotoxaemia). The treatment and cure of such diseases by veterinary practitioners, who are themselves often at a loss in such circumstances, is very laborious and certainly costly.

## Nutritional and physiological principles of the weaner diet

In the first week post-weaning, the piglet must become accustomed to a totally new diet. At first the piglet eats very little and maintenance requirements are not met. Fat, protein and energy reserves are mobilized, with the result that the regulatory systems switch over to 'hunger mode'. At this stage the feed conversion ratio (kg feed:kg gain) is typically between 3 and 4. In the second week, after the piglet has adapted to the new diet, feed efficiency improves rapidly. Body weight gain jumps to over 300 g per day. It is predominantly protein that is accumulated and food intake per kg of body weight gain falls to 1.5 kg. This highly compensatory and very intensive period of growth lasts for weeks, with individual piglets of the modern meat breeds gaining 1000 g per day at a body weight of 25 kg.

This short period of low intake (relative to gain) is not dangerous to the weaner's metabolism. All organisms are provided with adequate regulatory mechanisms and storage capacity to be able to cope with such situations. The one danger that does exist concerns the intestinal flora. The intermittent passage of food during the hunger period and the subsequent hyperphagia generate excellent conditions for microbial multiplication. Moreover, a potentially fatal shift in the intestinal bacterial population can result from the change from milk to solid feed and incorrect feeding (strongly buffering, high-nutrient food, based solely on nutrient requirements). The favourable lactobacilli disappear and conditions encourage the growth of acid-intolerant coliform bacteria with strong pathogenic potential. Unfortunately, the pig's defences against the full force of such an attack often prove too weak. The few defence measures such as stomach acidity, pancreatic capacity, or establishment of a resistant flora in the colon are still underdeveloped.

The success of the nutritional program will depend largely on how these physiological changes are dealt with. In the two to three weeks after weaning, the feed must meet the following three requirements:

1. **The diet must have a functional ability to inhibit certain bacterial populations**. Of importance are a low buffering capacity and the ability to encourage material passage through the intestine.

2. **Diet components must support the rapid establishment of a stable colon microflora.** A certain fraction of dietary fibre from long-chain hydrocarbons should be incorporated.

3. **The diet ingredients should act as a substrate intervening in the reorganization of the intestinal microflora.** Eubiosis can be effectively promoted by encouraging lactic acid-producing flora or blocking the attachment of pathogenic bacteria onto the intestinal wall.

These requirements cannot be met by simply making changes to the mineral fraction of the diet to reduce buffering capacity. In our studies, a basic feed mix of wheat-barley (approximately 1:1), soya (44% crude protein), and 3% each of fishmeal and soyabean oil has proved useful. Relevant reference values are for example an energy value of 13.2 MJ ME/kg, a crude protein content of 17.5–18% and a crude fibre content of 3.5–4%. Premixes are used containing amino acid supplements (12–13 g lysine/kg feed), minerals and vitamins to achieve typically 7 g calcium, 5 g phosphorus and 15,000 IU vitamin A/kg feed. This feed mixture is capable of meeting important physiological functions (low acid-binding capacity, ease of passage due to the dietary fibre content) and is also able to generate increases in body weight of 400–450 g per day in four-week-old weaners in the rearing section through 25 kg liveweight. However, the frequency of diarrhoea in such feeding groups can be 10% or higher, as was reported from Sweden following the ban on the use of antibiotics in 1986. The question raised is thus whether further, special feed additives can improve performance and reduce diarrhoea to the same extent that was achieved using antibiotics (additional weight gains of 15% and a reduction in diarrhoea of 50–66%).

## The effects of dietary additives

Feed components that may be considered useful in gaining the three objectives of weaner diet formulation mentioned above are carbohydrates, oligosaccharides, organic acids, metals, minerals, enzymes, probiotics and herbs. This chapter gives the results of our investigations involving acids and oligosaccharides together with investigations using phytase. Earlier work involving zinc and copper and absorbent materials such as diatomaceous earth and bentonite produced favourable results in the treatment of diarrhoea. However, for ecological reasons in the case of zinc, and for energetic/metabolic reasons in the case of bentonite, these additives should not be used prophylactically for diarrhoea.

ORGANIC ACIDS

Of the available alternatives to performance-enhancing drugs, the most important dietary components are the organic acids. The highly reproducible positive effects of organic acids on growth, feed utilization and alleviation of diarrhoea are indisputable. Indeed organic acids are in widespread use at present, being administered in addition to antibiotics.

In addition to the two methods of lowering buffering capacity mentioned earlier (calcium and crude protein reduction), acid supplements can also be used to reduce feed pH to 4.8–5. Apart from promoting stomach function (maintenance of the bacterial barrier in the stomach, optimum pepsin activity, more rapid evacuation), a lower buffering capacity also increases the rate of absorption of trace elements and the pre-caecal digestibility of organic materials (Blank *et al.,* 1988; Decuypere *et al.,* 1997).

In fourteen investigations using different acids, we observed an average 11% increase in body weight, an inhibition of stomach fermentation by a factor of one third and an 18 % increase in the gastric emptying time (Bolduan, 1988). The blood urea levels also appeared to be lower. Recent evaluation of 144 experiments in the pig rearing sector have shown that formic acid caused a 15% additional increase in bodyweight and a 7% improvement in the feed conversion ratio (Freitag, 1998; Table 1). These data showing benefits of dietary acids confirmed earlier results with sorbic acid and potassium formate (Kirchgessner *et al.,* 1997). Acids are now a recognized dietary supplement used to support stomach function in weaner pigs. Volatile acids are to be preferred as they also act to control microbial contamination of feeds.

**Table 1.  Improvements in performance of piglets receiving acid supplements compared with a control group (piglets reared from 8 to 25 kg).**

| Acid supplement | Formic acid | Sorbic acid | Potassium formate[1] |
|---|---|---|---|
| Inclusion rate, % | 0.65 | 1.8 | 1.2/0.9[2] |
| | *% of control* | | |
| Increase in bodyweight | 117 | 126 | 125 |
| Feed conversion ratio | 86 | 78 | 85 |
| Frequency of diarrhoea | 36 | 23 | 39 |
| Fraction of severe diarrhoea | 59 | 37 | 15 |

[1]Potassium diformate (Norsk Hydro, Norway).
[2]1.2% in the week of weaning/0.9% during subsequent 5 weeks.

## OLIGOSACCHARIDES AND PHYTASE

A normal diet contains over 10% sugar polymers of various chain lengths. They are of little energetic value and since they cannot be digested enzymatically by the host; and they pass through the intestine to become a substrate for fermentation by colon bacteria. By virtue of their fermentability these sugar polymers sustain important functions of the colon such as material transport and waste excretion.

When considering applications for weaner pigs, both the great variety of this class of substances and the predicament of the piglet should be considered. In addition to crude fibre detected by proximate analysis (lignin, cellulose and hemicellulose, which together account for about 5% of the ration), developments over the last few years have focused increasingly on short chain compounds appropriately named non-starch polysaccharides (NSPs). These compounds make up a further 5-8% of the ration. To improve utilisation of dietary gross energy, the biotechnology industry has developed suitable enzyme complements (pentosanases, glucanases, etc.) used as feed additives in the pig production sector to improve feed utilization and weight gains by 3–4%.

From a dietary standpoint, this is only of significance in that the enzyme supplements reduce digesta viscosity, which is typically determined by the swelling and gelling capacity of most polymers from glucan to pectin. The reduction in viscosity due to enzyme supplementation has had beneficial effects in the poultry industry, in particular for chick starter diets. Feed viscosity is not as important when rearing piglets as the glucans are hydrolzed in the pre-caecal region by the lactic acid-producing bacteria. In additon, we continue to detect diarrhoea when enzymes of this type are administered, as well as a significant hyper-proliferation of the intestinal flora in the frontal region of the jejunum (Bolduan, 1995). Obviously sugar molecules are a welcome substrate for the flora of the small intestine.

With regard to the piglet, oligosaccharides can be assessed as follows:

- The NSP fraction is retained in the ration as valuable dietary fibre.
- Search for a specific enzyme that does not degrade NSP but does break down other polysaccharide compounds thereby lowering viscosity.
- Search for oligosaccharides from natural sources that help the piglet control the negative shift in intestinal flora toward pathogens.

Our recent developmental work with piglets has indicated that phytase and the mannanoligosaccharides and fructo-oligosaccharides (MOS and FOS) are substances that are able to meet these high demands. MOS and FOS pass through the large intestine and act as a bacterial substrate specific to the bifidobacteria and lactobacilli (Spring, 1996). In our investigations, phytase proved able to enhance performance on its own and proved useful in combination with FOS and organic acids.

### Fructo-oligosaccharides

For the investigations with FOS we used inulin, which is present in Jerusalem artichoke (*Helianthus tuberosus*). The extract was a solution containing 40% inulin. Inulin, with a molecular weight of 5000, is comprised of about thirty fructose molecules joined by 1,2 glycosidic linkages. Bolduan *et al.* (1993) demonstrated that a 0.2% FOS feed supplement reduced blood urea by 24%, increased gastric emptying rate by some 11%, and increased the concentration of lactic acid in the colon five-fold.

In the rearing trials, FOS was administered as a syrup concentrate of Jerusalem artichoke juice containing 30% inulin. In six experiments performance of piglets receiving FOS was compared with that of piglets given in-feed antibiotic additives (50 ppm zinc bacitracin). Average weight gain was 96% of that in the control group and the average feed conversion ratio was 98% of the group receiving antibiotics. Adjusting the inclusion rate resulted in performance equal to the group given antibiotics. Average values from three experiments clearly demonstrate the effect of changing use rate in response to need (data refer to weaners on a four week feeding regime, Table 2).

Table 2.    Effects of inulin[1] (FOS) dosage on bodyweight gain and feed efficiency of piglets[2].

| Inulin (FOS) dosage scheme | 0.7% throughout | Step-down program weeks 1–4[3] |
|---|---|---|
| Increase in bodyweight, g/day | 417 | 461 |
| % of control[4] | 100 | 111 |
| Feed conversion ratio, kg/kg | 1.76 | 1.70 |
| % of control[4] | 100 | 97 |

[1] Jerusalem artichoke juice concentrate.
[2] Values are the mean of three trials.
[3] 2.5, 1, 0.5 and 0% in weeks 1, 2, 3 and 4, respectively.
[4] 50 ppm zinc bacitracin (control).

The decreasing dosage scheme also allowed a 25–30% saving in the quantity of FOS used. This effect underscores the fact that several starter mixtures covering a range of concentrations are beneficial from a dietary point of view because it ensures that the weaners are, in all events, supplied with sufficient additive in the early stages of weaning. This is important as colienterotoxaemia will begin within the first ten days. The additive could be discontinued as early as the fourth week. The use of FOS was not accompanied by diarrhoea though faeces were somewhat softer due to the stimulation of the colon.

### Mannanoligosaccharide

Linked mannose polymers are present in the walls of yeast cells (*Saccharomyces cerevisiae*). They also act as a substrate for lactic acid bacteria and in addition possess the ability to block bacterial attachment by occupying bacterial fimbria specific for mannose lectins in several strains of salmonella and *E. coli*. This essentially lowers pathogenicity of these coliforms and allows the potential pathogens in the lumen to be washed through the gastrointestinal tract (Spring, 1996). This should result in better growth performance. In an investigation of this, Bio-Mos mannan added to a pig starter feed gave a 10% improvement in growth rate of weaner pigs compared with an untreated control. An established growth promoter (olaquindox) gave only a 6% improvement (Bolduan *et al.*, 1997). In both cases the treatments were applied with 0.65% formic acid.

In our experiments we used washed yeast cell walls from brewing yeast strains including, amongst others, Bio-Mos from Alltech Inc. with a mannan content of between 21 and 30%. Weaner pigs at four weeks of age were subjected to four-week rearing tests in which the feed contained no antibiotics. It follows from these results that Bio-Mos represents an excellent alternative to in-feed antibiotics with an added advantage when used in combination with organic acids. The preferred approach utilizes graduated doses and administration in combination with formic acid where growth rate improved by 11 % and no diarrhoea was reported.

**Table 3.** **Effects of yeast cell wall, Bio-Mos and formic acid treatments on piglet performance weeks 1-4 post-weaning.**

| Feed additive | Use rate (%) | Weight gain[1] (%) | Comment |
|---|---|---|---|
| Without acid additives | | | |
| Yeast cell walls | 1.0 | 111 | 18% reduction in diarrhoea |
| Yeast cell walls | 1.5 | 113 | 12% reduction in diarrhoea |
| Yeast cell walls + formic acid | 2.0 + 0.65 | 120 | 53% reduction in diarrhoea |
| Bio-Mos + formic acid | 0.20 + 0.50 | 104 | FCR improved |
| Bio-Mos + formic acid | 0.6 to 0[2] + 0.50 | 111 | FCR improved |
| With 0.65% formic acid supplement | | | |
| Yeast cell walls | 2.5 | 113 | no diarrhoea in test |
| Bio-Mos | 0.2 | 110 | no diarrhoea in test |

[1]Values are % of control (no additive) response.
[2]Bio-Mos use rate: 0.6, 0.3, 0.1 and 0% weeks 1-4, respectively.

## Summary

Diets designed to respond to the phasing out of feed antibiotics should exhibit a low buffering capacity to promote the proper function of the stomach and an optimized crude fibre content to ensure the passage rate through the intestine. Organic acid supplements are clearly able to improve performance, with weight gain increases of between 11 and 25% and a reduction in diarrhoea observed. Of the various enzyme additives, only phytase can be recommended for use. Within the oligosaccharide group of substances, it is the polymers of mannose and fructose which, in specific doses and in combination with organic acids, result in improvements in performance of between 4 and 20%.

# References

Blank, R., R. Mosenthin and W.C. Sauer. 1988. Effect of fumaric acid supplementation and dietary buffering capacity on ileal and fecal nutrient and energy digestibilities in early weaned pigs. Vortr. Jahrestagung GfE , Göttingen.

Bolduan, G. 1988. Die Steuerung der Darm-Flora bei Ferkeln und Sauen. Chemie und Ernährung. *( Controlling the intestinal flora of piglets and sows. Chemical and nutritional studies. )* 3. BASF - Forum Tierernährung, Ausg. 23, Nr. 11.

Bolduan, G. 1995. Carbohydrasen in der Schweineernährung. *( Carbohydrases in the diet of pigs)* Lohmann - Informat. Sept.-Dez. Nr. 4:15.

Bolduan, G., M. Beck and C. Schubert. 1993. Zur Wirkung von Oligosacchariden in der Ferkelfütterung. *( On the effects of oligosaccharides in pig feeds)* Arch Anim. Nutr. Berlin 44:21.

Bolduan, G.A., Schuldt and W. Hackl. 1997. Diet feeding in weaner pigs. (Arch. Tierz., Dummerstorf, Sonderheft 95–100.

Decuypere, J., M. De Brun and N. Dierick. 1997. Influence of buffering capacity of the feed on the pre-cecal digestibility in pigs. Proceed. 7. Internat. Symp. Nutr. Physiol. Pigs. Saint Malo.

Freitag, N. 1998. Wirkungen von Futterzusätzen zur Ablösung der Leistungsförderer in der Schweineproduktion. *( The effects of feed additives as substitutes for performance enhancers in pig production)* Forschungsber. FH Soest.

Kirchgessner, M., B.R. Paulicks and F.X. Roth. 1997. Effects of supplementation of diformate complexes on the growth and carcass performances of piglets and fattening pigs in response to application time. Agribiol. Res. 50:1

Spring, P. 1996. Effects of mannanoligosaccharide on different cecal parameters and on cecal concentrations of enteric pathogens in poultry. Diss. ETH Zürich, Nr. 11 897.

# SILAGES: PROGRESS IN ANALYSIS AND MANAGEMENT

# Silage management in North America in the 1990s

KEITH K. BOLSEN

*Department of Animal Sciences and Industry, Kansas State University, Manhattan, Kansas, USA*

## Introduction

Advances in silage technology, including high-capacity precision chop harvesters, improved silos, polyethylene sheeting, shear-cutting silage unloaders and total mixed rations, made silage a principal method of forage preservation for dairy and beef cattle producers in North America in the 1990s. Silage quality and nutritional value are influenced by numerous biological and technological factors including: the crop species, stage of maturity and dry matter (DM) content at harvest, chop length, type of silo, rate of filling, forage density after packing, sealing technique, feedout rate, weather conditions at harvest and feedout, additives, timeliness of the silage-making activities, and the training of personnel (Bolsen, 1995). Because many of these influences are interrelated, it is difficult to discuss their significance individually. However, there are two dominant features of every silage: 1) the crop, including its stage of maturity and its "ensileability" and 2) the management and 'know-how' imposed by the silage maker.

To understand the effect of inoculants, other additives, and ensiling practices on silage quality, it is necessary to know how preservation occurs in ensiled forages (McDonald *et al.*, 1991). In 'perfect' silage, available carbohydrates are converted by anaerobic bacteria (mainly homofermentative lactic acid bacteria) to lactic acid. This bacterial activity lowers the pH rapidly and preserves the silage. In even the best of circumstances, some dry matter is lost during lactic acid production. However, the ensiling process is seldom perfect. Whenever oxygen is present, carbohydrates are converted to carbon dioxide and water, accompanied by the generation of considerable heat. The result is a serious loss of silage dry matter. Many of the good silage-making techniques involve eliminating as much oxygen as possible (Pitt, 1990).

233

## Silage additives

Additives have been used throughout the 20th century to improve silage preservation by ensuring that lactic acid bacteria (LAB) dominate the fermentation phase. However, the silage additive industry did not play a significant role in silage production in the USA until the past two or three decades. Additives can be divided into three general categories: 1) fermentation stimulants, such as bacterial inoculants and enzymes, 2) fermentation inhibitors such as propionic, formic, and sulfuric acids and 3) substrate or nutrient sources such as molasses, urea and anhydrous ammonia (Bolsen *et al.*, 1995).

Perhaps no other area of silage management has received as much attention among both researchers and livestock producers in recent years as bacterial inoculants. Effective bacterial inoculants promote a faster and more efficient fermentation of the ensiled crop, which increases both the quantity and quality of the silage. The bacteria in commercial products include one or more of the following species: *Lactobacillus plantarum* or other lactobacillus species, various pediococcus species and *Enterococcus (Streptococcus) faecium*. These strains of LAB have been isolated from silage crops or silages and were selected because: 1) they are homofermentative (i.e., ferment sugars predominantly to lactic acid) and 2) they grow rapidly under a wide range of temperature and moisture conditions. Bacterial inoculants have inherent advantages over other additives, including low cost, safety in handling, a low application rate per ton of chopped forage, and no residues or environmental problems.

Enzymes are capable of degrading plant cell walls and starch which could provide additional sugars for fermentation to lactic acid and increase the nutritive value of the ensiled material. Although enzymes offer potential to improve silage quality, considerable work needs to be done before they will become commonly used additives.

The justifications for using nonprotein nitrogen (NPN) have been prolonged aerobic stability during the feedout phase and the addition of an economical nitrogen source to low protein crops such as corn and sorghum. However, major drawbacks to ammoniation are the potentially dangerous volatile properties of anhydrous ammonia and its caustic nature plus the need for specialized application and safety equipment. Additionally, NPN always acts as a buffer during fermentation, requiring extra lactic acid to be produced to lower the pH enough for preservation. Thus, NPN addition always increases dry matter loss.

## Silage additive research at Kansas State University

Evaluation of silage additives began in 1975 in the Department of Animal Sciences and Industry and continues today. These 20 years have led to the following general conclusions about when bacterial inoculant and NPN additives such as urea or anhydrous ammonia should be used:

- Bacterial inoculants should be applied to every load of forage ensiled.
- NPN additives should never be used unless NPN is the only means of preventing aerobic deterioration during the feedout phase.

Results from over 200 laboratory-scale studies involving nearly 1,000 silages and 25,000 silos indicated that bacterial inoculants were beneficial in over 90% of the comparisons. Inoculated silages had faster and more efficient fermentations. The pH was lower, particularly during the first 2-4 days of the ensiling process. Lactic acid content and the lactic to acetic acid ratio were higher than in control silages. Inoculated silages also had lower ethanol and ammonia nitrogen values compared to untreated silages.

Results from 28 farm-scale trials evaluating 71 silages showed that bacterial inoculants consistently improved fermentation efficiency, dry matter recovery, food efficiency, and liveweight gain per ton of crop ensiled in both corn and forage sorghum silages (Bolsen *et al.*, 1992). Applying urea or anhydrous ammonia adversely affected fermentation efficiency, dry matter recovery, average daily liveweight gain, feed efficiency and liveweight gain per ton of crop ensiled, particularly for the higher moisture forage sorghums. An additive with a urea/molasses blend had less of a negative influence on silage preservation and cattle performance than urea or anhydrous ammonia.

## Economics of bacterial inoculants and NPN silage additives

An effective bacterial inoculant is a sound investment for any beef or dairy cattle producer who makes and feeds silage. Based on the results at Kansas State University, a 3–4 lb increase in gain per ton of crop ensiled produces $2-4 increases in net return per ton of corn or sorghum ensiled. If producers use NPN, they actually lose $4–6 per ton of crop ensiled because of the decreased dry matter recovery, increased feed to gain ratio, and added cost of replacing the loss of volatile nitrogen. These results apply to beef producers who background cattle and to beef and dairy producers that grow replacement heifers.

The use of a bacterial inoculant by dairy producers who include whole-plant corn or sorghum silages and alfalfa silage or haylage in lactation rations is also a good management decision. The additional 'cow days' per ton of crop ensiled, because of the increased dry matter recovery and the increased milk produced from the inoculated silage or haylage (0.25–0.5 lbs) results in $4-8 increases in net return per ton of corn or sorghum ensiled and $6-10 increases in net return per ton of alfalfa ensiled. A 'bottom line' calculation of the value of inoculating corn silage and alfalfa haylage is presented in the following example based on a herd with 97 cows in lactation producing an average of 87 lbs of milk daily with a daily dry matter intake of 54.2 lbs of the ration listed in Table 1. The increase in net income per ton of forage ensiled is realized from increases in both preservation and feed utilization improvements (Table 2).

**Table 1.   Silage and grain mix inputs in the example herd diet.**

| Ration | Dry matter (lbs) | Dry matter (%) | Amount as-fed (lbs) | $ per lb | Ration cost/day ($) |
|---|---|---|---|---|---|
| Corn silage | 11.4 | 35 | 32.6 | 0.011 | 0.36 |
| Alfalfa haylage | 11.2 | 40 | 28.0 | 0.0225 | 0.63 |
| Grain mix | 31.6 | 90 | 35.1 | 0.08 | 2.81 |
| Total | 54.2 | | 95.7 | | 3.80 |

# Recommendations for silage management and inoculant use

Why leave the critical fermentation phase to chance by assuming that the epiphytic microorganisms (those occurring naturally on the forage) will be effective in preserving the silage crop? Even if a dairy or beef cattle producer's silage has been acceptable in the past, because silage-making conditions in most regions of North America are generally good, there are always opportunities for improvement.

Although whole-plant corn and sorghum ensile easily, research data clearly show that the quality of the fermentation and subsequent preservation and utilization efficiencies are improved with bacterial inoculants. Alfalfa (and other legumes) are usually difficult to ensile because of a low sugar content and high buffering capacity. However, adding an inoculant helps ensure that as much of the available substrate as possible is converted to lactic acid thereby removing some of the risk of having a poorly preserved, low-quality silage.

Finally, if producers are already doing a good job but using a bacterial inoculant for the first time, they probably will not see a dramatic difference in their silage, but the benefit will be there: additional silage dry matter recovery and significantly more beef or milk production per ton of crop ensiled.

## SELECTING A BACTERIAL INOCULANT

The inoculant should provide at least 200,000 colony-forming units of viable LAB per gram of forage. These LAB should dominate the fermentation, produce lactic acid as the sole end product, be able to grow over a wide range of pH, temperature and moisture conditions and ferment a wide range of plant sugars. Purchase an inoculant from a reputable company that can provide quality control assurances along with independent research supporting the product's effectiveness.

## PROTECTING SILAGE FROM AIR AND WATER

Horizontal silos (i.e. bunker, trench, or pile) are economically attractive for storing large amounts of ensiled forage, but because so much of the

236

**Table 2.** Comparison of preservation efficiency and feed utilization efficiency with and without an inoculant.

| | Corn silage | | Alfalfa haylage | |
|---|---|---|---|---|
| | Untreated | Inoculant | Untreated | Inoculant |
| **Preservation efficiency** | | | | |
| Dry matter recovery, % | 90.0 | 91.3 | 88.7 | 90.0 |
| Dry matter recovered/ton ensiled, lbs | 1800 | 1826 | 1774 | 1800 |
| Amount fed daily, lbs | 32.6 | 32.6 | 28.0 | 28.0 |
| Cow days per ton ensiled | 55.2 | 56.0 (+0.8) | 63.3 | 64.3 (+1) |
| Milk gained per ton ensiled, lbs | | 69.6[1] | | 87.0[5] |
| Milk value gained per ton ensiled, | | $8.70[2] | | $10.87 |

| | | |
|---|---|---|
| **Utilization efficiency** | | |
| Milk yield/cow/day, lbs | Inoculated corn silage = +0.25 lbs. milk/cow/day. | Inoculated alfalfa haylage = +0.25 lbs. milk/cow/day. |
| Milk gained per ton ensiled, lbs | 56.0 cow days x 0.25 lbs. of milk = 14.0 lbs. milk gained/ton ensiled. | 64.3 cow days x 0.25 lbs. of milk = 16.0 lbs. milk gained/ton ensiled. |
| Milk value gained/ton ensiled, $ | 14.0 lbs. of milk × $0.125/lb. = $1.75 gained value/ton ensiled. | 16.0 lbs. of milk × $0.125/lb. = $2.00 gained value/ton ensiled. |
| **Combined efficiencies** | ($8.70 + $1.75) – ($2.75 + $1.00)[3,4]= $6.70 gained value/ton of crop ensiled. | ($10.87 + $2.00) – ($3.17 + $1.00)[7,4] = $8.70 gained value/ton of crop ensiled. |
| **Bottom line** | | |
| Additional cost | 32.6 lbs. x 305 days ÷ 200 = 4.97 tons/cow/year 4.97 tons/0.913 = 5.44 tons to ensile/cow/year[8] 5.44 tons x $1.00/ton = $5.44/cow/year $5.44/305 days = $0.018/cow/day | 28.0 lbs. x 305 days ÷ 200 = 4.27 tons/cow/year 4.27 tons/0.9 = 4.75 tons to ensile/cow/year[8] 4.75 tons x $1.00/ton = $4.75/cow/year $4.75/305 days = $0.016/cow/day |
| Additional income | 5.44 tons x $6.70 = $36.45/cow/year $36.45/305 days = $0.120/cow/day | 4.75 tons x $8.70 = $41.32/cow/year $41.32/305 days = $0.135/cow/day |
| Increased net income | $0.120 - $0.018 = $0.102/cow/day $0.102 x 305 days = $31.11/cow/year | $0.135 - $0.016 = $0.119/cow/day $0.119 x 305 days = $36.30/cow/year |

[1]87 lbs. of milk/cow day x 0.8 cow days gained = 69.6 lbs milk gained.
[2]69.6 lbs. of milk x $0.125/lb. = $8.70 gained value/ton ensiled.
[3]Haylage + grain mix costs/cow/day = $3.44 × 0.8 cow days = $2.75 added cost/ton ensiled.
[4]Treatment (inoculant) cost = $1.00/ton ensiled.
[5]87 lbs. of milk/cow day x 1.0 cow days gained per ton ensiled.
[6]87.0 lbs. of milk x $0.125 lb. = $10.87 gained value/ton ensiled.
[7]Corn silage + grain mix costs/cow/day = $3.17 x 1.0 cow day = $3.17 added cost/ton ensiled.
[8]Assumes a 91.3% forage in vs. silage out for the corn silage, 90.0% for alfalfa haylage.

surface of the ensiled material is exposed to air and rain or snow, dry matter and nutrient losses can be extensive. If left unprotected, losses in the top 2—4 feet can exceed 50%. This is particularly disturbing when one considers that in the typical horizontal silo, over 20% of the silage might be within the top three feet.

Top spoilage losses can be minimized by sealing (covering) the ensiled mass with polyethylene sheets which are usually weighted with tires or soil. Although this method minimizes losses, it is so awkward, cumbersome, and labor intensive that many producers feel the silage saved is not worth the time and effort required.

Top spoilage research has been conducted at Kansas State University since 1989 and the results document the magnitude of the dry matter and nutrient losses in the original top three feet of the ensiled crop. However, these losses cannot be seen until the silo is opened. Even then, the spoilage might be apparent only in the top 6–12 inches of silage, obscuring the fact that this area of spoiled silage represents substantially more silage as originally stored.

Provided here are a few simple equations that can be easily calculated or incorporated into a computer spreadsheet. The equations allow producers to estimate the value of silage saved by sealing based on crop value, silo dimensions, cost of the sealing material and labor to cover the silage.

### *Calculations demonstrating economic value of covering the silo*

Calculating the value of silage saved by sealing is based on four economic inputs and two silo/silage inputs. The four economic inputs are:

1. Value of the silage ($/ton)
2. Cost of the polyethylene sheet ($/ft$^2$ x number of ft$^2$)
3. Cost of the weighting material (zero was used in the examples)
4. labor cost ($/hr x number of hrs).

Ten hours of labor required per 4,000 ft$^2$ of polyethylene sheet were used in calculating the labor cost. In order to account for overlap from sheet to sheet and along the side walls or base, we assumed a covering efficiency of 80%. The first of the two silo/silage inputs determined the amount of silage within the original top three feet of the silo after filling is complete. This is determined by multiplying the silo width (ft) by length (ft) by depth of interest (3 ft) by the silage density (lb/ft$^3$) and dividing the product by 2,000 (lb/ton).

The second silo/silage input estimates the amount of silage within the original top three feet of the silo that is lost as spoilage. These values (20% if sealed, 50% if unsealed) are based on research conducted at Kansas State University and published in Kansas Agricultural Extension Station Reports of Progress (Dickerson *et al.*, 1991; Holthaus *et al.*, 1995, Bolsen *et al.*, 1993).

The following example estimates the net return from sealing a horizontal silo 40 ft wide by 100 ft long (4,000 ft$^2$).

*Economic assumptions:*

1. Corn silage price: $25/ton
2. Polyethylene film: $.055 per ft$^2$, $.055 x 4,000 ft$^2$ = $220
3. Weighting material: zero cost assumed
4. Labor cost: 10 hr/4,000 ft$^2$ sheet x $20/hr = $200

Sealing cost = $220 + $200 = $420

*Silo/silage assumptions:*

1. Assuming a silage density of 45 lb/ft$^3$ (4000 ft$^2$ surface x 3 ft deep x 45 lb/ft$^3$)/2000 = 270 tons of silage within the original top 3 ft (total silo capacity is about 1,080 tons)
2. Assume 20% loss in the top 3 ft if sealed, 50% loss if unsealed.

*Loss, unsealed:*

270 tons x $25/ton x 50% = $3,375

*Loss, sealed:*

270 tons x $25/ton x 20% = $1,350
Cost of sealing = $420
Net = $1,770

Net return to sealing:
$3,375 – $1,770 = $1,605

The concepts shown above are presented in a user-friendly spreadsheet format in Table 3. The first nine lines are economic inputs determined by the producer, and the following six lines are results based on formulas utilizing the producer's inputs. They can be programmed easily into the spreadsheet using the row letters as guides.

The most important single factor influencing preservation efficiency of ensiled forages is the degree of anaerobic conditions achieved and maintained during the fermentation and storage phases. When silage is not sealed or when the seal is inadequate, air and moisture enter the mass and affect both the ensiling process and silage quality during the storage and feedout phases. Based on the examples in Table 3, sealing a 40 ft × 100 ft silo could save approximately $1,600 worth of silage. Using the same concept, covering a 100 ft x 400 ft silo could save the producer over $16,000.

Although future technology might introduce a more environmentally and user-friendly product, polyethylene (6 mil) is the most effective sealing material available today. The most common sealing method is to place the polyethylene sheet over the ensiled forage and weight it down with rubber tires (20 to 25 tires per 100 ft$^2$). Research-based calculations confirm that the financial loss incurred by not sealing silage is substantial and reinforces our recommendation that sealing the exposed surface of a horizontal silo is one of the most important management decisions in any silage program.

Table 3.  Value of silage saved by sealing three horizontal silos differing in size.

| Economic inputs Silage crop | Corn | Corn | Corn | | Spreadsheet Formulas |
|---|---|---|---|---|---|
| Silage value, $/ton | 25 | 25 | 25 | A | |
| Silage density, lb/ft$^3$ | 45 | 45 | 45 | B | |
| Silo width, ft | 40 | 100 | 100 | C | |
| Silo length, ft | 100 | 250 | 400 | D | |
| Cost of 40 ft × 100 ft poly sheet, $ | 175 | 175 | 175 | E | |
| Efficiency of sheet, % | 80 | 80 | 80 | F | |
| Silage lost if unsealed, % | 50 | 50 | 50 | G | |
| Silage lost if sealed, % | 20 | 20 | 20 | H | |
| Labor cost, $/hr | 20 | 20 | 20 | I | |
| **Results** | | | | | |
| Silage in the top 3 ft, tons | 270 | 1,688 | 2,700 | J | (C×D×3×B)/2000 |
| Silage value lost if unsealed, $ | 3,375 | 21,094 | 33,750 | K | J× (G/100) ×A |
| Silage value lost if sealed, $ | 1,350 | 8,438 | 13,500 | L | J× (H/100) ×A |
| Cost per ft$^2$ of poly sheet, ¢ | 5.5 | 5.5 | 5.5 | M | ([E/(F/100)]/4000) ×100 |
| Sealing cost, $ | 419 | 2,617 | 4,188 | N | [(C×D×M)/100)]+ [(I×C×D×10)/4000] |
| Value of silage saved, $ | 1,606 | 10,039 | 16,063 | P | K–(L+N) |

# Questions and answers about silage in the 1990s

WHAT ARE THE CHARACTERISTICS OF A GOOD CORN HYBRID FOR SILAGE?

A corn hybrid must be capable of producing a high whole-plant dry matter yield and a high grain to forage ratio in the silage. It should also have a whole-plant dry matter content of 30–36% when the kernel is in the 60–80% milk-line stage of maturity.

HOW DO SORGHUMS COMPARE TO CORN AS SILAGE CROPS?

Grain sorghum compares very favorably to corn as a whole-plant silage. Grain sorghum should be harvested at the mid to late dough stage of kernel maturity. It usually has a higher crude protein content than corn silage, but slightly lower net energy values for beef and dairy cattle.

The agronomic and nutritional quality traits of forage sorghum silages are far more variable than those of whole plant corn or grain sorghum silages. Therefore, hybrid or variety selection is critical for forage sorghum and a good rule-of-thumb is to avoid the phenotypic extremes.

IS IT BETTER TO HARVEST (ENSILE) THE SILAGE CROP TOO EARLY OR TOO LATE?

For corn, sorghum, and small grain cereals it is probably better to harvest too early rather than too late but excessive effluent must be avoided (i.e.

do not harvest above 70–72% moisture). The earlier-harvested silage will have a lower pH, a higher acid content and the chance of a greater dry matter loss in the silo than later-harvested silage. The later-harvested crop will be more difficult to chop and pack and the drier silage will be more aerobically unstable during the feedout phase than earlier-harvested silage.

For field-wilted forages that are more difficult to ensile, it is probably better to harvest too late (i.e. at a lower moisture) rather than too early (i.e. at a higher moisture). When these forages are ensiled too wet, chances are greater for a clostridial fermentation and high butyric acid and ammonia nitrogen levels in the silage. When field-wilted forages are ensiled at a lower moisture they are more difficult to pack and present risks of heat damage (i.e., a decrease in nutrient availability) and a high mold content. Regardless of the length of the field-wilting period, these forages must be cut at the correct stage of maturity.

## HOW DO I ENSILE VERY WET GRASSES OR LEGUMES?

These forages should be field-wilted whenever possible. If weather conditions do not allow field wilting to at least 25% dry matter prior to chopping, then one of several strategies should be followed. First, these forages must be ensiled with an effective bacterial inoculant. Add 30–50 lbs of either dry or wet molasses or 100–200 lbs of a dry feedstuff or by-product per ton of chopped forage. Ground grain, wheat bran, wheat midds, rice bran, or citrus or beet pulps all have been used to ensile wet forages. Finally, the material added should be mixed as uniformly as possible with the wet forage.

## WHAT IS THE PROPER SIZE FOR A BUNKER, TRENCH, OR PILE SILO?

The tons of crop to be ensiled and the projected tons of silage to be fed daily determine the proper size for a bunker, trench, or pile. The height, width, and depth dimensions should be small enough to allow a rapid progression through the silage mass during the feedout phase. Most silos are too large. Large silos take too long to fill and the feedout rate is too slow.

## HOW LONG AFTER FILLING CAN THE SILO BE OPENED FOR FEEDING?

The fermentation phase should be completed before the silo is opened for feeding. This normally takes 2–3 weeks after filling. If silage is fed after only a few days in the silo, both dry matter intake and milk production are likely to be affected adversely. Inoculants should reduce the time required for the fermentation phase to be completed. Because grasses and legumes usually ferment slower than corn (or sorghum), grass or legume silages should not be fed until at least three weeks after filling.

## WHAT ARE EXPECTED LOSSES IN A VERY GOOD SILAGE?

The losses in a very good silage will range from 5–15% whereas the losses in a very bad silage will range from 25–50%. Loss is defined as the amount of forage dry matter put in a silo minus the amount of silage dry matter removed from the silo and fed. These losses are the result of effluent, respiration, primary and secondary fermentation and aerobic activity during the storage and feedout phases.

## HOW DOES THE TYPE OF SILO AFFECT DRY MATTER LOSSES AND SILAGE QUALITY?

The type of silo does affect losses and silage quality; however, minimum losses and high quality silage can be achieved in any type of silo if it is well managed. In general, vertical silos (towers) are more efficient than horizontal silos (bunkers, trenches, piles, and bags), and smaller-capacity silos are less efficient than larger-capacity silos (if filling is not delayed and the silage removal rate is not too slow). 'Forage in' versus 'silage out' losses range from as low as 5% to more than 40%.

## HOW DO I MANAGE THE SILAGE FACE DURING THE FEEDOUT PHASE?

The silage face should be maintained as a smooth surface perpendicular to the floor and side walls (in bunker and trench silos). This will minimize the surface exposed to air. The rate of progression through the silage mass must be sufficient to prevent the exposed silage from heating and spoiling. An average removal rate of 6–12 inches from the face per day is a common recommendation.

## WHAT ARE THE BENEFITS OF HAVING A ROOF OVER THE SILO?

A roof placed over the silo protects the exposed face from rain and snow during the feedout phase. The result is a more consistent dry matter content of the silage from day to day and week to week. This allows an accurate feeding rate of the silage on a dry matter basis, particularly in total mixed rations.

## WHAT PROBLEMS ARE ASSOCIATED WITH SILAGE EFFLUENT?

Silage effluent has a very high biological oxygen demand and therefore is an environmental hazard, particularly if it is allowed to enter a watercourse. Most forages ensiled below 26–28% dry matter can produce effluent during the first few days post-filling. Effluent is very nutrient-rich and contains soluble sugars, nitrogen, and minerals.

242

WHAT IS THE REAL COST OF SILAGE?

A common method of calculating the real cost of silage is to divide the actual cost per ton of forage after the silo is filled by the percent of the silage that is actually removed and fed when the silo is empty. For example, if 1,000 tons of whole-plant corn are ensiled in a bunker silo at a cost of $25 per ton and 900 tons of corn silage are removed and fed, the real cost is $25 divided by 90% (0.9), which equals $27.78. If only 750 tons of corn silage are removed and fed, the real cost is $25 divided by 75% (0.75), which equals $33.33.

## Conclusions

In general, silages in North America have improved considerably in terms of 'visually appraised' quality in the past 8-10 years. Many dairy cattle ranch owners and managers have initiated significant changes to improve their silage programs. These changes include shorter chop lengths, correct sizing of the silo's width and height, faster removal rates, improved corn and/or sorghum hybrids, more effective sealing and the use of an inoculant. However, problematic silages still occur far too often and typically are caused by the following:

1. **Delayed filling**. A few bunkers of corn silage take 2-4 weeks to fill.
2. **Forages ensiled too wet or too dry.** This is often related to the corn or sorghum hybrids grown and unfavorable field-wilting conditions for alfalfa, ryegrass and other hay crop silages.
3. **Chop lengths that are too long.** This is particularly evident in alfalfa, wheat, barley, oat and ryegrass silages in bunker, trench, or pile silos.
4. **Inadequate sealing of the ensiled forage.** In most instances, the polyethylene sheets are not properly weighted.
5. **Slow removal of silage during the feedout phase.** This is usually the result of the exposed face being too large.
6. **Failure to apply an effective bacterial inoculant.** Inoculants are responsible for more uniform and consistent silages throughout the silo for many dairy and beef operations. This observation is probably the most important reason to use an inoculant.

## References

Bolsen, K.K. 1995. Silage: basic principles. In: Forages, Vol. II, The Science of Grassland Agriculture. (R.F. Barnes, D.A. Miller and C.J. Nelson, eds.). (5th ed.). Iowa State University Press, Ames, Iowa. pp. 163–176.
Bolsen, K.K., R.N. Sonon, Jr., B. Dalke, R. Pope, J.G. Riley and A. Laytimi. 1992. Evaluation of inoculant and NPN silage additives: a summary of 26 trials and 65 farm-scale silages. Kansas Agric. Exp. Sta. Rpt. of Prog. 651:101–102.

Bolsen, K.K., J.T. Dickerson, B.E. Brent, R.N. Sonon, Jr., B.S. Dalke, C.J. Lin and J.E. Boyer, Jr. 1993. Rate and extent of top spoilage in horizontal silos. J. Dairy Sci. 76:2940–2962.

Bolsen, K.K., G. Ashbell and J.M. Wilkinson. 1995. Silage additives. In: Biotechnology in Animal Feeds and Animal Feeding. A. Chesson and R.J. Wallace (eds.). VCH Press, Weinhein, Germany. pp. 33–54.

Dickerson, J.T., Y. Niwa, K.K. Bolsen, B.E. Brent, C. Lin and J.E. Bradford. 1991. Rate and extent of top spoilage losses of alfalfa silage stored in horizontal silos. Kansas Agric. Exp. Sta. Rpt. of Prog. 623:74–77.

Holthaus, D.L., M.A. Young, B.E. Brent and K.K. Bolsen. 1995. Losses from top spoilage in horizontal silos. Kansas Agric. Exp. Sta. Rpt. of Prog. 727:59–62.

McDonald, P., A.R. Henderson and S.J.E. Heron. 1991. The Biochemistry of Silage (2nd ed.). Chalcombe Publ., Church Lane, Kingston, Canterbury, Kent, UK.

Pitt, R.E. 1990. Silage and hay preservation. Cornell University Cooperative Ext. Bulletin No. NRAES-5, Ithaca, NY.

# Analytical and nutritional assessment of alfalfa silage fermentation

G. PICHARD[1], F. BAS[1], M. THEODOROU[2], A. HARGREAVES[1], J. SCARPA[1], A. BIANCO[3] and M.A. BRUNI[3]

[1]Departamento de Zootecnia, Facultad de Agronomía, Pontificia Universidad Católica de Chile
[2]Institute of Grassland and Environmental Research, Aberystwyth, Wales, UK
[3]Facultad de Agronomía, Universidad de la República Oriental del Uruguay

## Introduction

In temperate regions of the world forage legumes growing in spring and summer are frequently stored as silage for delayed use during periods of feed shortage. However, in contrast with most grass species, they often undergo fermentation pathways that are detrimental from a nutritional perspective.

In the ensilage process there is an early and short aerobic phase followed by a major anaerobic phase during storage time, and finally a new exposure to air when feeding the ensiled forage. A wide range of epiphytic organisms are brought into silage fermentation at harvest time with enterobacteria, lactobacilli and clostridia the main groups involved in the anaerobic phase. Yeasts and molds are also present in quantities that are related to the amount of oxygen available (Woolford, 1984).

Under ideal conditions plant sugars should ferment to lactic acid in the shortest possible time and achieve a pH low enough to preserve forage from further fermentation. When an early acidic condition is established, plant nutrients are largely preserved and animals show good responses to inclusion of silage in the diet.

However, there are a number of interactions among plant composition, microbial populations and environmental factors that make it very difficult in practice to achieve such ideal conditions. Probably the most significant factors involved are the availability of plant sugars, the plant buffering capacity, the amount of oxygen permitted in the system and the initial numbers of different epiphytic organisms. These factors vary with plant species, plant morphology, agronomic traits, weather and ensiling management, resulting in significant variation in silage quality.

In this respect, there has been a special interest in legume silage research, not only because such silages can provide high levels of protein of plant origin, but also because they are the most difficult to ensile. This difficulty is due to low sugar content, high buffering capacity, high protein and high moisture contents.

The practical result of undesirable fermentation patterns is a reduced performance in animals fed such silage (McDonald *et al.*, 1991). One would assume that proper laboratory analyses would identify any nutrient deficiency or imbalance so that appropriate supplementary feeds could be provided. However, routine crude analyses have been shown to poorly reflect animal performance (Jones *et al.*, 1996). In particular, the ammonia level in silage has been extensively used to describe fermentation quality and nutritional value of silages (Wilkinson, 1990). However, other than in very poorly preserved silages this index is unsatisfactory for explaining animal performance/silage quality relationships. There are other low molecular weight nitrogenous compounds which are also precursors of an early rumen ammonia peak (Pichard and Rybertt, 1993) but they are ignored when relying solely on ammonia levels as an index of plant protein breakdown during ensiling.

Silage acidity is also frequently regarded as an important quality index; however, modern silage making has evolved to rather restricted fermentation systems by means of wilting and use of certain additives that promote a faster endpoint. Etheridge *et al.* (1993) and Choung and Chamberlain (1993) have reviewed the problems of silage acids with regard to voluntary intake.

Silage *in vitro* digestibility is another important analysis performed on silage samples. It is used either as such or as a basis for further estimation of metabolizable energy (ME), but those values can be very misleading when the weight and energy contribution of volatile compounds are ignored. In fact, well-fermented silages show a significant reduction in plant cell wall digestibility with respect to the original forage (Jaurena, 1996), but direct calorimetry on original and ensiled forages show minor or even positive changes in energy concentrations after ensiling (McDonald *et al.*, 1991). In this respect, estimations of ME on the basis of plant cell wall disappearance (Goering and Van Soest, 1970) fail to recognize the higher energy value of silages derived from alcohols and some acids.

In silage feeding, kinetics of rumen fermentation may be critical due to the asynchrony between massive release of low molecular weight nitrogenous compounds and the supply of readily available energy sources for rapid microbial mass growth (Pichard and Rybertt, 1993). When planning silage feeding strategies, digestion values obtained after 48 hrs incubation in rumen fluid coupled with knowledge of crude protein levels provide only limited nutritional meaning. The amount of rumen fermentable energy in silages is low in comparison to fresh forages, thus reducing the potential value of metabolizable protein estimates (AFRC, 1992). In turn, the supply of nitrogen from feed to the rumen is often well beyond the animal's ability to utilize it prior to salivary urea recycling. Also, the severe protein breakdown in poorly preserved silages further reduces the supply of metabolizable protein to the host animal and may also be limiting for rapid microbial growth.

It is well known that ultimately the best assessment of silage quality is obtained by animal performance experiments, but the need for rapid laboratory results is also recognised. The challenge is to provide meaningful analyses to nutritionists who assemble feeding strategies for diverse animal production situations.

## Objectives of the current work

In this work we collected a number of alfalfa silages being used by dairy farmers in order to subject them to a comprehensive analytical assessment and discussion of the nutritional implications. Additionally, alfalfa silages made from a known fresh forage were prepared in order to obtain four types of fermentation patterns and investigate the meaning of their differing analytical profiles.

MATERIALS AND METHODS

*Survey of farm silages*
Eleven silages were sampled from an equal number of farms. All silages had been made in the spring-summer period from essentially pure alfalfa stands (*Medicago sativa* L.). In each silo the external face was discarded and several representative subsamples were pooled to make one sample of approximately 10 kg. These samples were sealed in air tight bags and stored in boxes with dry ice until arrival in the laboratory where they were divided for fresh analyses, freeze-drying, oven drying and juice extraction. Analyses of fresh material were conducted immediately and the others stored at –20 °C.

*Experimental silages*
Alfalfa was ensiled in experimental silos of 1 m³ volume following four different strategies in order to obtain fermentation types the closest possible to homolactic, heterolactic, acetic and butyric patterns. The first was wilted and inoculated with *Lactobacillus plantarum*, well compacted and rapidly sealed. Heterolactic fermentation was obtained with similar but less strict techniques and inoculation with a mixture of lactobacilli, clostridia and coliforms. The acetic pattern was obtained with direct cut silage and coliform inoculum. The butyric type was obtained by slow filling and application of an inoculum cultured from soil spores obtained near animal facilities. All silages were stored for 90 days and then opened for sampling and analysis.

*Laboratory analyses*
In fresh forage pH and buffering capacity were determined as in Playne and McDonald (1966) and the titratable acidity determined as milliequivalents of sodium hydroxide (NaOH) per kg of dry matter required to raise silage pH to 7. Total nitrogen was determined by Kjeldhal (AOAC, 1984). Insoluble nitrogen was determined in the filter residue after a mineral-buffer extraction and the soluble nitrogen calculated as the difference from total nitrogen (Pichard, 1977). Ammonia nitrogen was determined by the

catalyzed indophenol reaction (Chaney and Marbach, 1962) in protein-free extracts as described by Pichard (1977). The unavailable nitrogen was measured as the residual nitrogen insoluble in acid detergent (ADIN) as per Goering and Van Soest (1970).

Extraction of protein for determining true protein and running electrophoresis utilized samples of 100 mg freeze-dried and finely ground silages or 10 ml of pressed juice mixed with 50 ml buffer (borax, 1 mM; sodium phosphate, 26 mM; citric acid, 10 mM, sodium taurocholate, 0.0091%; β-mercaptoethanol, pH 9.0). The samples were heated to 100 °C in a water bath and thoroughly mixed until complete cleared of solids. Subsamples of this extract were centrifuged at 1000 rpm for one minute and supernatants analysed for protein and subjected to electrophoresis.

Protein nitrogen was determined in the extract by the modified Lowry method developed by Tan *et al.* (1984) in order to avoid interference from phenolic compounds. The molecular weights of remaining proteins were determined in silage extracts prepared by the same procedure but substituting the sodium taurocholate by sodium dodecyl sulfate. Gel electrophoresis (PAGE-SDS 12.5%) was performed according to the method of Laemmli (1970) in a sodium chloride-enriched buffer as modified by Lobos and Mora (1991).

Amino acids were determined by high pressure liquid chromatography (HPLC) following acid hydrolysis and derivatization using a reverse phase column C18 3.9 x 300 mm at 46 °C in a dilution gradient for 67 minutes (Cohen, 1990). The amines putrescine, cadaverine, histamine and γ-aminobutyric acid were determined as their benzoic derivative benzilamides by HPLC as described by Krizek (1993).

Plant cell wall fractions were determined by the detergent system (Van Soest *et al.*, 1991). Reducing sugars were determined in filtrates of water extracts boiled with sulfuric acid by the Somogy reaction as described by McDonald and Henderson (1964). Starch was determined as free glucose (glucose oxidase Sigma Kit 315) in the residue washed with 85% ethanol and sequentially treated with α-amylase and amyloglucosidase based on the methods of McRae (1994) and Karkalas (1985).

Organic acids (citric, malic, succinic) were determined by HPLC (Schneider *et al.*, 1987) and volatile fatty acid (VFA) and lactic acid in silage extracts by gas chromatography in a Carbopack BDA column 4% Carbowax 20M (Supelco 1-1889) using a Fisons GC8000 instrument (Fussell, 1987).

*In vitro* rumen digestions were determined after 24 and 48 hrs incubation by the method of Goering and Van Soest (1970) in freeze-dried coarsely ground samples. The rumen inoculum donor was a mature cow fitted with a rumen cannula and fed a mixed alfalfa silage wheat straw diet (50:50).

# Results and discussion

## CHEMICAL CHARACTERIZATION OF FARM AND EXPERIMENTAL SILAGES

All farm silages had been wilted to approximately 30%, including two which were heavily wilted to 37 and 46 % dry matter (DM). The fermentation parameters differed widely among samples, revealing the diversity and complexity of the microbe-plant-silage management interactions (Table 1). The pH ranged from 4.2 to 5.9, being related to moisture content and quality of fermentation. Similarly, titratable acidity varied widely from 166 meq/100g in a badly conserved silage to 812 meq/100g in a well-preserved forage. The fatty acid profiles in farm silages yielded an average 8 and 3% lactic and acetic acids, respectively, with acetic acid less variable among samples than lactic acid. There were two very high butyric samples (I9 and J10) plus four other samples that contained more than 5% of total acids as butyric. Ethanol was found in all samples at an average concentration of 0.4%, and deviations had no biological significance.

The experimental silages were less wilted and their composition confirms that four different fermentation patterns were successfully obtained. All but the butyric sample had the same pH and similar titratable acidity. The lactic-type silage had the largest quantity of total acids and a wide lactic/acetic ratio. The heterolactic and acetic silages had very similar fermentation patterns, although the former had a greater quantity of total acids. The composition of the butyric silage represented a typically poor fermentation dominated by clostridia with high pH, low titratable acidity and lactic acid representing only 20% of total fatty acids.

## FATES OF NITROGENOUS COMPOUNDS

The total nitrogen content of silages ranged from 2.49 to 3.65% due mainly to different plant morphological stages at harvest time (Table 2). The buffer solubility of nitrogenous fractions showed significant variation among samples and values were not in agreement with the expected ranking based on the fermentation pattern of each sample. In samples that had the best fermentation, such as A1 and M13, we observed high percentages of soluble nitrogen. Conversely, both in farm and experimental samples, a relatively lower solubility was observed in low-lactic high-butyric silages. The fact that all farm silages had been wilted suggested that during fermentation there was a temperature-induced condensation and polymerisation of amino-aldehyde bases, thus reducing the solubility of nitrogenous compounds. Even though ADIN values were not very high (with the exception of sample J10), values were well above the normal ranges for fresh alfalfa. The average buffer solubility in the farm silage samples was close to 60% and ranged from 46 to 69%.

The soluble nitrogen fraction has frequently been considered to be mainly non-protein nitrogen (NPN). However, even though most NPN must be

Table 1.   Dry matter content and fermentation profile of farm and experimental alfalfa silages.

| Sample | Dry matter | pH | Titratable acidity | LA | AC | PR | BT | IB | Total | Ethanol |
|--------|-----------|-----|-------------------|-----|-----|-----|-----|-----|-------|---------|
|        | (%)       |     | meq/kg            |     |     | %ofDM |   |     |       |         |
| *Farm silages* | | | | | | | | | | |
| A1  | 33.36 | 4.64 | 377.15 | 5.04  | 3.30 | 0.23 | 0.03 | 0.07 | 8.66  | 0.58 |
| B2  | 27.15 | 4.85 | 496.13 | 5.18  | 2.82 | 0.00 | 0.79 | 0.00 | 8.78  | 0.42 |
| C3  | 24.58 | 4.65 | 487.86 | 7.61  | 3.42 | 0.00 | 0.47 | 0.00 | 11.49 | 0.48 |
| D4  | 36.62 | 4.53 | 466.39 | 4.71  | 2.20 | 0.00 | 0.09 | 0.18 | 7.18  | 0.23 |
| F6  | 22.38 | 4.89 | 506.36 | 10.65 | 4.36 | 0.32 | 0.11 | 0.13 | 15.56 | 0.54 |
| H8  | 31.61 | 5.10 | 624.80 | 5.88  | 2.65 | 0.35 | 0.37 | 0.34 | 9.58  | 0.09 |
| I9  | 30.06 | 5.86 | 166.14 | 6.43  | 2.87 | 0.56 | 4.90 | 0.26 | 15.01 | 0.54 |
| J10 | 27.54 | 5.39 | 424.50 | 11.62 | 2.88 | 0.53 | 3.56 | 0.25 | 18.83 | 0.60 |
| K11 | 31.41 | 5.08 | 707.67 | 10.88 | 5.01 | 0.03 | 0.04 | 0.08 | 16.03 | 0.32 |
| L12 | 46.08 | 4.79 | 310.79 | 5.80  | 1.65 | 0.00 | 0.03 | 0.03 | 7.50  | 0.18 |
| M13 | 31.47 | 4.20 | 812.86 | 13.79 | 2.39 | 0.10 | 0.00 | 0.04 | 16.31 | 0.45 |
| | | | | | | | | | | |
| *Average* | 31.11 | 4.91 | 489.15 | 7.96 | 3.05 | 0.19 | 0.94 | 0.12 | 12.27 | 0.40 |
| S.D.  | 6.39 | 0.45 | 180.19 | 3.18 | 0.96 | 0.22 | 1.67 | 0.12 | 4.17 | 0.17 |
| C.V.  | 0.21 | 0.09 | 0.37   | 0.40 | 0.31 | 1.13 | 1.78 | 0.93 | 0.34 | 0.43 |
| | | | | | | | | | | |
| *Experimental silages* | | | | | | | | | | |
| Homolactic   | 25.33 | 4.39 | 703.00 | 10.36 | 2.91 | 0.53 | 0.09 | 0.27 | 14.15 | 0.05 |
| Heterolactic | 25.16 | 4.32 | 703.22 | 7.17  | 3.57 | 0.07 | 0.24 | 0.11 | 11.15 | 0.12 |
| Acetic       | 24.92 | 4.32 | 767.75 | 5.67  | 2.93 | 0.11 | 0.06 | 0.18 | 8.94  | 0.04 |
| Butyric      | 27.07 | 5.33 | 274.11 | 2.42  | 3.63 | 0.74 | 3.92 | 0.61 | 11.31 | 0.02 |
| | | | | | | | | | | |
| Average | 25.62 | 4.59 | 612.02 | 6.40 | 3.26 | 0.36 | 1.07 | 0.29 | 11.39 | 0.06 |
| S.D.    | 0.98  | 0.50 | 227.33 | 3.30 | 0.39 | 0.32 | 1.90 | 0.22 | 2.13  | 0.04 |
| C.V.    | 0.04  | 0.11 | 0.37   | 0.52 | 0.12 | 0.90 | 1.77 | 0.76 | 0.19  | 0.75 |

[1]LA=lactic, AC=acetic, PR=propionic, BT=butyric, IB=isobutyric

in the soluble fraction, our results show that in good silages there is a significant amount of soluble nitrogen that corresponds to true protein and peptides, which is consistent with the findings of Rooke and Nsereko (1993) in grass silages. In Figure 1 the points above the line show the fraction of nitrogen not accounted for by the NPN. This corresponds to true protein contained in the soluble nitrogen fraction, in spite of the fact that the NPN fraction would be inflated by ADIN. In other terms, not all the true protein can be found in the insoluble nitrogen fraction.

Ammonia accounted for 7–37% of total nitrogen and was especially high in silages I9 and J10. Within experimental samples, the butyric-type silage also had 20% ammonia. Amines were found to be quite high in several samples, even in some that exhibited rather low ammonia levels. Samples B2, C3, F6, H8, I9 and J10 contained more than 4% total amines, with cadaverine, putrescine and γ-aminobutyric the most important (Table 3). In all experimental silages including the lactic acid one, which presumably underwent a very good fermentation, the amine levels (mainly cadaverine and putrescine) were quite high. The fact that silages with good volatile fatty

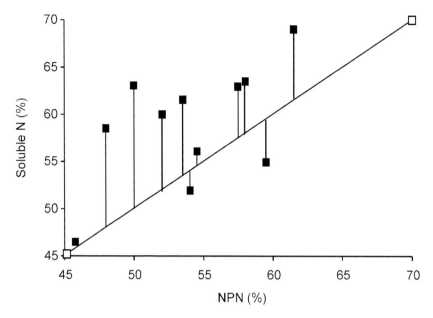

**Figure 1.** Relationship between soluble nitrogen and non-protein nitrogen fractions in farm silages.

acid profiles contained significant amounts of biogenic amines may be one of the factors involved in the poor animal responses frequently noted in legume silages (Gill *et al.*, 1987). These findings, however, would not be supported by Van Os *et al.* (1995) who found that biogenic amines from silages are degraded by rumen microbes with increasing efficiency as they adapt to diets with high amine content. This feature would prevent passage of amines to the intestine. Earlier work by Buchanan-Smith (1972) proved, however, that plasma infusion of amines caused a significant intake depression. Bends in the silage titration curves due to the presence of amines (Offer *et al.*, 1994) were clearly shown. Amines have been closely correlated with voluntary intake in the animal. The large amount of nitrogenous compounds found as amines represent reduction in the amino acid fraction, and this may be the main negative effect of amines, particularly if there is a selective utilization of certain labile amino acids for their formation.

Within the NPN fraction the amino acids represent the main compound not accounted for beyond ammonia, amines and ADIN. Interestingly, in high-lactic low-ammonia low-amine silages 25–45% of the total nitrogen was found in this amino acid-rich fraction. Even though this fraction might contain other compounds like amides or nitrogen oxides not reduced to free ammonia, the size of this fraction may have great significance in the utilization of proteins by ruminants fed silages.

The protein breakdown observed in a set of samples with very distinct fermentation patterns showed that a variable quantity of nitrogenous compounds remained insoluble through silage fermentation. If ADIN

**Table 2.** Composition of nitrogenous compounds in alfalfa silages (% of total N).

| Silage | | Buffer solubility | | Protein nature | | | NPN components | | |
|---|---|---|---|---|---|---|---|---|---|
| Sample | Total N (%) | Soluble | Insol-uble | Protein N | NPN | ADIN | NH$_3$ | Amines | AA[1] |
| *Farm silages* | | | | | | | | | |
| A1 | 3.22 | 68.99 | 31.0 | 38.78 | 61.22 | 10.3 | 9.22 | 1.04 | 40.66 |
| B2 | 2.78 | 62.53 | 37.47 | 50.35 | 49.66 | 11.8 | 15.18 | 4.68 | 18.00 |
| C3 | 3.65 | 62.70 | 37.31 | 42.26 | 57.74 | 7.51 | 11.25 | 7.05 | 31.93 |
| D4 | 3.64 | 55.26 | 44.74 | 40.81 | 59.20 | 9.34 | 6.63 | 0.15 | 43.08 |
| F6 | 2.78 | 46.17 | 53.83 | 54.17 | 45.83 | 9.75 | 11.71 | 4.04 | 20.33 |
| H8 | 2.55 | 59.90 | 40.10 | 47.99 | 52.02 | 11.42 | 13.68 | 5.05 | 21.87 |
| I9 | 2.49 | 55.31 | 44.70 | 45.75 | 54.25 | 11.07 | 36.94 | 7.07 | -0.83 |
| J10 | 2.76 | 52.37 | 47.63 | 46.25 | 53.76 | 18.74 | 20.40 | 8.04 | 6.58 |
| K11 | 2.51 | 61.24 | 38.77 | 46.54 | 53.47 | 12.87 | 15.21 | 2.06 | 23.33 |
| L12 | 2.64 | 58.41 | 41.59 | 51.83 | 48.17 | 11.66 | 8.93 | 0.03 | 27.56 |
| M13 | 3.43 | 63.48 | 36.53 | 41.90 | 58.10 | 5.62 | 7.72 | 0.28 | 44.48 |
| Average | 2.95 | 58.76 | 41.24 | 46.05 | 53.95 | 10.92 | 14.26 | 3.59 | 25.18 |
| S.D. | 0.45 | 6.23 | 6.23 | 4.84 | 4.84 | 3.32 | 8.51 | 3.03 | 14.48 |
| C.V. | 0.15 | 0.11 | 0.15 | 0.10 | 0.09 | 0.30 | 0.60 | 0.84 | 0.57 |
| *Experimental silages* | | | | | | | | | |
| Homolactic | 3.58 | 68.14 | 31.86 | 35.47 | 64.53 | 8.42 | 10.16 | 2.99 | 42.96 |
| Heterolactic | 3.83 | 73.91 | 26.09 | 32.05 | 67.95 | 9.19 | 12.20 | 4.48 | 42.08 |
| Acetic | 3.52 | 64.50 | 35.50 | 33.71 | 66.29 | 7.52 | 10.70 | 4.41 | 43.66 |
| Butyric | 3.13 | 59.99 | 40.01 | 42.45 | 57.55 | 11.35 | 22.37 | 7.33 | 16.50 |
| Average | 3.52 | 66.63 | 33.37 | 35.92 | 64.08 | 9.12 | 13.86 | 4.80 | 36.30 |
| S.D. | 0.29 | 5.89 | 5.89 | 4.57 | 4.57 | 1.63 | 5.74 | 1.82 | 13.21 |
| C.V. | 0.08 | 0.09 | 0.18 | 0.13 | 0.07 | 0.18 | 0.41 | 0.38 | 0.36 |
| Fresh alfalfa | 3.35 | 14.16 | 85.84 | 68.49 | 31.51 | 4.81 | 0 | 1.1 | 25.6 |

[1]Amino acid-rich fraction estimated as total NPN minus ADIN, ammonia-N and amine-N.

is subtracted from this insoluble fraction, the rest would presumably correspond to high molecular weight true proteins. This fraction ranged from 21 to 44%, being little affected by the quality of the fermentation and quite independent of the amounts of ammonia and amines often used as indicators of the extent of protein breakdown. This fraction of insoluble proteins preserved in spite of poor silage fermentation may be less degradable, probably due to structural protection within plant tissues or to a combined effect of heating during fermentation. The possibility of acid inhibition of proteases should be ruled out because most of the silages had fairly high pH values, particularly those with poor fermentation.

The electrophoretic analyses of extractable proteins showed a massive breakdown of high molecular weight proteins in most silage samples. The large subunit of Rubisco (54 kDa), which is clearly seen in fresh alfalfa, essentially disappeared and very weak and diffuse bands were observed in all samples. Only in silage M13 did a new and thick band appear at 30 kDa with several smaller bands in other positions (Figure 2). This is consistent with the good fermentation pattern of this sample derived from a crop

**Table 3.    Amines in alfalfa silages (% of total N).**

| Silage | Putrescine | Histamine | γ-aminobutyric | Cadaverine | TOTAL |
|---|---|---|---|---|---|
| *Farm silages* | | | | | |
| A1 | 0.38 | 0.05 | 0.32 | 0.29 | 1.04 |
| B2 | 1.52 | 0.21 | 1.40 | 1.55 | 4.68 |
| C3 | 1.84 | 0.20 | 1.88 | 3.13 | 7.05 |
| D4 | 0.04 | 0.00 | 0.06 | 0.05 | 0.15 |
| F6 | 1.19 | 0.12 | 1.44 | 1.29 | 4.04 |
| H8 | 1.55 | 0.19 | 1.54 | 1.77 | 5.05 |
| I9 | 2.39 | 0.35 | 1.99 | 2.34 | 7.07 |
| J10 | 2.79 | 0.25 | 2.11 | 2.89 | 8.04 |
| K11 | 0.72 | 0.07 | 0.67 | 0.60 | 2.06 |
| L12 | 0.01 | 0.00 | 0.01 | 0.01 | 0.03 |
| M13 | 0.24 | 0.03 | 0.01 | 0.00 | 0.28 |
| | | | | | |
| Average | 1.15 | 0.13 | 1.04 | 1.27 | 3.59 |
| S.D. | 0.96 | 0.11 | 0.84 | 1.17 | 3.03 |
| C.V. | 0.83 | 0.86 | 0.81 | 0.92 | 0.84 |
| | | | | | |
| *Experimental silages* | | | | | |
| Homolactic | 1.25 | 0.19 | 0.99 | 1.16 | 3.59 |
| Heterolactic | 1.58 | 0.28 | 2.05 | 1.49 | 5.40 |
| Acetic | 1.99 | 0.32 | 0.66 | 2.15 | 5.12 |
| Butyric | 2.19 | 0.38 | 1.83 | 2.10 | 6.50 |
| | | | | | |
| Average | 1.75 | 0.29 | 1.38 | 1.73 | 5.15 |
| S.D. | 0.42 | 0.08 | 0.66 | 0.48 | 1.20 |
| C.V. | 0.24 | 0.27 | 0.48 | 0.28 | 0.23 |

ensiled very quickly under excellent field conditions using a lactic acid bacterial inoculant. In the other samples most of the protein was washed out of the gel, i.e., under 10 kDa.

The amino acid profile of farm silages showed a wide variation among samples. Some consistency was found regarding a few amino acids when grouping and comparing the best fermented four silages and the poorest four silages. It was observed that arginine, alanine and phenylalanine had significantly higher values in poorly preserved silages, but for serine and threonine the reverse was observed (Table 4). For the other amino acids, no relationship could be found with any of the composition and fermentation parameters studied. In samples of farm silages there was no information about the original composition of the forages ensiled, but if we compare the composition of good silages with reported values for legume forage species (Table 5), it can be observed that arginine, lysine, histidine and aspartic acid are in low levels; in the poorly fermented ones, the same amino acids remain low with the addition of serine. When comparing the amino acid profiles of silages and rumen microbes it was found that aspartic and glutamic acids, arginine, tyrosine, methionine and lysine were very low.

Many of the amino acids show increased values with respect to original

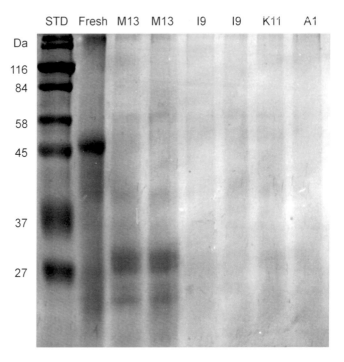

**Figure 2.** Protein electrophoresis of silage extracts with contrasting fermentation patterns.

**Table 4.** Major changes observed in amino acid profile in alfalfa silages with contrasting fermentation patterns[1].

| Amino acids | Type of fermentation | | Ratio |
|---|---|---|---|
| | Good | Poor | Good/poor |
| Arginine | 1.10 (0.22) | 2.38 (0.19) | 0.46 |
| Alanine | 11.74 (1.43) | 17.58 (4.23) | 0.67 |
| Phenylalanine | 5.21 (1.84) | 8.75 (1.54) | 0.60 |
| Serine | 6.06 (0.97) | 2.75 (1.86) | 2.20 |
| Threonine | 6.94 (0.93) | 4.10 (1.15) | 1.69 |

[1]Values between brackets are standard deviations of the mean.

forages, but it must be kept in mind that when reporting molar proportions the reduction of any one causes a proportional increase in all the others. In fact, during fermentation some amino acids have been degraded and the values in Table 5 indicate that there was a selective utilization of some. Also it shows that the profile in silage amino acids deviates significantly from the typical composition of rumen microbes that are supposed to provide a high quality protein to the host animal.

In terms of protein quality for high-producing ruminants and the existing concept about the importance of protein solubility, these findings allow

**Table 5.** Amino acid profile in good and poor silages compared with fresh legumes and rumen microbes[1].

| Amino acid | Fresh legume | Rumen microbes | Good silages | Poor silages | Ratios | | | |
|---|---|---|---|---|---|---|---|---|
| | A | B | C | D | C/A | D/A | C/B | D/B |
| | | | | (%) | | | | |
| Aspartate | 11.7 | 12.3 | 7.5 | 5.1 | 0.6 | 0.4 | 0.6 | 0.4 |
| Glutamine | 9.9 | 13.4 | 9 | 7.6 | 0.9 | 0.8 | 0.7 | 0.6 |
| Serine | 4.8 | 4.4 | 6.3 | 2.9 | 1.3 | 0.6 | 1.4 | 0.7 |
| Glycine | 7.3 | 5.4 | 9.9 | 10.2 | 1.4 | 1.4 | 1.8 | 1.9 |
| Histadine | 4.4 | 2.1 | 2.7 | 4 | 0.6 | 0.9 | 1.3 | 1.9 |
| Arginine | 8.8 | 5.1 | 1.1 | 2.5 | 0.1 | 0.3 | 0.2 | 0.5 |
| Threonine | 4.7 | 5.7 | 7.2 | 4.4 | 1.5 | 0.9 | 1.3 | 0.8 |
| Alanine | 8.3 | 6.9 | 12.1 | 18.7 | 1.5 | 2.3 | 1.8 | 2.7 |
| Proline | 4.5 | 3.7 | 8.7 | 8.7 | 1.9 | 1.9 | 2.3 | 2.4 |
| Tyrosine | 2 | 4.7 | 2.2 | 2.3 | 1.1 | 1.2 | 0.5 | 0.5 |
| Valine | 6.2 | 5.9 | 7.1 | 6.5 | 1.1 | 1 | 1.2 | 1.1 |
| Methionine | 1.4 | 2.5 | 1.4 | 1.3 | 1 | 0.9 | 0.6 | 0.5 |
| Isoleucine | 4.8 | 6 | 6.6 | 6.5 | 1.4 | 1.4 | 1.1 | 1.1 |
| Leucine | 8.8 | 8 | 9 | 8 | 1 | 0.9 | 1.1 | 1 |
| Phenylalanine | 4.9 | 5.1 | 5.4 | 9.3 | 1.1 | 1.9 | 1 | 1.8 |
| Lysine | 7.5 | 8.8 | 3.7 | 1.9 | 0.5 | 0.3 | 0.4 | 0.2 |
| | 100 | 100 | 100 | 100 | | | | |

[1]Good silages are L12, M13, A1 and D4. Poor silages are I9, J10, C3 and B2.

an opposing hypothesis for silages in regard to the role of soluble and insoluble proteins and the 'rumen bypass' phenomenon. First, the insoluble nitrogen components, either true protein or NPN, will be found mostly in the particulate fractions of the digesta. These will slowly release nitrogen to the rumen by means of progressive mechanical breakdown (mastication/rumination) and enzymatic activity of bacterial proteases. Consequently, this insoluble nitrogen fraction would have a low rumen by-pass potential because of the relatively slow particle breakdown rate, and conversely a good chance of being taken up by ruminal bacteria following enzymatic hydrolysis.

Our results, in agreement with the findings of Harrison and Blauwiekel (1994), suggest that in well-preserved silages amino acids and peptides are the most important components of the larger soluble nitrogen fraction. Considering that this fraction can either be used by rumen bacteria or pass through the rumen with the liquid phase, in animals fed silage with a high proportion of soluble N there is the probability this component will pass through the rumen without being taken up by bacteria. Such 'escape' might be enhanced because of the depletion in readily available energy that prevents bacteria from using large amounts of peptides and amino acids, although some of it could be inefficiently used as an energy source. In a theoretical calculation for a cow with a high level of silage intake one can assume a dilution rate of the liquid phase out of the rumen of 12 %/hr, a rate of carbohydrate digestion of 8 %/hr and a high microbial yield of 4 gN/100g fermented carbohydrate. Under such conditions a large proportion of soluble nitrogen compounds can escape microbial uptake. Ammonia can be absorbed across the rumen wall, but amino acids and peptides would be utilized to a lesser degree in the rumen epithelium and may be washed out with the liquid phase thus by-passing the rumen and providing a source of nutrients ready for absorption in omasum (Matthews and Webb, 1995) and duodenum. The hypothesis of intact peptides flowing post-ruminally has also been suggested by Wallace and Cotta (1988) on the basis of a high peptide accumulation found in rumen. The poor utilization of silage proteins for bacterial synthesis in the rumen reported by Tamminga *et al.* (1991) and his suggestion about the convenience of wilting grass to over 50% dry matter before ensiling in order to improve protein utilization, may be related to the hypothesis presented here. This is that soluble proteins in well-preserved silages, presumably rich in peptides and amino acids, have a good chance of escaping bacterial uptake in the rumen and would result in less efficient microbial protein synthesis. A severe wilting would lead to heated silages, reduced solubility of nitrogen compounds and increased ruminal retention time, thus improving the synchrony with the energy made available from slow fermentation of structural carbohydrates. This would in turn improve the efficiency of protein synthesis. The strategy suggested by these authors is in agreement with the objective of maximizing ruminal protein synthesis, but it fails to recognise that soluble peptides and amino acids may be more efficiently utilized by the host animal if by-passed and not recycled through rumen microbes. Such behaviour of soluble nitrogen compounds in well-preserved silages, namely peptides and amino acids, is of great nutritional interest although the problem of amino acid balance at that level remains an open question.

ANALYSIS OF ENERGY YIELDING COMPOUNDS FOUND IN FERMENTED SILAGES

Silages are known to consume plant sugars during anaerobic fermentation in quantities dependent on the extent of the fermentation. When fresh, most legume species have low sugar content and consequently the residual quantity after ensiling is very low (or is essentially nil). The majority of alfalfa silages surveyed (11/15) had less than 1.0 % residual sugars regardless of the quality of the fermentation. The remaining samples (4/15) had between 1.0 and 3.8% sugars. In turn, the residual quantity of starch ranged from 1.6 to 3.6% which is much lower than normal values reported in samples of fresh alfalfa by Van Soest (1994) and Jaurena (1996). Although some authors have suggested that to a large extent starch is not a fermentable substrate in the silage (Woolford, 1984), these low values confirm the findings of Valinotti and Pichard (1993) who reported that most of alfalfa starch disappeared during ensiling. Endogenous plant amylases may be responsible for this (Goodwin and Mercer, 1990), which might be envisaged as a positive fate as it helps provide fermentable energy in legume silages as long as it yields sugars at early fermentation times.

The total amount of nonstructural carbohydrate was on average 3.2%, ranging from 1.8 to 5.8% (Table 6). These are low values with respect to

**Table 6.** Residual carbohydrates and organic acids in silages available for rumen fermentation (% of dry matter).[1]

| | Free sugars | Starch | Organic acids | Rumen fermentable Cellulose + Hemicellulose | | Total rumen fermentable |
|---|---|---|---|---|---|---|
| | | | | 24 hrs | 48 hrs | 48 hrs |
| *Farm silages* (% DM) | | | | | | |
| A1 | 1.14 | 1.77 | 1.12 | 13.32 | 13.46 | 17.49 |
| | *6.52* | *10.12* | *6.40* | *76.16* | *76.96* | *100.00* |
| B2 | 0.27 | 2.22 | 2.5 | 12.85 | 16.83 | 21.82 |
| | *1.24* | *10.17* | *11.46* | *58.89* | *77.13* | *100.00* |
| C3 | 0.63 | 2.22 | 2.21 | 12.27 | 14.56 | 19.62 |
| | *3.21* | *11.31* | *11.26* | *62.54* | *74.21* | *100.00* |
| D4 | 2.69 | 2.32 | 3.75 | 14.72 | 16.53 | 25.29 |
| | *10.64* | *9.17* | *14.83* | *58.20* | *65.36* | *100.00* |
| F6 | 0.40 | 2.24 | 2.2 | 17.79 | 20.91 | 25.75 |
| | *1.55* | *8.70* | *8.54* | *69.09* | *81.20* | *100.00* |
| H8 | 0.45 | 1.80 | 1.72 | 14.53 | 17.16 | 21.13 |
| | *2.13* | *8.52* | *8.14* | *68.76* | *81.21* | *100.00* |
| I9 | 0.69 | 1.95 | 0.62 | 14.42 | 16.31 | 19.57 |
| | *3.53* | *9.96* | *3.17* | *73.68* | *83.34* | *100.00* |
| J10 | 0.38 | 1.50 | 1.44 | 8.83 | 13.25 | 16.57 |
| | *2.29* | *9.05* | *8.69* | *53.29* | *79.96* | *100.00* |
| K11 | 0.69 | 2.01 | 1.9 | 15.87 | 18.01 | 22.61 |
| | *3.05* | *8.89* | *8.40* | *70.19* | *79.66* | *100.00* |
| L12 | 3.78 | 2.04 | 2.75 | 16.53 | 18.09 | 26.66 |
| | *14.18* | *7.65* | *10.32* | *62.00* | *67.85* | *100.00* |
| M13 | 1.14 | 2.68 | 2.21 | 13.35 | 13.36 | 19.39 |
| | *5.88* | *13.82* | *11.40* | *68.85* | *68.90* | *100.00* |
| *Experimental silages* | | | | | | |
| Homolactic | 0.28 | 3.28 | 1.36 | 16.56 | 19.78 | 24.70 |
| | *1.13* | *13.28* | *5.51* | *67.04* | *80.08* | *100.00* |
| Heterolactic | 0.55 | 3.30 | 3.06 | 14.05 | 15.07 | 21.98 |
| | *2.50* | *15.01* | *13.92* | *63.92* | *68.56* | *100.00* |
| Acetic | 0.30 | 3.63 | 1.36 | 16.76 | 21.63 | 26.92 |
| | *1.11* | *13.48* | *5.05* | *62.26* | *80.35* | *100.00* |
| Butyric | 0.21 | 1.59 | 0.66 | 15.23 | 20.16 | 22.62 |
| | *0.93* | *7.03* | *2.92* | *67.33* | *89.12* | *100.00* |
| *Fresh forage* | | | | | | |
| Alfalfa | 1.12 | 4.2 | 9.7 | 21.2 | 22.14 | 37.16 |
| | *3.01* | *11.30* | *26.10* | *57.05* | *59.58* | *100.00* |

[1]Italic numbers represent % of total.

the high ruminal energy demand for efficient utilization of the large early supply of nitrogen. Other ingredients in the silage that help to support this energy demand are the residual organic acids, mainly succinic, but acids account for only an additional 1.9% of the fermentable dry matter. The amount of readily fermentable components including starch was on average only 5% of the plant weight. This accounts for less than 25% of the total fermentable carbohydrate. In contrast, over 60% of the silage nitrogen is in low molecular weight compounds that will be released in the rumen shortly after consumption.

Most of the fermentable carbohydrates correspond to plant cell wall components which have a reduced availability in the rumen owing to the silage fermentation. In the silo hemicellulose is exposed to acid solubilization of the most labile fractions thus becoming more refractory to rumen bacteria compared to the original forage (Huhtanen and Jaakkola, 1993). This was confirmed in the experimental silages. Plant cell wall digestibility decreased from 52% in the fresh forage to 48 and 42% in silages with lactic and butyric-type fermentations, respectively. Even though in all alfalfa silages a large proportion of the cell wall fermentation was accomplished by 24 hrs (Table 6), the small quantity of readily fermentable carbohydrate suggests that in early stages of fermentation this source of ATP is limiting and bacteria must take a less efficient route by burning proteins in order to obtain the required energy. The energy pattern observed in these farm and experimental silage samples is well recognised in the RFE system used in the UK for calculation of potential metabolizable energy (AFRC, 1992).

Based on the composition of fresh alfalfa samples reported by Smith (1973), Dijkshoorn (1973), Pichard and Innocenti (1987) and Van Soest (1994), the authors have calculated that the sum of sugars, starch, organic acids and digestible plant cell wall components adds up to 35–40 % of the plant weight with 55% of it derived from structural carbohydrates. In the silage samples studied, the sum of the same fractions added up to only 22% with 77% of it being structural components (Table 7). This represents a contrasting situation regarding the quantity and quality of energy sources available for rumen fermentation. The fraction that disappeared is partially converted to fatty acids which do not provide energy for microbial growth in the rumen. The results confirm that the pattern of energy supply to the rumen bacteria is much altered as a consequence of silage fermentation.

## Conclusions

The examination of very diverse alfalfa silages provided new insights regarding the interpretation of analytical results and their nutritional meaning. A comprehensive assessment of nitrogenous compounds and energy sources as well as their expected behaviour in the ruminant animal allowed distinctions to be made among silages which are not recognized by means of the most traditional analyses. These findings suggest the convenience of adopting some critical analytical strategies for ensiled forages.

Within the complex protein systems in plant, silage and animal, the

**Table 7.** Summary of rumen fermentable carbohydrates and organic acids in alfalfa silages (% of dry matter)[1].

| | Alfalfa silages | | | Fresh alfalfa |
|---|---|---|---|---|
| | Average | Lowest[2] | Highest[3] | |
| Sugars | 0.9 (4.1) | 0.21 | 3.78 | 1.12 |
| Organic acids | 1.9 (8.6) | 0.62 | 3.75 | 9.7 |
| Starch | 2.3 (10.4) | 1.50 | 3.63 | 4.2 |
| Cellulose + hemicellulose | 17.0 (76.9) | 13.36 | 21.63 | 22.14 |
| Total | 22.1 (100) | 16.57 | 26.92 | 37.16 |

[1]Values between brackets show the contribution (%) of fractions to total fermentable matter.
[2]Lowest absolute value found among 15 silage samples.
[3]Highest absolute value found among 15 silage samples.

results suggest that a restricted protein breakdown, as occurs in well-fermented silages, yields high quantities of peptides and amino acids. These compounds have a good chance of by-passing the microbial hydrolysis or uptake in the rumen by flowing with the liquid phase post-ruminally thus being directly absorbed in the omasum and small intestine. The capacity of rumen bacteria for rapid interception of these soluble compounds would be directly related to the amount of energy that is readily available soon after silage ingestion. Oppositely, the products of amino acid deamination and decarboxylation become more significant in poorly preserved silages with increased levels of ammonia, amines and butyric acid which have detrimental effects on animal performance.

Regarding the sources of energy that would be readily available for rumen microbes, it was found that in all alfalfa silages there was a vast utilization of sugars, starch, organic acids and pentoses derived from the acid hydrolysis of the most labile hemicellulose components. The better-fermented silages had higher residual amounts of these types of energy sources than poorly fermented silages. As a consequence, the consumption of low quality silages leads to an important imbalance in the rumen due to the excess of ammonia precursors and the depletion of rumen readily fermentable energy, which is further affected by the asynchrony in times at which they are made available.

# Acknowledgement

The authors wish to thank Mr. Bruno Tesser and Mr. Eduardo Leiva for their valuable assistance in the forage research programme. This work was supported by Conicyt under Grant No. 1960643.

# References

Agricultural and Food Research Council. 1992. Nutritive Requirements of Ruminant Animals: Protein. Report N° 9, Nutr. Abstr. and Rev., Series B. Vol. 62(12). CAB International, Wallingford, Oxon, England.

A.O.A.C. 1984. Association of Official Analytical Chemists. Official Methods of Analysis. 14th Ed., Washington D.C., USA.

Buchanan-Smith, J.G. 1972. Forage protein in ruminant animal production, BSAP Occasional Publication 6:611-617.

Chaney, A.L. and E.P. Marbach, 1962. Modified reagents for the determination of urea and ammonia. Clin. Chem. 8:130–132.

Choung, J.J. and D.G. Chamberlain. 1993. Effects of addition of lactic acid and post-ruminal supplementation with casein on the nutritional value of grass silage for milk production in dairy cows. Grass & Forage Sci. 48:380-386.

Cohen, S.A. 1990. Analysis of amino acids by liquid-chromatography after pre-column derivatization with 4-Nitrophenylisothiocyanate. J. of Chromatography 512:283–290.

Dijkshoorn, W. 1973. Organic acids and their role in ion uptake. *In:* Chemistry and Biochemistry of Herbage Vol. 2:163–188 (G.W. Butler and R.W. Bailey, eds.) Academic Press, London and New York.

Etheridge, M.O., C.R. Stockdale and P.D. Cranwell. 1993. Influence of method of conservation of lucerne on factors associated with voluntary intake in sheep. Australian J. Exp. Agric. 33:417–423.

Fussell, R.J. 1987. Determination of volatile fatty acids (C2-C5) and lactic acid in silage by gas chromatography. Analyst 112:1213–1216.

Gill, M., L.R.S. Thiago and J.G. Buchanan-Smith. 1987. Intake problems associated with ensiled forages. *In:* Feed Intake by Beef Cattle (F.N. Owens, ed.) Oklahoma State University Misc. Publ. 121:341–352.

Goering, K.H. and P.J Van Soest. 1970. Forage fiber analysis. USDA-ARS, Agric. Handbook 379.

Goodwin, T.W. and E.I. Mercer. 1990. Introduction to Plant Biochemistry. 2nd Ed., Pergamon Press, Oxford, New York.

Harrison, J.H. and R. Blauwiekel. 1994. Fermentation and utilization of grass silage. J. Dairy Sci. 77:3209–3235.

Huhtanen, P. and S. Jaakkola. 1993. The effects of forage preservation method and proportion of concentrate on digestion of cell wall carbohydrates and rumen digesta pool size in cattle. Grass and Forage Sci. 48:155–165.

Jaurena, G. 1996. Análisis de la contribución de los granos como aditivos para ensilajes de alfalfa. Tesis grado de Magister, P. Universidad católica de Chile.

Jones, R., A. Winters and J. Cockburn. 1996. Change in amino acid content of inoculated grass silage and its effect on animal production. *In:* Biotechnology in the Feed Industry. Proc. 12th Annual Symposium (T.P. Lyons and K.A. Jacques, eds). Nottingham University Press, Nottingham, Leics. UK. pp. 249–259.

Karkalas, J. 1985. An improved enzymatic method for the determination of native and modified starch. J. Sci. Food and Agric. 36:1019–1027.

Krizek, M. 1993. Biogenic amines in silage. 2. The occurrence of biogenic amines in silages. Arch Tierernahr. 43(2): 169–177.

Laemmli, U.K. 1970. Cleavage of structural proteins during the assembly of the head of bacteriophage T4. Nature, Aug. 15, 227(259):680–685.

Lobos, S. and S.G. Mora. 1991. Alteration in the electrophoretic mobility of OmpC due to variation in the ammonium sulphate concentration in sodium dodecyl sulphate policrylamide gel electrophoresis. Electrophoresis 12:448–450.

Matthews, J.C. and K.E. Webb, Jr. 1995. Absorption of L-carnosine, L-methionine and L-methionylglycine by isolated sheep ruminal and omasal epithelial tissue. J. Anim. Sci. 73:3464–3475.

McDonald, P., A.R. Henderson and S.J.E. Heron. 1991. The biochemistry of silages, 2nd Ed., Chalcombre Publications, U.K.

McDonald, P. and A.R. Henderson. 1964. Determination of water-soluble carbohydrates in gass. J. Sci. Food Agric. 15:395–398.

McRae, G. 1983. Starch analysis. In: Methods for the analysis of feeds eaten by ruminants. Division of Animal Production, Ian Clunies Rooss Animal Res. Lab., CSIRO, Melbourne, Australia.

Offer, N.W., R.J. Dewhurst and C. Thomas. 1994. The use of electrometric titration to improve the routine prediction of silage intake by lambs and dairy cows. Proc. 50th Winter Meeting, British Society of Animal Production, Scarborough, Paper 1.

Playne, M.J. and P. McDonald. 1966. The buffering constituents of herbage and of silage. J. Sci. Food Agric. 17:264–268.

Pichard, G. 1977. Forage nutritive value. Continuous and batch rumen in vitro fermentation and nitrogen solubility. PhD Thesis, Cornell University, Ithaca, New York.

Pichard, G. and E. Innocenti. 1987. Tabla de composición de forrajes de la zona central de Chile. Ciencia e Inv. Agr. 14(2):143–158.

Pichard, G. and G. Rybertt. 1993. Degradación de las proteínas en el proceso de ensilaje. Ciencia e Inv. Agr. 20 (2):402–429.

Rooke, J.A. and V.L. Nsereko. 1993. Peptide nitrogen in grass silages. In: Proc. 10th Intl. Conf. on Silage Research, Dublin, pp. 62–63.

Schneider, A., V. Gerbi and M. Redoglia. 1987. A rapid HPLC method for separation and determination of major organic acids in grapes, musts and wines. Am. J. Enol. Viticult. 38(2):151–155.

Smith, D. 1973. The nonstructural carbohydrates. In: Chemistry and Biochemistry of Herbage, Vol. 1:106–156. (G.W. Butler and R.W. Bailey, eds.) Academic Press, London and New York.

Tamminga, S., R. Ketelaar and A.M. Van Vuuren. 1991. Degradation of nitrogenous compounds in conserved forages in the rumen of dairy cows. Grass and Forage Sci. 46:427–435.

Tan, L.U.L., M.K.H. Chan and J.N. Sadler. 1984. A modification of the Lowry method for detecting protein in media containing lignocellulosic substrates. Biotechnol. Lett. 6(3):199–204.

Valinotti, P. and G. Pichard. 1993. "Efecto de la inoculación bacteriana sobre la fermentación del ensilaje de alfalfa fresca suplementada con carbohidratos solubles". XIII Reunión Asociación Latinoamericana de Producción Animal. (ALPA). Ciencia e Investigación Agraria. Mayo-Agosto. 22 (2):38–39.

Van Os, M., B. Lassalas, S, Toillon. and J.P. Jouany. 1995. *In vitro* degradation of amines by rumen micro-organisms. J. of Agric. Sci. Camb. 125:299–305.

Van Soest, P.J., J.B. Robertson and B.A. Lewis. 1991. Methods for dietary fiber, neutral detergent fiber, and nonstarch polysacharides in relation to animal nutrition. J. Dairy Sci. 74:3583–3597.

Van Soest, P.J. 1994. Nutritional Ecology of the Ruminant. 2nd Ed., Cornell University Press, Ithaca, New York

Wallace, R.J. and M.A. Cotta. 1988. Metabolism of nitrogen-containing compounds. *In:* The rumen microbial ecosystem (P.N. Hobson, ed.), Elsevier Applied Science, London and New York.

Wilkinson, M. 1990. Sampling and analysing silage. *In:* Silage U.K., 6th Edition. Chalcombe Publications.

Woolford, M.K. 1984. The silage fermentation. Microbiology Series Volume 14, Marcel Dekker, Inc., New York. 13

# MEDICINAL PLANTS IN HUMAN AND ANIMAL NUTRITION AND HEALTH

# Medicinal plant diversity of Mexico and its potential for animal health sciences

ROBERT BYE and EDELMIRA LINARES

*Jardín Botánico, Instituto de Biología, Universidad Nacional Autónoma de México, 04510 México, DF, México*

## Medicinal plants of Mexico

Herbal remedies are deeply rooted as an integral component of Mexican cultures. The variety of plants used to treat the many maladies of humans and animals is based on the rich biological and cultural diversity which Mexico is privileged to shelter (Bye *et al.*, 1995; Ramamoorthy *et al.*, 1993). Even though much of the pre-hispanic physical evidence of their medical traditions was destroyed by the Spaniards, Mesoamerican cultures have shared their experiences through early colonial documents and contemporary health concepts and practices.

The Europeans quickly recognized the value of the vegetal remedies of Mexico and catalogued their virtues. Aztec healers and scholars produced the colorful "Badianus Manuscript" in 1552 that documented the curative importance of 263 plants, of which 185 are recognized scientifically (Cruz, 1991). The scholarly friar (Bernardino de Sahagún 1979), worked from 1558 to 1582 to compile the detailed ethnographic record 'Florentine Codex' that summarized the contributions and philosophy of the Aztecs at the time of their contact with the Old World. Over 724 useful plants are described, of which 266 have medicinal properties. King Philip II sent his personal physician, Francisco Hernández (1959), to record the curative flora, which resulted in the 3,076 plants found in 'Natural History of New Spain'. Today we can identify only 667 species. These and later documents strongly suggest that plants were a central part of native Mexican life and that today we are aware of only a fraction of that rich flora.

### BOTANICAL AND ECOLOGICAL DIVERSITY

After the early colonial period, the fever to discover and record medicinal plants subsided. Sporadic events (e.g., Royal Expeditions of the late 1700s and early 1800s) sparked renewed interest although their results were hidden for almost a century. It was not until the end of the 19th century, when Mexico began to consolidate Mexican botanical data from earlier studies and to promote its own investigations, that information about the Mexican flora blossomed. The critical institution for this consolidation and growth was the Instituto Médico Nacional (IMN), an interdisciplinary research institute that functioned between 1888 and 1915. Martínez (1990) summarized much of the data, as well as that generated by IMN, in his classical book first published in 1933. Subsequent efforts to consolidate historical and subsequent information were carried out at the Instituto Mexicano sobre el Estudio de Plantas Medicinales (Díaz, 1976a, b). This multidisciplinary effort was repeated nearly 20 years later with the publication of the 'Atlas de las Plantas de la Medicina Tradicional Mexicana' (Argueta et al., 1994) and related bibliography (Argueta and Zolla, 1994) and dictionary (Mata et al., 1994).

Although current estimates of the extent of the medicinal flora vary between 3,352 species in 166 families (Bye et al., 1991) and 3,103 in 183 families (Argueta et al., 1994), only about 15% of the Mexican vascular flora (with a conservative estimate of 21,600 species) is employed for curative purposes. Even though there are studies in most parts of the country, certain areas, such as the arid central highlands and coastal regions, are sparsely covered. The dominant botanical families in terms of species numbers are: Asteraceae (383), Fabaceae (324), Euphorbiaceae (137), Lamiaceae (92) and Solanaceae (92). Diverse life forms are represented in the medicinal flora with herbs dominating (45.2%), followed by shrubs (28.2%), trees (27.7%) and vines (5.7%). The dry tropical forest, which covers 17% of the country, harbors 44.4% of the medicinal flora; the other vegetation types tend to cover greater geographic areas but contribute fewer species (oak and pine forests with 21% area and 44.1 and 37.5% taxa, respectively; desert with 50% area and 34.6% taxa; and humid tropical forest with 11% area and 32.5% taxa).

SPECIAL CONSIDERATIONS OF MEDICINAL PLANTS

The phytochemical and pharmacological basis as well as the cultural foundation of this diverse medicinal flora are under exploration. Up to 1994, laboratory investigations of remedial plants focused on the chemistry (394 species), chemistry and pharmacology (280 species), chemistry, pharmacology and toxicology (177 species), and chemistry, pharmacology, toxicology and active principles (69 species) (Argueta et al., 1994). Also, many indigenous groups are making inventories of their natural remedies and producing mini-floras (Aguilar et al., 1994b).

The relative practical use of medicinal plants is important in addition to their taxonomic diversity. A nation-wide survey of government rural clinics (Lozoya et al., 1988) revealed a 'basic set of medicinal plants' with the ten most widely consumed herbal remedies being derived from native flora (*Zea mays*, POA; *Artemisia ludoviciana*, AST; *Chenopodium ambrosioides*, CHN; *Calamintha macrostema*, LAM; *Heterotheca inuloides*, AST) and from introduced species (peppermint, *Mentha piperita*, LAM;

rue, *Ruta chalepensis*, RUT; chamomile, *Matricaria recutita*, AST; basil, *Ocimum basilicum*, LAM; and aloe, *Aloe barbadensis,* LIL). A list of the scientific and common names along with the acronym designating the plant family is in Table 1.

Table 1.  Scientific and common names of plant families for the acronyms used with scientific names in the text.[1]

| Scientific name | Common name | Plant family acronym |
|---|---|---|
| Agavaceae | Century plant | AGA |
| Amaranthus | Amaranth | AMA |
| Apiaceae | Carrot | API |
| Asteraceae | Aster | AST |
| Cactaceae | Cactus | CAC |
| Chenopodiaceae | Goosefoot | CHN |
| Cucurbitaceae | Cucumber | CUC |
| Euphorbiaceae | Spurge | EUP |
| Fabaceae | Bean | FAB |
| Fagaceae | Beech | FAG |
| Lamiaceae | Mint | LAM |
| Lauraceae | Laurel | LAU |
| Liliaceae | Lily | LIL |
| Loasaceae | Loasa | LOA |
| Magnoliaceae | Magnolia | MAG |
| Malpighiaceae | Barbados cherry | MLP |
| Moraceae | Mulberry | MOR |
| Myrtaceae | Myrtle | MRT |
| Nyctaginaceae | Four-o'clock | NYC |
| Onagraceae | Evening primrose | ONA |
| Passifloraceae | Passion flower | PAS |
| Poacaceae | Grass | POA |
| Pinaceae | Pine | PIN |
| Plataginaceae | Plantain | PTG |
| Rosaceae | Rose | ROS |
| Rutaceae | Rue | RUT |
| Salicaceae | Willow | SAL |
| Scrophulariaceae | Figwort | SCR |
| Theaceae | Tea | TEA |
| Urticaceae | Nettle | URT |
| Valerianaceae | Valerian | VAL |
| Verbenaceae | Verbena | VRB |

[1]Weber, 1982.

Traditional medicine frequently involves plants which share a common name but are taxonomically distinct. An analysis of collections of these plants in the field and in the markets of Mexico has brought to light 'medicinal plant complexes' in which a common name is applied to taxonomically distinct plants sharing medicinal use and morphological, organoleptic, pharmacological, and (in some cases) chemical properties (Linares and Bye, 1987). Usually there is a dominant species that people consider to be the most effective and is marketed beyond its native geographic range. The other species are used locally and usually when the dominant plant is unavailable. These subordinate taxa are usually employed within their natural geographic range and have little acceptance among people outside the area. Hence, for each region, one encounters a different species that is generally known only to the inhabitants in addition to the widespread, dominant species. An example is 'árnica' (*Heterotheca inuloides*, AST), which is valued for treating bruises, wounds and skin ailments as well as gastric ulcers. Although restricted to the mountains of central Mexico, the yellow flowers are found in markets throughout Mexico and various industrialized products are available. This plant is rapidly gaining popularity around the world as a substitute for the naturally rare 'árnica' (*Arnica montana*, AST) which has toxic constituents. In various parts of Mexico, residents employ for the same purpose herbs with similar composite flowers (usually yellow in color) but from different botanical genera of the Asteraceae (e.g., *Aster gymnocephalus, Haplopappus spinolosus, Tithonia diversifolia, Trixis inula, Verbesina greenmannii, Zexmenia pringlei*) and even plants from different botanical families (*Galphimia glauca*, MLP; *Mentzelia conzattii*, LOA).

In order to treat illnesses that are perceived to be caused by multiple factors, mixtures of different plants are employed. An ailment may be classified as belonging to a certain class of maladies and, depending upon the individual's symptoms and history, will be treated with a polyherbal formulation containing standard plant ingredients or 'fundamental plants'. In such cases as diarrhea with its many variants, five main or fundamental plants are employed and one or more of 12 supplementary plants are adjuncts depending upon the diagnosis (for details, see Bye *et al.*, 1995). Problems said to be associated with the cardiovascular system may manifest themselves as 'nervios' (nervousness), 'presión' (pressure), 'susto' (fright), 'corazón' (e.g., irregular heart beat), 'circulación' (weak blood circulation), and 'varices' (varicose veins). Certain species, such as *Ternstroemia* spp. (TEA) are always part of any herbal remedy mixture for all these illnesses, while others may be found in mixtures for only three of the six categories, as in the case of *Valeriana procera* (VAL) (Table 2).

CONSERVATION OF MEDICINAL PLANTS

Medicinal plants continue to play an important role in the health care of rural and urban Mexico. With the increased popularity of natural remedies on a national and international level, the demand for wild medicinal plants is increasing. In response to this commercial pressure, concern for their conservation has grown. Some 35 medicinal plants are threatened with extinction (Loa *et al.*, 1998), the main causes being overcollection and habitat destruction. A recent review of the conventional and biotechnological propagation of medicinal plants in arid regions of Mexico (where most of these plants are derived from wild populations) indicates that horticultural techniques exist for only a handful of species (Zárate *et al.*, 1996). Conservation practices integrating *in situ* conservation with plant propagation for subsequent reintroduction and for commercial cultivation are urgently needed.

Table 2. **Examples of fundamental plants used to treat ailments associated with various maladies based upon samples of medicinal plants in the Mercado Sonora in Mexico City.**

| Plant | Nervios (nervousness) | Presión (pressure) | Susto (fright) | Corazón (irregular heartbeat) | Circulación (circulation) | Varices (varicose veins) |
|---|---|---|---|---|---|---|
| *Citrus* spp. | X | X | X | X | X | X |
| *Ternstroemia* spp. | X | X | X | X | X | X |
| *Haematoxylon brasilleto* | X | X | X | X | X | X |
| *Agastache mexicana* | X | | X | X | X | X |
| *Ipomoea stans* | X | X | | X | X | X |
| *Chiranthodendron pentadactylon* | X | X | X | X | | |
| *Valeriana procera* | X | | X | X | | |
| *Taxodium mucronatum* | | | | X | | X |
| *Juglans regia* | | | | | X | X |

The Convention on Biological Diversity has become a focal point for promoting the conservation of organisms as well as developing biological resources for human benefit (United Nations Environment Program, 1992). In order to implement such a program, local communities, universities, government and nongovernment agencies and industry need to join forces to ensure the perpetuation of natural diversity and its wise use by humans. Mexico established CONABIO (Comisión Nacional para el Conocimiento y Uso de la Biodiversidad) as a central clearing house for information related to the country's biota. A status report (Conabio, 1998) summarizes the knowledge available and the challenges ahead for Mexico. Specific projects are underway to promote the conservation and utility of the medicinal plant diversity such as the International Cooperative Biodiversity Group's program (ICBG) on bioactive agents from drylands of Latin America (Bye *et al.*, 1997). The three main objectives of ICBG are: 1) conservation of biological diversity, 2) discovery of pharmaceutical substances from natural sources for treating diseases in developed and developing nations, and 3) promotion of sustained economic activities associated with the natural resources.

# Ethnoveterinary research

Ethnoveterinary research is the study of empirical knowledge and practices of traditional peoples in relation to their world views, management and utilization of animal resources. It is sometimes considered as a subdiscipline or parallel field of ethnobiology. Ethnoveterinary research and its application have been growing in recent years, especially in countries with limited financial resources and a strong traditional medicine heritage such as India (e.g., Padmakumar, 1998). In order to appreciate the embryonic state of ethnoveterinary research in Mexico, a brief history and results are presented. After that, forage plants with medicinal properties are examined in a preliminary manner to identify correlations that may exist between taxonomic diversity and medicinal plant uses.

Behavior studies show that animals select certain types of plants within the same species while foraging and when ill (Cowen, 1990). The behaviour of wild animals can also provide leads to useful plants. Native Americans acknowledge respectfully the acquisition of certain medicinal plants as gifts from animals. A popular salve used by people in northern Mega-Mexico[1] for treating body aches and noxious animal stings is derived from the 'chuchupate' roots (*Ligusticum porteri*, API). Among indigenous peoples (e.g., Navajo and Zuni), the herb is referred to as 'bear's herb', 'bear medicine' or 'smelly root' (Camazine and Bye, 1990). Black bears chew the aromatic root and rub it on their bodies (Sigstedt, 1990). Hence native mythology and contemporary utilization of medicinal plants associated with animals appear to have a biological basis that is culturally labeled.

Ethnobotanical information on relationships between plants and animals was examined with reference to plants used in veterinary medicine and to forage plants. An initial search for this information was made in selected literature (e.g., Alcorn, 1984; Bennett and Zingg, 1935; Esquivel, 1982; Langman, 1964; Lozano and López, 1988; Martínez *et al.*, 1995; Matuda and Piña, 1980; Mejía and Dávila 1992; Pennington, 1963, 1969, 1980; Sepulveda and Medina, 1993; Tilford, 1997) as well as databases in the Botanical Garden of the Institute of Biology, National University of Mexico (UNAM) (i.e., BADEPLAM and that of the Edward Palmer Ethnobotanical File (Bye, 1991)). Plant classification and nomenclature[2] were revised using selected floristic literature and standard references (Bailey and Bailey, 1976; Cronquist, 1981). Spanish and indigenous terms applied to medicinal plants were compared with the standard definitions (Aguilar *et al.*, 1994a; Díaz, 1976a; Esquivel, 1982; Mata *et al.*, 1994). Remedial attributes of the forage plants were derived from the nation-wide compilation of Mexican traditional medicinal plants (Argueta *et al.*, 1994). The properties of the medicinal plants were classified according to an internationally recognized arrangement of body systems and medical problems (Cook, 1995) and included the following categories: circulatory system (CS), digestive system (DS), genitourinary system (GU),

---

[1] Mega-Mexico is a term applied to Mexico and regions beyond its contemporary border that share similar floristic composition and often represent the biogeographic frontiers of essentially Mexican plant genera and families (Rzedowski, 1993). Interestingly, these provincial extensions correspond to the prolongation of the Aztec Empire in the south and to the extent of the Spanish colony of New Spain (and later Mexico) prior to the reduction of Mexico's territorial limits in the 19th century.

[2] The scientific names for plants mentioned in the text are incomplete in that they lack the author citation. Also, many of the plants mentioned do not have common English names; to aid the reader in recognizing the plants, a plant family acronym follows the scientific name (Weber, 1982). See Table 1 for the complete family name.

ill-defined symptoms (ID), inflammation (IF), infections and infestations (II), injuries (IJ), nervous system (NS), pregnancy/birth/puerperium disorders (PP), poisonings (PS), respiratory system (RS), skin/subcutaneous cellular system (SC), and sensory system (SS). In addition, a category (CL) for ailments that are culturally defined and recognized in Mexico was added. Lists of the plants used in ethnoveterinary medicine and the forage plants with medicinal use are found in Tables 3 and 4.

ETHNOVETERINARY MEDICINAL STUDIES IN MEXICO

In recent years, ethnoveterinary studies have increased as this interdisciplinary field combines elements from anthropology, biology, nutrition, veterinary medicine, zootechnology and social development. The medicinal applications, in particular, have drawn attention on a worldwide basis (Mathias-Mundy and McCorkle, 1989). In Mexico, the role of plants in veterinary science has received little attention until recently. During the late 19th century, few studies of medicinal plants were carried out on domestic animals. A century later, the Faculty of Veterinary Medicine and Zootechnology (FMVZ) of UNAM has reinitiated investigation in this area.

The study of the effects of medicinal plants, especially on animals, was secondary in the 28-year long national program of the Instituto Médico Nacional. The majority of the studies focused on botany, pharmacology and chemistry of medicinal plants, clinical cases and physiology. In the IMN's major publications (four volumes of El Estudio and 12 volumes of Anales del Instituto Médico Nacional; Fernández, 1961), at least eight articles reported results of studies conducted on animals.

The UNAM initiated the consolidation of studies on medicinal plants ('herbolaria') for animals in 1988 with the first of three seminars on this theme (Lozano and López, 1988). Of the 5,700 student theses written between 1916 and 1987 in the FMVZ, only 24 (or 0.04%) treated some aspect of traditional medicine in the care of animals (Lozano, 1988). Of these theses, 13 tested the effects of a specific plant, two examined the combination of plants, three compared a plant extract with a commercial product, three tested various plants against commercial products, two discussed compilations of contemporary and historical information on medicinal plants in general and one (Esquivel, 1982) was the result of field interviews with farmers concerning illnesses of their animals and the plant remedies employed. Other contributions in the publication discuss initial laboratory studies of certain plants: *Aloe vera* (LIL), *Mimosa tenuiflora* (FAB), and *Desmodium plicatum* (FAB) to heal burns (Sumano et al., 1988); *Arnica montana* [probably *Heterotheca inuloides*] (AST), *Passiflora* sp. (PAS), *Valeriana* sp. (VAL), *Eucalyptus globulus* (MRT), *Bougainvillea spectabilis* (NYC), *Verbascum thapsus* (SCR), *Cinnamomum zeylanicum* (LAU), *Crataegus pubescens* (ROS), and *Citrus aurantiifolia* (RUT) for treating trachobronchitis in dogs (Vázquez et al., 1988); antifungal properties of *Helenium quadridentatum* (AST) against

271

Table 3.  Plants used in ethnoveterinary medicine. (CS = circulatory system, CL = Cultural defined illnesses, DS = digestive system, IS = immune system, ES = endrocine system, GU = genitourinary system, ID= ill-defined symptoms, II = infections/infestations, IF = inflammation, IJ = injuries, MT = metabolic system disorders, MS = muscular-skeletal system, NP = neoplasms, NS = nervous system disorders, NT = nutritional disorders, PN = pain, PS = poisonings, PP = pregnancy/birth/puerperium disorders, RS = respiratory system disorders, SS = sensory system disorders, SC = skin/subcutaneous cellular system, nl = medical application not listed).

| Family | Species | Animal treatment category | | | | |
|--------|---------|------|------|------|------|------|
| Agavaceae | *Agave cupreata* | PS | | | | |
| | *Agave wocomahi* | CL | | | | |
| | *Dasylirion sereke* | CL | | | | |
| Anacardiaceae | *Schinus molle* | II | PS | SS | | |
| Annonaceae | *Annona reticulata* | DS | | | | |
| Apiaceae | *Ligusticum porteri* | CL | | | | |
| Apocynaceae | *Thevetia thevetoides* | SC | | | | |
| Arecaceae | *Brahea dulcis* | NS | | | | |
| Aristolochiacea | *Aristolochia mexicana* | DS | | | | |
| Asclepiadaceae | *Asclepias curassavica* | II | | | | |
| Asteraceae | *Acourtia sp.* | IF | | | | |
| | *Brickellia squarrosa* | II | SC | | | |
| | *Calea zacatechichi* | II | | | | |
| | *Cirsium pinetorum* | GU | SC | | | |
| | *Conyza flaginoides* | DS | | | | |
| | *Gymnosperma glutinosa* | CL | | | | |
| | *Helenium quadridentatum* | II | | | | |
| | *Heliopsis longipes* | II | | | | |
| | *Heterotheca inuloides* | CS | DS | IF | IJ | SC |
| | *Matricaria recutita* | DS | | | | |
| | *Montanoa tomentosa* | CS | DS | GU | RS | |
| | *Ratibida mexicana* | CL | | | | |
| | *Salmea scandens* | II | | | | |
| | *Stevia eupatoria* | DS | | | | |
| | *Tagetes erecta* | DS | II | | | |
| | *Verbesina capitaneja* | II | SC | | | |
| Bignoniaceae | *Crescentia alata* | IJ | | | | |
| | *Parmentiera edulis* | DS | IF | II | | |
| | *Tecoma mollis* | DS | | | | |
| Bromeliaceae | *Bromelia sylvestris* | II | | | | |
| Buddlejaceae | *Buddleja elliptica* | nl | | | | |
| | *Buddleja perfoliata* | DS | | | | |
| Burseraceae | *Bursera sp.* | CL | | | | |
| | *Bursera trijugum* | DS | | | | |
| Cactaceae | *Hylocereus undatus* | PP | | | | |
| | *Stenocereus marginatus* | ID | | | | |
| | *Opuntia lasiacantha* | II | | | | |
| Campanulaceae | *Lobelia laxiflora* | nl | | | | |
| Chenopodiaceae | *Teloxys ambrosioides* | DS | II | | | |
| | *Teloxys graveolens* | II | | | | |
| Chrysobalanacea | *Licania arborea* | II | | | | |
| Convolvulaceae | *Ipomoea arborescens* | II | PS | | | |
| | *Ipomoea dumosa* | PP | | | | |
| Cucurbitaceae | *Cucurbita ficifolia* | GU | | | | |
| Cupressaceae | *Cupressus lusitanica* | CL | | | | |
| Dioscoreaceae | *Dioscorea decomposita* | PP | | | | |

**Table 3. continued**

| Family | Species | Animal treatment category | | | |
|---|---|---|---|---|---|
| Euphorbiaceae | *Acalyphya arvensis* | IJ | | | |
| | *Cnidoscolus urens* | II | | | |
| | *Croton cortesianus* | II | | | |
| | *Croton draco* | nl | SS | | |
| | *Euphorbia lancifolia* | ID | | | |
| | *Ricinus communis* | IF | IJ | | |
| Fabaceae | *Caesalpinea coriaria* | SC | | | |
| | *Calliandra anomala* | DS | | | |
| | *Cassia ornithopoides* | PS | | | |
| | *Desmodium plicatums* | II | SC | | |
| | *Erythrina americana* | NS | | | |
| | *Eysenhardtia polystachya* | DS | ID | II | nl |
| | *Haematoxylum brasiletto* | DS | | | |
| | *Leucaena glauca* | II | | | |
| | *Mimosa tenuiflora* | SC | | | |
| | *Phaseolus vulgaris* | DS | PS | | |
| | *Pithecellobium dulce* | DS | | | |
| | *Prosopis laevigata* | ID | | | |
| Hamamelidaceae | *Liquidambar macrophylla* | nl | | | |
| Hydrophyllaceae | *Nama undulatum* | SC | | | |
| Julianiaceae | *Amphypterygium adstringens* | DS | SC | | |
| Lamiaceae | *Hyptis stellulata* | SC | | | |
| | *Hyptis verticillata* | ID | | | |
| | *Marrubium vulgare* | DS | RS | | |
| | *Mentha piperita* | DS | | | |
| | *Ocimun micranthum* | IF | | | |
| | *Salvia coccinea* | DS | | | |
| | *Salvia polystachya* | SC | | | |
| Lauraceae | *Cinnamomum zeylanicum* | IF | | | |
| Liliaceae | *Allium cepa* | DS | GU | | |
| | *Allium sativum* | II | PS | | |
| | *Aloe vera* | SC | | | |
| | *Aloe vulgaris* | II | | | |
| | *Amarylidaceae sp.* | SC | | | |
| | *Schoenocaulon ghiesbreghtii* | II | | | |
| Loganiaceae | *Buddleja cordata* | CL | | | |
| Magnoliaceae | *Talauma mexicana* | CS | | | |
| | *Byrsonima crassifolia* | DS | SC | | |
| | *Malpighia glabra* | DS | | | |
| Malvaceae | *Abelmoschus moschatus* | PS | | | |
| | *Malva rotundifolia* | DS | GU | II | |
| | *Sida acuta* | DS | | | |
| Meliaceae | *Swietenia humilis* | SC | | | |
| | *Trichilia havanensis* | II | | | |
| Moraceae | *Brosimum alicastrum* | DS | | | |
| Musaceae | *Musa sapientum* | SC | | | |
| Myrtaceae | *Eucalyptus globulus* | IF | | | |
| | *Psidium guajava* | DS | | | |
| Nyctaginaceae | *Bougainvillea spectabilis* | IF | | | |
| Oleaceae | *Fraxinus papillosa* | CL | | | |
| | *Fraxinus uhdei* | II | | | |
| | *Fraxinus uhdei* | IJ | | | |
| Passifloraceae | *Passiflora coriacea* | IJ | | | |

**Table 3.** continued

| Family | Species | | Animal treatment category | |
|---|---|---|---|---|
| Phytolaccaceae | *Petiveria alliacea* | IJ | RS | |
| | *Petiveria alliacea L.* | ID | II | |
| | *Phytolacca octandra* | II | | |
| | *Stegnosperma holimifolium* | II | | |
| Pinaceae | *Pinus ayacahuite* | PS | SC | |
| | *Pinus sp.* | CL | | |
| Plumbaginaceae | *Plumbago scandens* | IJ | | |
| Poaceae | *Arthrostylidium racemiflorum* | DS | | |
| | *Zea mays* | CL | | |
| Polygonaceae | *Antigonon leptopus* | IF | | |
| Ranunculaceae | *Clematis dioica* | GU | II | |
| | *Clematis grossa* | RS | | |
| Rosaceae | *Crataegus pubescens* | IF | | |
| | *Rosa centifolia* | DS | IF | |
| Rubiaceae | *Coffea arabica* | II | | |
| | *Exostema caribaeum* | SC | | |
| | *Hamelia patens* | IJ | nl | |
| Rutaceae | *Citrus aurantiifolia* | IF | II | SC |
| | *Ruta chalepensis* | IF | | |
| | *Zanthoxylum fagara* | RS | | |
| Sapindaceae | *Serjania rachiptera* | DS | nl | |
| Scrophulariaceae | *Scoporia dulcis* | IJ | | |
| | *Verbascum thapsus* | IF | | |
| Simaroubaceae | *Castela tortuosa* | NL | | |
| Smilacaceae | *Smilax domingensis* | PP | nl | |
| Solanaceae | *Capsicum annuum var. glabriusculum* | IJ | CL | |
| | *Capsicum annuum var. acuminatum* | II | | |
| | *Capsicum annuum var. longum* | CL | DS | |
| | *Lycopersicum lycopersicum* | DS | II | |
| | *Solanum verbascifolium* | DS | II | |
| Sterculiaceae | *Guazuma ulmifolia* | DS | IJ | PP |
| | *Waltheria americana* | DS | | |
| Theophrastaceae | *Jacquinia aurantiaca* | SC | DS | RS |
| | *Jacquinia pungens* | IF | | |
| Tiliaceae | *Heliocarpus donnell-smithii* | PP | | |
| Turneraceae | *Turnera diffusa* | IF | | |
| Valerianaceae | *Valeriana sp.* | IF | | |
| Verbenaceae | *Lantana camara* | II | | |
| | *Vitex mollis* | DS | | |
| Vitaceae | *Cissus sicyoides* | SC | | |

*Saprolegnia* spp. in talapia fish (Auró and Sumano, 1988); the effect of *Talauma mexicana* (MAG) on arterial pressure in dogs (Durán *et al.*, 1988); uses of *Allium sativum* (LIL) as a nematodicide in carp (Peña *et al.*, 1988) and antibacterial, antiparasitic, and toxicological properties of *Heliopsis longipes* (AST) in sheep, horses, and laboratory rats (Romero *et al.*, 1988). A database (HERBVET10) was initiated to maintain information on the application and evaluation of herbal remedies on animals (López *et al.*, 1988). The research continues to apply the initial findings to resolving

Table 4.    Forage plants with medicinal uses for humans. (CS = circulatory system, CL = Cultural defined illnesses, DS = digestive system, IS = immune system, ES = endrocrine system, GU = genitourinary system, ID= ill-defined symptoms, II = infections/infestations, IF = inflammation, IJ = injuries, MN = mental disorders, MT = metabolic system, MS = muscular-skeletal system, NP = neoplasms, NS = nervous system disorders, NT = nutritional, PN = pain, PS = poisonings, PP = pregnancy/birth/puerperium disorders, RS = respiratory system, SS = sensory system, and SC = skin/subcutaneous cellular system).

| Family | Species | Treatment class |
|---|---|---|
| Agavaceae | *Agave lecheguilla* | EN GU II   IJ   SN |
| | *Agave salmiana* | BS  EN  IF   IJ   RS  SC |
| | *Yucca schidigera* | DS  GU  IF   II   IJ   MS  SC |
| Amaranthaceae | *Alternanthera repens* | CL  DS  GU  II   MS  NS  PN  RS |
| | *Amaranthus hybridus* | DS  PN  PP  RS  SC |
| | *Iresine celosia* | CL  DS  GU  IF   II   PP  SC |
| Anacardiaceae | *Cyrtocarpa procera* | DS  II   IJ   PN  RS |
| | *Schinus molle* | CL  CS  DS  GU  IF   II   IJ   MS  PN  PP  SS   RS |
| | *Spondias mombin* | DS  GU  IF   II   PN  PS  RS  SC  SS |
| Apiaceae | *Arracacia atropurpurea* | CL  II |
| Araceae | *Syngonium podophyllum* | IJ   SC  SS |
| Arecaceae | *Cocos nucifera* | CS  DS  II   PP  SC |
| Asclepiadaceae | *Asclepias brachystephana* | SC |
| Asteraceae | *Ageratum corynbosum* | DS |
| | *Aster subulatus* | II |
| | *Bidens odorata* | CL  DS  II   MN MS  PN  SC |
| | *Bidens pilosa* | BS  DS  EN  GU  IJ   MS  NT  PN  SC |
| | *Cosmos bipinnatus* | RS |
| | *Gutierrezia sarothrae* | DS  IJ   PN |
| | *Helianthus annuus* | IJ   MN MS  PN  RS |
| | *Melampodium divaricatum* | CL  DS  ID  II   IJ   MS  PP  PS   RS  SC |
| | *Polymnia maculata* | IJ |
| | *Simsia amplexicaulis* | DS  GU  RS |
| | *Sonchus oleraceus* | BS  DS  GU  IF   II   IJ   PN  SC  SS |
| | *Viguiera dentata* | RS  SC |
| Bignoniaceae | *Cydista aequinoctialis* | SC |
| Bombacaceae | *Ceiba pentandra* | DS  EN  IF   II   IJ   MS  NP  PN  SC |
| Boraginaceae | *Cordia alliodora* | CL  DS  GU  ID  II   IJ   MN RS  SC |
| Brassicaceae | *Brassica rapa* | PN |
| | *Lepidium virginidum* | CL  DS  IF   II   PN  PP  RS  SC |
| Burseraceae | *Bursera microphylla* | DS  IF   II   IJ   PN  RS  SC |
| Buxaceae | *Simmondsia chinensis* | CS  GU  IJ   NP  PN  PP  RS  SC  SS |
| Cactaceae | *Mammillaria microcarpa* | PN |
| | *Nopalea cochenillifera* | EN  IF   II   IJ   NP  PN  RS  SC  SS |
| | *Opuntia ficus-indica* | DS  EN  IF   PP |
| | *Opuntia fulgida* | DS  GU  II   PN |
| | *Opuntia imbricata* | EN  GU  MS  RS |
| | *Opuntia leptocaulis* | PN  RS |
| Chenopodiaceae | *Beta vulgaris* | BS  DS  EN  ID |
| | *Teloxys amobrosioides* | CL  CS  DS  GU  ID  IF   II   IJ   MN MS  MT  NS  PN  PP  PS   RS  SC |
| Cochlospermaceae | *Cochlospermum vitifolium* | DS  EN  GU  II   IJ   PP  PS   RS  SC |
| Convolvulaceae | *Bonamia brevipedicellata* | SC |
| | *Ipomoea purpurea* | DS  PP |
| | *Jacquemontia pentandra* | DS |
| | *Merrenya aegyptia* | SC |
| Cucurbitaceae | *Lagenaria siceraria* | DS  IF   II   RS |
| | *Sechium edule* | CS  DS  GU  II   MN PP  RS |
| Cyperaceae | *Cyperus esculentus* | CS  DS  GU  ID  IJ   PN  PP  SC |
| Euphorbiaceae | *Adelia barbinervis* | IJ   PN  SC |
| | *Dalechampia scandens* | PN |
| | *Euphorbia hypericifolia* | DS  IF   IJ   PS   SC |

**Table 4.** **continued**

| Family | Species | Treatment class |
|--------|---------|-----------------|
| Fabaceae | *Acacia angustissima* | CS DS GU IF II IJ |
| | *Acacia cymbispina* | IF                       IF |
| | *Acacia farnesiana* | DS GU IF II IJ MS PN PS SC |
| | *Acacia pennatula* | CS DS GU IF II IJ MNPN SC SS |
| | *Arachis hypogaea* | CS EN ID IF II MNNS PP |
| | *Bauhinia divaricata* | CL DS IF II IJ PP RS SC |
| | *Caesalpinia gaumeri* | IJ |
| | *Caesalpinia pulcherrima* | DS GU IF II IJ PN PP PS RS SC |
| | *Cajanus cajan* | IF IJ MS |
| | *Cassia biflora* | DS |
| | *Ceratonia siliqua* | DS |
| | *Enterolobium cyclocarpum* | CS DS IF RS SC |
| | *Eysenhardtia polystachya* | DS EN GU IF IJ PP SC |
| | *Gliricidia sepium* | CL CS DS GU II IJ PN PP PS SC SS |
| | *Glycine max* | MT |
| | *Leucaena leucocephala* | CS EN IF MN |
| | *Lupinus elegans* | PP |
| | *Lysiloma divaricatum* | IJ |
| | *Mimosa laxiflora* | NS |
| | *Mimosa purpurascens* | DS |
| | *Olneya tesota* | II |
| | *Phaseolus vulgaris* | DS GU PN PP SC |
| | *Pithecellobium dulce* | DS IF II IJ PN PP SS |
| | *Prosopis juliflora* | DS GU IF II IJ PN SC SS |
| | *Prosopis laevigata* | DS IF II PN RS SC SS |
| | *Quercus candicans* | IJ |
| | *Quercus laurina* | DS GU ID IF II IJ RS SC |
| | *Quercus rugosa* | DS GU IF II RS |
| | *Quercus urbanii* | II |
| Geraniaceae | *Erodium cicutarium* | DS GU IF II IJ PN PP RS SC SS |
| Juglandaceae | *Juglans mollis* | SC |
| Lamiaceae | *Salvia hispanica* | DS SS |
| | *Salvia reflexa* | DS |
| Malpighiaceae | *Malpighia glabra* | CL DS PN |
| Malvaceae | *Anoda cristata* | CL CS DS GU II IJ PP RS SC |
| | *Gossypium hirsutum* | IJ PP RS |
| | *Hibiscus sabdariffa* | DS GU II PN |
| | *Sida rhombifolia* | DS IF II IJ NP PN SC |
| | *Sphaeralcea coulteri* | DS |
| Moraceae | *Brosimum alicastrum* | BS CS DS EN GU IF II NP PP PS RS SC |
| | *Ficus continifolia* | GU IF II |
| | *Ficus pertusa* | IF PN |
| | *Morus celtifolia* | DS PN PP SC |
| Moringaceae | *Moringa oleifera* | DS GU RS |
| Musaceae | *Musa acuminata* | CL CS DS GU II |
| | *Musa paradisiaca* | DS GU SC |
| | *Musa sapientum* | DS ES GU II IJ RS SS |
| Onagraceae | *Gaura coccinea* | IF IJ PS |
| Papaveraceae | *Papaver somniferum* | II MNNS RS |
| Pedaliaceae | *Sesamum indicum* | PP RS |
| Phytolaccaceae | *Phytolacca icosandra* | DS II IJ MS NT PN PP SC |
| Plantaginaceae | *Plantago major* | DS GU IF II IJ MS PN RS |
| Poaceae | *Arundinella berteroniana* | GU PN |
| | *Arundo donax* | GU ID IF II IJ MT PP PS SS |
| | *Avena sativa* | DS ID IF II IJ PN PP RS SC |
| | *Bambusa longifolia* | GU |
| | *Bouteloua gracilis* | DS |
| | *Cenchrus echinatus* | DS GU II IJ PN PP PS |
| | *Cymbopogon citratus* | CS DS IF II MNMS MT PN RS SC |

**Table 4. continued**

| Family | Species | Treatment class |
|--------|---------|-----------------|
| | *Cynodon dactylon* | BS DS EN GU ID IF PN PP SC |
| | *Cynodon plectostachyus* | BS DS EN GU PN PP SC |
| | *Eleusine indica* | GU II PN PP RS SC |
| | *Hordeum vulgare* | DS GU ID IF II RS SC |
| | *Lasiacis ruscifolia* | DS GU PN RS |
| | *Muhlenbergia dumosa* | DS II |
| | *Oryza sativa* | DS IF II RS SC |
| | *Panicum maximum* | PP |
| | *Paspalum paniculatum* | DS PN |
| | *Pennisetum purpureum* | MS PN |
| | *Saccharum officinarum* | DS EN II IJ PN PP PS RS SC |
| | *Sorghum bicolor* | II NT |
| | *Sorghum halepense* | II |
| | *Zea mays* | CL CS DS GU IF II MT NT PN RS SC |
| Polygonaceae | *Polygonum aviculare* | GU II SC |
| | *Polygonum hydropiperoides* | DS II SC |
| | *Rumex crispus* | DS GU II IJ PN |
| Portulacaceae | *Portulaca oleracea* | CS DS EN IF II |
| Primulaceae | *Anagallis arvensis* | DS IJ PN PP SC |
| Rhamnaceae | *Ceanothus ochreaus* | ID |
| | *Colubrina glomerata* | SC |
| | *Colubrina greggii* | PP |
| Rhizophoraceae | *Rhizophora mangle* | DS EN II IJ NT PN PP SC |
| Rubiaceae | *Bouvardia ternifolia* | CS DS II MN PN PP PS RS |
| Rutaceae | *Citrus aurantium* | DS PN |
| Solanaceae | *Physalis phyladelphica* | RS |
| | *Solanum hirtum* | IF RS |
| | *Solanum torvum* | CL PN SC |
| | *Solanum tuberosum* | SC |
| Sterculiaceae | *Guazuma ulmifolia* | DS EN II |
| | *Helicteres barvensis* | RS |
| | *Theobroma cacao* | II PP |
| Ulmaceae | *Celtis iguanaeus* | SC |
| Verbenaceae | *Callicarpa acuminata* | DS II |
| | *Duranta repens* | BS |
| | *Lantana camara* | DS PN |
| | *Lippia berlandieri* | DS IF IJ PN PP RS SC |
| | *Lippia graveolens* | DS IF IJ PN PP RS SC |
| Zygophyllaceae | *Guaiacum coulteri* | IF PP |
| | *Kallstroemia grandiflora* | II |
| | *Larrea tridentata* | BS CS DS EN GU ID IF II IJ MS PN PP RS SC |

practical problems such as the use of a preparation based upon *Aloe vera* (LIL) in the treatment of milk cow lacerations (Jiménez *et al.*, 1995).

Despite the sporadic geographic coverage of Mexico with respect to ethnoveterinary studies, certain patterns emerge from the 135 vascular plant species (distributed in 124 genera and 64 families) registered as medicines for such animals as cattle, horses, mules, donkeys, sheep, goats, hogs, chickens, and dogs. The treatment categories with the most taxa (in terms of number of families and species) (Figure 1) are digestive system (22/39), infections and infestations (20/37), skin/subcutaneous cellular system (14/17), inflammations (14/17), and injuries (11/12). Nonspecific records (10) and ill-defined symptoms (6) are not included in the graphic analysis. The digestive system section includes such ailments as diarrhea, colic, 'empacho', 'timpanismo', and vermifuge. Infections and infestations include such illnesses as cholera, dysentary, erysipela, lice, and sarna as well as plants with antibacterial, antihelminthic, antiparasitic, and anti-rabies properties.

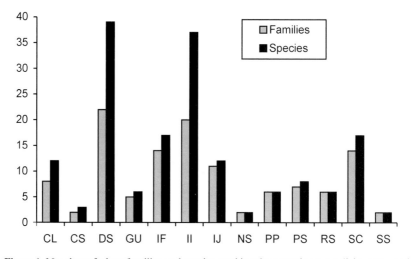

**Figure 1.** Number of plant families and species used in ethnoveterinary medicine arranged by systems of the body and important medicinal problems (CL=culturally-defined ailments, CS=circulatory system, DS=digestive system, GU=genitourinary system, IF=inflamm-ation, II=infections and infestations, IJ=injuries, NS=nervous system, PP=pregnancy/birth/puerperium disorders, PS=poisonings, RS=respriatory system, SC=skin/subcutaneous cellular system, and SS=sensory system).

The most important family is the Asteraceae with 15 genera and 16 species registered for nine of the 13 defined ailment classes. The subsequent three families in descending order of importance (numbers of genera/species/illness categories) are Fabaceae (12/12/5), Lamiaceae (5/7/5), and Liliaceae (4/5/5). For the five highest ranking medical categories, the relationship of native (n) to introduced (i) taxa is as follows: digestive system (32 n; 7 i), infections and infestations (29 n; 8 i), skin/subcutaneous cellular system (19 n; 3 i), inflammations (8 n; 9 i), and injuries (9 n; 3 i). The majority of the medicinal plants are native in all illness categories except inflammations, where more than half of the vegetal remedies are derived from such cultivated exotics as *Cinnamomum zeylanicum* (LAU), *Eucalyptus globulus* (MRT), *Rosa centifolia* (ROS) and *Citrus aurantiifolia* (RUT) and naturalized weeds as *Ricinus communis* (EUP) and *Verbascum thapsus* (SCR).

In addition to caring for their valued animals, the farmers have used livestock for conducting empirical experiments with remedial plants. Recently, the powdered bark of 'tepezcohuite' (*Mimosa tenuiflora*, FAB) has become very popular in Mexico for treating burns, wounds, infected gums and other skin lesions. Family ranchers in Chiapas credit its 'discovery' to the efficacious results of bark poultices applied to wounds of their donkeys, cattle and horses.

RELATIONSHIPS BETWEEN FORAGE AND MEDICINAL PLANTS

Plants provide for the well-being of the organism and, in the case of livestock, are considered forage, fodder and pasturage. An interesting academic debate exists (with interesting legal implications for USA's Food and Drug Adminstration's classification) on whether food and drug plants are the same or different. Based upon speculation on the evolution of human dietary behavior, some authors (Etkin and Ross, 1983; Johns, 1990) support the sameness of these plant categories. On the other hand, an analysis of native North American food and drug plants provides support for the hypothesis that food knowledge and drug knowledge are distinct yet may overlap (Moerman, 1996).

Traditional medicine in Mexico recognizes the importance of plants as a whole in maintaining the well-being of the body, i.e., a medicinal plant and a food plant are one. Such a holistic approach diminishes the distinction based upon intention between plants ingested for food (e.g., daily sources of energy and structural material) and those applied as medicine (e.g., prescribed dosage to remedy an illness). For instance, 'epazote' (*Teloxys ambrosioides*, CHN) is consumed as a condiment and an edible green and also drunk as a tea to treat intestinal parasites. Alternative practices to institutional medicine in the USA have a similar concept and are gaining popularity as we see more 'nutraceuticals' and 'pharmafoods' that people routinely ingest in their daily diet (Etkin and Johns, 1998). One such product is milk thistle (*Silybum marinanum*, AST) with its active principle silyarin, that is a powerful antioxidant and protects the liver from cell damage (Hobbs, 1995). The incorporation of local food plants (e.g., tepary beans (*Phaseolus acutifolius*, FAB; mesquite (*Prosopis* spp, FAB); plantago (*Plantago* spp., PTG); acorns (*Quercus* spp., FAG); chia (*Salvia* spp. and *Hyptis* spp., LAM); and prickly-pear fruits and pads (*Opuntia* spp., CAC)) which contain gums, pectins and complex carbohydrates into the Native American diet has been shown to control blood sucrose and cholesterol levels in obese diabetics (Nabhan, 1985). The benefits of consuming plant mixtures (such as the fundamental medicinal plants mentioned above) may be due to synergistic effects as seen in the combination of pygeum (*Pygeum africanum*, ROS) and nettle (*Urtica dioica*, URT) in the treatment of prostate disease (Hartmann *et al.*, 1996). Browsing on various plants by livestock may reflect their innate ability to combine therapeutic plants during feeding. When considering the role of edible and medicinal plants in the relationships between humans and domestic animals, two aspects may be considered. The first is the experience of humans in the management of animals or animal husbandry; and second, the ability of the animals to recognize and take advantage of the plants upon which they feed.

Even though the Aztec Indians had no experience with European livestock or similar beasts[3] before the conquest, animal husbandry was well developed in pre-Cortesian Mexico, both in Mesoamerica and in the northern Aridoamerican region. The care given to the animals reflected profound biological knowledge as well as technology transfer among indigenous cultures. Plants were used in transcultural native zootechnical practices as seen in archaeological and historical documentation. Scarlet macaws (*Ara macao*) were raised methodically for ceremonial and commercial purposes at Paquimé (Casas Grandes, Chihuahua), far to the north of their biogeographic range during the Medio Period (1060-1340 AD). Despite the diverse diet of amaranth (*Amaranthus* spp., AMA), squash (*Cucurbita* spp., CUC), maiz (*Zea mays*, POA) and maguey (*Agave* spp., AGA), archaeological bones of the captive birds suggest an unbalanced diet due to faulty calcium absorption (DiPeso, 1974). Native turkeys (*Meleagris gallopavo*) were raised here as well as in the Anasazi settlements to the north and Mexica urban centers to the south (DiPeso, 1974). Hairless dogs (*Canis americanus* and *C. caribaeus*) were important to pre-Cortesian cultures as pets, food and elements in ceremonies. In Chapter 1 of Sahagún's early colonial masterpiece, he describes the treatment of 'xoloitzcuintli' puppies with pine pitch (*Pinus* spp., PIN) to assure the removal of all their hair (Sahagún, 1963).

Records of the early Mexican colonial period affirm the depth of pre-conquest indigenous knowledge. Of the 608 useful plants recorded by Sahagún (1979), 14 were attributed forage properties (Estrada, 1989). Of this subset, four plants (chia: Salvia and Hyptis, LAM; maguey: Agave, AGA; maíz: *Zea mays*, POA; and tuna: Opuntia, CAC) also had edible and medicinal properties while a fifth shared only medicinal virtues. This last plant, 'tonalchichicaquilitl' (*Oenothera lacinata*, ONA), was considered a bitter herb which aided the digestion, soothed irritated intestines and was prized as a remedy for internal fevers. It is interesting to note that various North American species of Oenothera are currently under development in Great Britain as a nutraceutical containing $\gamma$-linolenic acid for treating atopic eczema (Horrobin and Lapinskas, 1998).

In 1527, quantities of cattle, horses, donkeys, mules, hogs, goats and sheep arrived in the Spanish colony of New Spain in the region of present-day Pánuco, Veracruz (Barrera, 1996). By 1620, over 1,300,000 head of cattle and 8,100,000 goats and sheep covered central Mexico. The introduction of indigenous peoples to European livestock was probably through the religious mission centers (Pennington, 1963). Trusted Indians were chosen as herdsmen for the mission cattle. Later they obtained their own animals as payment for services, by trading or by rounding up strays. Over

---

[3]The first encounter with of the Aztecs with Old World livestock, the European horse, was probably awe inspiring. Chapter 35 of Book 12 of Sahagun's (1975) Florentine Codex describes how, after the first military encounters of the Aztec warriors with Cortes' army, the captured Spanish soldiers were ceremonially slain and their heads along with the heads of their horses were strung up on the sacrificial skull rake of the main temple in the Empire's capital.

time, these animals became an important source of energy and material for the rural populations. Not only did the animals supply the force for labor and transport, but also various food products. The grazing of the animals in the fields and forests and their subsequent corralling provided a concentrated dung deposit of converted wild biomass that was used to fertilize cultivated fields. During the herding process, the caretakers introduced the exotic animals to the native vegetation and, in turn, observed the livestock's behavior toward specific plants.

Since the Conquest of Mexico nearly 480 years ago, rural peoples of Mexico have had much opportunity to learn from their observations as the number of European domestic animals rose. Today, there are more than 77 million head of livestock (Figure 2). During this century, the Mexican population increased dramatically (e.g., between 1902 and 1981, the human population grew to over five times that at the beginning of this century (Instituto Nacional de Estadística, Geografía e Informática, 1986; Figures 2 and 3). The urban population exploded 11.5 times while the rural population expanded by a factor of 2.3. Certain livestock (e.g., horses and mules) that are strongly linked to rural lifestyles increased at a rate greater than that of the rural population while others (e.g., sheep and goats) expanded at a slightly lower rate. Growth of the bovine and porcine populations probably reflects more the large scale ranching to satisfy increased demand by city consumers. These general data suggest that domestic animals continue to be important for farmers and that opportunities remain to observe animal preferences for plants as forage and for automedication. Conversations with rural people today reveal their keen sense of observation of animal behavior and availability of grazing resources (e.g., concerns of indigenous peoples of the northwestern Mexico, see Pennington, 1963; 1969; 1980). Thus, forage plants and animal behavior are valuable information sources on contemporary and future useful plants.

An example of a browse plant with international commercial value is Mexican oregano (*Lippia berlandieri* and *Lippia graveolens*, VRB). The leaves, stems and flowers are popular ingredients in local medicine used to treat respiratory ailments, gastrointestinal illnesses and dermatologi-cal maladies. Local farmers of the Chihuahuan Desert of northern Mexico purposely herd their goats in wild stands of this shrub so that the goat's meat acquires naturally the wild seasoning for the favorite 'cabrito' goat dishes. Mexican oregano became internationally important after the Chernobyl nuclear plant explosion in 1986 when it replaced the European cultivated oregano (*Origanum vulgare*, LAM) which suffered long-term contamination with radioactive fallout.

A preliminary approximation of the potential of medicinal plants in animal husbandry can be made by correlating forage plants and their medicinal uses for humans. A similar approach was considered by IMN for forage plants of the family Fabaceae with medicinal properties (Villada, 1894-1898). The consumption of various plants by livestock, especially when seeking to relieve illnesses, parallels the human practice of mixing

281

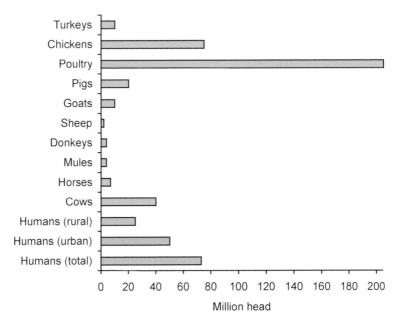

**Figure 2.** Human and livestock populations in Mexico in 1981.

fundamental medicinal plants. Hence, vegetal food contains different phytochemicals which can produce additive and/or synergistic effects.

Animals' interactions with plants are correlated strongly with their perception of the plant's bioactive principles. First, it is important to recognize that animals can detect differences among plants, even those within the same species. Second, indigenous peoples have incorporated animals' choice of plants into their mythology as well as utilitarian way of life. Third, this process continues today with introduced as well as native animals where one observes the effects of certain vegetal remedies after their application to animals as well as the consequences of ingestion of certain plants when the animals are feeding.

Foraging behavior of animals, especially domestic mammals, is known to be strongly influenced by secondary metabolites that are toxic to mammals, insects and microbes (Bryant *et al.* 1991). Food selection and ingestion of plants are regulated by phytotoxins through the animal's sensitivity to taste, odor and sight. Animals constantly sample foods and regulate their intake of nutritious plants that contain these phytotoxins. The concentrations of these secondary metabolites vary in the plant depending upon the environment, season, development phase, physiological age and part. Also, the presence of a particular class of biosynthetic compounds is less important than the activity of the specific substance; a specific monoterpene may have a dramatically different effect on an herbivore than that of other structurally related terpenes.

Since activity of toxic principles (rather than inhibition of protein or

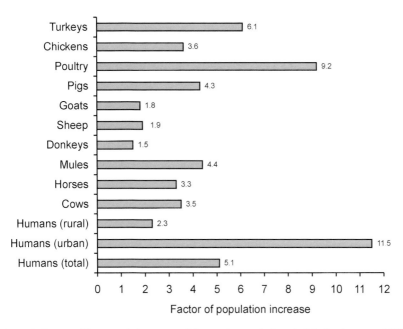

**Figure 3.** Factor of increase in human and livestock populations in Mexico between 1902 and 1981.

carbohydrate digestion) is the primary factor in an animal's interaction with forage plants, the chemical quality of plants can be recognized, learned and passed onto other members of the social and maternal group. Diet selection is known to be flexible and permits the animals, with their innate ability to detect secondary compounds, to experiment cautiously with unknown plants, hence providing greater opportunities to test the floristic diversity and pass on their experiences to others. This learning system of post-ingestive feedback has been shown to have both affective and cognitive components. In addition, the mixture of different phytochemicals (that grazers encounter as a consequence of ingestion of different plants or plant parts) could result in additive and/or synergistic effects. This situation was demonstrated with six monoterpenes in balsam poplar (*Populus blasamifera*, SAL) and their effect on snowshoe hare (Jogia *et al.*, 1989; Reichardt *et al.*, 1990).

As a consequence of demonstrated animal sensitivity to biochemical differences in plants, and of learning abilities that permit careful exploration, balanced intake of nutritive and toxic substances and communication of such information, the foraging behavior of domestic animals can be useful in the exploration and evaluation of medicinal plant diversity. In order to be of benefit to science, these plant-animal interactions need to be recognized and acted upon by humans. Unfortunately, there are few documented cases that clearly show how human societies have exploited animal behavior in response to plants. None the less, fragments of ethnobiological data related to Mexican Indians of the past and present suggest that empirical animal ethnoscience exists. Whether this line of research (known as zoopharmacognosy or the study of the use of plant medicines by animals; Rodriguez and Wrangham, 1993) will be important in the future development of medicinal plants will depend upon our recognition of the cultural and theoretical principles of the plant-animal interactions as well as systematic documentation of such interactions (McCorkle, 1986).

Even though incomplete, the compilation of forage plants revealed 953 species known to be consumed by livestock animals in Mexico. The grass family (Poaceae) has the greatest number of taxa, which account for more than half of those registered. Of these forage plants, 151 species (about 16%) have medicinal uses among Mexican people and are distributed in 128 genera and 50 families (Figure 4). The ailment classes with the greatest species richness are: digestive system (90), infections and infestations (72), skin/subcutaneous cellular system (66), pain (61), and injuries (54).

The richest botanical families (in terms of number of genera and species) are: Fabaceae (19/24), Poaceae (19/21), Asteraceae (11/12), Malvaceae (5/5), Verbenacae (4/5), and Cactaceae (3/5). This taxonomic pattern varies from that of medicinal plants in Mexico (Asteraceae, Fabaceae, Euphorbiaceae, Lamiaceae, and Solanaceae) and the USA and Canada (Asteraceae, Rosaceae, Apiaceae, Ranunculaceae, and Ericaceae) (Bye *et al.*, 1995; Moerman, 1996). These differences in the order and taxonomic composition may be due to: 1) the diverse origins of the Mexican flora (which is derived mostly from the Neotropical floristic kingdom with the major families in descending order of species richness being Asteraceae, Fabaceae,

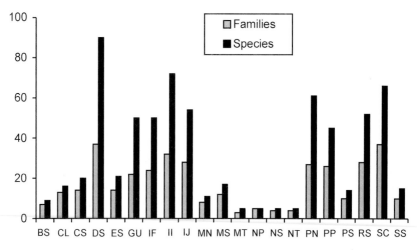

**Figure 4.** Number of plant families and species of livestock forage plants with human medicinal uses arranged by systems of the body and important medicinal problems (see text for explanation of abbreviations; Cook, 1995) (NOTE: records of 9 families with 13 species for ill-defined symptoms are not included).

Poaceae, Orchidaceae and Cactaceae) (Rzedowski, 1993); 2) the sampling bias towards grazed and browsed plants (predominantly the Asteraceae and Fabaceae); and 3) the successful evolutionary adaptation of these plant groups to Mexico's predominantly arid environment.

Of the 151 forage plants with medicinal properties, only 60 are cultivated (39 known only from cultivation, the remainder also found as wild or weedy populations; 31 native and 29 introduced). Many of these plants (especially trees and shrubs) have multiple uses including human food, shade, living fences, soil retainer and firewood. The incorporation of these plants into an integrated on-the-farm production system as additives to silage for local livestock or as raw material for industrial transformation could be attractive to small farmers. Such plant uses could satisfy domestic needs and at the same time increase monetary income. Along with these cultivated plants are species that exist both as cultivated and wild populations in Mexico. Examples include *Leucaena leucocephala* (FAB) and *Gliricidia sepium* (FAB), which again are multiple-use plants native to southern Mexico and adjacent Central America. Over the centuries, indigenous and mestizo groups have widened their geographic distribution due to the trees' utility and ease of propagation. In fact, Leucaena is now found as a livestock forage tree around the world (National Research Council, 1984). In addition to providing immediate benefits through farming domesticated races and sustainably harvesting wild plants, the natural populations are valuable genetic reserves that future plant breeders will seek as starting material for modifying nutritional, phytochemical and horticultural characteristics of cultivated plants.

The herbaceous weedy species (26 plants; 16 native and 10 natural-ized) are common in and along cultivated fields. In some cases growth is encouraged so that people can collect forage to bring to the corralled animals or so that the animals can be turned out onto the harvested fields and devour the crop's companion weeds. In the tropical regions, natural forest regeneration includes many woody plants (e.g., Acacia, Caesalpinia, Cassia, Bauhinia, FAB; Lantana, VRB) as part of the early succession after the abandonment of cultivated fields. Certain trees (*Brosimum alicastrum*, MOR) are encouraged in the 'potreros' (or pastures carved out of the forest) so as to prolong the utility of these lands for the local farmers. Taking advantage of forage/medicinal plants with these ecologi-cal characteristics and of the people's appreciation for them would be indispensable in promoting ecological recovery of destroyed tropical areas. With deforestation of Mexican humid tropical forests advancing at an annual rate of 4.2%, only 9% of the area with original vegetation will exist in the year 2000 (Dirzo, 1992) with the consequential loss of half of the species of this region (Peña and Neyra, 1998). The local communi-ties can have a vested interest in participating in the recovery of the vegeta-tion through enrichment management (Ricker *et al.*, 1999) and in protecting natural resources for the future while obtaining immediate benefits through controlled browsing in these plots and sustainable harvesting of local plants of industrial interest.

RELATIONSHIP AMONG ETHNOVETERINARY MEDICINAL
PLANTS, FORAGE PLANTS AND TRADITIONAL MEDICINAL
PLANTS OF MEXICO

With the preliminary data available, it is possible to determine the relationships among the plants used in ethnoveterinary medical practice, those
consumed by livestock as forage, and those applied in traditional medicine
in Mexico. Using the previous two analyses in terms of body system/medical
problem classification, a comparison is made with the summary data on
2854 remedial plants reported in the national atlas (Argueta *et al.*, 1994).
In order to be consistent, the following classes were accepted: culturally
defined illnesses, digestive system, respiratory system, skin/subcutaneous
cellular system, and sensory system. Part of the genitourinary system
ailments of the Mexican compilation are included in the
pregnancy/birth/puerperium disorders group. Due to their low representa-
tion, metabolic system and nutritional disorders are combined. Because
the Mexican study did not summarize data on the circulatory system,
endocrine system, infections/infestations, inflammation, injuries, mental
disorders, muscular-skeletal system, neoplasms, nervous system, pain, and
poisonings, they are not considered here.

Even though the relative proportions are numerically different, the body
system/problem categories of the three usage groups possess, for the most
part, the same order of importance (Figure 5). The largest number of
plants is employed in the digestive system. The second largest category
is the skin/subcutaneous cellular system. The third category is culturally
defined ailments for the ethnoveterinary medicine group, but respiratory
system for the other two groups. The fourth and fifth standings are held
by the female reproductive system and genitourinary system.

Such close agreement (taking into consideration the minor values of
differences in the lower rankings) in the relative order of groupings of
plants with medicinal properties from three separate analyses suggests
that there is a common basis for the plants' employment and biological
activity. Although the foundation for the explanation of such a pattern
was not developed fully in this text, certain possibilities can be considered.
The database indicates that the plants are distributed throughout the
vascular plants rather than concentrated in a particular taxonomic (and
phytochemically related) group. In the first two analyses, each family had
on average three species. On one hand, the plants of different taxonomic
position may share similar bioactive principles. For instance, hypoglycemic
principles of taxonomically distinct plants with anti-diabetic activity share
certain complex carbohydrates, peptides and terpenoids (Marles and
Farnsworth, 1995); anti-diarrhoeal plants are rich in polyphenols and
polysaccharides (Heinrich, 1998). On the other hand, different compounds
with similar pharmacological properties may result in the clustering of
taxonomically diverse medicinal plants. Sharing these attributes along with
morphological, organoleptic and cultural features strengthens the concept
of 'medicinal plant complexes' that humans have developed over time,
perhaps having incorporated plants from their observations on grazing

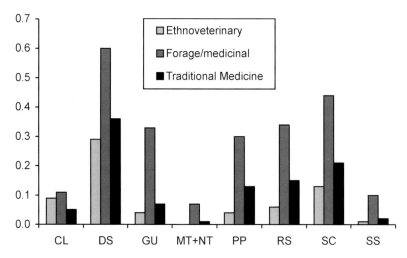

**Figure 5.** Comparison among plants used in ethnoveterinary medicine (n=135 spp.), forage plants with medicinal properties (n=151 spp.), and medicinal plants use by humans (n=2854 spp.) as the proportion of species utilized in body systems and important medicinal problems (CL=culturally defined ailments, DS=digestive system, CS=circulatory system, GU=genitourinary system, MT + NT = metabolic system and nutritional disorders, PP=pregnancy/birth/puerperium disorders, RS=respiratory system, SC=skin/subcutaneous cellular system, SS=sensory system).

behavior of animals. Such an example from this study is the 'orégano'. The characteristic odor and taste, common name and use as a condiment and medicinal herb are applied to members of four different families: Asteraceae (Brickellia), Fabaceae (Dalea), Lamiaceae (Calamintha, Coleus, Hedeoma, Hyptis, Monarda, Oreganum, and Poliomintha) as well as Verbenaceae (Lantana and Lippia).

## Conclusions

Despite the sporadic geographic coverage and uneven taxonomic treatment of the ethnoveterinary medicinal plants and forage plants, the preliminary patterns are reasonable approximations of the merits of plants applied to afflicted livestock and those consumed by animals. The purported properties of ethnoveterinary vegetal medicines parallel those of forage plants consumed by livestock and medicinal plants employed by humans. In particular, plants used in the digestive system predominate. This pattern, in turn, suggests future application of ethnoveterinary practices in livestock management as well as in commercial development and ecological restoration. There appears to be a biological and phytochemical foundation to this pattern. Further work needs to be carried out in order to corroborate the pharmacological activity of the plants and their value to animals and humans as well as to detect chemovarieties of plants (Tétény, 1970) for future application in the medical sciences and the conservation of genetic diversity of plants. In addition, certain parallels in ethnomedicine and ethnoveterinary science are apparent and need explanation. The potential of Mexican medicinal plants for improving the health of animals and humans is promising. We have much to learn from the 480 years of Old World domestic animals' experience in Mexico and to share with the indigenous and mestizo livestock managers.

# References

Aguilar, A., A. Argueta and L. Cano. 1994a. Flora Medicinal Indígena de México. Instituto Nacional Indigenista, México, DF.

Aguilar, A., J.R. Camacho, S. Chino, P. Jácquez and M.E. López. 1994b. Herbario Medicinal del Instituto Mexicano del Seguro Social - Información Etnobotánica. Instituto Mexicano del Seguro Social, México, DF

Alcorn, J.B. 1984. Huastec Mayan Ethnobotany. University of Texas Press, Austin, TX.

Argueta Villamar, A., L.M. Cano Asseleihand M.E. Rodarte. 1994. Atlas de las Plantas de la Medicina Tradicional Mexicana. Instituto Nacional Indigenista, México, DF.

Argueta Villamar, A. and C. Zolla (eds.). 1994. Nueva Bibliografía de la Medicina Tradicional Mexicana. Instituto Nacional Indigenista, México, DF.

Auró Angulo, A. and H. Sumano López. 1988. Uso de la manzanilla (*Helenium quadridentatum*) para el tratamiento de la saprolegniasis (*Saprolegnia* spp.) en tilapias (*Tylapia mossaambica*): estudio comparativo con la acriflavina, In: Memorias: Primera Jornada sobre Herbolaria Medicinal en Medicina Veterinaria, (coords. L. Lozano Nathal and G. López Buendía), Facultad de Medicina Veterinaria y Zootecnia, Universidad Nacional Autónoma de México, México, DF. pp. 90–95.

Barrera, N.B. 1996. Los orígenes de la ganadería en México. Ciencias 44:14–17.

Bailey, L.H. and E.Z. Bailey. 1976. Hortus Third. Macmillan Publishing Co., Inc., New York, NY.

Bennett, W.C. and R.M. Zingg. 1935. The Tarahumara, An Indian Tribe of Northern Mexico. University of Chigaco Press, Chicago, IL.

Bryant, J.P., F.D. Provenza, J. Pastor, P.B. Reichardt, T.P. Clausen and J.T. du Toit. 1991. Interactions between woody plants and browsing mammals mediated by secondary metabolites. Annual Review of Ecology and Systematics 22:431–446.

Bye, R. 1991. Documentación de los Recursos Vegetales en México: Las Colecciones Etnobotánicas del Dr. Edward Palmer. Informe Téncico, CONACYT POZOCCR 892320, México, DF.

Bye, R., E. Linares Mazari and E. Estrada Lugo. 1991. Recursos genéticos en plantas medicinales de Mexico. In: Advances en el Estudio de los Recursos Fitogenéticos de México, (eds. R. Ortega Paczka, G. Palomino

Hasbach, F. Castillo González, V.A. González Hernández, M. Livera Muñoz), Sociedad Mexicana de Fitogenética, Chapingo, Mexico. pp. 341–359.

Bye, R., E. Linares and E. Estrada. 1995. Biological diversity of medicinal plants in Mexico. Recent Advances in Phytochemisty 29:65–82.

Bye, R., R. Mata and R. Pereda Miranda. 1997. Avances en el Programa del International Cooperative Biodiversity Group en México. Noticero de la Sociedad de Biología de Chile 5(2):41–45.

Camazine, S. and R. Bye. 1990. A study of the medical ethnobotany of the Zuni Indians of New Mexico. Journal of Ethnopharmacology 2:365–388.

Conabio. 1998. La Diversidad Biológica de México: Estudio de País, 1998. Comisión Nacional para el Conocimiento y Uso de la Biodiversidad, Mexico, DF.

Cook, F.E.M., 1995. Economic Botany Data Collection Standard. Royal Botanial Gardens, Kew.

Cowen, R. 1990. Medicine on the wild side. Science News 138:280–282.

Cronquist, A. 1981. An Integrated System of Classification of Flowering Plants. Columbia University Press, New York, NY.

Cruz, M. de la. 1991. Libellus de Medicinalibus Indorum Herbis. Fondo de Cultura Económica y Instituto Mexicano del Seguro Social, México, DF.

Díaz, J.L. (ed.). 1976a. Usos de las Plantas Medicinales de México. Instituto Mexicano para el Estudio de las Plantas Medicinales, México, DF.

Díaz, J.L. (ed.). 1976b. Índice y Sinonimia de las Plantas Medicinales de México. Instituto Mexicano para el Estudio de las Plantas Medicinales, México, DF.

DiPeso, C.C. 1974. Casas Grandes: A Fallen Trading Center of the Gran Chichimeca. Vol. 2. The Amerind Foundation, Dragoon, AZ.

Dirzo, R. 1992. Diversidad florística y estado de conservación de las selvas tropicales de México, In: México ante los Retos de la Biodiversidad, (comps. J. Sarukhán and R. Dirzo), Comisión Nacional para el Conocimiento y Uso de la Biodiversidad, México, DF.

Durán Vázquez, A., L.C. Lozano Nathal and C. Calderón Figueroa. 1988. Contribución al estudio del yoloxochitl (*Talauma mexicana*), In: Memorias: Primera Jornada sobre Herbolaria Medicinal en Medicina Veterinaria, (coords. L. Lozano Nathal and G. López Buendía), Facultad de Medicina Veterinaria y Zootecnia, Universidad Nacional Autónoma de México, México, DF. pp. 96–107.

Esquivel Mendoza, G. 1982. Pensamiento Magico–Religioso de un Grupo Nahua del Estado de Guerrero con Respecto al Origen y Tratamientos de las Enfermedades en su Animales. Tesis, Facultad de Medicina Veterinario y Zootecnia, Universidad Nacional Autónoma de México, México, DF.

Estrada Lugo, E.I.J. 1989. El Códice Florentino, su Información Etnbotánica. Colegio de Postgraduados, Montecillos, México.

Etkin, N.L. and T. Johns. 1998. "Pharmafoods" and "nutraceuticals": paradigm shifts in biotherapeutics, In: Plants for Food and Medicine, (H.D.V. Prendergast, N.L. Etkin, D.R. Harris and P.J. Houghton, eds.), Royal Botanic Gardens, Kew. pp. 3–16.

Etkin, N. and P. Ross. 1983. Malaria, medicine and meals: plant use among the Hausa and its impact on disease. In: The Anthropology of Medicine – From Culture to Method, (L. Romanucci-Ross, D.E. Moerman and L. Tancredi, eds.), Bergin and Garvey, New York, NY. pp. 231–259.

Fernández del Castillo, F. 1961. Historia Bibliográfica del Instituto Médico Nacional de México, Antecesor del Instituto de Biología de la Universidad Nacional Autónoma de México. Imprenta Universitaria, México, DF.

Hartmann, R.W., M. Markand F. Soldati. 1996. Inhibition of 5-a-reductase and aromatase by PHL-00801, a combination of PY 102 (*Pygeum africanum*) and UR 102 (*Urtica dioica*) extracts. Phytomedicine 3:121–128.

Heinrich, M. 1998. Plants as antidiarrhoeals in medicine and diet. In: Plants for Food and Medicine, (H.D.V. Prendergast, N.L. Etkin, D.R. Harris and P.J. Houghton, eds.), Royal Botanic Gardens, Kew. pp. 17–30.

Hernández, F. 1959. Historia Natural de las Plantas de Nueva España, In: Historia Natual de Nueva España, Obras Completas, Tomos II y III. Universidad Nacional Autónoma de México, Mexico, DF.

Hobbs, C. 1995. Milk Thistle: The Liver Herb. Botanica-Interweave, Austin, TX.

Horrobin, D.F. and P. Lapinskas. 1998. The commercial development of food plants used as medicines. In: Plants for Food and Medicine, (H.D.V. Prendergast, N.L. Etkin, D.R. Harris and P.J. Houghton, eds.), Royal Botanic Gardens, Kew. pp. 75–81.

Instituto Nacional de Estadística, Geografía e Informática. 1986. Estadísticas Históricas de México. Secretaría de Programación y Presupuesto, México, DF.

Jiménez L, E., H. Sumano L.and G. Mateos T. 1995. Uso de la zábila (*Aloe vera*) para el tratamiento de laceraciones y grietas en tetas de vacas lechera. Vet. Mex. 26:271–272.

Jogia, M.K., A.R.E. Sinclair and R.J. Anderson. 1989. An antifedent in balsam poplar inhibits browsing by snowshoe hares. Oecologia 79:189–192.

Johns, T. 1990. With Bitter Herbs They Shall Eat It: Chemical Ecology and the Origins of Human Diet and Medicine. University of Arizona Press, Tucson, AZ.

Langman, I.K. 1964. A Selected Guide to the Literature on the Flowering Plants of Mexico. University of Pennsylvania Press, Philadephia, PA.

Linares, E. and R. Bye. 1987. A study of four medicinal plant complexes of Mexico and adjacent United States. Journal of Ethnopharmacology 19:153–183.

Loa Loza, E., M. Cervantes Ábrego, L. Durand Smith and A. Peña Jiménez. 1998. Uso de la Biodiversidad, In: La Diversidad Biológica de México: Estudio de País, (Conabio), Comisión Nacional para el Conocimiento y Uso de la Biodiversidad, México, DF. pp. 103–154.

López Buendía, G., L.C. Lozano Nathal and I. Aubert de la P. 1988. Aspectos teórico-practico para el desarrollo de na base de datos relacional sobre plants medicinales para uso en medicina veterinaria, In: Memorias: Primera Jornada sobre Herbolaria Medicinal en Medicina Veterinaria, (coords. L. Lozano Nathal and G. López Buendía), Facultad de Medicina Veterinaria y Zootecnia, Universidad Nacional Autónoma de México, México, DF. pp. 144–155.

Lozano Nathal, L.C. 1988. Las tesis de licenciatura sobre plantas plantas medicinales en la Facultad de Medicina Veterinaria y Zootécnia, UNAM (1916–1987), In: Memorias: Primera Jornada sobre Herbolaria Medicinal en Medicina Veterinaria, (coords. L. Lozano Nathal and G. López Buendía), Facultad de Medicina Veterinaria y Zootecnia, Universidad Nacional Autónoma de México, México, DF. pp. 23–32.

Lozano Nathal, L. and G. López Buendía. 1988. Memorias: Primera Jornada sobre Herbolaria Medicinal en Medicina Veterinaria. Facultad de Medicina Veterinaria y Zootecnia, Universidad Nacional Autónoma de México, México, DF.

Lozoya, X., G. Velázquez D. and A. Flores A. 1988. La medicina tradicional en México – Experiencia del programa IMSS-COMPLAMAR 1982–1987. Instituto Mexicano del Seguro Social, México, DF.

Marles, R.J., and N.R. Farnsworth. 1995. Antidiabetic plants and their active constituents. Phytomedicine 2:137–189.

Martínez, M. 1990. Las Plantas Medicinales de México. Ediciones Botas, Mexico, DF.

Martínez Alfaro, M.A., V. Evangelista Oliva, M. Mendoza Cruz, Gustavo Morales García, G. Toledo Olazcoaga and A. Wong León. 1995. Catálogo de Plantas Útiles de la Sierra Norte de Puebla, México. Instituto de Biología, Universidad Nacional Autónoma México, México, DF.

Mata Pinzón, S., D. Méndez Granados, M.A. Marmolejo Monsivais, J.A. Tascón Mendoza, M. Zurita Esquivel, Y. Galindo Manrique, G.I. Lozano Mascarúa and C. Zolla. 1994. Diccionario Enciclopédico de la Medicina Tradicional Mexicana. Instituto Nacional Indigenista, México, DF

Mathias-Mundy, E. and C.M. McCorkle. 1989. Ethnoveterinary Medicine: An Annotated Bibliography. Iowa State University, Ames, IA.

Matuda, E., and I. Piña Lujan. 1980. Las Plantas Mexicanas del Género Yucca. Gobierno del Estado de México, Toluca, Méx.

McCorkle, C.M. 1986. An introduction to ethnoveterimary research and development. Journal of Ethnobiology 6:129–149.

Mejía-Saulés, M.T. and P. Dávila Aranda. 1992. Gramíneas Útiles de México. Instituto de Biología, Universidad Nacional Autónoma México, México, DF.

Moerman, D.E. 1996. An analysis of the food and drug plants of native North America. Journal of Ethnopharmacology 52:1–22.

Nabhan, G.P. 1985. Gathering the Desert. Univesity of Arizona Press, Tucson, AZ.

National Research Council. 1984. Leucaena: Promising Forage and Tree Crop for the Tropics. National Academy Press, Washington, DC.

Padmakumar, V. 1998. Farmers' reliance on ethnoveterinary practices to cope with common cattle ailments. Indigenous Knowledge and Development Monitor 6(2):14–15.

Peña Haaz, N., M.E.A. Auró Angulo and H. Sumano López. 1988. Evaluación comparativa del efecto nematodicida del ajo (*Allium sativum*), sus extractos liposoluble e hidrosoluble y el tartrato de amonio y potasio en carpa (*Cyprinus carpio*), In: Memorias: Primera Jornada sobre Herbolaria Medicinal en Medicina Veterinaria, (coords. L. Lozano Nathal and G. López Buendía), Facultad de Medicina Veterinaria y Zootecnia, Universidad Nacional Autónoma de México, México, DF. pp. 124–129.

Peña Jimenéz, A. and L. Neyra González. 1998. Amenazas de la biodiversidad. In: La Diversidad Biológica de México: Estudio de País (Conabio), Comisión Nacional para el Conocimiento y Uso de la Biodiversidad. Mexico, DF. pp. 157–181.

Pennington, C.W. 1963. The Tarahumar of Mexico: Their environment and material culture. University of Utah Press, Salt Lake City, UT.

Pennington, C.W. 1969. The Tepehuan of Chihuahua: Their material culture. University of Utah Press, Salt Lake City, UT.

Pennington, C.W. 1980. The Pima Bajo of Central Sonora, Mexico: Their material culture. University of Utah Press, Salt Lake City, UT.

Ramamoorthy, T.P., R. Bye, A. Lot and J. Fa (eds.). 1993. Biological Diversity of Mexico: Origins and Distribution. Oxford University Press, New York, NY.

Reichardt, P.B., J.P. Bryant, B.R. Mattes, T.P. Clausen and F.S. Chapin. 1990. The winter chemical defense of balsam poplar against snowshoe hares. Journal of Chemical Ecology 16:1941–1960.

Ricker, M., R. Bye, G. Ibarra-Manríquez, M. Martínez-Ramos, C. Siebe, J.L. Palacio P., R. Valenzuela R. and G. Ángeles. 1999. Diversidad y manejo de los bosques mexicanos: aspectos microcecnómicos. Investigación Económico 59:77–109.

Rodriguez, E. and R.Wrangham. 1993. Zoopharmacognosy: medicinal plant use by wild apes and monkeys. Recent Advances in Phytochemistry 27:89–105.

Romero Ramírez, C.M., A.R. del Castillo R., A.C. Martinez M. and C.J. Calderón F. 1988. Estudios preliminares de los efectos antibacterianos, antiparasitarios y toxicologicos de la raíz del chilcuan (*Heliopsis longipes*), In: Memorias: Primera Jornada sobre Herbolaria Medicinal en Medicina

Veterinaria, (coords. L. Lozano Nathal and G. López Buendía), Facultad de Medicina Veterinaria y Zootecnia, Universidad Nacional Autónoma de México, México, DF. pp. 34–143.

Rzedowski, J. 1993. Diversity and origins of the phanerogamic flora of Mexico. In: Biological Diversity of Mexico: Origins and Distribution, (T.P. Ramamoorthy, R. Bye, A. Lot and J. Fa, eds.), Oxford University Press, New York, NY.

Sahagún, B. 1963. Florentine Codex: General History of the Things of New Spain. Book 11 – Earthly Things. University of Utah Press, Salt Lake City, UT.

Sahagún, B. 1975. Florentine Codex: General History of the Things of New Spain. Book 12 – The Conquest of Mexico. University of Utah Press, Salt Lake City, UT.

Sahagún, B. 1979. Códice Florentino. Archivo General de la Nación, Mexico, DF.

Sepulveda Betancourt, J.I. and A.L. Medina. 1993. Manejo de poblaciones de *Yucca schidigera* como un recursos sostenible, In: Making Sustainability Operational (coords. H. Manzanilla, D. Shaw, C. Aguirre-Bravo, L. Iglesias Gutierrez and R.H. Harme), U.S. Department of Agriculture, Forest Service, General Technical Report RM-240, Fort Collins, CO. pp. 164–171.

Sigstedt, S. 1990. Bear medicine: self-medication by animals. In: Abstracts of Thirteenth Annual Ethnobiology Conference, (Society of Ethnobiology), Arizona State University. Tempe, AZ. p. 4.

Sumano López, M., A. Auró Angulo and L. Ocampo Camberos. 1988. Comparación del efecto cicatrizante de varios preparados de la medicina tradicional y la medicina de patenete, In: Memorias: Primera Jornada sobre Herbolaria Medicinal en Medicina Veterinaria, (coords. L. Lozano Nathal and G. López Buendía), Facultad de Medicina Veterinaria y Zootecnia, Universidad Nacional Autónoma de México, México, DF. pp. 80–85.

Tétény, P. 1970. Intraspecific Chemical Taxa of Medicinal Plants. Chemical Publishing Co., New York, NY.

Tilford, G.L. 1997. Edible and Medicinal Plants of the West. Mountain Press, Missoula, MT.

United Nations Environment Program. 1992. Convention on Biological Diversity. United Nations Environment Program, Geneva, Switzerland.

Vázquez Manríquez, L., H. Sumano López and L.A. Calzada Nova. 1988. Evaluación comparativa de un remedio de la medicina tradicional para el tratamiento de traqueobronquitis en caninos, In: Memorias: Primera Jornada sobre Herbolaria Medicinal en Medicina Veterinaria, (coords. L. Lozano Nathal and G. López Buendía), Facultad de Medicina Veterinaria y Zootecnia, Universidad Nacional Autónoma de México, México, DF. pp. 85–89.

Villada, M.M. 1894–1898. Apuntes acera de plantas medicinales indígenas de la familia de las Leguminosas. Gaceta Médica de México 31:194–202; 34:211–227; 35:157–164.

Weber, W.A. 1982. Mnemonic three-letter acronyms for the families of vascular plants: a device for more effective herbarium curation. Taxon 31:74–88.

Zárate Pedroche, S., R. Bye, M.A. Elechosa, M.A. Monroy de la Rosa, G. Morales and M. Mendoza. 1996. Métodos de propagación convencionales y biotecnológicos de especies medicinales en zonas áridas, In: Técnicas Convencionales y Biotecnológicas para la Propagación de Plantas de Zonas Áridas, (eds. J. Izquierdo and G. Palomino), Organización de las Naciones Unidas para la Agricultura y la Alimentación, Santiago, Chile. pp. 305–347.

## Acknowledgements

We acknowledge the assistance of Myrna Mendoza, Gustavo Morales, Laura Cortes and Hector Sumano in the preparation of the manuscript. Francisco Basurto, Carmen Y. Chávez, Virginia Evangelista and Jorge Saldivar provided support for the development of information used in this report. We appreciate the valuable work of Javier Caballero and Laura Cortés (project coordinator and technician, respectively) of BADAPLAM (Base de Datos Etnobotánicos sobre Plantas de México). Concepts and data were derived from field studies and laboratory work that have been supported by: International Cooperative Biodiversity Group: Bioactive Agents from Dryland Plants of Latin America (Grant UO1 TW 00316 from the National Institutes of Health (NIH), National Science Foundation (NSF) and U.S. Agency for International Development (USAID); Consejo Nacional de Ciencias y Tecnología (CONACYT proyecto POZOCCOR 892320); UNAM (DGAPA-PAPIIT proyecto IN208094; Jardín Botánico del Instituto de Biología); Palmer Study Fund; National Geographic Society; Sigma Xi Society; The Royal Society of London and Botanical Museum of Harvard University. Encouragement and suggestions were provided by many colleagues. We are especially thankful to W.A. Archer, C.W. Pennington, and friends at the Centre of Economic Botany of Royal Botanic Gardens Kew (Frances Cook, Penny Davis, Steve Davis, David Fields, Christina León, and Hew Prendergast).

# Herbs as a source of nutrition *versus* herbs as a source of drugs: A matter of claims, biology and regulations

MARK D. NEWCOMB

*Heinz Specialty Pet Food, Newport, Kentucky, USA*

## Introduction

Use of herbs and other functional ingredients in humans and in animal species has increased dramatically over the last 5-years in the United States. Articles on herb uses are found in popular magazines displayed at grocery stores and more recently, in the Journal of the American Medical Association (Benoussan *et al.*, 1998). Apparently, the use of herbs has gone mainstream and is no longer just in the arena of a few eccentric users. As awareness of the uses of herbs and other functional ingredients increases, a greater demand is being made to verify that uses are at least 'safe' and preferably that they are effective as either a preservative, a nutrient or as a therapeutic agent. As one reviews both the popular and scientific literature regarding herb uses in both human and animal populations, it is often confusing as to whether the addition of the functional ingredient is intended to be therapeutic (drug) or whether the ingredient is added as a 'nutrient'. Many authors attribute pharmacological action(s) to the herb, when in reality, the action may as easily be as a source of 'nutrition' to the animal. Usually, it is not important from the author's viewpoint whether the activity is clearly a pharmacological action or an attribute of the ingredient as a source of a nutrient. To most authors, the importance is the biology of the ingredient as a dietary addition. The differentiation may become important as it relates to use in animal feed, since a pharmacological action approval (i.e., alters structure or affects function) would be subject to a different regulatory approach by FDA than would approval as a source of a nutrient.

## What is a nutrient and what can be added to animal feed?

The definition of 'nutrient' is somewhat difficult to define from a functional perspective. The definition is however, important as it helps to define what potentially may or may not be viewed as a feed. To classically trained

295

nutritionists, it is almost unquestionably agreed that water, amino acids, vitamins, minerals, fats, fiber and carbohydrates are nutrients. It is less clear however, whether items provided for their *in vivo* antioxidant function would be viewed as a nutrient. How would vitamin C be viewed given that it is required for hydroxylation of proline in collagen synthesis? It is known that ascorbic acid is a powerful antioxidant due to it powerful reducing potential, but this role is less clearly assigned as a part of vitamin C's status as a nutrient. A food is a substance that provides taste, flavor, or nutritive value. However, it can be argued that nutrition is an evolving science and that 'nutrients' should perhaps include a broader array of dietary compounds than have been thought of classically in our nutrition training.

Attributing a biological function to a nutrient can have interesting implications as well. An example can be seen with the recent FDA approval for label claims that a diet rich in soluble fiber from oats or psyllium may lower cholesterol. The definition of the soluble fiber as a nutrient (hence a part of a food) served to allow it to be listed as a component of the food. To discuss the biological response of the fiber on the label required approval since it was viewed as a 'health' claim—lowered cholesterol—which was allowed by the FDA Modernization Act of 1990. An approved health claim becomes generic and is allowed to be used on all products meeting the approved claim. The adage that the difference between a 'food' and a 'drug' is in the 'claim' is true in this example.

There is likely a continuum between nutrition and pharmacology. We all know from classic nutrition studies that overt deficiency of nutrients may result in a disease state. This disease is either reversible or preventable by inclusion of the deficient nutrient in the diet. A classical example would be found in the zinc response of animals with parakeratosis. A less nutritionally distinct example would be seen in the case of selenium deficiency. Clinically, selenium deficiency would present as either white muscle disease or as mulberry heart disease. These clinical conditions as related to selenium deficiency may be a secondary manifestation of low selenium dependent glutathione peroxidase activity resulting in increased oxidative stress and tissue damage. The continuum from nutritional deficiency to clinical symptoms in this example routes through the low activity of an antioxidant enzyme system. The question remains would zinc or selenium be defined as a drug or a nutrient? In these cases, it is likely that no marketing claims would be listed on a product due to the common use of these ingredients across most diets. However, the use of marketing claims such as 'selenium added to prevent mulberry heart disease' would likely result in the 'nutrient' becoming a 'drug' from a regulatory perspective.

A similar continuum between drug and nutrient may well be involved with responses observed by the uses of some herbal ingredients. In a review of the literature relative to uses of *Ginkgo biloba* (or standardized extracts), several studies have evaluated the impact of dietary additions as a method of decreasing tissue damage in the face of experimentally induced oxidative stress situations. Diabetes is known to cause retina damage by increased peroxidation of the retina lipids in some species. In an experimentally induced diabetic rat, oral dosing of EGb1 (100 mg/kg) eliminated diabetes induced changes to an electroretinogram. The same report following an ischemia—reperfusion sequence in an *in vitro* system subsequent to a 10 day oral dose of either 25,50, or 100 mg/kg/d of EGb1, noted altered retina tissue accumulation of various ions in a dose dependent manner. A pharmacological agent (drug) designed to be effective in the treatment of diabetes might be expected to lower blood glucose or perhaps provide increased secretion of insulin. However, Ginkgo in this example is likely acting as an antioxidant at the tissue level to provide some degree of protection to prevent retinal lipid oxidation. Again, it is reasonable to question whether the response to *Ginkgo biloba* is most appropriately viewed as drug or nutrient.

It is interesting that most classically trained animal nutritionists have been slow to consider the data surrounding the use of herbs in the diet of animals. It is intriguing to review the data further on the uses of *Ginkgo biloba*. A study evaluated a 10-day oral dose of 100 mg/kg/d of Egb1 followed by harvesting rat retina and placing it in a Na-ascorbate oxidizing system to evaluate antioxidant activity in the retina. Egb1 resulted in less alteration of the electroretinogram analysis suggesting inhibition of oxidative tissue damage in this *in vitro* system. Another report evaluated ischemia induced tissue damage response to ginkgolides. The extract, BN 52021, was fed at 20 mg/kg at 45 minutes prior to ischemia induced by occlusion of the mesenteric artery. Ginkgolide response was measured as effective by reduced necrosis, hemorrhage, edema, and neutrophil invasion into the intestinal tissue when measured at necropsy after 24 hr or reperfusion. Similar reports are available in the literature describing the effects of other botanicals on antioxidant status of the animal. Examples of reports showing antioxidant activity are found for items such as Siberian ginseng (Bekenev *et al.*, 1982), garlic, onion, shallot (Yin *et al.*, 1998), milk thistle (Konya *et al.*, 1993), and lycopene derived from Tomato (Clinton, 1998).

In the human food arena, there is discussion that the terminology 'desirable food constituent' be used to expand the concepts of 'essential' or 'conditionally essential' nutrients to a broader concept that would denote a nutrient(s) that is considered a part of a balanced long-term diet. This nutrient may function *in vivo* as an antioxidant, a soluble fiber important in the maintenance of a normal gut mucosa, or as some other functional component that would not easily be defined under the traditional concept of 'essentiality'.

## How does the GRAS listing relate to functional ingredients?

One interesting nuance of the existing regulatory system is that ingredients appearing on the Generally Recognized as Safe (GRAS) list in the Code of Federal Regulations are considered GRAS for only a specific use. This affects the use of GRAS ingredients in feeds in that if this particular ingredient is used, only its GRAS approved use may be discussed in packaging or other marketing material used to promote the product. While not a botanical, this concept affects uses of common items such as the aluminosilicates if used as an aflatoxin-binding agent. Aluminosilicates are approved only as anticaking agents. In this particular example use of aluminosilicates as an insurance policy against low level aflatoxin contamination could be considered as an adulterant. While it is not likely to be subject to regulatory action, the current system may encourage use of an ingredient for a specific purpose that cannot be discussed on the labeling. It seems reasonable that the GRAS listing should be a listing of acceptable ingredients allowable up to a given level regardless of the reason for use. Obviously, a marketing claim would need to be scientifically substantiated; however, this subtle change in the GRAS regulation would move violations from being considered 'adulterated' to being considered 'misbranded.' 'Safety' at a given dietary level is not dependent on marketing verbiage, but rather is a function of ingredient biology.

## Humans use many herbs and so-called nutraceuticals—How does DSHEA apply to animals?

The Dietary Supplement and Health Education Act (DSHEA) of 1994 opened the door for the human supplement industry to sell and market health or nutrient supplements in a fairly broad format within the United States. It is doubtful if anyone has not seen the supplement section in stores expanding almost exponentially to carry products from new companies as well as new products from existing pharmaceutical companies. It is evident that a large amount of the US population is interested in the uses of these supplements as this has been estimated to be a 4 billion-dollar market segment. Dietary supplements are available in forms ranging from tablets to powder drinks and for inclusion directly into foods such as power bars, juices and soft drinks. However, it must be noted that DSHEA specifically does not apply to use of dietary supplements in animal species (Federal Register, 2/22/96).

ARE DIETARY SUPPLEMENTS AVAILABLE FOR ANIMALS?

Dietary supplements are not defined in animal feeding regulation as they are in human regulation. Dietary ingredients are either 'drug' or 'feed' and are regulated as such. Any item not viewed as a feed, or approved as a food additive is by default unapproved. New legislation would be required to allow the use of dietary supplements for animals. The FDA usually allows regulatory discretion for the use of ingredients defined by the Official Publication of the American Association of Feed Control Officials (AAFCO) with respect to ingredients for which no safety concerns exist. FDA does have a significant role in the AAFCO ingredient definition approval process ensuring that an AAFCO definition has been either officially or unofficially evaluated by FDA prior to being assigned and approved by AAFCO. The Official Publication lists ingredients that are defined with respect to their availability as a feedstuff for animals in general. No differentiation exists between companion animals and livestock, so that all feed ingredients positively defined by AAFCO are available for any animal classification with only a few minor exceptions.

## Update on current regulatory efforts

Regulation of the evolving uses of functional foods is a difficult issue. AAFCO has established a Nutraceutical Regulatory Advisory Panel (NRAP) consisting of regulators from academia, AAFCO and the FDA to consider the numerous issues surrounding uses of these ingredients. The NRAP has solicited comments from groups/individuals with stakes in potential regulatory outcomes. In addition, the Pet Food Institute (a trade organization representing a coalition of companies that market pet foods) has formed a Functional Foods Task Force to attempt to proactively respond to the regulatory issues and to provide a pet food industry perspective on workable regulatory approaches. It is currently unclear what scientific bodies may be utilized to formulate opinions relative to the safety and efficacy considerations relating to specific ingredients. It is possible that AAFCO definitions similar to those assigned to enzymes could be implemented which would allow the uses of ingredients that have not easily been assigned to existing AAFCO feed categories. It is virtually certain that the regulatory efforts with respect to functional ingredients will continue to evolve.

## Definitions helpful in this discussion:

**AAFCO Definitions**:
    **Nutrient**: A feed constituent in a form and at a level that will help support the life of an animal. The chief classes of feed nutrients are proteins, fats, carbohydrates, minerals, and vitamins.
    **Feed(s)**: Edible material(s), which are consumed by animals and contribute energy and/or nutrients to the animal's diet. (Usually refers to animals rather than man).
    **Additive**: An ingredient or combination of ingredients added to the basic feed mix or parts thereof to fulfill a specific need. Usually used in micro quantities and requires careful handling and mixing.
    **GRAS:** Abbreviation for the phrase 'Generally Recognized as Safe.' A substance which is generally recognized as safe by experts qualified to evaluate the safety of the substance for its intended use.

**FDA Definition:**
**Food**: An article used for food or drink for man or other animals.

# References

Benoussan, A., N.J. Talley, M. Hing, R. Menzies, A. Guo, and M. Ngu. 1998. Treatment of Irritable bowel disease with Chinese herbal medicine. JAMA. 280(18):1585–1589.

Bekenev, V.A., and V.I. Khasnulin. 1982. Biolobical mechanisms of piglet adaptation to conditions of industrial technology. Sib. Res. Des-Technol. Inst. Anim. Husb. S-KH Biol. 17(1):113–116.

Clinton, S. 1998. Lycopene: chemistry, biology, and implications for human health and disease. Nutrition Reviews 56(2): 35–51.

Konya, L., V. Kekesi, S. Nagy, S. Feher. 1993. Effect of antioxidant treatment on the myocardium during reperfusion in dogs. ACTA Physiol. Hung. 81(3): 219–228.

Yin, Mei-Chin, and Wen-shen Cheng. 1998. Antioxidant activity of several allium members. J. Agric. Food Chem. 46:4097–4101.

# FOCUSING ON FORAGE UTILIZATION: ENZYMES, NDF DIGESTION AND FORMULATION STRATEGIES

# The use of exogenous fibrolytic enzymes to enhance microbial activities in the rumen and the performance of ruminant animals

KARL A. DAWSON AND JUAN M. TRICARICO

*Department of Animal Sciences, University of Kentucky, Lexington, Kentucky, USA*

## Introduction

Slow or incomplete digestion of fibrous substrates often limits the overall digestive process in the rumen and can significantly influence animal performance in livestock production systems that use forages as a major component of the diet. As a result, many strategies have been developed to stimulate the digestion of the fibrous components in ruminant feeds. These have included the use of specific nutrients which stimulate fiber digestion, processing feeds to increase the rate and extent of fiber digestion, and the use of direct-fed microbials and yeast culture to stimulate the natural ability of the microbial population in the rumen to digest fibrous substrates. Recent advances in fermentation technology and biotechnology have allowed for the economic production of large quantities of biologically active enzymes that can also be used as livestock feed supplements. These technologies provide new possibilities for altering digestive processes in a wide variety of animals. Specific enzyme preparations with specific activities can be designed and added as feed supplement. Such preparations can be used to drive specific metabolic and digestive processes in the gastrointestinal tract and may augment natural digestive processes to increase nutrient availability and feed intake. In the last decade, specific enzyme preparations have become valuable tools for economically manipulating digestive processes in monogastric animals and poultry (Johnson *et al.*, 1993; Annison and Choct, 1993); but there has also been considerable interest in using enzymes as supplements for ruminant diets (Dawson, 1993; Feng *et al.*, 1996; Lewis *et al.*, 1996; Annison, 1997; Howes *et al.*, 1998). Strategies that use supplemental enzyme activity in the rumen may be important since the digestibility of organic matter in the rumen does not reach 100% and even small changes in digestibility can influence the efficiency of ruminal fermentations.

While it is possible to define a number of enzyme systems or preparations that could be used to enhance digestive processes in the rumen, most enzyme applications in ruminants have focused on the use of polysaccharide-digesting enzymes to enhance the degradation of the slowly digested substrates in plant fiber. Two major types of enzyme activities are commonly considered in this respect. Cellulases are usually complex mixtures of proteins that act to hydrolyze ß1-4 linkages connecting the individual sugar molecules that make up the cellulose found in forages. In comparison, xylanases are enzymes that act on the xylans found in the hemicellulose fraction of many forages and in the fiber fractions of grains. Neither of these enzyme systems is found in the array of digestive proteins produced by animals and both are produced commercially using microbial fermentation processes.

In the past, the application of enzymes in ruminants has mainly focused on their use in young pre-ruminant animals or as a pretreatment for ruminant feed materials. Direct feed applications of exogenous enzymes to provide activities in the gastrointestinal tract of mature animals were not considered because of the potential destruction of the enzyme by the microbial population in the rumen. However, a number of recent microbiological studies and production trials have suggested that the addition of active enzyme preparations to ruminant diets prior to feeding may have a significant impact on microbial and digestive activities in the rumen. Enzyme-induced changes in digestive processes are reflected in both altered ruminal fermentation patterns and improved animal performance. This paper will review some of the recent data demonstrating the important effects of specific enzyme preparations on microbial activities in the rumen and discuss their impact on the performance of dairy cattle.

## Effects of specific exogenous enzymes on disappearance of fibrous substrates

A number of in vitro studies have demonstrated that it is possible to use specific fibrolytic enzyme preparations to enhance the processes associated with fiber digestion in the rumen. This can take place at several levels but is often associated with an increase in the initial rate of fiber disappearance. The response is generally measured as an increase in the initial rate of dry matter disappearance (Table 1) or as an increase in the rate of neutral detergent fiber (NDF) disappearance in batch cultures of ruminal bacteria that have been supplemented with enzyme preparations. This activity is believed to be the result of the ability of the enzyme preparation to render the fiber soluble or more available for microbial attack in the rumen. The most active period for enzyme effects appears to be during the first 6-12 hrs of the digestive process. In most instances, fibrolytic enzymes appear to have no significant effects on the total extent of fiber digestion after extended incubation periods.

The ability of specific exogenous enzyme systems to increase the initial rate of fiber digestion is important in many animal production systems because it influences the processes which control feed intake. In vitro digestion during the first 6-12 hrs of fermentation has been found to be closely correlated with voluntary dry matter intake in ruminant animals and is

Table 1.   Effects of an exogenous enzyme preparation (Fibrozyme) on the initial rate of dry matter disappearance in *in vitro* batch cultures of ruminal bacteria.

| Incubation time (h) | Dry matter digestion (%/h) in: | | Relative increase in the rate of dry matter digestion (%) |
|---|---|---|---|
| | Control | Fibrozyme (1g/kg) | |
| 12 | 3.63 | 4.25 | 17.1 |
| 18 | 2.90 | 3.01 | 3.8 |

[1]unpublished data from Dawson and Tricarico, 1998.

believed to be a measure that reflects the effects of plant fiber on the relative dry matter intake of ruminants fed forage based diets (Van Soest, 1994). As a result, the observed increases in the initial rate of fiber disappearance are consistent with the ability of certain fibrolytic enzyme systems to enhance feed intake in practical production systems. However, most of the available data have indicated that this type of enzyme activity can be influenced by the nature of the fiber, the age and maturity of the plant material, the nutritional status of the animal and the types of enzyme systems provided in the supplement. As a result, it is not yet possible to consistently predict responses to many types of enzyme supplements in all feeding and management systems.

## Effects of specific exogenous enzymes on *in vitro* ruminal microbial activities

While it is clear that exogenous enzymes can influence the solubilization of some types of dietary fiber, other enzyme-induced changes in ruminal microbial activities probably have the most significant impact on the overall production response to enzyme supplementation. A number of changes in ruminal fermentations have been associated with enzyme supplementation (Table 2). Several groups throughout the world are working to document and model these changes in ruminal fermentation. Currently, many of these changes can be demonstrated in batch cultures of ruminal bacteria by measuring the individual volatile fatty acid (VFA) production rates and by stoichiometrically estimating the amount of carbohydrates that are degraded to produce these volatile end products.

Studies of a number of enzyme preparations clearly show differences in the way individual enzymes and mixtures of enzymes alter ruminal microbial activities (Table 3). For example, use of enzyme preparations based on high levels of xylanase activity have been shown to enhance total VFA production and overall carbohydrate utilization by a ruminal microbial population in batch cultures provided with ground fescue hay as a substrate. This is consistent with the overall effects observed in studies that demonstrate enhanced dry matter digestion and fiber digestion. However, enzyme preparations that contain measurable levels of fungal cellulase

Table 2. Some measured changes in ruminal activities associated with exogenous enzyme supplementation.

---

Increased dry matter digestion
Increased NDF digestion
Increased VFA production
Increased carbohydrate utilization
Decreased acetate:propionate ratio
Altered ruminal pH
Enhanced microbial protein synthesis
Increased ammonia production
Increased urease activities

---

are more inclined to alter the relative proportions of VFA produced by a population of ruminal bacteria. This reflects rather dramatic changes in the physiological activities of the ruminal bacteria and can lead to a more efficient fermentation. These shifts in activity result in more propionate and butyrate production and less acetate production by the microbial population in the presence of the enzyme supplement. Combinations of the two enzyme systems not only increased the relative amounts of carbohydrate digested, but also beneficially decreased the acetate:propionate ratio. Such changes in the rumen suggest that certain types of enzyme preparations cannot only have a significant impact on the digestive process, but may also have dramatic effects on the overall fermentation activity in the rumen resulting in improvements in the efficiency of nutrient utilization. The fact that some specific enzymes can improve the efficiency of ruminant production without any concomitant increase in feed intake suggests that such fermentation shifts are important in explaining some of the overall production responses (Beauchemin *et al.*, 1995).

Table 3. Effects of various enzyme preparations on the fermentation of fescue hay by ruminal microbial populations in batch cultures.[1]

| Item | Treatment | | | |
|---|---|---|---|---|
| | Control | Cellulase | Xylanase | Cellulase + xylanase |
| Total VFA produced, mM | 40.9[a] | 50.1[b] | 58.3[c] | 61.5[d] |
| Acetate, mM | 26.5[a] | 25.1[a] | 38.1[b] | 28.0[c] |
| Propionate, mM | 7.8[a] | 13.4[b] | 11.0[c] | 18.9[d] |
| Butyrate, mM | 4.1[a] | 8.4[b] | 5.6[c] | 10.9[d] |
| Acetate/propionate ratio | 3.4[a] | 1.9[b] | 3.5[a] | 1.5[c] |
| Estimated carbohydrate utilization, mM | 22.5[a] | 29.3[b] | 32.0[c] | 37.0[d] |

[a,b,c,d] Means within each row with different superscripts differ (P<0.05).
[1] unpublished data from Dawson and Tricarico, 1998.

# Effects of a specific exogenous enzyme preparation on the ability of ruminal bacteria to degrade fiber

Fibrozyme is an enzyme supplement for ruminants prepared from the fermentation extracts of *Aspergillus niger* and *Trichoderma longibrachiatum*. It has been formulated on the basis of its ability to degrade the xylans found in the hemicellulose fraction. As a result, it was designed to aid in the breakdown of the fibrous matrix in plant structural carbohydrate complexes and expose many of the bound nutrients to digestive activities in the rumen. It may be especially useful in attacking the hemicellulose which makes up 80 % of the fiber found in grains. The enzyme preparation also contains measurable amounts of cellulase and protease activity that may augment other enzymatic activities in the rumen. As a result, its digestive activities are not limited to attack on hemicellulose. This enzyme preparation is of particular interest because many of the component proteins are produced in a naturally glycosylated form. Glycosylation is a post-translational modification of the protein molecule that is believed to be important in the processes that lead to secretion of the enzyme during production and in protecting the enzymes from destruction by the protein-degrading enzymes in the rumen (Annison, 1997; Chesson, 1993). This gives these enzymes a distinct advantage in the rumen where naturally-occurring proteolytic enzymes work to actively destroy proteins that enter with the feed. The ability of such fungal enzyme systems to withstand ruminal degradation has been demonstrated in a number of studies (Hristov *et al.*, 1996).

Studies have examined the effects of Fibrozyme on ruminal fermentations and have established its ability to alter microbial activities in the rumen. These effects can be rather dramatic and can be measured by removing ruminal fluid from animals receiving the enzyme supplement. Rumen fluid samples from animals receiving Fibrozyme have been consistently shown to have an enhanced ability to degrade and utilize the carbohydrates in grass hay (Table 4). These activities were often associated with an increase in the digestive activities during the initial stages of digestion and were often more pronounced in rumen fluid from animals receiving a high level of grain supplement than in rumen fluid from cattle receiving a hay based diet. It is interesting to note that the enhanced digestive abilities of these populations is not always reflected in *in vitro* dry matter digestion (IVDMD), but is often readily observed when examining the overall carbohydrate utilization (mM carbohydrates degraded) by the microbial population during a 12 hr incubation period (Table 4). Such studies have established a role for Fibrozyme and similar enzyme preparations in strategies for enhancing overall microbial activities in the rumen. The enzyme preparations appear to have the ability to change the way microbial populations in the rumen degrade and process fibrous substrates. Optimal applications of exogenous enzymes will require special consideration of diets and management practices, but it is clear that these types of preparations will have a place in modern ruminant feeding programs.

**Table 4.** The digestive activities of rumen fluid from animals fed either a grass hay diet or a 50% concentrate diet with or without supplemental Fibrozyme.[1]

| Item | Fluid from animals fed a grass hay diet | | Fluid from animals fed a 50% concentrate diet | |
| --- | --- | --- | --- | --- |
| | Without Fibrozyme | With Fibrozyme | Without Fibrozyme | With Fibrozyme |
| *In vitro* dry matter disappearance, % | | | | |
| 12 h | 26.1[a] | 37.7[b] | 29.6 | 28.7 |
| 24 h | 50.3 | 50.2 | 50.1 | 53.4 |
| Carbohydrate utilization, mM | | | | |
| 12 h | 16.4[a] | 18.6[b] | 19.9[a] | 23.5[b] |
| 24 h | 24.6 | 26.1 | 28.8[a] | 32.0[b] |

[a,b] Means within each row with different superscripts differ (P<0.05).
[1]Tricarico *et al.*, 1998.

# Effects of Fibrozyme on milk production in field trials

While laboratory studies have demonstrated the potential effects of Fibrozyme on digestive processes in the rumen, several recent field trials have demonstrated the impact of this exogenous enzyme preparation on the performance of dairy cattle in practical management systems (Table 5). Improved milk production in cattle receiving total mixed rations (TMR) or pelleted diets supplemented with 15 g of Fibrozyme per head per day range from no increase in milk production to an increase of 6.2 lbs of milk per cow each day in high-producing dairy cows. Such changes in milk production are often associated with increases in voluntary intake, but may also be the result of increases in the efficiency of the ruminal fermentation process as reflected in altered ruminal fermentation patterns. It is clear from the field data that responses to exogenous enzyme supplementation can be quite variable. This may be partially due to the inability of specific enzyme preparations to enhance the digestion of certain complex structural carbohydrates. Factors such as the maturity of the forage or the amount of lignification can influence the composition and structure of plant polysaccharide and can inhibit the activities of some enzyme preparations. Such factors could be expected to limit the ability of the enzyme preparation to stimulate animal performance. It will be important to identify plant, animal and microbial factors that influence exogenous enzyme activities in the rumen before predictable reponses to enzymes can be obtained.

# Defining appropriate dose rates for enzyme preparations

The level of enzyme supplementation is an important consideration when defining strategies for using specific enzyme preparations. Both *in vitro* digestion studies and production studies suggest that ruminal responses

**Table 5.  Milk production responses to Fibrozyme measured in field trials.**

| Site of trial/investigator | Change in yield (per day) | Response | Comments |
|---|---|---|---|
| Idaho dairy/Howes (1997) | 61.3 lb to 64.5 lb | Milk yield increased 3.2 lb (1.5 kg)/day, (also reported increased dry matter intake) | Heifers fed a TMR |
| Idaho dairy/Howes (1997) | 81.8 lb to 85.9 lb | Milk yield increased 4.1 lb (1.9 kg)/ day | High-producing cows fed a TMR |
| Southeastern US/Heintzelman (1998) | Variable with herd | Milk yield increased 1.8 lb (0.82 kg)/day | Mean of 14 herds fed pelleted supplements |
| California/Sawyer and Dildey (1998) | 104 lb to 115 lb in high cows (less in low cows) | Milk yield increased 6.2 lbs (2.8 kg)/day | High producing cows fed a TMR |
| China/Zi-Lin and Jian-Hua (1998) | 46.1 lb to 48.0 lb | Milk yield increased 1.9 lbs (0.86kg)/day | Paired Holsteins fed TMR base diet of corn silage, concentrate and Guinea grass |

to different levels of enzyme supplementation are not linear and that optimal activities of specific enzyme preparations occur over narrow ranges of inclusion rates. Inclusion of enzyme above the optimal level can depress microbial actives in *in vitro* systems (Figure 1). This type of depressed activity appears to be reflected in performance responses and has been demonstrated in studies with beef cattle (Figure 2). This characteristic of enzyme supplements can account for the lack of response to high levels of enzyme supplementation in dairy cattle (Sanchez *et al.*, 1996). The fact that it is possible to both over-feed and under-feed enzymes makes their application complex. The reason for depressed responses with increased levels of enzyme supplementation is not clearly understood, but may reflect the abilities of certain enzymes to down-regulate or depress the normal enzyme systems produced by the ruminal microbial population. Such depressions emphasize the need for dependable systems for evaluating enzyme activities and their effects on microbial activities in the rumen.

# Basic mechanisms which explain the effects of fibrolytic enzymes in the rumen

Exogenous enzyme preparations are often used at low concentrations. At these concentrations the enzymes would not be expected to contribute to extensive amounts of fiber digestion in the rumen even if conditions were optimal for their activities. For example, providing an animal with 1500 IU of xylanase, could only result in a 1 % increase in the soluble

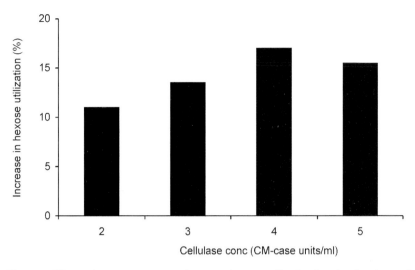

**Figure 1.** Effects of enzyme concentration on substrate utilization in a batch culture of ruminal microorganisms maintained on fescue hay for 12 hours (Unpublished data from Tricarico and Dawson, 1998.

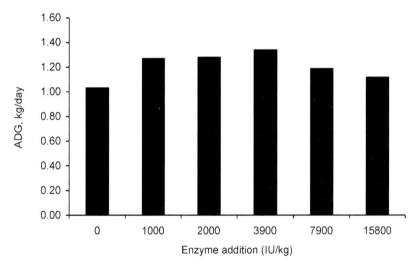

**Figure 2.** Effects of adding incremental levels of a fibrolytic enzyme preparation to an alfalfa diet on average daily gain of cattle. (Adapted from Beauchemin *et al.*, 1995)

xylose release from hemicellulose if optimal enzyme activities could be maintained in the rumen for a full 24 hrs. Since this is unlikely, the ability of low levels of exogenous enzyme to significantly enhance the solubilization of dietary fiber cannot account for all of the effects observed in the rumen. Instead, it appears that the beneficial activities of exogenous

310

fibrolytic enzymes are related to their ability to enhance the initial degradation of plant structural carbohydrates and complement normal enzymatic activities associated with ruminal microorganisms. It is likely that exogenous enzymes act in the rumen shortly after feeding and during a period just prior to bacterial colonization and prior to the time when naturally-occurring microbial enzymes develop and initiate fiber digestion. As a result, the exogenous enzymes can be expected to complement the endogenous enzyme systems associated with the fibrolytic activities of the microorganisms in the rumen and allow for greater digestion of fibrous substrates during the critical preliminary stages of digestion. The overall effects of enzyme supplementation may be a result of their ability to expose slowly-degraded substrates to microbial attack.

## Conclusions

Recent studies with specific enzyme supplements have shown that some of these preparations can enhance the solubilization of the fibrous components of ruminant diets. These activities can improve intake and stimulate animal performance. However, some enzyme supplementation strategies can also beneficially alter microbial activities in the rumen and change ruminal fermentation patterns. Some of these changes may have dramatic effects on production efficiency and may account for a large proportion of the beneficial activities associated with the use of low levels of exogenous enzyme in ruminant feeds.

## References

Annison, G. 1997. The use of enzymes in ruminant diets. In: Biotechnology in the Feed Industry, Proceedings of the 13th Annual Symposium. (T. P. Lyons and K. A. Jacques, eds.). Nottingham University Press, Nottingham, Leics., UK. p.115.

Annison, G. and M. Choct. 1993. Enzymes in poultry diets. In: Enzymes in Animal Nutrition: Proceedings of the 1st Symposium. Institut fur Nutzienwissenschaften, Zurich. (C. Wenk and M. Boessinger, eds.). p. 61.

Beauchemin, K. A., L. M. Rode and B. J. H. Sewlt. 1995. Fibrolytic enzymes increase fiber digestibility and growth rate of steers fed dry forages. Can. J. Anim. Sci. 75:641.

Chesson, A. 1993. Feed enzymes. Anim. Feed Sci. and Technol. 45:65.

Dawson, K. A. 1993. Probiotics and enzymes in ruminant nutrition. In: Enzymes in Animal Nutrition: Proceedings of the 1st Symposium. Institut fur Nutzienwissenschaften, Zurich. (C. Wenk and M. Boessinger, eds.). p. 89.

Feng, P., C. W. Hunt, G. T. Pritchard and W. E. Julien. 1996. Effect of enzyme preparations on *in situ* and *in vitro* degradation and *in vitro* digestive characteristics of mature cool-season grass forage in beef steers. J. Anim. Sci. 74:1349–1357.

Histrov, A., T. A. McAllister and K. -J. Chen. 1996. Exogenous enzymes for ruminants: Mode of action and potential applications. Proc. of the 17 Western Nutrition Conference, Edmonton, Alberta.

Howes, D., J. M Tricarico, K. A. Dawson and P. Karnezos. 1998. Fibrozyme: The first protected enzyme for ruminants: Improving fiber digestion and animal performance. In: Biotechnology in the Feed Industry, Proceedings of the 14th Annual Symposium (T.P. Lyons and K.A. Jacques, eds.) Nottingham University Press, Nottingham, UK. p.393.

Johnson, R., P. Williams and R. Campbell. 1993. Enzymes in pig production. In: Enzymes in Animal Nutrition: Proceedings of the 1st Symposium. Institut fur Nutzienwissenschaften, Zurich. (C. Wenk and M. Boessinger, eds.). p.49.

Lewis, G. E., C .W. Hunt, W. K. Sanchez, R. Treacher, G. T. Pritchard and P. Feng. 1996. Effect of direct-fed fibrolytic enzymes on the digestive characteristics of a forage-based diet fed to beef steers. J. Anim. Sci. 74:3020-3028.

Tricarico, J. M., K. A. Dawson and K. E. Newman. 1998. Effects of an exogenous microbial enzyme preparation (Fibrozyme) on ruminal digestion of fescue hay. J. Anim. Sci. 76 (Suppl. 1):289.

Sanchez, W. K., C. W. Hunt, M. A. Guy, G. T. Pritchard, B. Swanson, T. Warner and R. J. Treacher. 1996. Effect of fibrolytic enzymes on lactational performance of dairy cattle. Proceedings of the American Dairy Science Association. Corvallis Oregon.

Van Soest, P. J. 1994. Nutritional Ecology of the Ruminant (Second Edition). Cornell University Press, Ithaca. p. 119.

# Influence of Fibrozyme on digestive function and growth performance of feedlot steers fed a 78% concentrate growing diet

R. A. ZINN and J. SALINAS

*Department of Animal Science, University of California, Davis, California, USA*

## Introduction

The two most limiting factors affecting the rate of ruminal fiber digestion are pH and physical chemical interactions among cell wall constituents. Ruminal pH affects fiber digestion through its influence on the specific growth rates of cellulolytic bacteria. Growth of cellulolytic bacteria is optimal at ruminal pH of greater than 6.5. Between pH of 6.5 to 6.0, the specific growth rate decreases 14%/hr for every 0.1 unit decrease in ruminal pH. Cellulolytic bacteria do not grow at ruminal pH below 6.0. This toxicity is due apparently to the inability of cellulolytic bacteria to regulate intracellular anion concentrations at lower ruminal pH (Russell and Wilson, 1996).

In addition to specific growth rates of cellulolytic bacteria, the availability (or accessibility) of substrate to the cellulolytic process is also an important limitation to the rate of fiber digestion. Cellulose fibrils are cemented together in a matrix of hemicellulose, lignin, pectins, and extensins. In particular, the physical/chemical interactions of hemicellulose and lignin with cellulose present a formidable barrier to the cellulolytic process (Hatfield, 1993).

Ruminal deficiencies in fibrolytic enzymes may be partially overcome by dietary enzyme supplementation. Combinations of cellulase and xylanase enzymes have enhanced *in vitro* (Feng *et al.*, 1996; Howes *et al.*, 1998) and *in vivo* digestion (Lewis *et al.*, 1996), growth performance of steers fed forage-based diets (Beauchemin *et al.*, 1995) and milk production (Howes *et al.*, 1998).

Our objective in the present study was to evaluate the influence of a commercial enzyme supplement (Fibrozyme, Alltech, Inc.) containing xylanase and cellulase activity, on characteristics of digestion and performance of feedlot steers fed a high-energy growing diet. Hemicellulose is composed of dense pentose polymers called xylans. In this study we test the hypothesis that dietary enzyme supplementation will promote disruption of the hemicellulose-cellulose matrix thereby enhancing ruminal fiber digestion, and in turn, feed intake.

# Experimental procedures

## TRIAL 1. EFFECTS ON RUMINAL DIGESTION PARAMETERS

Eight Holstein steers (159 kg) with cannulas in the rumen and proximal duodenum (Zinn and Plascencia, 1993) were used in a crossover design to evaluate the influence of Fibrozyme supplementation (0 versus 15 g/steer/day) on digestive function. Fibrozyme is a rumen-stable (not rapidly degraded by ruminal proteolytic enzymes) fibrolytic enzyme supplement prepared from fermentation extracts of *Aspergillus niger* and *Trichoderma longibrachiatum*. Steers were individually maintained in slotted-floor pens (7.6 m2) with *ad libitum* access to water. Composition of the basal diet is shown in Table 1. Chromic oxide (0.40%) was included in the diet as a digesta marker. Fibrozyme (7.5 g/feeding) was added to the basal diet at the time of feeding. Intake of the basal diet was restricted to 3.5 kg dry matter per day. Diets were fed in equal portions at 0800 and 2000 daily. Experimental periods consisted of a 10-day diet adjustment period followed by a 4-day collection period. During the collection period duodenal and fecal samples were taken from all steers twice daily at the following times: day 1, 0750 and 1350; day 2, 0900 and 1500; day 3, 1050 and 1650; and day 4, 1200 and 1800. Individual samples consisted of approximately 500 ml duodenal chyme and 200 g (wet basis) fecal material. Samples from each steer and within each collection period were composited for analysis. During the final day of each collection period, ruminal samples were obtained from each steer at 4 hr after feeding via the ruminal cannula and ruminal fluid pH was determined. Ruminal fluid was composited for isolation of ruminal bacteria via differential centrifugation (Bergen *et al.*, 1968). The microbial isolates were prepared for analysis by oven-drying at 70°C and then grinding with mortar and pestle. Feed, duodenal and fecal samples were first oven-dried at 70°C and then ground in a laboratory mill (Micro-Mill, Bell-Arts Products, Pequannock, NJ). Samples were then oven-dried at 105°C until no further weight loss and stored in sealed glass jars. Samples were subjected to all or part of the following analysis: ash, Kjeldahl nitrogen (N), ammonia N (AOAC, 1975), neutral detergent fiber (NDF) (Goering and Van Soest, 1970; corrected for neutral detergent insoluble ash), purines (Zinn and Owens, 1986), chromic oxide (Hill and Anderson, 1958) and starch (Zinn, 1989). Microbial organic matter and microbial nitrogen leaving the abomasum were calculated using purines as a microbial marker (Zinn and Owens, 1986). Organic matter fermented in the rumen was considered equal to organic matter (OM) intake minus the difference between the amount of total OM reaching the duodenum and microbial OM reaching the duodenum. Feed N escape to the small intestine was considered equal to total N leaving the abomasum minus ammonia N and microbial N, and thus includes any endogenous contributions. The trial was analyzed as a crossover experiment (Cochran and Cox, 1950).

Table 1.   Composition of diet fed to steers (Trials 1[a] and 2).

| Item | Basal diet |
|---|---|
| Ingredient composition, % (dry basis) | |
| Alfalfa hay | 5.00 |
| Sudangrass hay | 17.00 |
| Steam-flaked corn | 65.50 |
| Limestone | 1.00 |
| Urea | 1.10 |
| Trace mineralized salt[b] | 0.40 |
| Yellow grease | 4.00 |
| Cane molasses | 6.00 |
| Nutrient composition (dry basis)[c] | |
| Net energy, Mcal/kg | |
| Maintenance | 2.16 |
| Gain | 1.49 |
| Crude protein, % | 12.25 |
| Calcium, % | 0.60 |
| Magnesium, % | 0.20 |
| Phosphorus, % | 0.27 |
| Potassium, % | 0.95 |
| Sulfur, % | 0.14 |

[a]In Trial 1, chromic oxide (0.40%, dry basis) was substituted for steam-flaked corn in the basal diet as a digesta marker.
[b]Trace mineral salt contained $CoSO_4$, 0.068%; $CuSO_4$, 1.04%; $FeSO_4$, 3.57%; ZnO, 1.24%; $MnSO_4$, 1.07%; KI, 0.052%; and NaCl, 92.96%.
[c]Based on tabular NE values for individual feed ingredients (NRC, 1996).

## TRIAL 2. EFFECT ON PERFORMANCE OF STEERS

Ninety-six crossbred steer calves were used in a 64-day receiving trial to evaluate the Fibrozyme supplementation on growth performance. The trial was initiated July 21, 1998. Calves were blocked by weight and assigned within weight groupings to 16 pens (6 steers/pen). Upon initiation of the trial steers were implanted with Synovex-S (Fort Dodge Animal Health, Overland Park, KS). Treatments were the same as in Trial 1 (Table 1). Calves were allowed *ad libitum* access to experimental diets. Fresh feed was provided twice daily (roughly 0700 and 1500 hr). Fibrozyme (7.5 g/steer, twice daily) was topdressed on the feed at the time of feeding. Assuming the primary determinant of energy gain was weight gain, energy gain was calculated by the equation: $EG = (0.0557 \, MBW^{0.75})ADG^{1.097}$, where EG is the daily energy deposited (Mcal/day), ADG is weight gain (kg/d) and MBW is the mean body weight (kg) (NRC, 1984). Maintenance energy expended (Mcal/day, EM) was calculated by the equation: $EM = 0.077MBW^{0.75}$ (NRC, 1984). From the derived estimates for energy required for maintenance and gain, the NE for maintenance ($NE_m$) and gain ($NE_g$) of the diets were obtained by means of the quadratic formula below. The trial was analyzed as a randomized complete block experiment (Cochran and Cox, 1950).

Formula for deriving net energy estimates for maintenance ($NE_m$) and gain ($NE_g$):

$$x= \frac{(-b \pm \sqrt{b^2-4ac})}{2c}$$

where a = -0.41EM, b = 0.877EM + 0.41DMI + EG, and c = -0.877DMI, and $NE_g$ = 0.877$NE_m$ - 0.41.

# Results and discussion

TRIAL 1

Treatment effects on characteristics of ruminal and total tract digestion (Trial 1) are shown in Table 2. There were no treatment effects (P>0.10) on ruminal

Table 2.   Influence of Fibrozyme supplementation on characteristics of ruminal and total tract digestion of organic matter, NDF, starch, and nitrogen (Trial 1).

| | Fibrozyme (g/d) | | |
|---|---|---|---|
| Item | 0 | 15 | SEM |
| Steer replicates | 8 | 8 | |
| Intake, g/d | | | |
| Dry matter | 3,484 | 3,499 | |
| Organic matter | 3,291 | 3,305 | |
| NDF | 600 | 603 | |
| Starch | 1,676 | 1,683 | |
| Nitrogen | 63.1 | 63.3 | |
| Leaving abomasum, g/d | | | |
| Organic matter | 1,765 | 1,713 | 25 |
| NDF[a] | 431 | 394 | 11 |
| Starch | 335 | 312 | 18 |
| Nonammonia N | 69.0 | 68.7 | 1.0 |
| Microbial N | 48.0 | 49.5 | 1.0 |
| Feed N[a] | 21.0 | 19.2 | 0.6 |
| Fecal excretion, g/d | | | |
| Organic matter | 768 | 768 | 21 |
| NDF | 364 | 362 | 16 |
| Starch | 24.7 | 26.9 | 2.1 |
| Nitrogen | 22.9 | 22.9 | 0.4 |
| Ruminal pH | 6.44 | 6.41 | 0.06 |
| Ruminal digestion, % | | | |
| Organic matter | 61.0 | 63.2 | 0.9 |
| NDF[a] | 28.2 | 34.7 | 1.8 |
| Starch | 80.0 | 81.5 | 1.1 |
| Feed N[a] | 66.6 | 69.8 | 0.9 |
| Microbial N efficiency[b] | 24.0 | 23.8 | 0.4 |
| N efficiency[c] | 1.09 | 1.08 | 0.02 |
| Total tract digestion, % | | | |
| Organic matter | 76.7 | 76.8 | 0.6 |
| NDF | 39.4 | 39.9 | 2.6 |
| Starch | 98.5 | 98.4 | 0.1 |
| Nitrogen | 63.7 | 63.9 | 0.6 |

[a]Treatments differ, P<0.05.
[b]Microbial N, g/kg organic matter fermented.
[c]Duodenal nonammonia N/N intake.

pH, ruminal microbial efficiency or ruminal and total tract digestion of organic matter and starch. Fibrozyme supplementation increased (P <0.05) ruminal digestion of NDF (23%) and feed N (5%). The increase in ruminal degradation of feed N is consistent with the associative effects of fiber on accessibility of forage protein to the proteolytic process. Total tract digestion of NDF and N were similar (P>0.10) across treatments.

TRIAL 2

Treatment effects on growth performance of feedlot calves during a 64-day feeding period (Trial 2) are shown in Table 3. Fibrozyme supplementation increased final weight (3%, P<0.10), average daily gain (6%, P = 0.13), and dry matter (DM) intake (4.5%, P<0.05). Consistent with the metabolism trial (Trial 1), Fibrozyme did not influence the NE value of the diet.

Table 3.    Influence of Fibrozyme supplementation on feedlot cattle growth performance (Trial 2).

| Item | Fibrozyme, g/d | | |
|---|---|---|---|
| | 0 | 15 | SD |
| Pen replicates | 8 | 8 | |
| Weight, kg[a] | | | |
| Initial | 223 | 226 | 2 |
| Final[b] | 308 | 317 | 3 |
| Average daily gain, kg | 1.33 | 1.41 | 0.03 |
| Dry matter intake, kg/d[c] | 6.28 | 6.56 | 0.07 |
| Feed efficiency | 4.75 | 4.66 | 0.09 |
| Dietary NE, Mcal/kg | | | |
| Maintenance | 2.00 | 2.02 | 0.02 |
| Gain | 1.34 | 1.36 | 0.02 |

[a]Initial and final weights were reduced by 4% to account for digestive tract fill.
[b]Treatments differ, P<0.10.
[c]Treatments differ, P<0.05.

Treatment effects on DM intake (and consequently weight gain), can be explained by changes in ruminal NDF digestion (Trial 2). The rumen has an upper limit on its capacity. As energy density of the diet decreases, the amount of slowly digestible OM in the rumen increases. In situations where energy density of the diet is limiting, maximal DM intake (DMImax) can be explained on the basis of effective NDF (eNDF) intake and ruminal NDF digestion. A simple basic-language program for calculating DMImax is given in Table 4. Inputs for initial weight of cattle when first placed in the feedlot, average weight during the feeding trial, dietary NDF, dietary eNDF, and ruminal NDF digestion were 180 kg, 265 kg, 19%, 80%, and 28.2%, respectively, for controls and 180 kg, 271 kg, 19%, 80%, and 34.7%, respectively, for Fibrozyme treatment. Accordingly, the 23% increase in ruminal NDF digestion due to Fibrozyme supplementation (Trial 1, Table 2) is expected to permit a 12% increase in DM intake.

Because the forage level of the basal diet was only marginally limiting energy intake, the observed increase in DM intake (4.5%, Table 3) with Fibrozyme supplementation was less then projected.

**Table 4.** Basic language program for calculation of maximal dry matter intake, and ruminal passage and digestion rates of NDF for feedlot cattle, as influenced by eNDF intake and ruminal NDF digestion.

```
INPUT "INITIAL WEIGHT OF CATTLE WHEN FIRST PLACED ON FEED, KG"; IW
INPUT "AVERAGE WEIGHT DURING PERIOD OF INTEREST, KG"; BW
INPUT "DIETARY NDF, % (DM BASIS)"; RNDF
INPUT "EFFECTIVE NDF, % OF NDF"; ENDF
INPUT "% RUMINAL NDF DIGESTION"; PRDNDF
FILLNDF = (((.098 * IW) + 26.24) * (BW ^ .75))
DMIMAX = FILLNDF / ((.01 * RNDF * (1 - (.01 * PRDNDF))) / ((.77 - (.00386 * ENDF)) *
(-.037 + (.042 * RNDF) - (.00031 * (RNDF ^ 2)))))
NDFI = DMIMAX * (RNDF / 100)
EDNDF = NDFI * (1 - (PRDNDF / 100))
RDNDF = NDFI * (PRDNDF / 100)
KPNDF = ((EDNDF / 24) / FILLNDF)
KDNDF = ((PRDNDF / 100) * KPNDF) / (1 - (PRDNDF / 100))
PRINT "MAXIMUM DM INTAKE, G/D";DMIMAX
PRINT "RUMINAL NDF PASSAGE RATE"; KPNDF
PRINT "RUMINAL NDF DIGESTION RATE"; KDNDF
PRINT "RUMINAL NDF FILL"; FILLNDF
PRINT "RUMINAL NDF TURNOVER";FILLNDF/ NDFI
END
```

## Conclusions

We conclude that supplementation of high-energy growing diet for feedlot cattle with Fibrozyme will enhance ruminal fiber digestion and thereby enhance dry matter intake and growth performance.

## References

AOAC. 1975. Official Methods of Analysis (12th Ed.). Association of Official Analytical Chemists, Washington, DC.

Beauchemin, K.A., L.M. Rode and V.J.H. Sewalt. 1995. Fibrolytic enzymes increase fiber digestibility and growth rate of steers fed dry forages. Can. J. Anim. Sci. 75:641–644.

Bergen, W. G., D. B. Purser and J. H. Cline. 1968. Effect of ration on the nutritive quality of rumen microbial protein. J. Anim. Sci. 27:1497.

Cochran, W. G. and G. M. Cox. 1950. Experimental Designs. John Wiley & Sons, Inc., New York.

Feng, T., C. W. Hunt, G. T. Pritchard and W. E. Julien. 1996. Effects of enzyme preparations on *in situ* and *in vitro* digestive characteristics of mature cool-season grass forage in beef steers. J. Anim. Sci. 74:1349.

Goering, H. K. and P. J. Van Soest. 1970. Forage fiber analysis. Apparatus, reagents, procedures and some applications. ARS, USDA Agr. Handbook No. 379.

Hatfield, R. D. 1993. Cell wall polysaccharide interactions and degradability. In: Forage Cell Wall Structure and Digestibility. Am. Soc. Agron., Crop Sci. Soc. Am., and Soil Sci. Soc. Am., Madison, WI. Page 285.

Hill, F. N., and D. L. Anderson. 1958. Comparison of metabolizable energy and productive energy determinations with growing chicks. J. Nutr. 64:587.

Howes, D., J. M. Tricarico, K. Dawson, and K. Karnezo. 1998. Fibrozyme, the first protected enzyme for ruminants: Improving fiber digestion and animal performance. In: Biotechnology in the Feed Industry, Proceedings of the 14th Annual Symposium (T.P. Lyons and K.A. Jacques, eds). Nottingham University Press. UK.

Lewis, G. E., C. W. Hunt, W. K. Sanchez, R. Treacher, G. T. Pritchard and P. Feng. 1996. Effects of direct fed fibrolytic enzymes on the digestive characteristics of a forage-based diet fed to beef steers. J. Anim. Sci. 75:3020.

NRC. 1984. Nutrient Requirements of Beef Cattle (6th Rev. Ed.). National Academy of Press, Washington, DC.

NRC. 1996. Nutrient Requirements of Beef Cattle (7th Rev. Ed.). National Academy of Press, Washington, DC.

Russell, J. B., and D. B. Wilson. 1996. Why are ruminal cellulolytic bacteria unable to digest cellulose at low pH? J. Dairy Sci. 79:1503.

Zinn, R. A. 1989. Influence of steaming time on site of digestion of flaked corn in steers. J. Anim. Sci. 68:776.

Zinn, R. A. and F. N. Owens. 1986. A rapid procedure for purine measurements and its use for estimating net ruminal protein synthesis. Can. J. Anim. Sci. 66:157.

Zinn, R. A. and A. Plascencia. 1993. Interaction of whole cottonseed and supplemental fat on digestive function in cattle. J. Anim. Sci. 71:11.

# Formulating the fourth diet

JAY D. JOHNSTON[1] and IAN C. SHIVAS[2]

[1] Ritchie Feed & Seed, Gloucester, Ontario, Canada
[2] Agri-Smart Consulting, St. Marys, Ontario Canada

## Introduction

Producers have long known of the adage that there are three types of dairy cow diets: the one designed on paper, the one mixed, and the one eaten by the cow. A *fourth diet,* the one digested by the cow, should be added to this list. Historically the analytical techniques we have used for feed ingredients and consequently the models we have used in ration formulation have fallen short of providing the information we need to formulate that fourth diet. While prediction of biological events is still at best an inexact science, advances in our understanding of fiber digestion, in analytical methods for useful fiber analysis and in computer models for their practical application have made it possible for nutritionists to get much closer. This presentation discusses from a feed industry perspective an approach to forage analysis and ration formulation that can be used in a practical, time saving fashion at the farm level to help producers maximize cost effective milk production

## Meeting the producer's needs: approaches to ration formulation

Nutritional problems such as ration formulation are met using a wide variety of software developed by both universities and private industry. There are numerous software programs available (Eastridge *et al.*, 1998b), and an excellent review of the most popular programs offered (Eastridge *et al.*, 1998a). The reviewed programs were all based on sound scientific data and represent those most commonly used in the field. Each has its own benefits and drawbacks, be they ease of application or ability to incorporate newer forms of analytical data. Most of these programs are mechanistic in nature and their use faces understandable problems due to assumptions that have to be made (Kohn, 1997).

For example the recently released Cornell-Penn-Miner (CPM) program predicts among other things metabolizable protein, and milk and plasma urea nitrogen values, yet reports have shown that these predictions may not be accurate over a wide range of rumen undegradable protein levels (Moscardini *et al.*, 1998). Differences in dry matter intake predictions between programs have also been noted across varying days in milk (Fox *et al.*, 1992) and environmental conditions, as some of the programs do not include temperature in their prediction equation (VandeHaar *et al.*, 1992).

Despite these criticisms, it must be remembered that predicting biological results over a variety of cattle sizes, environments, and production goals is at best an inexact science. Even with the greatest of care taken in ration programming, animal response is still predicated on the accuracy of the ingredient analyses, the formulation used by the producer, the ration mixed by the equipment and the amount of the diet absorbed by the cow. The potential for variation in any one of the above is large enough that concern over micro management of diets must be tempered with an appreciation for what is actually happening at the farm level. In a recent review article, Kertz (1998) demonstrated just how wide these variations are when ingredient databases from both public and private laboratories in the US and Canada were considered. Similar observations were made by Hutjens (1998), who reported on the many areas in dairy feeding where unnecessary variations lead to avoidable financial losses. Some of these losses such as shrink or poor mixing are easily rectified, while concerns over nutrient fluctuations and measurement are far harder to quantify and remedy. Basic feed sampling will take care of a lot of these problems, and should be taken as a logical step. Unfortunately, this is not always the case despite reports showing that the economic value of such testing is US$0.27/cow/day when uncertainty in the composition of feedstuffs is considered (St. Pierre and Harvey, 1986). While a decision to sample feeds seems obvious, the problem then becomes one of deciding what to measure and how to interpret the results.

## Interpreting forage analyses

Traditional analyses included protein, ether extract, crude fiber, and minerals. This basic list was soon expanded when the understanding of detergent fiber (NDF) values became more widespread. Most farmers are now aware of the importance of measuring acid detergent fiber (ADF) and NDF levels, thanks to the efforts of extension and industry personnel. However, with this increasing level of knowledge has come the understandable questioning of feed programs, as many simply do not work because digestibility was not taken into account.

The importance of measuring digestibility has been reported widely (Dhanoa *et al.*, 1995), as have the implications of rate of passage (Mertens, 1993). Because the ruminal digestibility of most nutrients is affected by residence time, any assessment of overall digestion is best considered with approaches that combine the kinetics of digestion with those of passage (Firkins *et al.*, 1998). The ultimate goal, however, remains that of assessing the amount of ruminally degraded organic matter, as microbial protein synthesis in the rumen is highly dependent on this number. The relationship between NDF and animal performance is also important. Allen and Oba, 1996) showed a positive relationship between NDF digestibility, dry matter intake, milk production and body weight change in lactating cows. The increase in milk production can be substantial, as a 1% improvement in digestibility can result in a 0.57 kg increase in milk production in early lactation (Allen *et al.*, 1997). The production response to increased NDF digestibility diminishes as days in milk increase; but the same authors showed that it can be 0.15 kg of 3.5% fat-corrected milk (FCM) for mid- to late lactation cows. With milk prices in the CA$ 56.00/HL range this could mean additional revenue of $0.09 per cow per day for each unit improvement in digestibility. When viewed in terms of large herds or multiple unit increases in digestibility, the effects on revenue are large.

MEASURING NDF DIGESTIBILITY

Measurements of digestibility rates can be achieved using *in vivo, in situ*, or *in vitro* techniques. The *in vivo* method is undoubtedly the best but it is very costly. *In situ* techniques have been shown to offer an accurate measurement of rumen degradation rates over various outflow rates (Arieli *et al.*, 1996), but the logistics of chemical analysis of the digested samples are time consuming and do not lend themselves to automation. *In vitro* analyses on the other hand have been greatly simplified by new analytical systems such as that available from Ankom Technologies and their use in measuring 30 hr *in vitro* NDF (IVNDF) digestibilities has grown. This type of analysis is not without its problems, as its use relies on several assumptions for pH and residency times. These *in vitro* techniques are, however, a tool that can be used to screen large numbers of samples in an effective and affordable manner. Methodology is obviously of critical importance, as the technique used must demonstrate accuracy without interfering in fermentation in order to describe feed ingredients in a manner that can be used in rumen models.

Grant and Mertens (1992) reported that lag times were an important concern as they can be lengthened by decreased pH levels or by the inclusion of non-structural carbohydrates. Recently reported work has shown that neither the lag time nor the extent of NDF digestion is affected by pH in the 6.2 to 6.8 range, although the overall rate can be diminished (Piwonka and Firkins, 1996). Several studies (Grant and Weidner, 1992; Hiltner and Dehority, 1983) have shown that a range of 6.2–6.8 is the threshold for optimal NDF digestion. Hence any *in vitro* analyses should be conducted with the inoculum pH in this range. The data reported in Tables 1 and 2 were generated from an *in vitro* system with pH ranging between 6.8 to 6.2 when measured at 0, 3, 6, 30 and 48 hrs.

The *in vitro* measurement of digestibility has progressed from the early two-stage technique (Tilley and Terry, 1963) to the more automated systems of today. Several authors have reviewed the newer techniques and have shown that the results obtained from the new systems are reliable and repeatable (Garmen *et al.*, 1997; Cohen *et al.*, 1997). One of the techniques reported was the Ankom Daisy II with which the NDF digestibility can be measured for forages, grains, or total mixed rations. The system utilizes miniature filter bags immersed in filtered rumen inoculum and buffer. The fermenting chamber holds up to four jars that can each contain up to 20 filter bags. This system offers a great deal of flexibility as far as experimental design is concerned. Analysis of results using the system has shown that similar samples can be successfully fermented within one jar or mixed with other samples within the same jar. As the samples are digested in separate Dacron bags, sequential ADF and NDF analyses can be performed with a minimum of problems once the fermentation is complete. Work by several authors (Komarek *et al.*, 1994a,b) has demonstrated that sequential ADF and NDF determinations provide repeatable and accurate results.

USING *IN VITRO* NDF ANALYSES

The use of *in vitro* systems to measure 30 hr IVNDF digestion is certainly of value and it has been used as a method of ranking corn silage varieties (Thomas *et al.*, 1998). In this work, several nutrients were measured in silage varieties from three different companies. *In vitro* true dry matter disappearance was shown to be statistically (P=0.07) different among varieties, as was *in vitro* NDF disappearance. Further work conducted at the Miner Institute showed IVNDF digestion rates for corn silages ranging from 24.87 to 61.56% (coefficient of variation = 19.53%) for samples obtained from farms throughout New England (Allshouse *et al.*, 1998). Multivariate analysis of these samples demonstrated that rainfall and temperature also contributed significantly to the variation in *in vitro* true dry matter disappearance (Majewski *et al.*, 1998).

A similar use of *in vitro* analyses began at Ritchie Feed & Seed in Ontario in the summer of 1997. The initial goal was to categorize forage samples by variety and geographic area. This effort soon proved to be all but futile, as large intra- and intervarietal differences were observed both within and between regions. Some of this variability was anticipated given the soil variability of Eastern Ontario, but the variation was not expected to be so large. Upon realizing the degree of variability (Table 1), work began to further quantify the differences among forage samples. Production differences among herds of similar days-in-milk fed total mixed rations (TMRs) based on corn silages with like 30 hr IVNDF digestion rates led us to believe that the answer perhaps lay in the degree and extent of digestion expressed at various time points.

## Field data: Differences among silages

Given the wide variety of factors affecting NDF levels in corn silage, a field study was undertaken to see if there was a pattern to NDF disappearance rates. It was hoped that such a pattern would reveal one time point for measuring NDF disappearance that would allow silage samples to be described in a comparative manner. All samples were collected during the fall of 1998 from farms in Eastern Ontario after a fermentation of 90 days. There is not a wide variation in the climatic conditions of Eastern Ontario; hence the samples came from farms that experienced the same weather last summer: warm, overcast, with lots of rain during the growing period followed by a rapid drying period. The data set excludes silages treated with inoculants and represents a mixture of randomly selected silage hybrids. While hybrid was not a criterion for inclusion, 62% of the samples were of dual purpose or grain varieties.

NDF levels were measured at 0, 3, 6, 30 and 48 hrs. The procedure utilized the Ankom technique, with amylase and sodium sulfite added. The rumen inoculum came from lactating Holsteins producing in excess of 35 kg of milk per day, and the Kansas State buffer system was utilized. Disappearance rates were calculated using time 0 hrs as a reference point.

The variability in either NDF content or NDF disappearance rate was large regardless of the time point examined (Tables 1 and 2). While a range in the NDF or NDF disappearance rates was anticipated, such a wide variance was not expected nor was the low correlation between any of the time points (Table 3). In terms of applicability to field use, these results make clear that corn silage samples had best be considered individually when *in vitro* techniques are used. Of further interest was that NDF disappearance continued past 30 hrs in most cases. The 30 hr time point used by many laboratories to calculate total NDF digestion rates does not appear to be correct.

Table 1.  *In vitro* NDF content of corn silage.

|  | Measurement time | | | | |
|  | 0 hrs | 3 hrs | 6 hrs | 30 hrs | 48 hrs |
| --- | --- | --- | --- | --- | --- |
| NDF, %[1] | 44.598 | 40.489 | 38.415 | 24.526 | 20.249 |
| Standard deviation | 5.9941 | 4.6858 | 4.8739 | 4.5757 | 3.6616 |
| Standard error of the mean | 0.5689 | 0.4448 | 0.4626 | 0.4343 | 0.3475 |
| Coefficient of variation, % | 13.440 | 11.573 | 12.687 | 18.656 | 18.083 |

[1]% of original dry matter.

# Incorporating *in vitro* data into feeding programs

High-producing herds today are continuously looking for ways to improve efficiency as producers are facing a market that is gradually returning less per liter of milk shipped. One of the largest costs on the farm is feed

Table 2.   *In vitro* NDF disappearance (% of original) for corn silage samples (n=100) measured at 3, 6, 30 and 48 hrs.

|  | Measurement time | | | |
|---|---|---|---|---|
|  | 3 hrs | 6 hrs | 30 hrs | 48 hrs |
| Mean disappearance, % | 8.6166 | 13.230 | 44.479 | 54.076 |
| Standard deviation | 6.5711 | 8.3803 | 10.542 | 8.3193 |
| Standard error of the mean | 0.6237 | 0.7954 | 1.0006 | 0.7896 |
| Coefficient of variation, % | 76.261 | 63.341 | 23.701 | 15.385 |
| Minimum | 0.0000 | 0.8900 | 8.2000 | 32.1000 |
| Maximum | 31.700 | 47.600 | 67.400 | 83.500 |

Table 3.   Correlations between NDF and NDF disappearance rates at 0, 3, 6, 30 and 48 hrs (N=100).

|  | NDF (%) | | | | | NDF disappearance, (%) | | |
|---|---|---|---|---|---|---|---|---|
|  | 0 hrs | 3 hrs | 6 hrs | 30 hrs | 48 hrs | 3 hrs | 6 hrs | 30 hrs |
| NDF 0 hrs | 0 |  |  |  |  |  |  |  |
| NDF 3 hrs | 0.8500 |  |  |  |  |  |  |  |
| NDF 6 hrs | 0.6972 | 0.9040 |  |  |  |  |  |  |
| NDF 30 hrs | 0.3620 | 0.5888 | 0.6365 |  |  |  |  |  |
| NDF 48 hrs | 0.4138 | 0.5524 | 0.5498 | 0.5833 |  |  |  |  |
| NDF disappearance, 3 hrs | 0.5167 | −0.0039 | −0.1364 | −0.2577 | −0.1026 |  |  |  |
| NDF disappearance, 6 hrs | 0.4681 | 0.0290 | −0.1928 | −0.3023 | −0.1123 | 0.8513 |  |  |
| NDF disappearance, 30 hrs | 0.3716 | 0.0451 | −0.1014 | −0.7238 | −0.2593 | 0.6301 | 0.6452 |  |
| NDF disappearance, 48 hrs | 0.3625 | 0.1102 | 0.0146 | −0.2848 | −0.6664 | 0.5115 | 0.4951 | 0.5445 |

(OMAFR, 1991). Nutritionists formulating diets for these farms strive to meet these demands by looking for formulation techniques or additives that will reduce the cost of milk production. The problem is how do you put a realistic economic value on a feeding program prior to its use in the field? The use of *in vitro* laboratory analysis and new ration formulation tools are gradually eliminating this hurdle.

The lowest cost ingredients in dairy diets are forages. Therefore, the goal needs to be the maximization of their use. Formulators must therefore increase the percentage of forage in the ration in a manner that yields the most cost effective mixture of milk volume and total components. Nutritionists today recognize that if milk production and the returns from milk components within Multiple Component Pricing (MCP) systems are to be maximized they must optimize the growth of rumen microorganisms from rumen fermentation. The advent of formulation tools such as the CPM, Cornell Net Carbohydrate and Protein Systems (CNCPS) and Dalex models offer the ability to design diets that optimize the conditions in the rumen for the fermentation of nutrients.

As nutritionists, we need to adopt rumen models in ration formulation to help:

- Maximize dry matter intake.
- Maximize microbial protein yields.
- Optimize forage intake.
- Ensure an adequate fiber mat.
- Balance carbohydrate fractions and protein fractions.
- Address environmental concerns: lower fecal, urine and methane output per unit of milk.

## DRY MATTER INTAKE AND NDF DISAPPEARANCE RATE

The dairy industry is all about maximizing dry matter intake. The more dry matter a cow consumes, the more milk and milk components the cow will produce. Thus it is important to understand the quality and digestibility of the forage we are feeding. The techniques currently used in North America that predict energy from ADF or NDF are unsatisfactory as the values give variable production responses. The basic assumption in these approaches is that all fibers are digested at the same rate and are passed from the rumen at the same rate. These techniques worked initially, but newer data have shown that it is time to move on. Japanese workers have developed the Oa and Ob system (Sniffen and Chalupa, 1998), which delineates fast and slow fiber fractions. The Oa fraction is the amount of fiber that disappears in a 4 hr digestion with a fiber digesting enzyme system, while the Ob fraction represents the slower fraction. A similar approach can be taken using the data shown in Tables 1 and 2.

New feed formulation programs that include predictions of rumen yield allow us to change the rates of digestion of the carbohydrate and protein fractions for various feedstuffs. If the correct fractional rates for a feedstuff can be defined, milk production differences can be demonstrated. The technique found to be most successful was use of time point analyses to estimate rapid and slow NDF disappearance rates. These figures are then considered in conjunction with lignified NDF levels as determined by the 48 hr NDF disappearance. Results from this approach are demonstrated in Table 4, which shows how a swing of 10 points in the soluble NDF fraction can have a dramatic effect on milk production and predicted net energy (lactation) ($NE_L$) levels. Figure 1 compares forage NDF and NDF disappearance rates. The rations in Table 5 were generated based on *in vitro* analyses using the CPM model and corrected 48 hr NDF levels. The carbohydrate $B_2$ ($C:B_2$) fraction is equivalent to the rate of NDF disappearance.

Table 6 demonstrates how predicted milk yield and $NE_L$ can be affected by the levels of lignin (as a % of NDF). Lignin content was derived from 48 hr NDF content. Note that as the amount of lignified NDF increases, the amount of fermentable NDF decreases and milk yields suffer.

The initial reaction to these results is usually healthy skepticism, but with experience this skepticism is replaced with an appreciation of how fractional digestion rate changes can have a large effect on production.

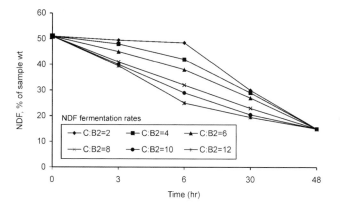

**Figure 1.** Comparison of NDF disappearance rates.

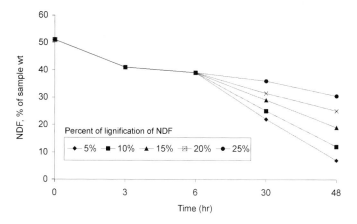

**Figure 2.** The effect of lignification on NDF disappearance.

**Table 4.** **The effect of NDF disappearance rate on predicted milk yield and predicted NE_L level.**

| Carbohydrate $B_2$ disappearance rate[1], (%/hr) | Milk yield (kg CPM) | Predicted $NE_L$, (Mcal/kg) |
|---|---|---|
| 2 | 31.8 | 1.43 |
| 4 | 34.0 | 1.60 |
| 6 | 35.6 | 1.70 |
| 8 | 36.7 | 1.77 |
| 10 | 37.6 | 1.82 |
| 12 | 38.3 | 1.86 |

[1]Equivalent to NDF disappearance rate.

**Table 5.   Diets used on a 140 cow dairy using corn silages with different NDF disappearance rates (carbohydrate B$_2$ digestion rates).**

|  | Carbohydrate B$_2$ digestion rate | |
|---|---|---|
|  | 3.0%/hour | 7.0%/hour |
| Haylage | 5.0 | 5.0 |
| Corn silage | 22.5 | 24.3 |
| Brewer's grains | 7.0 | 11.9 |
| Ground corn | 6.3 | 5.2 |
| Barley | 1.0 | 1.0 |
| Wheat shorts |  | 1.5 |
| Protein mix | 2.4 | 2.799 |
| Feed costs, $/cow/day | 4.05 | 3.37 |
| Crude protein, % | 18.22 | 17.96 |

**Table 6.   The effect of lignified NDF on milk production and predicted NE$_L$.**

| Lignin (% of NDF) | Milk production (kg/day) | NE$_L$ (Mcal/kg) |
|---|---|---|
| 5 | 36.3 | 1.75 |
| 10 | 35.3 | 1.62 |
| 15 | 34.2 | 1.50 |
| 20 | 33.1 | 1.37 |
| 25 | 32.0 | 1.24 |

For example, Figures 3 and 4 are typical of the NDF disappearance graphs for leafy and grain–type corn silages and demonstrate how the lag time differs between these two types of hybrids.

Recently, a producer asked us if these differences in NDF disappearance could pay for a bunker silo in feed cost savings. The results are shown in Table 5 with the protein mixes being unique to each ration. The ration formulated using the NDF digestibility rate (C:B$_2$) of 7%/hr had a higher microbial yield from the rumen and as a result required less bypass protein. The protein added to this ration was predominately cheaper sources of

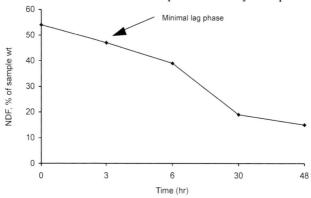

**Figure 3.** The *in vitro* NDF disappearance for a leafy corn silage.

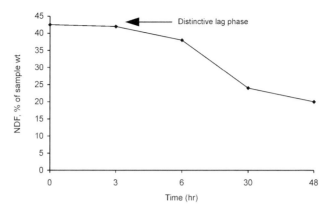

**Figure 4.** The *in vitro* NDF disappearance for a grain variety of corn silage.

rumen degradable proteins such as soybean meal, canola meal and urea. The ration formulated using corn silage with a C:B$_2$ of 3%/hr yielded less microbial protein and had to be supplemented with bypass sources of protein, such as fish meal and blood meal to attain the same amino acid balance. The cost difference between these two rations was CA $0.68 per head per day.

Differences among various legume and grass/legume haylages are not as dramatic as those seen in corn silages, but they can affect milk production levels (Figures 5 and 6). The data in Figure 7 demonstrate the effect of time of cutting on NDF disappearance rates with samples taken at the same geographic point in a field when first and second haylages were harvested. The samples were fermented in mini silos and the poor results for the second cut were reflected in production when the crop was actually fed to lactating cows.

The effect seasonality has on haylages can be duplicated in corn silages

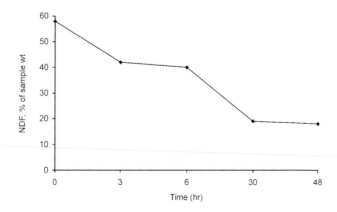

**Figure 5.** Typical *in vitro* NDF disappearance of a grass haylage.

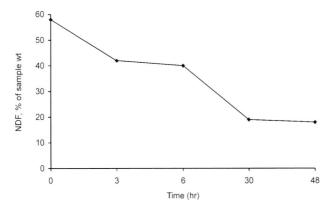

**Figure 6.** Typical *in vitro* NDF analysis of an alfalfa haylage.

when processing techniques are used. Kernel processors are gaining increased acceptance in North America as more reports of improved NDF digestibility are published. Another option is use of a re-cutter screen where harvested corn silage is forced through a further screen in order to reduce chop length. It would be reasonable to assume that the effect of using the screen would be to decrease the lag time before silage digestion begins in the rumen. As illustrated in Figure 8 this did not happen, but the rate and extent of NDF disappearance did increase. The data points used came from the analysis of a grain hybrid that had been dried to 32% DM prior to harvest.

## UNDERSTANDING THE RESPONSE TO SILAGE AND RUMEN FERMENTATION AIDS

### The effect of silage inoculants on NDF disappearance
As processing of haylages is not a very practical proposition, other techniques need to be found to alter NDF disappearance rates. One indirect

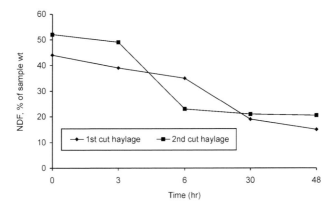

**Figure 7.** The effect of date of harvest on NDF disappearance.

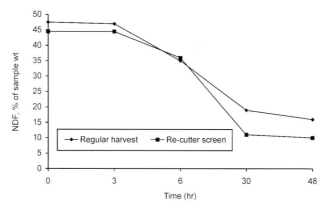

**Figure 8.** Effect of re-cutter screen on NDF disappearance for corn silage.

approach is the use of inoculants, which while intended to improve the ensiling process, can also affect NDF and protein digestion characteristics. The impact of altering silage fermentation with an inoculant on forage digestion characteristics was illustrated in a trial using mini silos. Haylage was ensiled following a 24-hour wilting period and treatment with or without a silage inoculant (Sil-All, Alltech Inc.). The silos were opened after a 30-day ensiling period and composite samples analyzed for both treated and control groups. There were improvements in the NDF disappearance and a protein sparing effect when haylage was inoculated with Sil-All (Figures 9 and 10).

A similar trial tested effects of inoculation with Sil-All on corn silage with 1 tonne silos being used instead of mini silos. The inoculant was applied in both the wet and dry form at ensiling and samples were taken after 110 days. Inoculation resulted in a protein sparing effect at the 30 hr measurement (P<0.05) while NDF disappearance was increased at the 3 hr time point

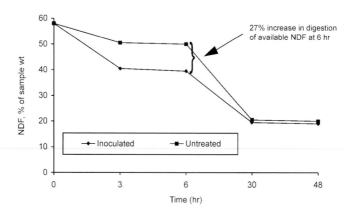

**Figure 9.** The effect of inoculation on NDF disappearance of grass haylage.

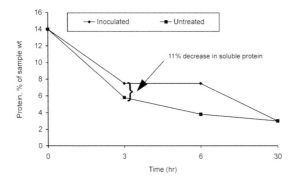

**Figure 10.** The effect of inoculant on the protein disappearance of grass silage.

(P<0.08) (Table 7). The importance of these results lies in the fact that while Sil-All is designed as an aid to improve fermentation, its use does positively modify the ruminal digestion characteristics of corn silage.

**Table 7.** Effects of inoculation with water-soluble (WS) or dry forms of Sil-All on *in vitro* digestibility characteristics of corn silage.

| | | | Time (h) | | |
|---|---|---|---|---|---|
| | 0 | 3 | 6 | 30 | 48 |
| **Protein, g** | | | | | |
| WS[1] | 6.4 | 2.2 | 1.9 | 1.5[a] | – |
| Dry[2] | 6.6 | 2.3 | 2.1 | 1.5[a] | – |
| Control | 6.9 | 2.1 | 1.9 | 1.1[b] | – |
| P value | 0.48 | 0.34 | 0.59 | 0.04 | – |
| **Protein disappearance, % of initial weight** | | | | | |
| WS | – | 62.8[a] | 67.5 | 75.3[a] | – |
| Dry | – | 65.6[ab] | 68.2 | 77.4[ab] | – |
| Control | – | 69.3[b] | 71.8 | 84.1[b] | – |
| P value | – | 0.11 | 0.43 | 0.05 | – |
| **NDF, %** | | | | | |
| WS | 51.7[ab] | 45.6 | 43.0 | 27.5 | 21.7 |
| Dry | 52.4[a] | 44.9 | 43.6 | 28.0 | 23.2 |
| Control | 50.8[b] | 45.0 | 43.1 | 26.6 | 22.8 |
| P value | 0.10 | 0.75 | 0.73 | 0.54 | 0.23 |
| **NDF disappearance, % of initial weight** | | | | | |
| WS | – | 12.1[a] | 16.8 | 46.8 | 57.9 |
| Dry | – | 14.3[a] | 16.8 | 46.5 | 55.7 |
| Control | – | 11.3[b] | 15.1 | 47.7 | 55.1 |
| P value | – | 0.03 | 0.36 | 0.87 | 0.15 |

[1]Sil-All Water Soluble
[2]Sil-All Dry Inoculant
[ab]Values within columns with different superscripts are significantly different (P<0.05).

### The effect of Fibrozyme on in vitro NDF disappearance

The potential milk production per acre from corn silage can be affected greatly by variety, stage of maturity, processing technique, and environment (Undersander *et al.*, 1993). The use of enzymes has also been suggested as another technique to increase silage digestion or feeding value (Yang *et al.*, 1999) with some of the positive responses in production coming from increased dry matter intake and some from improved digestibility. Yang *et al.* (1999) reported that addition of an enzyme containing xylanase and cellulase activities to the diets of lactating dairy cattle improved ruminal NDF digestion by up to 6%, and 4% FCM production by 2.2 kg.

As the mode of action of the various enzyme products appears to vary according to the activities included relative to the feed substrate, generalized conclusions cannot really be drawn. With this in mind a further field trial was undertaken to see if the enzyme product Fibrozyme affected *in vitro* NDF disappearance rates, and if so in what manner. The study involved the use of four corn silage hybrids planted at three densities of 22K, 27K and 32K plants per acre. Samples were taken following a 90 day fermentation and NDF disappearance rates were calculated from the results of *in vitro* analyses. Fibrozyme was added to the treatment groups at a rate equivalent to 15 g/head/day. Fibrozyme improved NDF disappearance across hybrids and planting rates within the first 6 hours ($P<0.05$) (Table 8). Further work is needed to explain hybrid and planting density effects, but the concept of enzyme supplementation of dairy diets is another tool that can be used to produce cost effective milk.

Table 8. Effects of Fibrozyme on the rate and extent of NDF disappearance in four corn silage hybrids.

| All hybrids | Initial rate of digestion (6 h) | | | Extended rate of digestion (30 h) | | | NDF remaining (48 h) | |
|---|---|---|---|---|---|---|---|---|
| | Control | Fibro-zyme | Increase (%) | Control | Fibro-zyme | Increase (%) | Control | Fibro-zyme |
| 22K | 1.39 | 2.13 | 72.8 | 13.08 | 12.86 | 19.9 | 20.10 | 19.27 |
| 27K | 2.49 | 3.32 | 69.3 | 14.83 | 12.81 | −11.7 | 19.89 | 19.86 |
| 32K | 2.57[a] | 4.66[b] | 196.7 | 14.35 | 15.17 | 13.3 | 21.20 | 20.37 |
| Overall | 2.15[a] | 3.38[b] | 112.9 | 14.09 | 13.61 | 7.1 | 20.39 | 19.83 |

[a,b] Means in a row with different superscripts differ ($P<0.05$).

## ECONOMIC IMPACT

Any successful ration formulation becomes part of an effective production health program. Formulating rations to increase digestible fiber intake has resulted in a better rumen environment. Rations formulated at the Elora Dairy Research Center on this basis have resulted in higher rumen pH values and fewer rumen health incidents (Livingston, personal communication). Rumen pH was recorded once per minute over 24 hours

334

in eight ruminally-canulated cows or 1,440 times per day. Rumen pH ranged from 6.25 to 6.35 and compared closely to the predictions by the CPM model. Cows on these programs appear to have greater dry matter intakes in early lactation and less severe body weight loss.

In reviewing high-producing dairy herds, all have a percentage of dietary NDF supplied as fermentable material. Feedstuffs that are highly fermentable result in increased microbial yields from the rumen. The formulator can produce the same amount of milk by feeding more forage and decreasing non-forage costs. Data were collected on a 150 cow herd housed in free stalls producing approximately 30 liters per cow per day. The farm had two silos for corn silage. One silo had corn silage stored at 36% DM with a C:B$_2$ rate of 3.07 %/hr and the other silo had corn silage at 32% DM with a C:B$_2$ rate of 7.0%/hr. Switching from the silo containing the forage with the slower C:B2 digestion rate to the other will result in 0.75 liter in increase in milk (DFO, 1999).

Formulating diets with the 7.0% C:B2 fermentation rate allows for either increased potential milk production or a savings in feeding costs. When reviewing the rations (Table 9), the diet using the corn silage with a C:B2 of 7.0% per hour gave an improvement in feeding costs of CA$0.60 per day over the diet using the silage with a C:B$_2$ of 3.0% per hour. On an annualized basis with 150 cows, this difference will contribute CA$32,850 to the producer's bottom line.

Table 9.   Feeding cost per cow per day for test farm using corn silage with either 3 or 7 %/hr C:B$_2$ digestion rate.

| Date | Feed cost (CA$/cow/day) |
| --- | --- |
| September[1] | 3.14 |
| October[1] | 3.07 |
| November[2] | 3.63 |
| December[2] | 3.75 |
| January[2] | 3.71 |

[1]Ration based on the corn silage with C:B$_2$ digestion rate of 7 %/hr.
[2]Ration based on the corn silage with C:B$_2$ digestion rate of 3 %/hr.

OTHER BENEFITS: ENVIRONMENTAL IMPACT

Of all the problems facing the modern dairy operation none has the potential to cause as much controversy as that of environmental pollution. Farm nutrient cycles have been reviewed by several authors (Chandler, 1996; Beegle, 1998) and options to minimize nitrogen or phosphorous pollution have been discussed. Most of these options involve the measurement of whole farm nitrogen and phosphorus use and production rates; and it has proven very difficult to avoid nutrient excesses. Different cropping procedures certainly have merit, but another option is to alter the diet so as to maximize nitrogen use in the cow and minimize its overfeeding

(Chase, 1998). The concept of synchronization of ruminal protein and carbohydrate levels has met with mixed success. The accepted theory is that rate of digestion of the carbohydrates is the principal factor controlling the amount of energy available for microbial growth, while proteins affect the extent of microbial production (Hoover and Stokes, 1991). *In vitro* studies have shown both success and failure when protein and carbohydrate needs were matched (Newbold and Rust, 1992; Henning *et al.*, 1991). Lactation studies have met with similar results (Robinson and McQuenn, 1994); but it would appear that understanding the interactions between ruminally degraded organic matter and protein is key to solving the problem. A recent report has shown that plasma urea nitrogen levels can be manipulated by changes to the diet (Shabi *et al.*, 1998), as can urinary creatinine and purine derivative levels (Moscardini *et al.*, 1998). These results have implications for total farm nitrogen balance, an increasingly important concern.

Notwithstanding the obvious financial loss due to overfeeding protein, the belief amongst many producers that high dietary protein content is necessary for high production levels will be hard to change. Altering the views of producers on protein needs will not be easy, but with the release of the CPM program they can be shown that nitrogen excretion can be changed if enough information on the diet is obtained. Measurements such as ruminal degradability of proteins and organic matter are needed, however they are not always easy to obtain. *In vitro* analyses allow one more method of gathering data; and the technique can be used to predict the extent and degree of both protein and NDF digestion. Once these rates are known they can then be used in the CPM model to modify the nitrogen cycle in lactating cattle with a resulting decrease in environmental concerns.

## Implications for the future

One of the principle truths in the world of animal agriculture is that change is inevitable, necessary, and ultimately the foundation for future survival. This is not to say that every new idea is to be embraced without review of potential consequences, as there is a fine line between rejection of new ideas for perceived lack of supporting evidence, and embracing them skeptically while further research is conducted. The analysis of feed ingredients and interpretation of analytical results has long been a dilemma as can be seen from the following quote:

> *"Meanwhile, experimental inquiry has been increasingly active; the laws of animal nutrition are getting to be better understood, the theories have been put to the test of actual experience. While their value to the farmer has been developed in ways which improvements have become apparent, we are constantly working toward a clearer understanding of the principles of feeding and a more successful application of them to the practice of the farm. With the rest it has become evident that to meet the demands*

*of physiological chemistry and practical feeding, the chemist must devise more accurate methods of estimating the nutritive value of feeding stuffs"*
*(W.O. Atwater, 1891).*

This quote could just as easily have come from a current article on dairy nutrition. Past, present and future nutritionists have been or will be faced with the same dilemma of incomplete knowledge of important variables. Successfully handling this lack of complete knowledge is the challenge facing anyone providing services or products to the dairy industry. Those with a firm grasp of the relationships at play in the biological systems involved in producing cost effective milk will prosper. Those that do not face a more clouded future. The problem becomes one of being able to use today's knowledge in a manner that will lead to the breakthroughs necessary for tomorrow's survival.

## Conclusions

Fiber analyses have evolved from proximate to detergent measurement systems, while the protein component of the diet has gone from being viewed as a single entity to one where fractions and amino acid composition are now accepted as the standard (Clark *et al.*, 1992; Sniffen *et al.*, 1992; Schwab, 1995). Thoughtful new approaches on carbohydrate fractions have been proposed (Hall *et al.*, 1998), as have new techniques to measure them (Pell and Schofield, 1993). Research on sugars and starches (Hoover and Miller, 1995) has also added to the base of knowledge being applied in the field and has been shown to offer a usable method of improving rumen productivity. Improvements in our understanding of how rumen function can be affected by changes in fiber digestion have been afforded by the release of the CPM model. When applied in conjunction with measurements of fractional digestion rates the results achieved in the field have been significant, especially if compared to those obtained from older models. The improvements have generally arisen from being able to make adjustments for lag times and extent of disappearance. Taken as a whole, these scientific advances afford today's nutritionists with a wide variety of techniques to improve milk production by minimizing the number and extent of the variables that must be dealt with.

The release of newer computer models designed to predict the performance of dairy cattle under a variety of environmental and nutritional conditions has caused a major shift in the manner in which diets are designed. Given that this new generation of computer programs allows nutritionists an opportunity to improve microbial yield, the possibilities of cutting ration costs while also avoiding formulation mistakes that reflect on animal health are very real. Utilizing this approach to diet formulation does, however, require a greater knowledge of the nutritional characteristics of the ingredients in the ration.

# References

Allen, M. and M.Oba. 1996. Fiber digestibility of forages. Proc. 57th Minnesota Nutrition Conf. and Provita Technical Symposium. Extension Special Programs, Univ. of Minnesota, P.O. Box 64780, St Paul MN 55164–0780.

Allen, M., M. Oba and B.Y. Choi. 1997. Nutritionist's perspective on corn hybrids for silage. Proc. Silage: Field to Feedbunk. NRAES. 152 Riley-Robb Hall, Ithaca, New York 14853–5701.

Allshouse, R.D., C.J. Majewski and C.J. Sniffen. 1998. Investigations in forage quality. Variation in forage quality in the Northeast. W.H. Miner Agricultural Research Institute. 98–8.

Arieli, S.J., J. Mabjeesh, Z. Shabi, I. Bruckental, Y. Aharoni, S. Zamwel and H. Tagari. 1996. *In situ* assessment of degradability of organic matter in the rumen of the dairy cow. J. Dairy Sci. 81:1965–1990.

Atwater, W.O. 1891. The fuel value of feeding stuffs. Storrs Agricultural Experiment Station Annual Report. 3:174.

Beegle, D. 1998. Managing dairy feed, manure, and fertilizer in nutrient cycles. Dairy Feeding Systems. NRAES. 152 Riley-Robb Hall, Ithaca, New York 14853–5701. Pp. 333–344.

Chandler, P.T. 1996. Environmental challenges as related to animal agriculture-dairy. In: Nutrient Management of Food Animals to Enhance and Protect the Environment . CRC. Press, Inc. New York p.7.

Chase, L.E. 1998. Animal management strategies to reduce nutrient excretion. Dairy feeding systems. NRAES. 152 Riley-Robb Hall, Ithaca, New York 14853-5701. Pp. 324–332.

Clark, J.H., T.H. Klusmeyer and M.R. Cameron. 1992. Symposium: nitrogen metabolism and amino acid nutrition in dairy cattle. J. Dairy Sci. 75:2304.

Cohen, M.A., H.E. Maslanka and L. Kung. 1997. An evaluation of automated and manual *in vitro* methods for estimation of NDF digestion. Conference on Rumen Physiology, Chicago, Il.

Dairy Farmers of Ontario (DFO).1999. Milk Shipments, February.

Dhanoa, M.S., J. France, R.C. Siddons, S.Lopez and J.B. Buchanan-Smith. 1995. A non-linear compartmental model to describe forage degradation kinetics during incubation in polyester bags in the rumen. Br. J. Nutr. 73:3–15.

Eastridge, M.L., H.F. Bucholtz, A.L.Slater and C.S. Hall. 1998a. Nutrient requirements for dairy cattle of the National Research Council versus some commonly used ration software. J.Dairy Sci. 81:3059–3062.

Eastridge, M.L., H.F. Bucholtz, A.L.Slater and C.S.Hall. 1998b. Nutrient Requirements: a buyers guide to software. Dairy Herd Mgt. 32(4):48–54.

Firkins,J.L., M.S. Allen, B.S. Oldick,and N.R. St. Pierre. 1998. Modeling ruminal digestibility of carbohydrates and microbial protein flow to the duodenum. J. Dairy Sci. 81:3350–3369.

Fox, D.G., C.J. Sniffen, J.D. O'Connor, J.B. Russell and P.J. Van Soest. 1992. A net carbohydrate and protein system for evaluating cattle diets: III Cattle requirements and diet adequacy. J. Anim. Sci. 70:3578–3596.

Garmen, C.L., L.A. Holden and H.A. Kane. 1997. Comparison of *in vitro* dry matter digestibility of nine feedstuffs using three different methods of analysis. J. Dairy Sci. 80(Suppl. 1):260.

Grant, R. J. and D.R. Mertens. 1992. Development of buffer systems for pH control and evaluations of pH effects on fiber digestion In vitro. J. Dairy Sci. 75:1581–1587.

Grant, R.J. and S.J. Weidner. 1992. Digestion kinetics of fiber: influence of *in vitro* buffer pH varied within observed physiological range. J. Dairy Sci. 75:1060.

Hall, M.B. , A.N. Pell and L.E. Chase. 1998. Characteristics of neutral detergent soluble fiber fermentation by mixed ruminal microbes. Anim. Feed Sci. Technol. 70:23.

Henning, P.H., D.J. Steyn and H.H. Meissner. 1991. Effect of synchronization of energy and nitrogen supply on ruminal characteristics and microbial growth. J. Animal Sci. 71: 2516–2528.

Hiltner, P. and B.A. Dehority. 1983. Effect of soluble carbohydrates on digestion of cellulose by pure cultures of rumen bacteria. Appl. Environ. Microbiol. 46:642.

Hoover,W.H. and T.K. Miller. 1995. Optimizing carbohydrate fermentation in the rumen. 6th Annual Florida Ruminant Nutrition Symposium.

Hoover, W.H. and S.R. Stokes. 1991 Balancing carbohydrates and proteins for optimum rumen microbial yield. J. Dairy Sci. 74:3630.

Hutjens, M. 1998. Considerations in feeding systems. pp. 32–38. In: Dairy Feeding Systems: Management, Components and Nutrients. N.R.A.E.S. Dec. 1998.

Kertz, A.F. 1998. Variability in delivery of nutrients to lactating dairy cows. J. Dairy Sci. 81:3075–3084.

Kohn, R. 1997. The use of mechanistic models to evaluate dairy rations. In: Proc. Tri-State Dairy Nutr. Conf. (M.L. Eastridge, ed.) Ft. Wayne IN. The Ohio State Univ,. Columbus. Pages 159–169.

Komarek, A.R., J.B. Robertson and P.J. Van Soest. 1994a. A comparison of methods for determining ADF using the filter bag technique versus conventional filtration. J. Dairy Sci. Vol. 77(Suppl. 1).

Komarek, A.R., J.B. Robertson and P.J. Van Soest. 1994b. Comparison of the filter bag technique to conventional filtration in the Van Soest analysis of 21 feeds. Presented at the National Conference on Forage Quality, Evaluation and Utilization Proceedings (University of Nebraska).

Majewski, C.J., R.D. Allshouse and C.J. Sniffen. 1998. Investigations in forage Quality. II. Variability in forage quality parameters for corn hybrids. W.H. Miner Agricultural Research Institute. 98–8.

Mertens, D.R. 1993. Rate and extent of digestion. In: Quantitative Aspects of Ruminant Digestion and Metabolism. (J.M. Forbes and J. France, eds.) CAB Int. Wallingford, United Kingdom. Pp. 13–51.

Moscardini, S., T.C. Wright, P.H. Luimes, B.W. McBride and P. Susmel. 1998. Effects of rumen-undegradable protein and feed intake on purine derivative and urea nitrogen: comparison with predictions from the Cornell Net Carbohydrate and Protein System. J. Dairy Sci. 81:2421–2429.

Newbold, J.R. and S.R. Rust. 1992. Effect of asynchronous nitrogen and energy supply on growth of ruminal bacteria in batch culture. J. Dairy Sci. 70:538–546.

Ontario Ministry of Agriculture Food and Rural Affairs. 1991.Ontario Farm Management Analysis Project.

Pell, A.N. and P. Schofield. 1993. Computerized monitoring of gas production to measure for digestion in vitro. J. Dairy Sci. 76:1063.

Piwonka, E.J. and J.L. Firkins. 1996. Effect of glucose fermnentation on fiber digestion by ruminal microorganisms *in vitro*. J. Dairy Sci. 79:2196–2206.

Robinson, P.H., and R.E. McQuenn. 1994. Influence of supplemental protein source and feeding frequency on rumen fermentation and performance in dairy cows. J. Dairy Sci. 77: 1340–1353.

Shabi, Z., A. Ariel, I. Bruckental, Y. Aharoni, S. Zamwel, A. Bor and H. Tagari. 1998. Effect of the synchronization of the degradation of dietary crude protein and organic matter and feeding frequency on ruminal fermentation and flow of digesta in the abomasum of dairy cows. J. Dairy Sci. 81:1991–2000.

Schwab, C. 1995. Rumen protected amino acids. Tri State Dairy Conference, Fort Wayne, Ind., pp. 85–110.

Sniffen C.J. and W. Chalupa. 1998. Protein and amino acid nutrition of lactating cows – an update. Dairy Professional Program, Cornell 1998.

Sniffen, C.J., J.D. O'Connor, P.J. Van Soest, D.G. Fox and J.B. Russell. 1992. A net carbohydrate and protein system for evaluating cattle diets: II. Carbohydrate and protein availability. J. Anim. Sci. 70:3562.

St. Pierre, N.R. and W.R. Harvey. 1986 Uncertainty in composition of ingredients and optional rate of success for a maximum profit total mixed ration. J. Dairy Sci. 76:3160–3178.

Stokes, M.R. and S. Zheng. 1995. The use of carbohydrate enzymes as feed additives for early lactation cows. 23rd Biennial Conf. Rumen Function, Chicago III 23:35 (Abstr.).

Tilley, J.M.A. and R.A. Terry. 1963. A two-stage technique for the *in vitro* digestion of forage crops. Journal of British Grassland Society 18:104–111.

Thomas, E.D., C.S. Ballard, C.J.Sniffen, D.S. Tsang, R.D. Allhouse and P. Mandebvu. 1998. Effect of hybrid on corn silage yield, nutrient composition, *in vitro* digestion, intake by Holstein heifers, intake and milk production by lactating Holstein cows. W.H. Miner Agricultural Research Institute, Chazy, N.Y. 98–13.

Undersander, D.J., W.T. Howard and R.D. Shaver. 1993. Milk per acre spreadsheets that bring yield and quality into a single term. J. Prod. Agric. 6:231–235.

VandeHaar, M.J., H.F. Bucholtz, M.S. Allen, J.R. Allen, J.R. Black, R.S. Emery C.J. Sniffen and R.W. Beverly. 1992. Spartan Ration Evaluator/Balancer for Dairy Cattle. Version 2.02. Michigan State University, East Lansing.

Yang, W.Z., K.A. Beauchemin and L. M. Rode. 1999. Effects of an enzyme feed additive on extent of digestion and milk production of lactating dairy cows. J. Dairy Sci. 82:391–403.

# Forage utilization efficiency: an Australian perspective

LES SANDLES

*BEST-fed NUTRITION, Shepparton, Victoria, Australia*

In recent times there has been a global shift back to pasture-based dairy farming led largely by the "clean green" push. Although philosophically this may be the correct move by the dairy industry, care must be exercised that it is achieved in a thoughtful, controlled way in order for the appropriate management to be employed and sensible decisions made. The danger is in embracing radical changes without thoughtful and balanced evaluation of the potential consequences. Many times we see well-meaning farmers get into trouble changing too quickly with too little homework.

The key to profitability in pasture-based dairy farming is in understanding that balanced rations are more difficult to achieve, and stockmanship reigns as the most important skill. One needs to be very cow-focused to assess the need for diet changes. Computers and consultants cannot substitute for stockmanship. This paper will provide some basic concepts that need to be considered if pasture-based dairy production is your quest.

## The major factors affecting milk yield

Milk production is the result of the coordination of many, many complex metabolic and physiological events in the cow. Numerous factors affect the efficiency with which the multitudes of cascades of biochemical processes are carried out. Yet, only a handful of factors need be attended with reasonable diligence by the farmer to allow all of the necessary events to proceed successfully, such that good milk responses are achieved in response to improved feeding levels.

For all intents and purposes, there are only seven factors that require significant management attention to maximise farm productivity. These factors are presented in Figure 1. Of these seven management areas, only cow condition and the four factors associated with the feed require day-to-day attention. Unexpressed genetic potential lies latent in most herds, and its improvement and the changing of calving patterns both require strategic decision-making processes to be employed.

343

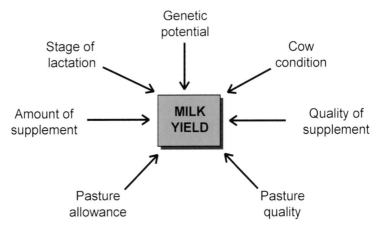

**Figure 1.** The seven major factors influencing milk production.

## Cow condition: evaluating diet balance

If one adheres to the 80/20 principle in farm management, body condition management is the 20% which leads to 80% of the success on the animal side. Cow condition is, in fact, the most important criterion for assessing the success of dietary balance when used in conjunction with milk production. It is also the key factor contributing to milk components, health and fertility. You must become very astute at monitoring and measuring, i.e., managing, body condition when most of the diet is 'unknown'.

## Forage quality and pasture utilization

With cow condition as a benchmark, this leaves the feed side, i.e., the pasture (or any other forage for that matter) and supplements (concentrate or roughage). It is the daily interaction of these that primarily determines day-to-day milk yield and composition, body condition, animal health and fertility. There is no difference between a total mixed ration (TMR) and a pasture-based ration in this respect; it is just a little more challenging to get it all right when basing the diet on pasture. My own experience is that when the shift from TMR to pasture is executed properly, yield and profitability can both be preserved. Moreover, health and fertility will improve if we manage the transition to pasture well.

FORAGE GROWING COSTS

As an observer to Australian and New Zealand dairy industries, you could be easily convinced that pasture is very cheap – so cheap that we waste more than half of what we grow. Unfortunately this is not a rare mindset. Australian and New Zealand farmers are still trying to survive while working an out-dated paradigm – that pasture is cheap. Even now, many advisers are still fertilising this perception. A recent conference paper (Tease, 1997) discussed several case studies in which pasture costs were apparently consistently low, arguing that supplementary feed costs were threatening our farmers' prosperity. His own data do not even support this conclusion (Figure 2). It is evident from this figure that the cash outlay for home-grown feed is low, and that purchased feed is of similar magnitude. Neither feed category threatens farm prosperity. However, when analysing farm cash flows of pasture-based dairy farm businesses, with an ounce of commonsense one quickly realises that most farm expenses relate, either directly or indirectly, to the cost of growing pasture. I suspect the same is true of other forage-based dairy farms, although it may be diluted a little as farms move from home-grown forage to higher inclusions of concentrates and purchased forage.

By including the labour, overhead and depreciation costs, a very different picture of pasture begins to emerge (Table 1). In the table we see that pasture is quite expensive to grow. Also illustrated is the effect of increased pasture yield on the unit cost of growth. Although it may cost more to increase pasture dry matter yields, the higher yields produce significantly cheaper feed.

PASTURE UTILIZATION EFFICIENCY: THE LARGEST IMPACT ON PROFITABILITY

It is not enough simply to grow more pasture. Tonnes of pasture *consumed* is the key to farm profitability. First we have to grow more pasture to

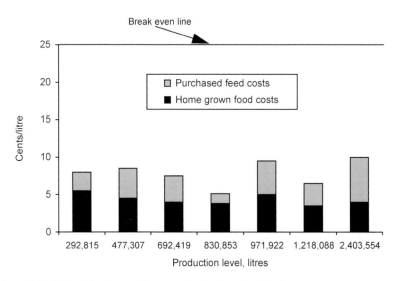

**Figure 2.** Relationship between farm production level and feed cost.

**Table 1. What is the real cost of growing pasture?**

| Pasture inputs | Pasture grown | |
|---|---|---|
| | 8 t/Ha | 14 t/Ha |
| Opportunity cost (eg., $6250/Ha @ 8% interest) | $500 | $500 |
| Seeds and sprays | $35 | $55 |
| Water | – | – |
| Labour | $120 | $120 |
| Repairs and maintenance | $150 | $200 |
| Fertiliser | $250 | $400 |
| Total cost per hectare | $1055 | $1275 |
| Total cost per kg DM | 13.2¢ | 9.1¢ |

reduce the unit growing cost, and then we have to harvest the pasture efficiently. To make total sense out of this picture, we need to provide a series of examples. Table 2 expands on the previous table illustrating the effects of land values and farming systems and the effects of pasture utilisation on the true cost of pasture as a feed. Once the real-cost adjustments are made and pasture utilisation is considered, the homegrown feeds take on a new aura – they are not automatically cheap feeds. Growing costs (in Table 2) range from 10-13.6 c/kg DM. However, it is not until you consider the utilised pasture dry matter (UDM) costs that the real picture emerges. As you can see, every effort must be made to maximise the yield (total tonnes) of harvested pasture dry matter.

**Table 2. Estimated costs of growing pasture at different land prices and the resulting unit cost of utilised pasture dry matter (UDM) at various utilisation efficiencies.**

| Expense category ($/Ha) | Land price | | | |
|---|---|---|---|---|
| | $2000 per acre | $3000 per acre | $3000 per acre (irrigated) | $4000 per acre |
| *Finance costs* | | | | |
| Seeds and sprays | 35.0 | 35.0 | 35.0 | 35.0 |
| Irrigation expenses | 0.0 | 0.0 | 300.0 | 0.0 |
| Fertiliser | 265.0 | 265.0 | 365.0 | 265.0 |
| Labour | 80.0 | 80.0 | 200.0 | 80.0 |
| Repairs and maintenance[1] | 120.0 | 120.0 | 200.0 | 120.0 |
| Depreciation * | 200.0 | 200.0 | 300.0 | 200.0 |
| Totals | 1100.0 | 1300.0 | 2000.0 | 1500.0 |
| *Growing costs (c/kg DM)[2]* | 10.0 | 11.8 | 13.3 | 13.6 |
| UDM (c/kg DM) | | | | |
| @ 40% utilisation | 25.0 | 29.5 | 33.3 | 34.0 |
| @ 50% utilisation | 20.0 | 23.6 | 26.6 | 27.2 |
| @ 60% utilisation | 16.7 | 19.7 | 22.2 | 22.7 |
| @ 70% utilisation | 14.3 | 16.9 | 19.0 | 19.4 |

[1]Guesstimates of category costs relating to the proportion of total costs dedicated to pasture growth only.
[2]Assuming 11 tonnes DM/Ha grown on dryland, 15 tonnes DM/Ha grown on irrigation.

Pasture utilisation efficiency is the factor with greatest impact on farm profitability. Figure 3 illustrates the relationship between gross margin and pasture utilisation (UDM/ha). Clearly, as the UDM increases, gross margin also increases. The poorer the pasture utilisation, the more expensive the feed (Table 2). Once this is established, the relationship between UDM and farm profitability becomes very strong as can be seen from making these adjustments in the case study analysis (Figure 4). Real pasture costs were in the order 14–28 cents/kg DM ($140–280/t) which is precisely the same story illustrated in Table 2. Without focus and an understanding of the real costs of pasture production, it would be easy to romance the pasture-based farming system with disastrous consequences.

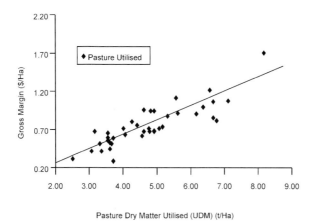

**Figure 3.** Relationship between pasture dry matter utilised and gross margin.

## Maximising pasture use efficiency

Only two aspects of pasture management require discussion:

1. Increasing the harvest efficiency of pasture currently grown.
2. Improving pasture yields.

Management priorities must, very definitely, be in this order since there are few farms on which grazing is the dominant means of harvest where utilisation of pasture is optimal. Improving pasture yield is outside the scope of this presentation. Suffice to say that species selection, grazing, fertiliser and irrigation management are all vital components.

## Increasing pasture utilisation efficiency: forage quality is the key

Numerous management factors influence the efficiency with which pasture is harvested. The most obvious are presented in Figure 5 and three of these are closely related: grazing management, pasture species and fertiliser management. Each of these has a tremendous impact on forage quality.

The quickest and most significant means of increasing pasture use efficiency is to optimise rotation length (i.e., the period from one grazing to the next).

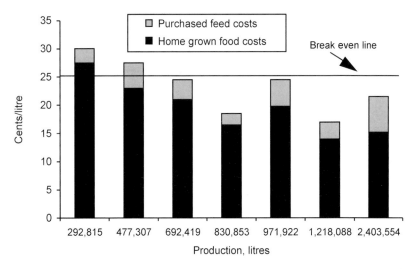

**Figure 4.** Relationship between farm production level and component cost of production (with revised home-grown feed costs).

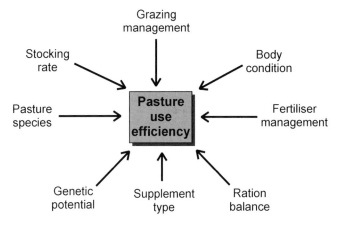

**Figure 5.** Major factors affecting pasture utilisation efficiency.

Rotations that are too short reduce dry matter yields, while rotations that are too long limit pasture consumption by the cow as forage quality declines.

Owing to the relationship between neutral detergent fibre (NDF) and intake, no amount of concentrates can compensate for a poor quality forage base (Van Soest, 1994; Mertens, 1983). In Figure 6, this is illustrated on three basal rations containing either A) good quality (lucerne), B) fair quality (corn silage), and S) poor quality (bermuda grass) forages, all optimised for fibre. Without going into mathematical detail, the relationship described below in Equation 1 can be used to describe the limitations to intake, and thus production level (Mertens, 1983):

Dry matter intake (% of liveweight) = $\dfrac{120}{NDF}$       Equation 1

The underlying mechanism for the relationship between intake and NDF in Equation 1 is obvious. As fibre quality improves, intake, digestibility and passage rate all increase. The line in Figure 6 is there as a reminder that as milk yield improves, the percentage of NDF in the ration can be reduced since the maintenance of the rumen mat requires kilograms of NDF, not percentages.

An understanding of the physical role of NDF leads us to the limitations of our pasture-based management system. Figure 7 clearly illustrates the intake boundaries for our pasture (or forage)–based dairy rations. Once we accept that intake is primarily determined by dietary NDF, we quickly recognise that there is a limited number of feasible ration solutions for cows at different production levels. More importantly, the number of feasible rations diminishes as production expectations rise and/or forage quality declines. It is rather simplistic, but it serves as a guideline to get diet components in the right ballpark and is an incredibly good tool when educating farmers on the importance of fibre quality. Simply put, as NDF increases, dry matter intake decreases.

Typically our pasture NDF values increase quickly after optimum grazing height (maturity). A rotation only seven days too long may result in a 7-10% unit increase in pasture NDF and cause intakes to fall by up to 0.7% of liveweight (Table 3) or 2 kg DM/day. Not only will dry matter intake decrease, but energy density of the pasture also falls (by ~1 MJ ME/kg DM), ultimately sacrificing 7–8 liters of milk/day. Table 3 clarifies this point, and the important role concentrates play in increasing total dry matter intake.

**Table 3.**   **Effects of NDF on dry matter intake predicted by Equation I.**

|  | NDF (% Dry matter) | Dry matter intake (% of liveweight) |
|---|---|---|
| Excellent pasture | 35 | 3.40 |
| Average pasture | 45 | 2.70 |
| Poor pasture | 55 | 2.18 |
| Pasture hay | 60 | 2.00 |
| Oats | 30 | 4.00 |
| Barley | 20 | 6.00 |
| Wheat | 13 | 9.20 |

From the perspective of Figure 7, we can assemble a second equation:

NDF intake (kg/day) = 1.2% of liveweight (kg)       Equation 2

Thus, the limit to feasible intakes is determined with liveweight as the controller, and NDF as the key variable to be managed. In practical terms this means:

*A 500 kg cow will have an intake limitation of approximately 6.0 kg NDF.*

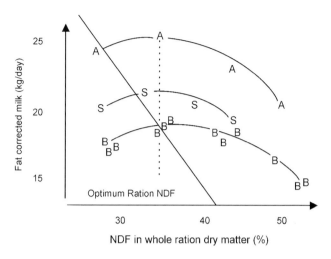

**Figure 6.** The relationship between milk yield and NDF.

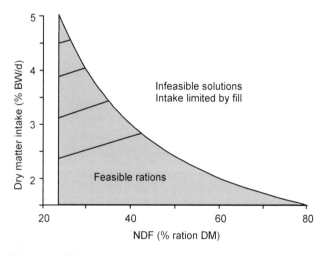

**Figure 7.** Using the NDF-energy intake system to identify the range of feasible rations for cows of different production levels (Mertens, 1992).

*A 600 kg cow will have an intake limitation of approximately 7.2 kg NDF.* This is incredibly important to understand when managing a pasture-based dairy ration. A cow can only fit so much in! Pasture quality management is the most challenging aspect of low-cost dairying systems. Even relatively small changes in pasture quality have an enormous impact on dry matter intake as noted in Table 3. The other challenges such as dealing with differences in genetic potential, nutrient balance, etc., pale by comparison.

# Using supplements to maximise profits from pasture

It is the number of tonnes of pasture dry matter harvested that primarily determines whether profits are made or lost. The most profitable means of achieving high levels of pasture utilisation is to take advantage of the complementary properties concentrates offer.

## THE ROLE OF SUPPLEMENTS IN THE PASTURE-BASED FARMING SYSTEM

Supplements provide the vital links between pasture management and animal management. More aggressive grazing reduces the pasture allocation per cow, often reducing the consumption of pasture per cow. This in turn compromises the efficiency of feed conversion. More importantly, the risk of running out of feed increases as grazing management is intensified through higher stocking rates, restricted use of fibrous supplements and improved genetic potential of the herd. Supplements, therefore, play the critical role of insurance against running out of feed, and help maintain high feed conversion efficiencies. If used as an integral part of the management system, supplements result in significant profits. However, this is rarely seen in practice.

## ECONOMICS OF CONCENTRATES IN PASTURE-BASED DAIRY RATIONS

Dairy farmers in southeastern Australia and New Zealand rely heavily on pastures to provide the nutrients required for milk production. Typically, lactating dairy cows receive rations similar to those presented in Table 4. The most common 'reason' for concentrates to be used on farm is the recognition that they contain the potential to realise high production levels per cow and simultaneously per hectare by intensifying grazing management. In practice, this rarely happens without external guidance due to a fall in pasture utilisation when supplements are fed. The net result is usually a marginal cost/benefit scenario from supplement use (Table 5). Even if production per cow and per hectare are improved, responses such as this fail to capture our audience, but rather leave them a little frustrated.

## SUBSTITUTION

In understanding Equation 2, it becomes obvious that as NDF intake approaches maximum, the use of supplements will force some forage out of the diet. The frustration of substitution is that the theoretical responses to supplements are rarely met.

The energy in cereal grain (12.2–12.7 MJ ME/kg DM) is sufficient for

**Table 4.   Typical dairy cow diets in Victoria.**

|  | Pasture only | Clients (Pre-BEST-*fed* Nutrition) |
|---|---|---|
|  | kg  per  cow  per  year | |
| Pasture | 3300 | 2800 |
| Conserved forage | 1100 | 1100 |
| Concentrates | 0 | 1000 |
| Milk yield | 4350 | 5200 |

**Table 5.   Cost/benefit from feeding concentrates to lactating dairy cows.**

|  | No concentrates | 1000 kg/cow/year (as fed) |
|---|---|---|
| Milk yield, liters/cow/year | 4350 | 5200 |
| Response |  | 0.84 kg milk/kg concentrate |
| Concentrate cost |  | 23.1 cents/kg |
| Milk return |  | 25 cents/liter |
| Cost/ benefit |  | −2.1 cents/ kg |

about 2.3 litres of milk. At 23.1 cents/kg for concentrate and 25 cents/liter for milk, this represents an enormous opportunity for profit. Even if you only get half of this, it still represents pretty good value for money! Yet typical responses to concentrate supplements are sufficiently poor that their value is still subject to a good deal of debate.

Cereal grain, specifically wheat with an energy density of 12.7 MJ/kg DM, contains sufficient energy for about 2.6 liters of milk, yet such responses are never recorded. The extent to which the response falls short of the 2.6 liters/kg DM wheat is the extent to which one or other of the following have occurred:

- substitution
- the imbalance of nutrients in the rumen, or
- the partitioning of nutrients between milk production and body tissue

Since substitution refers to the drop in pasture intake caused by the intake of supplements, the production response is usually less than the potential intake. In turn, the marginal rate of response often becomes just that – marginal.

### Managing substitution

Management of fibre quality alone is insufficient to extract the best from pasture-based dairy systems. The seeking of feasible dietary solutions also entails a quest for matching supplements to pasture (forage) to ensure maximum use and control of quality pasture.

Substitution will be minimised by dietary balance, body condition management and grazing management; however, an element will remain. This can be eliminated by additional cows to maintain or increase the effective grazing pressure. When the system is managed well the profitability cannot be disputed. Table 6 shows the progress made by BEST-*fed* Nutrition clients as our working relationship develops.

**Table 6.** The impact of Best-*fed* Nutrition's feeding philosophy on production, ration costs and margins over feed costs.

| | Pasture only * | Year 0 | Year 1 | Year 2 | Year 3 |
|---|---|---|---|---|---|
| Milk yield, litres/cow | 4350 | 5194 | 6072 | 6612 | 7087 |
| Milk return, cents/litre net | 25 | 25 | 25 | 25 | 25 |
| Milk return, $net/cow | 1088 | 1299 | 1518 | 1653 | 1772 |
| | | | | | |
| Ration components, DM intake/cow/year | | | | | |
| Pasture | 3.3 | 2.8 | 2.8 | 2.9 | 3.0 |
| Hay and silage | 1.0 | 1.1 | 1.1 | 1.1 | 1.1 |
| Concentrate | - | 1.0 | 1.5 | 1.7 | 2.0 |
| Total | 4.3 | 4.9 | 5.4 | 5.7 | 6.1 |
| Pasture use efficiency | | | | | |
| Stocking rate, cows/hectare | 2.1 | 2.3 | 2.5 | 2.6 | 2.7 |
| Pasture utilisation, % | 50 | 45 | 55 | 60 | 65 |
| Pasture UDM, tonnes DM/hectare/year | 6.6 | 6.2 | 7.0 | 7.5 | 8.1 |
| Pasture costs, c/kg UDM | 24.4 | 19.8 | 18.2 | 16.9 | 16.3 |
| | | | | | |
| Ration costs, $/cow/year | | | | | |
| Pasture | 779 | 734 | 601 | 570 | 489 |
| Hay and silage | 130 | 143 | 143 | 143 | 143 |
| Concentrate | 0 | 250 | 375 | 425 | 500 |
| Total ration cost | 909 | 1127 | 1119 | 1138 | 1188 |
| Ration cost, c/kg/DM | 21.1 | 23.0 | 20.7 | 20.0 | 19.5 |
| | | | | | |
| Ration response, litres/kg DM | 1.01 | 1.06 | 1.12 | 1.16 | 1.16 |
| Concentrate response, litres/kg | - | 0.84 | 1.15 | 1.33 | 1.37 |
| | | | | | |
| Margins over feed cost | | | | | |
| Per liter of milk, cents | 4.1 | 3.3 | 6.6 | 7.8 | 8.2 |
| Per cow per year, $ | 179 | 377 | 399 | 515 | 584 |
| Per hectare per year | 357 | 867 | 998 | 1338 | 1577 |

*Extrapolated data set for demonstration purposes only

Unless moderate increases in stocking rate occur in conjunction with significant increases in milk yield, supplements will provide little economic benefit to the farm business. When used as an integral part of the management of the dairy feedbase, supplements have a large positive cost/benefit ratio (Table 6). It is also evident that as production per cow rises, margin over feed cost also rises. When the effects of increased concentrate use combine with increased stocking rates and higher production per cow, the effects on margin over feed costs per hectare are huge.

# References

Mertens, D.R. 1983. Using neutral detergent fibre to formulate dairy rations and estimate the net energy content of forages. Proc. Cornell Nutrit. Conf. Ithaca, NY pp 60–68.

Mertens, D.R. 1992. Nonstructural and structural carbohydrates. In: Large Dairy Herd Management, American Dairy Sci. Assoc. (Ed: HH Van Hern and C.J. Hilcox) p 219.

Tease, I. 1997. The economics of increasing milk production. Gipps Dairy Conference. Dept Natural Resources and Environment. pp 12–26.

Van Soest, P.J. 1994. Nutritional ecology of the ruminant. Cornell University Press, Ithaca, NY.

# MANAGING MYCOTOXIN IMPACT

# Global climatic effects on livestock and human health

SIMON M. SHANE

*School of Veterinary Medicine, Louisiana State University,
Baton Rouge, Louisiana*

## Introduction

The agricultural and livestock industries of the world are under increasing pressure to produce sufficient food for expanding populations, especially in the tropical areas of the world. Seasonal climatic extremes involving drought and flooding detract from optimal production, which can affect the availability and cost of food for livestock and human populations on a regional or worldwide basis.

Advances in meteorology and allied disciplines have increased the precision and reliability of short-term weather forecasts, but only recently has it been possible to predict global weather patterns on a seasonal or annual basis. The introduction of remote sensing by weather satellite and the deployment of remotely-operated buoys and weather stations reporting oceanic and atmospheric data have created new opportunities to study weather patterns. Advances in computerized processing of large databases and the development of models of increasing complexity and refinement can correlate predictions with actual climatic events. The purpose of predicting major changes in rainfall pattern and temperature are evident. Selection of appropriate crops, provision for enhanced storage and handling of products, and contingency plans for disease outbreaks and disruption of infrastructure can be completed in advance of severe changes in order to reduce their impact.

The most recent 1997/1998 *El Niño* event illustrates the global effect of profound weather changes and the various responses that were applied at the international, regional and local levels.

## The ENSO phenomenon

ENSO is an acronym for *El Niño* and Southern Oscillation which comprises the cyclic warming of the ocean in the eastern equatorial Pacific and changes in precipitation extending from the western

Indonesian archipelago (100° E) to central South America (60° W) along a band extending from 10° N to 10° S of the equator. Although ENSO events have their greatest impact in the Pacific, it is now evident that a major disturbance in the temperature of the Pacific Ocean and consequential displacement of jet streams has obvious effects on temperature and precipitation in North America, sub-Saharan Africa, northern Australia, mainland Asia and the Middle East. At 2–7 year intervals, a climatic phenomenon referred to as an "*El Niño*" occurs off the equatorial coast of Latin America extending from central Peru (8° S) to southern Colombia (5° N) encompassing the coastline of Ecuador. Normally an annual increase in surface water temperature of 1–2 °C occurs during late-December and extends through to February of the following year. This regular phenomenon is associated with decreased landings of pelagic fish.

At variable intervals, the normal ocean warming is intensified, resulting in a complete collapse of the fishing industry. These events, long recognized by fisherman, are referred to as an *El Niño* ("the little one") in reference to the Christ child, since the ocean warming was noted during late December. The term "Southern Oscillation" was applied to the differential in atmospheric pressure between eastern and western regions of the Pacific first recorded in the mid-1920s by Sir Gilbert Walker. There is evidence that *El Niño* events have occurred throughout recorded history, but strong events occurred in 1982–1983, and most recently in 1997–1998. Moderate to weak *El Niño* cycles were recorded in 1977–1978, 1987–1988 and 1991–1992.

Studies were initiated in the mid-1960s by Bjerkness based on data accumulated during the International Geophysical year of 1957 which coincided with an El Niño event. Studies on the ENSO phenomenon were intensified following the severe 1972–1973 event that resulted in the complete collapse of the Peruvian fishing industry. In addition, this El Niño was associated with severe droughts in India, western Indonesia, Hawaii, sub-Saharan Africa and the Soviet Union. In contrast, excessive rainfall and flooding occurred along coastal Peru, the Philippines and the western seaboard of the United States.

Since the early 1980s it has become evident that the southern oscillation is coupled with the occurrence of anomalous warming of the equatorial Pacific Ocean, although the specific global climatic factors which trigger an El Niño event have not been defined or quantified.

The southern oscillation represents a differential in atmospheric pressure between the northwest and southeast Pacific regions. A high pressure zone is located over Easter Island at 30°S and 110°W. This interacts with a large low pressure trough which is located variably in the western Pacific between the Indonesian island of Kalimantan and northern Australia. The normal westward movement of the easterly trade winds, which increase in intensity during January of each year, maintains the normal sea temperature and atmospheric conditions associated with periods between El Niño events. Surface water is driven across the Pacific resulting in a differential in sea surface level of 40–100 cm between the eastern and western Pacific. This results in a depression in the thermocline in the western Pacific, which lies at a depth of approximately 200 m. The westward movement of surface water promotes the upwelling of cold and nutrient-rich water from the Humboldt current, which originates in Antarctica and traverses the western coastline of Latin America. The thermocline or transition zone between warm and cold water lies at approximately 50 m in depth along the Peruvian coast. The cold water flowing from Antarctica is rich in phytoplankton; and the presence of sunlight filtering through the surface water stimulates the food chain, resulting in acceptable harvests by the fishing industry.

**Normal**

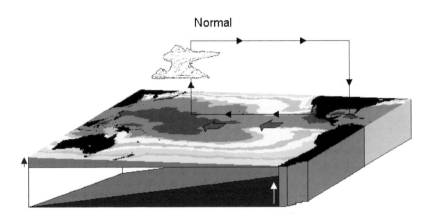

**Figure 1a.** The normal situation: Annual occurrence of easterly trade winds moves surface water westward across the Pacific from the equatorial coast of Latin America. Thermocline rises adjacent to the coasts of Northern Peru and Ecuador. Upward flow of air over Indonesia results in regional seasonal precipitation.

## Reynolds Monthly SST (°C)

**Figure 1b.** The normal situation: Annual depression of surface temperature in the eastern and central equatorial Pacific contrasting with the higher surface temperature in the western Pacific.

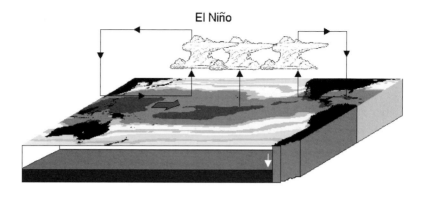

**Figure 2a.** *El Niño* phenomenon: Failure of easterly trade winds is associated with eastward movement of warm surface water extending to the equatorial coast of Latin America. Depression in the thermocline, cyclonic conditions in the central Pacific and drought over the Indonesian archipelago result from disturbances in movement of air over the Pacific.

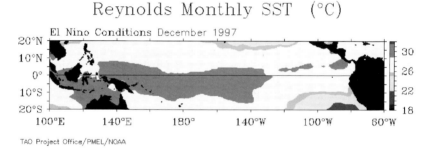

**Figure 2b.** *El Niño* conditions: Extensive warming of the equatorial Pacific extending to the coast of Latin America.

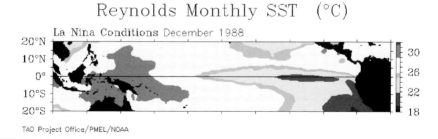

**Figure 2c.** *La Niña* conditions: Lower than normal surface temperature along coastal Latin America and the eastern equatorial Pacific Ocean.

The easterly trade winds eventually meet westerly winds over Indonesia. (Figures 1a and 1b). The upward flow of air results in condensation and heavy precipitation over the tropical islands of the western Pacific. Dry air returns eastward at high altitude, eventually sinking over the eastern Pacific and the equatorial desert-coastline of Ecuador and Peru. With a decline in the intensity of the southern oscillation index, the normal cycle is reversed and water moves eastward across the Pacific, resulting in a moderate (1–2°C) warming over a 5° band above and below the equator. This normal warming is of relatively short duration and extends from December through February.

*El Niño* events are preceded by a collapse of the easterly trade winds. (Figures 2a, b and c). Under severe conditions there may even be a reversal of winds accompanied by equatorial cyclones. The seasonal westward movement of surface water is impeded and the thermocline along the equatorial Pacific coastline is depressed. This results in a warming of the surface water and a reduction in plankton necessary to maintain the food chain. The cyclones which form above and below the equator in the Indonesian low pressure trough stimulate sub-surface Kelvin waves which move eastward across the Pacific during a 3 month period. The warm Kelvin waves contribute to an increase in surface temperature and further depress the thermocline along the coast of Peru and Ecuador, intensifying the *El Niño* event. In severe *El Niño* years, residual warm water in the central equatorial Pacific contributes to repeated and prolonged cyclones which stimulate new cycles of Kelvin waves, intensifying the warming of surface water in the eastern Pacific.

Although the collapse of the seasonal easterly trade winds is the immediate precursor of an *El Niño* event, the reason for the change is unknown. Meteorologists are currently developing models incorporating atmospheric pressure, water temperature and ocean currents. It is evident that the model termed the canonical *El Niño*, based on the southern oscillation, is inadequate to account for the initiation, occurrence or intensity of *El Niño* events. It is possible that seasonal trade winds are influenced by irregular atmospheric disturbances in the Indian Ocean. Non-seasonal but intense westerly winds of about one week in duration in the western Pacific may interfere with the regular onset and maintenance of the southern oscillation.

The severe damage caused by the 1982–1983 *El Niño* event, estimated to exceed $13 billion, stimulated research into global weather systems. The World Meteorological Association established a program to monitor sea temperature and air movement in the equatorial Pacific. The US National Oceanic and Atmospheric Administration deployed an array of 70 moored Atlas and Proteus buoys as a component of the TOGA-TAO program (Temperature of the Oceans and Global Atmosphere - Temperature of the Atmosphere and Oceans). An international CLIVAR (climate variability and predictability program) and the joint US GOALS (Global Ocean Atmosphere Land System) research initiatives will provide data in future years to resolve many of the unknown factors relating to the onset and severity of *El Niño* events.

The ENSO cycle is represented by both *El Niño* events and the subsequent counterpart, the *La Niña*. This phenomenon, also called the ENSO cold phase, or *El Viejo*, is characterized by more intense easterly trade winds and a corresponding decline in surface temperature in the equatorial coastal regions of Peru and Ecuador.

The *El Niño/La Niña* extending from early-1997 through late-1998 has been studied more intensively than any other previous ENSO event. Anomalies in water temperature and sea surface levels were documented and correlations were made between the observations and global climate patterns using advanced meteorologic techniques. Analysis of data during the next two years will identify factors contributing to perturbation of the ENSO cycle and will be used to predict the onset and intensity of *El Niño* events.

## Effects of a severe *El Niño*

The 1982–1983 *El Niño* was estimated to have resulted in $13 billion in damage and over 2,000 deaths. The effects of the 1997–1998 event have yet to be calculated, but the combined effects of flooding and drought in various areas of the world exceed $10 billion in direct crop losses and damage to property and infrastructure. The environmental impact of the most recent *El Niño* includes loss of coral reefs and disruption of food chains. This has resulted in extensive mortality among seals along the Pacific coast of North America, and virtual elimination of the marine iguanas on the Galapagos Islands. The fish catch in Peru was reduced by 96% during the 1997–1998 season compared to the previous year. Chile experienced a 50% reduction in catches. The 1982–1983 *El Niño* event reduced the catches in Peru from 12 million metric tons in 1970 to under 0.5 million tons in 1983. Since most fishmeal produced by Chile, Peru and Ecuador is exported, increased demand for protein to compensate for the reduced supply increased the price of alternative ingredients, especially in countries without adequate supplies of soybean meal and other vegetable proteins. In 1998, the problem was exacerbated by the reluctance to use animal by-products due to the perceived risks associated with transmissible spongiform encephalopathy.

Severe *El Niño* events are associated with drought conditions in Indonesia extending through New Guinea and northern Australia. Low rainfall reduces coarse grain production in the Philippines and Indonesia and lowers the output of palm and coconut oils and copra used for human consumption, domestic livestock production and export to generate foreign exchange. Other areas affected by drought include the northern tier of Australia, New Zealand, Micronesia, southern India, sub-Saharan Africa, the Altiplano region of Peru, southern Mexico and Central America and the Iberian Peninsula. Excessive rainfall and flooding is experienced in the Gulf region of the US, Cuba, the coastal region of Peru, Bolivia, and southern Brazil and northern Argentina. Severe cyclones occur in the central Pacific affecting French Polynesia and Hawaii in addition to wind and flood damage along the western seaboard of the US and Mexico.

The effect of decreased supplies of coarse grains and soybeans on the world market in 1997–1998 was compensated by a decrease in demand associated with the economic crisis in southeast Asia. This fact, together with the large inventories in the US and Brazil, reduced the impact of the drought caused by the *El Niño* of 1997–1998. Some crops such as coffee, sugar and cocoa were affected by either drought or flooding and sharp rises in the prices of these commodities were recorded during 1998.

During a typical *El Niño*, the US Midwest Grain Belt experiences higher precipitation and cooler temperatures than normal. This generally increases crop yields with maize output approximately 5% above standard. During the past 22 *El Niño* events 7 crops, each 10% above the trend line, were harvested and only in 3 seasons was there a 10% reduction below standard yield. Two of these, in 1915 and 1993, were attributed to excessive rainfall. High precipitation in the Southwest during the fall and early winter of an *El Niño* year results in stressed crops, reduced yield associated with agricultural pests and weeds and lowered revenue due to mycotoxin contamination.

*La Niña* events generally follow severe *El Niño* disturbances. Water temperature along the western Pacific coastline of Peru and Chile may be reduced by 5°C, resulting in a restoration of the normal food chain and leading to recovery of fish populations. *La Niña* periods are approximately 12 months in duration. Due to a disturbance in the normal path of the jet stream across the North American subcontinent, the Northwest and Midwest experience increased precipitation and periods of extreme cold. In contrast, winters in the Southeast are on average warmer than normal in *La Niña* years and precipitation is reduced. Spring melt following high winter precipitation may result in flooding in water catchment areas. Hurricane activity in the mid-Atlantic, Caribbean and Gulf regions increases during *La Niña* periods, resulting in crop damage on the islands and the coastal areas of the American continent.

ENSO events have a severe impact on both livestock and human populations in affected areas. Climatic effects, including elevated temperature, precipitation and humidity, influence health through three related mechanisms. Flooding affects the quantity and potability of surface water. The vectors of disease, including mosquitoes and other arthropods, multiply rapidly during periods of high precipitation and flooding and may extend disease to previously unaffected but susceptible populations. Extensive outbreaks of malaria, dengue and Rift Valley fever were recorded in central and east Africa following unseasonal rains related to the 1997–1998 *El Niño* event. High temperatures in India, which attained 50°C, together with an extended monsoon period led to outbreaks of malaria, dengue and pneumonic plague. Unseasonal precipitation promotes water-borne disease including hepatitis, typhoid and cholera. Disturbance of ecosystems results in the emergence of rodent and insect pests. Rats and mice destroy stored crops and are reservoirs of diseases including Lhasa fever, leptospirosis, hantavirus and salmonellosis, all of which have followed the *El Niño* events of 1976, 1983 and 1993. Cholera is associated with increased water temperature in coastal regions of southeast Asia, Peru and Chile. In addition, cholera is disseminated during flooding, especially in densely populated urban areas with inadequate sewage and water supply.

Drought and consequential reduction in protein and caloric intake by livestock and human populations results in immunosuppression and increased susceptibility to parasitism, including nematodes, cestodes and trematodes. Deviations from normal temperature and precipitation patterns have far-reaching effects on the nutrition, health and well being of subsistence populations that rely on local production of grain, livestock or fish. This is illustrated by starvation among the one million inhabitants of the highlands of Papua New Guinea during the severe ENSO-induced drought of 1997–1998.

## Planning of agricultural production based on *El Niño* prediction

Based on the impact of ENSO cycles over the past 2 decades, the government of Peru issues a short-term forecast of climatic conditions each November. Predictions of rainfall and fishing conditions are based on sea temperature, strength and direction of the trade winds and meteorological data from the Pacific Ocean. Data are incorporated in a computerized model to provide a forecast of seasonal weather. Four possible alternative scenarios have been defined to guide responses during the following 6 month period. Near-normal conditions require no specific action. A weak *El Niño* will reduce fish catches and result in an adequate to above average rainfall along the coastal region. A severe *El Niño* will lead to the collapse of the fishing industry and will be associated with severe flooding. A *La Niña* will enhance fish catches, but will result in drought along the coastal zone. Based on forecasts, farmers' groups and government extension agents decide on the appropriate combination of rice and cotton, the 2 principal crops in northern Peru. Rice is favored under wet conditions and cotton is more tolerant of drought. Similar planning has been instituted in northern Australia, Brazil, Ethiopia and India. More precise and longer range forecasts in the future will facilitate the incorporation of climate predictions into decisions relating to allocation of land to specific crops, time of planting, storage requirements, fertilization patterns and selection of cultivars.

Faced with the potential of a drought in sub-Saharan Africa, the Southern Africa Regional Outlook Forum was organized in September of 1997 in Zimbabwe. A forecast based on previous meteorological data was developed. It was anticipated that the 1998 maize harvest would exceed the 1990–1997 average in Angola, Malawi and Mozambique. Problems were anticipated for Botswana (80% reduction), Lesotho and Namibia (30% reduction) and in South Africa, Zambia and Zimbabwe where yields were anticipated to be 5–15% lower than normal. Predictions were provided for the guidance of agricultural planners at the national and regional levels. Forecasts were used to develop contingency plans and extension advice for farmers. Suggestions included substitution of more drought-resistant cultivars for high yield varieties, planting sorghum and millet in place of maize and an emphasis on earlier planting.

Contrary to the predictions of a prolonged drought, rainfall was normal or exceeded the monthly average in January of 1998, offsetting the damage caused by low rainfall in November and December of 1997. Production was reduced in Lesotho, Southern Zimbabwe and Zambia, and in all but the coastal areas of Mozambique. Excess rainfall with resultant flooding limited yields in parts of Malawi and northern Zambia. Maize yields in South Africa were below normal although the country did not experience the severe drought associated with previous *El Niño* events. The exercise in forecasting and resource allocation demonstrated deficiencies in coordination and communication which should be resolved in subsequent years.

A specific project to predict the effect of ENSO effects on crop production in Zimbabwe was carried out by US researchers at Columbia University. Daily climatic data from 4 sites in Zimbabwe, extending over 39 years, were incorporated into a maize-growth model with parameters for soil type and cultivar for each of the areas. Maize yield was predicted based on sea surface temperatures in the Niño-3 region of the Pacific (5° N to 5° S and 90° W to 150° W) during the 3 month period extending from November to January each year. Each of the 4 sites showed decreased precipitation during *El Niño* years compared to *La Niña* and neutral years. It was determined that early planting in projected *El Niño* years could offset the effect of a shortened rainy season by ensuring that pollination occurred before the onset of drought-induced stress.

Depending on the availability of adequate storage facilities, it is possible to stockpile grain in anticipation of low yields resulting from *El Niño*-related drought. In 1997, the Central Marketing Board of Zimbabwe placed 500,000 metric tons of maize in reserve and entered into contracts with South Africa and other countries to supply an additional 400,000 metric tons. Adequate rains during the first three months of 1998 averted severe losses, but the steps taken would have prevented famine in the event of crop failure. Australian aid workers were able to ship grains and other foods to New Guinea, although deficiencies in infrastructure prevented distribution to isolated communities in the country's mountainous regions.

Predictions of high rainfall and flooding should stimulate appropriate reinforcement of dams and levies and the development of contingency plans for the distribution of food and other necessities to at-risk communities. Knowledge of an increase in livestock and animal diseases associated with contaminated water and a high prevalence of insect vectors should bring about stockpiling and distribution of vaccines along with implementation of appropriate preventive measures on a regional basis.

## Local adaptation and response to global climatic changes

Livestock producers are concerned with excessive heat or prolonged and unseasonal precipitation as the principal climatic factors affecting productivity. Heat stress decreases reproductive potential, egg production and growth rate. Excessive rainfall promotes the persistence and proliferation of protozoal and bacterial pathogens and exacerbates intestinal and respiratory infections in intensively-housed livestock. Exposure to extremes of either heat or cold results in immunosuppression with increased susceptibility of herds and flocks to disease-causing agents.

Global climatic changes, including high temperature and drought or low temperature accompanied by unseasonally high or erratic rainfall patterns, will result in mycotoxin contamination of feed ingredients. Production of toxins, both pre- and post-harvest, will have a deleterious effect on reproduction and growth when affected grains are included in diets. The effect depends on the type and level of mycotoxin and the age and species of livestock.

An appropriate response to the severe and prolonged high temperature recorded in the southeast United States during the 1982 *El Niño* event is reflected in the installation of evaporative cooling in both breeder and broiler housing. Evaporative cooling using cellulose pads reduces the severity of heat exposure in areas where maximum daily temperature exceeds 35°C. North Louisiana and South Arkansas have a cumulative production of 5 million broilers per week, representing 3% of the nation's total production of 165 million per week. A program of retrofitting evaporative cooling and fan-powered ventilation was undertaken. It was calculated that during the 13 weeks of excessive heat during an abnormal summer, hen-housed egg production of broiler breeders would decline by 10% and hatchability would be depressed by 8%. The loss associated with excessive heat over the 375 houses required to maintain a production level of 5 million broilers per week is estimated at 2.5 million chicks valued at $373,000. This value presumes purchase of chicks or fertile hatching eggs from other areas of the country to maintain production. In the event of non-availability of either fertile eggs or chicks, the affected complexes would experience a loss of 3,900 metric tons of processed meat valued at $761,000.

The capital cost of retrofitting a conventional breeder house is estimated at $4,000. Annual operating costs including depreciation, interest, maintenance and power for 375 houses would amount to $500,000 per annum. This value represents an expenditure of 0.2¢ per chick placed. Given the value of chicks lost as a result of heat, capital expenditure on installation of evaporative cooling would be recouped in 1.3 years. If, however, the broiler complexes were to experience a loss of throughput associated with lower broiler production, the payback period would be reduced to 6 months.

In evaluating the losses in broiler growing, a 13-week period of high temperature would depress broiler liveweight by 10%. With a margin of

3.6 ¢/kg, the loss in contribution would be $2,184,000 per season. In addition, the loss in remuneration to growers who are paid on the basis of liveweight would be decreased by approximately 14%. This is based on a 10% decline in liveweight from 2.28 kg per bird to 2.05 kg per bird. Collectively, contract growers would lose over $300,000 per season as a result of excessive heat. Based on the experiences of the *El Nino* events of the 1970s and 1980s, new broiler houses in the Southeast are constructed using longitudinal ("tunnel") ventilation with evaporative cooling despite the $120,000 cost of a house with a capacity of 25,000 broilers.

## MINIMIZING THE EFFECTS OF MYCOTOXINS

Simulation of the effect of low-grade aflatoxicosis following excessive rainfall suggests a marked decline in income in broiler complexes as a result of depressed live mass, inferior feed conversion ratio and elevated mortality and downgrades. In addition, chick production can be depressed by up to 5% in breeders consuming rations contaminated with 2-5 ppm aflatoxin $B_1$, 3 ppm *fusarium* T2 toxin or 1 ppm ochratoxin A. An appropriate response to mycotoxin contamination involves appropriate screening and storage of ingredients. In reality, farmers in many areas are obliged to make use of contaminated feed ingredients based on restraints of availability and cost. The effect of aflatoxin, fumonisin, zearalenone and to a lesser extent T-2 toxin can be offset by using mycotoxin binders and absorbers. Laboratory and field trials have shown that modified esterified glucomannan derived from the cell wall of a selected strain of *Saccharomyces cerevisiae* has a high affinity for these mycotoxins, both *in vitro* and within the intestinal tract. Addition of commercially-available Mycosorb™ at levels of up to 0.2% in diets has shown beneficial effects on growth rate, liveability, egg production and hatchability in the presence of aflatoxin contamination ranging from 50 to 200 ppb. The glucomannan compounds not only bind mycotoxins thereby reducing their immunosuppressive effect, but they also stimulate immune response resulting in higher levels of antibody in response to vaccines. In tropical countries adequate protection against velogenic Newcastle disease and highly pathogenic infectious bursal disease are critical to the survival of flocks and hence profitability. The cost effectiveness of incorporating mycotoxin binders in diets has been clearly demonstrated and benefit:cost ratios exceeding 25:1 can be attained.

Elevated ambient temperatures are responsible for mortality, decreased egg production and deterioration in shell integrity in commercial laying farms. Feed additives can be used to counteract the physiological responses to heat. These result in respiratory alkalosis and mineral depletion due to diuresis. Critical micronutrients, including manganese and zinc, play an important role in shell formation and are rate-limiting under conditions induced by high ambient temperature. Eggshell 49™, which contains highly-available bioplexes of essential trace minerals (zinc, manganese and copper), will contribute to improved shell strength, higher specific gravity and lower rejects, especially in high-producing Leghorn strain hens exposed to prolonged high temperature.

The immunosuppression associated with high ambient temperature is due to a reduction in the humoral immune response, resulting in lower antibody titers. In addition, cellular immunity is also suppressed through a T-cell or regulatory amplifier response. These changes are attributed to a corticosteroid-induced disturbance in serum ion concentration. Mannanoligosaccharides derived from yeast fermentation are available as a commercial supplement, Bio-Mos™. Laboratory studies have shown that the additive is capable of stimulating phagocytic and macrophage activity. Mannanoligosaccharides compete for binding sites on enterocytes, inhibiting colonization with intestinal pathogens including *Escherichia coli* and *Salmonella*.

Based on the intermediate and short-term forecasts of unseasonal temperature and rainfall following major disturbances in global climate patterns, it is possible to develop and implement appropriate responses. These will reduce both production and economic losses and contribute to continued supply of food for populations in affected areas.

# *In vitro* and *in vivo* testing of adsorbents for detoxifying mycotoxins in contaminated feedstuffs

DAVID R. LEDOUX[1] and GEORGE E. ROTTINGHAUS[2]

*Fusarium/Poultry Research Laboratory, [1]Department of Animal Science and [2]Veterinary Medical Diagnostic Laboratory, College of Veterinary Medicine, University of Missouri, Columbia, Missouri, USA*

## Introduction

Mycotoxins are a group of structurally diverse secondary fungal metabolites that occur as contaminants of grain worldwide. Aspergillus, Fusarium, Penicillium, and Claviceps species of fungi are ubiquitous in nature and under ideal conditions often infect economically important crops and forages in the field, during storage, transportation and processing. The most important mycotoxins found in the United States are aflatoxin $B_1$, fumonisin $B_1$, ochratoxin A, vomitoxin, zearalenone and the ergot alkaloids. Many of these mycotoxins can cause serious health problems in livestock and their presence in agricultural commodities may result in serious economic losses. Acute mycotoxicosis outbreaks do occur, but most mycotoxin-associated animal health problems are obscure chronic conditions related to reduced efficiency of production and increased susceptibility to infectious disease. Recognizing these potential problems, the grain industry, animal producers, overseas buyers and inspection agencies are promoting on-site testing using ELISA test kits for the various mycotoxins. Contaminated grains can be readily identified and at low levels of contamination can be safely used in livestock and poultry feed. Grain and screenings containing higher levels of mycotoxin contamination are generally unsafe for animal consumption. The use of microbial inactivation, mold inhibitors, fermentation, physical separation, thermal inactivation, irradiation, ammoniation (Goldblatt, 1971; Park *et al.*, 1984; CAST, 1989), ozone degradation (Mckenzie *et al.*, 1997, 1998), and sequestering agents have been reported for the decontamination and remediation of these highly contaminated feedstuffs. Unfortunately, most of these measures are costly, time-consuming, and only partially effective. At the present time, the most promising and practical approach has been the addition of adsorbents to contaminated feed to selectively bind the mycotoxin during the digestive process, allowing the mycotoxin to pass harmlessly through the animal. Research indicates that a number of adsorbents are capable of binding aflatoxin and reducing or preventing its toxic effects (Phillips *et al.*, 1988; Harvey *et al.*, 1989, 1991a, 1991b, 1993; Kubena *et al.*, 1990b, 1991, 1993; Ledoux *et al.*, 1999). Natural sorbents are generally recognized as safe (GRAS) for animal feeds at levels of 2 % or less by FDA.

The major advantages of adsorbents include low cost, safety and the ease with which they can be added to animal feeds. However, not all adsorbents are equally effective in protecting livestock against the toxic effects of aflatoxin and several adsorbents have been shown to impair nutrient utilization (Chung *et al.*, 1990; Kubena *et al.*, 1993; Scheideler, 1993). Recently, Dale (1998) noted that many of the adsorbents on the market today have not been adequately tested for *in vivo* efficacy, but are used based on *in vitro* data only. However, as Scheideler (1993) and Dwyer *et al.* (1997) have suggested, *in vitro* tests may not always be a reliable indicator of ability to bind a mycotoxin. Therefore, it is important that adsorbents be subjected to *in vivo* evaluation both with respect to efficacy and to determine if impaired nutrient utilization from diets occurs. The objective of this paper is to provide a model for *in vitro* and *in vivo* evaluation of the efficacy of adsorbents to ameliorate the toxic effects of mycotoxins.

## *In vitro* testing for mycotoxin binding by adsorbents

A search of the peer-reviewed scientific literature reveals that only limited information is available on *in vitro* mycotoxin binding studies. Information is almost exclusively limited to aflatoxin binding (Masimango *et al.*, 1978; Phillips *et al.*, 1988; Ramos and Hernandez, 1996; Grant and Phillips, 1998), although *in vitro* binding studies for zearalenone (Lemke *et al.*, 1998), ochratoxin A (Rotter *et al.*, 1989) and ergotamine (Chestnut *et al.*, 1992) have also been published. Phillips *et al.* (1988), using radiolabeled aflatoxin $B_1$, were the first to document that a variety of aluminum oxide compounds, silicas and aluminosilicates would bind aflatoxin in aqueous solution. The adsorbent with the strongest binding ability for aflatoxin $B_1$ was a hydrated sodium calcium aluminosilicate (HSCAS). The chemisorption of aflatoxin to HSCAS involves the formation of a complex by the $\beta$-keto-lactone or bilactone system of aflatoxin with uncoordinated metal ions in HSCAS (Phillips *et al.*, 1990; Sarr *et al.*, 1990). Commercialization of this product initiated a search to find other products that would bind aflatoxin as well as many of the other commonly occurring mycotoxins. Because of the expense and limited ability of laboratories to work with radiolabeled mycotoxins, a number of laboratories developed thin layer chromatography (TLC) and high performance liquid chromatography (HPLC) procedures to rapidly and inexpensively screen large numbers of samples for mycotoxin binding ability. These methods were developed to simply identify potential candidates for *in vivo* testing. The simple screening procedure we use is described below. It is typical of *in vitro* procedures used in most laboratories involved in testing the ability of adsorbents to bind mycotoxins.

David R. Ledoux and George E. Rottinghaus

EXPERIMENTAL DESIGN

Mycotoxins are readily available from Sigma Chemical Company. Primary stock solutions of each mycotoxin (1,000 µg/ml) are prepared in methanol or acetonitrile. Mycotoxin test solutions (2 µg/ml) for adsorption studies are prepared in distilled water from the methanolic stock solutions. Mycotoxin concentrations in the test solutions are not based on levels known to cause problems in livestock, but are based on 1) solubility of the mycotoxin in aqueous solution; 2) the relative ease of analysis by HPLC; and 3) cost of the mycotoxin.

Aliquots (10 ml) of the mycotoxin test solutions are added to screw cap test tubes along with 100 mg of adsorbent. In order to measure loss due to non-specific binding and to eliminate exogenous peaks, two controls are prepared by adding 10 ml of the mycotoxin test solution without the addition of adsorbent, and 10 ml distilled water plus 100 mg adsorbent to test tubes. Each sample and control is run in triplicate. The test tubes are placed on a rotator shaker for 1 hr at room temperature and centrifuged at 3,000 rpm for 10 minutes. A 2 ml aliquot of the aqueous supernatant is removed for mycotoxin analysis. The original mycotoxin test solution is used as the HPLC standard for each mycotoxin.

HPLC analyses are performed on a Perkin-Elmer Model 250 liquid chromatograph pump equipped with an Perkin Elmer ISS 200 autosampler, a Perkin-Elmer 8.3 cm $C_{18}$ cartridge column (3 µm particle size). Detection is with a Perkin-Elmer LS-4 fluorescence spectrophotometer or a Perkin Elmer LC 90 UV detector. Flow rate of mobile phase is 1 ml/min. The mobile phases and detection wavelengths used for each mycotoxin are presented in Table 1. Percent mycotoxin bound is calculated from the difference between the initial and final concentration of mycotoxin in the aqueous supernatant.

Table 1. HPLC mobile phase and detection wavelengths for mycotoxin analysis.

| Mycotoxin | Mobile phase | Detection* |
|---|---|---|
| Aflatoxin $B_1$, $B_2$, $G_1$, $G_2$ | Water:methanol:isopropanol (40:17:2) | F: Ex 365 nm Em 430 nm |
| Ergot alkaloids | Acetonitrile:water with 200 mg $(NH_4)_2CO_3$/L (38:62) | F: Ex 250 nm Em 420 nm |
| Fumonisin $B_1$. (OPA derrivative) | Acetonitrile:1% aqua KCl:acetic acid (40:60:1) | F: Ex 335 nm Em 440 nm |
| Ochratoxin A | Methanol:water:acetic acid (40:60:1) | F: Ex 365 nm Em 450 nm |
| Vomitoxin | Methanol:water with 3 g KCl/L (9:1) | UV 224 nm |
| Zearalenone | Water:methanol:acetic acid (45:55:1) | F: Ex 274 nm Em 465 nm |

*F=fluorescence, Ex=excitation wavelength, Em=emission wavelength, UV=ultraviolet

*In vitro* mycotoxin concentrations of 2 µg/ml in aqueous test solutions were selected because many of the mycotoxins have only limited solubility in water. For example, the solubility of aflatoxin $B_1$ in water is estimated to be 11-33 µg/ml by Grant and Phillips (1998), while the solubility of zearalenone in water is estimated to be less than 4 µg/ml by Lemke *et al.* (1998) at neutral pH and 37° C. Addition of higher levels of mycotoxins may result in precipitation and lead to erroneous adsorption results. The simple *in vitro* procedure allows a large number of samples to be examined rapidly and inexpensively. The absence of sample transfers and filtration steps minimizes error due to nonspecific binding, etc. The procedure is used as a yes/no test to identify sorbents that strongly bind mycotoxins relative to sorbents that have little if any binding ability. A sorbent demonstrating strong binding ability (>80-90%) in distilled water can be further evaluated *in vitro* for mycotoxin binding ability over a wide range of mycotoxin and adsorbent concentrations, temperatures, pHs, and time periods (Ramos and Hernandez, 1996; Grant and Phillips, 1998; Lemke *et al.*, 1998).

Additional *in vitro* information on surface adsorption of mycotoxins on binders can be obtained by using Langmuir and Freundlich adsorption isotherms (Ramos and Hernandez, 1996). Adsorption isotherms plot the amount of mycotoxin adsorbed per unit weight of adsorbent versus the mycotoxin concentration in solution at equilibrium and constant temperature (see Figure 1) and allow the determination of binding capacity and affinity of the sorbent for the compound adsorbed. Grant and Phillips (1998) were able to use multiple isotherm equations to determine not only capacity and affinity but also average capacity, enthalpy of binding, heterogeneity coefficient, multiple site distribution coefficients, and multisite capacity of HSCAS for aflatoxin $B_1$.

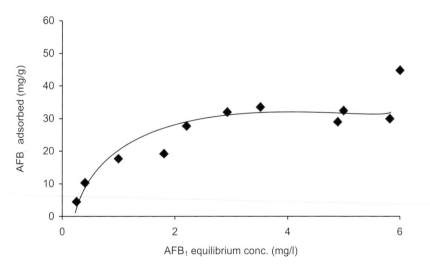

**Figure 1.** Isotherm plot of aflatoxin $B_1$ adsorption to a sorbent.

# Model for *in vivo* testing of adsorbents in poultry

## EXPERIMENTAL DESIGN

Once an adsorbent is identified from *in vitro* testing as a potential candidate for *in vivo* testing (>80-90% binding), the following approach is then used to evaluate the adsorbent. An example of dietary treatments required to evaluate the efficacy of an adsorbent to ameliorate the toxic effects of a single mycotoxin is presented in Table 2. Diet 1 is a control diet that should contain no mycotoxin or adsorbent. The diet should be a typical corn-soybean meal starter diet used in the broiler industry and should be formulated to meet or exceed the nutritional requirements of growing chicks as recommended by the National Research Council (NRC, 1994). In our laboratory, we usually formulate a basal diet that meets or exceeds NRC requirements and allows for the substitution of small quantities of the adsorbent and mycotoxin. The basal diet is then split into four portions and the adsorbent and clay are added to produce diets 2, 3, and 4. Diet 2 will contain the adsorbent to be tested and is included to provide information on the effects (negative or positive) of the adsorbent when fed alone. This treatment is critical because some adsorbents have been shown to compromise the nutritional integrity of the diet (Chung *et al.*, 1990; Kubena *et al.*, 1993; Scheideler, 1993). Diet 3 will contain the mycotoxin at a level that will ensure a measurable toxic response. It is essential to produce a measurable effect against which any reduction in toxicity due to the adsorbent can be measured. Diet 4 contains both the adsorbent and the mycotoxin and this treatment is included to demonstrate the ability of the adsorbent to ameliorate the toxic effects of the mycotoxin. Dietary mycotoxin concentrations are confirmed by analysis and all diets are screened (Rottinghaus *et al.*, 1982, 1992) for the presence of other mycotoxins including aflatoxin, citrinin, T-2 toxin, vomitoxin, sterigmatocystin, zearalenone, the fumonisins, diacetoxyscirpenol, and ochratoxin A prior to the start of the experiment.

Table 2. Dietary treatments for evaluating efficacy of an adsorbent to reduce the toxic effects of a mycotoxin.

| Diets | Adsorbent | Mycotoxin |
|---|---|---|
| 1 | 0 | 0 |
| 2 | 0.05-2% | 0 |
| 3 | 0 | (X) mg/kg |
| 4 | 0.05-2% | (X) mg/kg |

A minimum of five pen replicates of six day-old chicks should be assigned to each of the four dietary treatments for 21 days. Data are analyzed as a 2 × 2 factorial by analysis of variance using the General Linear Models procedure of SAS (SAS Institute, 1985). The means for treatments showing significant differences in the analysis of variance are then compared using the Fisher's protected least significant difference procedure (Snedecor and Cochran, 1967).

## LEVEL OF MYCOTOXIN AND ADSORBENT FOR *IN VIVO* TESTING

The level of mycotoxin to use will depend on the toxicity of the individual mycotoxin, and as indicated previously, on the level that will result in a measurable toxic effect. A list of mycotoxins and levels that have consistently been shown to cause a measurable toxic effect in broiler chicks is summarized in Table 3. T-2 toxin is recommended as being representative of the tricothecenes because of its greater toxicity compared with other tricothecenes.

The level of adsorbent to be used for testing will depend on two major considerations. First and most important is to test at a level that is being recommended for dietary inclusion. The second consideration is to include a level that represents the highest possible inclusion level. As indicated previously, most natural adsorbents are recognized as safe for animal feeds at levels of up to 2% by FDA. However, because some of the current adsorbents on the market may have been activated (chemically or physically treated) they may not be harmless at levels up to 2% of the diet. Therefore one approach is to test at least two levels, the recommended level and the highest possible inclusion level. Testing of the highest inclusion level serves as an additional demonstration of the safety of the product.

## SELECTION OF RESPONSE VARIABLES

The obvious and most important response variable of interest to producers is performance. However, as Dale (1998) correctly points out, evaluation of effects on performance (feed intake, body weight gain, feed conversion) is probably not adequate for satisfactory evaluation. Using aflatoxin as an example, Dale (1998) recommends that such sensitive parameters as serum proteins and carotenoids be evaluated, and that effects on immune response should also be measured. We use a number of response variables including performance, organ weights, serum chemistry, gross pathology, and histopathology. We have also recently developed and tested a panel of immune assays that will be used in the future to further evaluate mycotoxins (Li, 1998).

With respect to gross pathology, all birds are examined for signs of pathology due either to the mycotoxin or resulting from nutritional deficiencies that may have been caused by addition of the adsorbent. Brains are examined for the lesions of cerebellar swelling, edema, and hemorrhage as seen with vitamin E deficiency (Austic and Scott, 1997). The mucosal surface of the crop and esophagus are examined for the multiple white foci, indicative of squamous metaplasia of the subepithelial mucous glands, observed with vitamin A deficiency (Austic and Scott, 1997). The proximal

374

tibial growth plate is examined for widening of the zones of proliferation and/or hypertrophy as seen in cases of vitamin D, calcium and/or phosphorus deficiency (Austic and Scott, 1997). The tibia is also broken as a simple method to evaluate bone strength. The skeletal muscles and abdominal cavity are examined for the hemorrhages observed in cases of vitamin K deficiency (Austic and Scott, 1997). The legs are also examined for bowing and/or perosis as can occur with deficiencies in nicotinic acid, choline, and/or manganese (Austic and Scott, 1997). The skin and feathers of the chicks are also examined for indications of pantothenic acid and biotin deficiency (Austic and Scott, 1997). With respect to histopathology, only the target organs of the test mycotoxin are microscopically evaluated.

Table 3 contains a list of mycotoxins and their effects on various response variables in broiler chicks. Using this table it is relatively easy to select the appropriate response variables. For example, if evaluating aflatoxin, response variables should include performance, serum proteins, liver and kidney weights, and microscopic evaluation of liver and kidney for pathologic changes.

**Table 3. Toxic effects of selected mycotoxins in broiler chicks.**

| Mycotoxin | Dietary level[1] (mg/kg) | Effects |
|---|---|---|
| Aflatoxin | 3-4 | Decreased performance<br>Decreased serum proteins<br>Increased liver and kidney weights<br>Liver and kidney lesions |
| Ochratoxin A | 3-4 | Decreased performance<br>Decreased serum proteins<br>Increased uric acid<br>Increased liver and kidney weights<br>Kidney lesions |
| T-2 Toxin | 5-8 | Decreased performance<br>Decreased serum proteins<br>Oral lesions |
| Fumonisin $B_1$ | 300-400 | Decreased performance<br>Increased SA:SO[2] ratio<br>Increased liver and kidney weights<br>Liver lesions |
| Moniliformin | 100 | Decreased performance<br>Increased heart and liver weights<br>Cardiac lesions |

[1]Range reported to consistently cause toxic effects listed.
[2]SA:SO = sphinganine to sphingosine ratio.

# Efficacy of adsorbents to bind mycotoxins

Since it was first demonstrated (Phillips *et al.*, 1988, 1990) that a specific hydrated sodium calcium aluminosilicate (HSCAS) was effective in ameliorating the toxic effects of aflatoxin *in vivo*, a large number of other adsorbents have been tested for efficacy against aflatoxin. Results indicate that there is great variability in the efficacy of these compounds *in vivo;* and in many cases *in vitro* efficacy is not related to *in vivo* efficacy.

Recently, there has been a tremendous increase in the number of these adsorbents available commercially. In addition, claims are being made that these products are not only effective against aflatoxin but are also effective against a number of other mycotoxins including T-2 toxin, ochratoxin A, fumonisin $B_1$, and deoxynivalenol (vomitoxin). Unfortunately, most of these claims are based on *in vitro* evaluation, which as we have discussed previously is not always correlated with *in vivo* efficacy. To date, results of well-designed *in vivo* studies published in refereed journals indicate that none of the adsorbents tested provided any protection against T-2 toxin, ochratoxin A, cyclopiazonic acid, diacetoxyscirpenol, or fumonisin $B_1$ (Kubena *et al.,* 1990a, 1992, 1993, 1998; Brown *et al.*, 1992; Huff *et al.*, 1992; Dwyer *et al.*, 1997; Bailey *et al.*, 1998). *In vivo* studies conducted in our laboratory (Ledoux and Rottinghaus, unpublished) also indicate that none of adsorbents tested thus far have afforded protection against fumonisin $B_1$, moniliformin, ochratoxin A or vomitoxin.

A review of the hypothesized mechanism for the efficacy of the HSCAS against aflatoxin may well explain the lack of efficacy of these adsorbents against other mycotoxins. As indicated earlier, the chemisorption of aflatoxin to HSCAS involves the formation of a complex by the ß-keto-lactone or bilactone system of aflatoxin with uncoordinated metal ions in HSCAS (Phillips *et al.,* 1990; Sarr *et al.*, 1990). A review of the chemical structures of the other mycotoxins indicates, with the possible exception of ergot alkaloids, that none of them have a similar ß-keto-lactone or bilactone system that is thought to be essential for chemisorption to HSCAS to occur. Therefore, unless these mycotoxins have some other type of structural system that would allow chemisorption to HSCAS to occur, it is not surprising that HSCAS adsorbents are not effective in reducing or preventing the toxic effects of these mycotoxins.

# Conclusion

In conclusion, the *in vitro* and *in vivo* models outlined in this paper will provide the livestock industry with the means to critically evaluate adsorbents currently available. Additionally, these procedures can be used to develop and evaluate the efficacy of new products to alleviate the toxic effects of mycotoxins.

# References

Austic, R.E. and M.L. Scott. 1997. Nutritional diseases. In: Diseases of Poultry, 10th ed. (B.W. Calnek, H.J. Barnes, C.W. Beard, L.R. McDougald, and Y.M. Saif eds.), Iowa State University Press, Ames, Iowa. pp. 47–73.

Bailey, R.H., L.F. Kubena, R.B. Harvey, S.A. Buckley and G.E. Rottinghaus. 1998. Efficacy of various inorganic sorbents to reduce the toxicity of aflatoxin and T-2 toxin in broiler chickens. Poultry Sci. 77:1623–1630.

Brown, T.P., G.E. Rottinghaus and M.E. Williams. 1992. Fumonisin mycotoxicosis in broilers: Performance and pathology. Avian Diseases 36:450–454.

Council for Agricultural Science and Technology Task Force Report #16. 1989. Mycotoxins:Economic and Health Risks. Ames, IA.

Chestnut, A.B., P.D. Anderson, M.A. Cochran, H.A. Fribourg and K.D. Gwinn. 1992. Effects of hydrated sodium calcium aluminosilicate on fescue toxicosis and mineral absorption. J. Anim. Sci. 70:2838–2846.

Chung, T.K., J.W. Erdman, Jr. and D.H. Baker. 1990. Hydrated sodium calcium aluminosilicate: effects on zinc, manganese, vitamin A, and riboflavin utilization. Poultry Sci. 69:1364–1370.

Dale, N. 1998. Mycotoxin binders: It's time for real science. Poultry Digest 57:38–39.

Dwyer, M.R., L.F. Kubena, R.B. Harvey, K. Mayura, A.B. Sarr, S. Buckley, R.H. Bailey and T. D. Phillips. 1997. Effects of inorganic adsorbents and cyclopiazonic acid in broiler chicks. Poultry Sci. 76:1141–1149.

Goldblatt, L.A. 1971. Control and removal of aflatoxin. J. Am. Oil Chem. Soc. 48:605–610.

Grant, P.G. and T.D. Phillips. 1998. Isothermal adsorption of aflatoxin $B_1$ on HSCAS clay. J. Agric. Food Chem. 46:599–605.

Harvey, R.B., L.F. Kubena, T.D. Phillips, W.E. Huff and D.E. Corrier. 1989. Prevention of aflatoxicosis by addition of hydrated sodium calcium aluminosilicate to the diets of growing barrows. Am. J. Vet. Res. 50:416–420.

Harvey, R.B., L.F. Kubena, T.D. Phillips, M.E. Elissalde and W.E. Huff. 1991a. Diminution of aflatoxin toxicity to growing lambs by dietary supplementation with hydrated sodium calcium aluminosilicate. Am. J. Vet. Res. 52:152–156.

Harvey, R.B., T.D. Phillips, J.A. Ellis, L.F. Kubena, W.E. Huff and H.D. Petersen. 1991b. Effects on aflatoxin $M_1$ residues in milk by addition of hydrated sodium calcium aluminosilicate to aflatoxin-contaminated diets of dairy cows. Am. J.Vet. Res. 52:1556–1559.

Harvey, R.B., L.F. Kubena, M.H. Elissalde and T.D. Phillips. 1993. Efficacy of zeolitic ore compounds on the toxicity of aflatoxin to growing broiler chickens. Avian Dis. 37:67–73.

Huff, W.E., L.F. Kubena, R.B. Harvey and T.D. Phillips. 1992. Efficacy of hydrated sodium calcium aluminosilicate to reduce the individual and combined toxicity of aflatoxin and ochratoxin A. Poultry Sci. 71:64–69.

Kubena, L.F., R.B. Harvey, W.E. Huff, D.E. Corrier, T.D. Phillips and G.E. Rottinghaus. 1990a. Efficacy of a hydrated sodium calcium aluminosilicate to reduce the toxicity of aflatoxin and T-2 toxin. Poultry Sci. 69:1078–1086.

Kubena, L.F., R.B. Harvey, T.D. Phillips, D.E. Corrier and W.E. Huff. 1990b. Diminution of aflatoxicosis in growing chickens by the dietary addition of hydrated sodium calcium alumiunosilicate. Poultry Sci. 69:727–735.

Kubena, L.F., W.E. Huff, R.B. Harvey, A.G. Yersin, M.H. Elissalde, D.A. Witzel, L.E. Giroir, T.D. Phillips and H.D. Petersen. 1991. Effects of a hydrated sodium calcium aluminosilicate on growing turkey poults during aflatoxicosis. Poultry Sci. 70:1823–1830.

Kubena, L.F., R.B. Harvey, T.D. Phillips and B.A. Clement. 1992. Effects of several sorbent materials on mycotoxicosis in broiler chickens. Poultry Sci. 71(Suppl. 1):161.

Kubena, L.F., R.B. Harvey, W.E. Huff, M.H. Elissalde, A.G. Yersin, T.D. Phillips and G.E. Rottinghaus. 1993. Efficacy of a hydrated sodium calcium aluminosilicate to reduce the toxicity of aflatoxin and diacetoxyscirpenol. Poultry Sci. 72:51–59.

Kubena, L.F., R.B. Harvey, R.H. Bailey, S.A. Buckley and G.E. Rottinghaus. 1998. Effects of a hydrated sodium calcium aluminosilicate (T-Bind) on mycotoxicosis in young broiler chickens. Poultry Sci. 77:1502–1509.

Ledoux, D.R., G.E. Rottinghaus, A.J. Bermudez and M. Alonso-Debolt. 1999. Efficacy of a hydrated sodium calcium aluminosilicate to ameliorate the toxic effects of aflatoxin in broiler chicks. Poultry Sci. 78:204–210.

Lemke, S.L., P.G. Grant and T.D. Phillips. 1998. Adsorption of zearalenone by organophilic montmorillonite clay. J. Agric. Food Chem. 46:3789–3796.

Li, Y.C. 1998. Effects of *Fusarium* mycotoxins, fumonisin $B_1$ and moniliformin, on selected immune responses in broiler chicks and turkey poults. Doctoral Dissertation, University of Missouri, Columbia, Missouri.

Masimango, N., J. Remacle and J.L. Ramaut. 1978. The role of adsorption in the elimination of aflatoxin $B_1$ from contaminated media. Europ. J. Appl. Microbiol. 6:101–105.

McKenzie, K.S., A.B. Sarr, K. Mayura, R.H. Bailey, D.R. Miller, T.D. Rogers, W.P. Norred, K.A. Voss, R.D. Platner, L.F. Kubena and T.D. Phillips. 1997. Oxidative degradation and detoxification of mycotoxins using a novel source of ozone. Food and Chem. Toxicol. 35:807–820.

McKenzie, K.S., L.F. Kubena, A.J. Denvir, T.D. Rogers, G.D. Hitchens, R.H. Bailey, R.B. Harvey, S.A. Buckley and T.D. Phillips. 1998. Aflatoxicosis in turkey poults is prevented by treatment of naturally-contaminated corn with an ozone generated by electrolysis. Poultry Sci. 77:1094–1102.

National Research Council. 1994. Nutrient Requirements of Poultry, 9th ed. National Academy of Science, Washington, D.C.

Park, D.L., L.S. Lee and S.A. Kolton. 1984. Distribution of ammonia-related aflatoxin reaction products in cottonseed meal. J. Am. Oil Chem. Soc. 61:1071–1074.

Phillips, T.D., L.F. Kubena, R.B. Harvey, D.R. Taylor and N.D. Heidelbaugh. 1988. Hydrated sodium calcium aluminosilicate: A high affinity sorbent for aflatoxin. Poultry Sci. 67:243–247.

Phillips, T.D., A.B. Sarr, B.A. Clement, L.F. Kubena and R.B. Harvey. 1990. Prevention of aflatoxicosis in farm animals via selective chemisorption of aflatoxin. In: G.A. Bray and D.H. Ryan, ed. Pennington Center Nutrition Series Volume 1, Mycotoxins, Cancer, and Health, Louisiana State Univ. Press, Baton Rouge, LA. pp. 223–237.

Ramos, A.J. and E. Hernandez. 1996. *In vitro* aflatoxin adsorption by means of a montmorillonite silicate. A study of adsorption isotherms. Animal Feed Sci. Technology 62:263–269.

Rotter, R.G., A.A. Frohlich and R.R. Marquardt. 1989. Influence of dietary charcoal on ochratoxin A toxicity in Leghorn chicks. Can. J. Vet. Res. 53:489–453.

Rottinghaus, G.E., B. Olsen and G.D. Osweiler. 1982. Rapid screening method for aflatoxin $B_1$, zearalenone, ochratoxin A, T-2 toxin, diacetoxyscirpenol and vomitoxin. In: Proceedings of the 25th Annual American Association of Veterinary Laboratory Diagnosticians, Nashville, TN. Pages 477–484

Rottinghaus, G.E., C.E. Coatney and H.C. Minor. 1992. A rapid sensitive thin layer chromatography procedure for the detection of fumonisin $B_1$ and $B_2$. J. Vet. Diagn. Invest. 4:326–329.

Sarr, A.B., B.A. Clement and T.D. Phillips. 1990. Effects of molecular structure on the chemisorption of aflatoxin $B_1$ and related compounds by hydrated sodium calcium aluminosilicate. The Toxicologist 10(1):163.

SAS Institute. 1985. SAS User's Guide: Statistics. Version 6 Edition. SAS Institute Inc. Cary, NC.

Scheideler, S. E. 1993. Effects of various types of aluminosilicates and aflatoxin $B_1$ on aflatoxin toxicity, chick performance, and mineral status. Poultry Sci. 72:282–288.

Snedecor, G.W. and W.E. Cochran. 1967. Statistical Methods. 6th ed. The Iowa State University Press, Ames, IA.

# Nutritional approaches to reduce the impact of mycotoxins

ANDREA PIVA[1] and FABIO GALVANO[2]

[1]Dipartimento di Morfofisiologia Veterinaria e Produzioni Animali, Università di Bologna, Ozzano Emilia, Bologna, Italy.

[2]Dipartimento di Scienze e Tecnologie Agroforestali ed Ambientali, Università di Reggio Calabria, Reggio Calabria, Italy.

## Introduction

Mycotoxins are highly toxic secondary products of the metabolism of some fungi mainly belonging to Aspergillus, Penicillium and Fusarium species. A toxic syndrome caused by mycotoxin ingestion in man and animals is referred to as a mycotoxicosis. It has been estimated that at least 300 fungal metabolites are potentially toxic for man and animals, and that as much as 25% of the world's cereals are contaminated with known mycotoxins (Devegowda et al., 1998). Moreover, it can be realistically assumed that other mycotoxins are likely to be discovered. The most notorious and extensively investigated mycotoxins are aflatoxin $B_1$, ochratoxin A, fumonisin $B_1$, zearalenone, deoxynivalenol and T2-toxin. However, recently research interest in other toxins such as citrinin, sterigmatocistyn and diacetoxyscirpenol has been growing.

Chemical, biological and toxicological properties of mycotoxins are diverse. Hence, their toxic effects are extremely variable and also depend on toxin intake, duration of exposure, animal species, age, sex, physiological status, and eventual synergism among mycotoxins simultaneously present in feed or foods. However, the main toxic effects are carcinogenicity, genotoxicity, teratogenicity, nephrotoxicity, hepatotoxicity, reproductive disorders and immunosuppression. In addition, some mycotoxins are specifically indicated or strongly suspected to cause certain human and animal diseases such as Reye's disease (caused by aflatoxin $B_1$) (Becroft and Webster, 1972), equine leukoencephalomalacia and porcine pulmonary edema (caused by fumonisin $B_1$), human alimentary toxic aleukia (caused by T2-toxin) and Balkan endemic nephropathy (caused by ochratoxin). The positive correlation between the consumption of aflatoxin-contaminated foods and the increased incidence of liver cancer in several Asian and African populations has led to the classification of aflatoxins as group 1A carcinogens by the International Agency for Research on Cancer (IARC, 1993). In 1997, the Joint FAO/WHO Expert Committee on Food

Additives (JECFA) provided qualitative and quantitative information on aflatoxins and concluded that aflatoxins should be treated as carcinogenic food contaminants, the intake of which should be reduced to levels as low as could reasonably be acheived (JECFA, 1997). According to Kuiper-Goodman (1995), although human health risk assessment involves toxicological, epidemiological and exposure factors, in the risk management of mycotoxins it is necessary to take action before all this information is available. However, the lack of this information means some uncertainties in assessing human exposure and health risk and in establishing causal relationships between incidence of mycotoxins in foods and human disease (Smith *et al.*, 1995).

From a regulatory standpoint, different countries have enforced different thresholds to limit the passage of mycotoxins along the food chain. In the US it is required by law that aflatoxin $M_1$ in milk be less that 0.5 ppb, whereas in western Europe the regulations are more stringent, and maximum levels are set at 0.05 ppb (Boutrif and Canet, 1998). Currently the US Food and Drug Administration (FDA) regulates only aflatoxin among the mycotoxins and stipulates a maximum of 20 ppb of aflatoxin in grain shipped for interstate transit. Denmark, on the other hand, has decided that a level of 15 ppb of ochratoxin in the liver or kidney of pigs results in confiscation of those organs and that levels exceeding 25 ppb would result in condemnation of the entire carcass.

No doubt exists concerning the economic impact of mycotoxins. Recent studies (Charmley *et al.*, 1995; Garcia *et al.*, 1997) evidenced that economic losses occur at all levels of food and feed production including crop and animal production, processing and distribution. Even during favorable climatic periods millions of dollars are lost as a consequence of crop contamination. For all these reasons prevention, decontamination and detoxification of mycotoxins are issues of great importance.

Generally, any approach aimed to reduce the toxic and economic impact of mycotoxins should fulfill the following prerequisites:

1. prevent, destroy, remove or detoxify mycotoxins in feeds and foods
2. not produce nor leave toxic and/or carcinogenic/mutagenic residues in the final products
3. not significantly alter important technologic and nutritional properties
4. be technically and economically feasible (Piva *et al.*, 1995)

A wide range of chemical, physical and biological routes have been taken in the attempt to reduce the toxicity of mycotoxins. Although some chemical detoxification methods (i.e., ammonia, sodium bisulfite and calcium hydroxide treatments) are effective, they do not fulfill all the requirements, especially those concerning the safety of reaction products and the safeguarding of the nutritional characteristics of the treated foods and feeds (Piva *et al.*, 1995).

For these reasons nutritional approaches such as a) supplementation of nutrients, food components or additives with protective properties against toxicity, and b) addition of non-nutritive sorbents or bacteria, yeast and modified yeast cells capable of reducing mycotoxin bioavailability are assuming increasing interest.

# Nutritional routes to protection against mycotoxins

## ANTIOXIDANT SUBSTANCES

Since some mycotoxins are known to cause membrane damage through increased lipid peroxidation, the protective properties of antioxidant substances have been extensively investigated. Selenium, some vitamins (A, C and E) and their precursors have marked antioxidant properties acting as superoxide anion scavengers. For these reasons they have been investigated as protective agents against mycotoxins.

### Selenium

In a controlled *in vitro* study Lin *et al.* (1994) observed that selenium could reduce toxicity of T-2 toxin on cultured chicken embryonic chondrocytes. When sodium selenite was added to the culture in the presence of T-2 toxin there were no decreases in collagen microfibril, intramembrane particle numbers and enzyme (cytochrome c, oxidase and H+-ATPase) activities observed.

In an *in vivo* study in rats Shi *et al.* (1994) demonstrated that selenium inhibits aflatoxin $B_1$-DNA binding and adduct formation. Sodium selenite and a selenium-enriched yeast extract protected cultured hamster ovary cells from aflatoxin $B_1$ cytotoxicity, but not from mutagenicity (Shi *et al.*, 1995). In contrast, McLeod *et al.* (1997) reported that rats given a selenium-deficient diet were more resistant to aflatoxin $B_1$ than those given a selenium-sufficient diet. According to the authors the protection conferred by selenium deficiency was associated with the hepatic expression of an aldoketo reductase and a glutathione S-transferase subunit that efficiently metabolize the mycotoxin.

Based on a study on rats, Atroshi *et al.* (1995) concluded that selenium, vitamin E and vitamin C act as an antioxidant and free radical scavenger system that protects the spleen and brain against membrane damage caused by T-2 toxin and deoxynivalenol. Additionally, it has been postulated that higher levels of methionine supplementation would counteract the methionine depletion due to the fact that glutathione is composed of methionine and cystine (Devegowda *et al.*, 1998).

### Vitamins

Further evidence of protective effects of some vitamins and/or their precursors against mycotoxin-induced damage arises from numerous *in vivo* and *in vitro* studies. Grosse *et al.* (1997) observed that vitamin A, C and E reduced DNA adducts in kidney and liver by 70 to 90% in mice exposed to ochratoxin and zearalenone. Vitamin C can also protect guinea pigs from aflatoxin $B_1$ hepatotoxicity (Netke *et al.*, 1997). Vitamin C reduced abnormalities in both mitotic and meiotic chromosomes and morphologies of the sperm head in mice exposed to ochratoxin (Bose and Sinha, 1994). Analogous protective actions have also been attributed to vitamin E (Ibeh and Saxena, 1998) and vitamin A against exposure both to ochratoxin (Kumari and Sinha, 1994) and aflatoxin $B_1$ (Sinha and Dharmshila, 1994). Supplementary vitamin E administered to chickens partially counteracts the formation of lipid peroxides due to single and combined exposure to ochratoxin and T-2 toxin (Hoehler and Marquardt, 1996) while Coelho (1996) demonstrated that vitamin supplementation of turkey diets can reduce negative effects of mycotoxins and environmental stress.

Carotenoids (carotene and xanthophylls) are excellent antioxidants with antimutagenic and anticarcinogenic properties. They occur naturally in some foods such as carrots, red tomatoes, butter, cheese, paprika, palm oil, corn kernels, and red salmon. Dietary carotenoids inhibit aflatoxin $B_1$-induced liver DNA damage in rats as demonstrated by Gradelet *et al.* (1997; 1998). To the authors, ß-apo-8'carotenal, canthaxanthin and astaxanthin exert their protective effects altering aflatoxin $B_1$ metabolism toward pathways that lead to the formation of aflatoxin $M_1$, a less toxic metabolite. As specifically regards betacarotene, because it does not alter aflatoxin $B_1$ metabolism its protective action must be mediated by other mechanisms. No protective effects were observed by administration of supplementary lycopene (a carotenoid found in ripe fruit) and excess vitamin A.

In a study on antimutagenic activity of natural xanthophylls against aflatoxin $B_1$ in *Salmonella typhimurium,* González de Mejía *et al.* (1997) reported that xanthophylls inhibited the mutagenicity of aflatoxin $B_1$ in a dose-dependent manner.

Yu *et al.* (1994), using woodchuck hepatocytes as a model to investigate the effects of vitamin A, C, E and betacarotene on aflatoxin $B_1$-DNA adducts, reported contrasting results. In fact, they showed that vitamin C and particularly vitamin A were effective in reducing aflatoxin $B_1$-DNA binding, whereas vitamin E and betacarotene enhanced it. The authors concluded that additional studies are needed to understand the mechanism of enhanced adduct formation.

Two vitamin $A_2$ compounds (3-dehydroretinol and 3-dehydroretinyl palmitate) mainly present in freshwater fish have been shown to be very effective in inhibiting the microsome-catalyzed formation of DNA-aflatoxin $B_1$ adduct (Aboobaker *et al.*, 1997). The inhibition should be due to modulation of microsomal enzymes, which activate the carcinogen, hence suggesting a potential chemopreventive role of these compounds against carcinogenesis induced by aflatoxin $B_1$.

In a study conducted on *Bacillus subtilis* cells, vitamin E was able to prevent the genotoxicity of zearalenone (Ghédira Chékir *et al.*, 1998). The authors attributed the specificity of the prevention to the structural similarity of vitamin E and zearalenone.

## FOOD COMPONENTS AND ADDITIVES

Numerous food components, ingredients or additives with or without overall antioxidant properties have been investigated to verify their chemoprotective properties. Ellagic acid is a phenolic compound that occurs naturally in some foods such as strawberries, raspberries, and grapes. It has both antimutagenic and anticarcinogenic activity as demonstrated in a wide range of assays *in vitro* and *in vivo*. Loarca Piña *et al.* (1996; 1998), in *in vitro* tests on salmonella cells, showed that ellagic acid inhibits aflatoxin $B_1$ direct-acting mutagenicity, particularly when incubated with metabolic enzymes. The result of sequential incubation indicated that the formation of an aflatoxin $B_1$-ellagic acid chemical complex was the mechanism of inhibition.

Another study emphasized the role of phenolic compounds in the activation and detoxification processes and hence in modulating the carcinogenicity of aflatoxin $B_1$ (Aboobaker *et al.*, 1994). In tests performed on rats given a synthetic diet containing various food-associated phenolic compounds each at 0.5% level, the authors observed a marked decrease in the ability of liver microsomes to catalyze reactions of aflatoxin $B_1$ leading to its activation and DNA adduct formation. The phenolic compounds tested were several flavonoids (fisetin, kaempferol, morin, naringin and catechin), phenolic acids (caffeic acid and chlorogenic acid), other phenolic (eugenol, vanillin) and synthetic phenolic antioxidants butylated hydroxyanisole (BHA) and butylated hydroxytoluene (BHT). Some phenolic compounds (naringin, catechin, eugenol, vanillin and BHA) were also found to induce cytosolic glutathione S-transferase activity that stimulated the formation of specific aflatoxin $B_1$-glutathione conjugate.

Williams and Iatropoulos (1996) and Manson *et al.* (1997) confirmed that BHA and BHT inhibited the initiation of hepatocarcinogenesis by aflatoxin $B_1$ in rats. Soni *et al.* (1997) confirmed that ellagic acid and BHA ameliorate aflatoxin-induced mutagenicity and carcinogenicity. The same authors also found that certain food additives and/or active ingredients with general antioxidant properties such as turmeric (*Curcuma longa*), curcumin (diferlolyl methane) and garlic, have the same properties. Firozi *et al.* (1996) demonstrated that curcumin reduces the formation of aflatoxin $B_1$-DNA adducts by modulating cytochrome P450 function.

A range of natural dietary constituents including garlic oil, ethoxyquine, indole-3-carbinol and phenethyl isothiocynate have *in vitro* chemoprotective actions toward aflatoxin $B_1$ (Manson *et al.*, 1997). Some natural polyphenolic compounds, i.e., polyhydroxylated flavonoids and phenolic acids, were found to be effective in reducing aflatoxin $B_1$-DNA adducts (Firozi and Bhattacharya, 1995). S-methyl methanethiosulfonate (MMTS), a compound present in the juice of cabbage and onion, has a suppressive effect on aflatoxin $B_1$- or methyl methanesulfonate (MMS)-induced chromosome aberrations in rat bone marrow cells (Ito *et al.*, 1997). Also, the precursor of MMTS S-methyl-L-cysteinesulfoxide significantly suppressed aflatoxin $B_1$- or MMS-induced chromosome aberrations. According to the authors, although other mechanisms are not excluded,

385

the protective properties of MMTS may result from its ability to modify -SH groups in proteins.

Cavin *et al.* (1998), in a study on the effects of two diterpenes (cafestol and kahweol) present in green and roasted coffee beans against the covalent binding of aflatoxin $B_1$ metabolites to DNA of rats, identified these two substances as potentially chemoprotective agents. It has been postulated that these compounds may act as blocking agents by producing a coordinated modulation of multiple enzymes involved in carcinogen detoxification. Manson *et al.* (1997) found that caffeic acid has chemoprotective activity against aflatoxin $B_1$ *in vitro*.

Jesval (1998) attributed to berry and leaf juice of grape (*Vitis vinifera*) protective abilities against ochratoxin-induced hepatoma and renal carcinoma in mice. Propionic acid and potassium sorbate used as preservatives in bread making in France destroyed aflatoxin $B_1$ from 52 to 71% (Amra *et al.*, 1996).

## ASPARTAME

Three studies (Creppy *et al.*, 1995; 1996; Baudrimont *et al.*, 1997a,b) reported that aspartame (L-aspartyl-L-phenylanine methyl ester) has a wide protective action against ochratoxin-induced subchronic effects. Studies on monkey kidney cells showed that aspartame prevents or partially protects against some typical cytotoxic effects of ochratoxin such as inhibition of protein synthesis, lipid peroxidation and leakage of certain enzymes such as lactate dehydrogenase, gamma-glutamyl transferase and alkaline phosphatase. *In vitro*, aspartame prevented ochratoxin binding to plasma proteins. When given to rats, aspartame prevented ochratoxin genotoxicity and nephrotoxicity and washed out the toxin from the body efficiently. The protective action is thought to be due to its structural similarity to phenylanine and ochratoxin. To the authors, aspartame is the best candidate for preventing ochratoxin-induced subchronic effects, and the absence of side effects in humans and animals is worth noting.

## PIPERINE

According to Reen *et al.* (1997), piperine (1-piperoylpiperidine), the major alkaloid constituent of pepper (*Piper nigrum*), has considerable potential as protective agent against the carcinogenic effects of aflatoxin $B_1$. It is well known that aflatoxin $B_1$ toxicity is bioactivated by the cytochrome P450 monooxygenases (CYP450). In cultured rat cells piperine dramatically reduced $CYP4502B_1$ activity and counteracted $CYP4502B_1$-mediated toxicity of aflatoxin $B_1$, thus offering a chemopreventive effect against procarginogens activated by $CYP4502B_1$.

## COUMARIN

Coumarin (1,2-benzopyrone), a natural food constituent especially present in *Fava tonka*, has a chemoprotective action against aflatoxin $B_1$. As demonstrated by Goeger *et al.* (1998) in *in vitro* studies on hamster ovary cells, liver cells from rats and chick embryos, coumarin decreased cytotoxicity and mutagenicity of aflatoxin $B_1$, with marked species differences in chemoprotection. However, it must be considered that coumarin has also toxic properties and, due to their structural similarity, counteracts vitamin K absorption.

## CHLOROPHYLL AND ITS DERIVATIVES

Dashwood *et al.* (1998) demonstrated that chlorophylline (a food grade derivative of the green plant pigment chlorophyll) has chemopreventive properties against a wide classes of mutagens, including aflatoxin $B_1$. Both *in vitro* and *in vivo* studies showed that chlorophylline act as an interceptor molecule by forming a strong noncovalent complex with aflatoxin $B_1$ (Breinholt *et al.*, 1995) reducing hepatic aflatoxin $B_1$-DNA adducts and liver tumors.

## CYPROHEPTADINE

Cyproheptadine, a serotonin antagonist with appetite stimulant properties, has been tested to reduce feed refusal due to the presence of deoxynivalenol (Prelusky *et al.*, 1997). The authors observed that cyproheptadine effectively offset the reduction of feed intake. It was concluded that, although serotoninergic mechanisms are involved in reducing deoxynivalenol-induced feed refusal, further investigations are needed to better understand the reasons for the anorectic effect.

## MYCOTOXIN BINDING AGENTS

Addition of nutritionally inert sorbents is one of the most recent approaches to reduce mycotoxin effects in animals. After a general initial skepticism, the interest of researchers in sorbents has increased in the last years (Dale, 1998). Sorbents act to reduce the bioavailability of mycotoxins by adsorption. Indeed, if a stable sorbent-mycotoxin complex is formed, the absorption of mycotoxins in the gastrointestinal tract can be reduced thereby decreasing both toxic effects for animal and carry over in animal products for human consumption.

With this aim numerous sorbents of different sources have been tested including hydrated sodium calcium aluminosilicate (HSCAS), zeolites, bentonites, clays and activated carbons (Piva *et al.*, 1995; Ramos *et al.*, 1996).

### HSCAS
HSCAS, a phyllosilicate derived from natural zeolite, is perhaps the most extensively investigated sorbent. Evidence of a high affinity of HSCAS

387

for aflatoxin $B_1$ both *in vitro* and *in vivo* arises from numerous studies reviewed by Piva *et al.* (1995) and Ramos *et al.* (1996). However, enthusiasm for the efficacy of HSCAS must be tempered by other studies that have shown HSCAS to be ineffective in binding dangerous mycotoxins other than aflatoxin $B_1$. Indeed, its protective properties are very low toward ochratoxin and zearalenone and nil toward trichothecenes.

## Zeolites

Zeolites are hydrated aluminosilicates of alkali and alkaline-earth cations characterized by infinite three-dimensional structures (Ramos *et al.*, 1996). Although contrasting results are present in the literature, an overall efficacy of zeolite in binding aflatoxin $B_1$ and zearalenone has been reported (Piva *et al.*, 1995; Ramos *et al.*, 1996). As evidenced by Piva *et al.* (1995), the origin of zeolite can markedly affect results of adsorption tests. In fact, the pore size distribution of synthetic as opposed to natural zeolites varies very little. If pore size is compatible with that of the mycotoxin molecule, adsorption can occur. On the contrary, adsorption can be low or nil due to the absence of intermediate sized pores. The use of a zeolite, the clinoptilolite, reduced liver accumulation when administered to laying hens exposed to aflatoxin $B_1$ although it had no effect on liver mixed-function-oxygenase (MFO) activities (Zaghini *et al.*, 1998).

## Bentonites

Bentonites are sorbents with a layered (lamellar) crystalline microstructure and variable composition and adsorption properties, mainly depending on the interchangeable cations ($Na^+$, $K^+$, $Ca^{+2}$ and $Mg^{+2}$) present in the layers (Ramos *et al.*, 1996). Bentonite has been shown to bind aflatoxin $B_1$ *in vitro* and reduce its toxic effects in trout and pigs and also to reduce toxic effects of T2-toxin in rats (Ramos *et al.*, 1996). Sodium bentonite and a synthetic zeolite mixture (80:20 ratio) did not depress feed intake or nutrient apparent digestibility (Rizzi *et al.*, 1995) while preventing aflatoxin accumulation in the liver of growing lambs and decreasing aflatoxin recovery in urine by several fold (Zaghini *et al.*, 1993). To the authors, the detoxifying properties of bentonite could be enhanced by its ability to reduce the transit time of digestion through the gastrointestinal tract thus increasing the fecal loss of the toxins. However, this ability was not observed for zearalenone and nivalenol (Ramos *et al.*, 1996).

## Clays

Other clays such as kaolin, sepiolite and montmorillonite have a variable ability to reduce toxic effects of aflatoxin $B_1$ as reviewed by Ramos *et al.* (1996). However, their efficacy is limited to aflatoxin $B_1$ and is lower than that of HSCAS and bentonite.

## Activated carbons

Activated carbons are an important group of sorbents. They are a family of carbonaceous substances obtained by pyrolysis of several organic compounds and manufactured by activation processes aimed at developing a highly porous structure (Galvano *et al.*, 1996a). Generally, the adsorption properties of activated carbon are strictly dependent on the source materials and physicochemical parameters such as surface area and pore size distribution. As such, preparation methods and chemical treatments can strongly modify activated carbon surface characteristics. Because of the numerous possible combinations between typology of carbonaceous substances and activation processes, many activated carbons with quite different adsorbing properties exist. This fact could explain some contrasting results reported in a recent review concerning the ability of activated carbon to bind mycotoxins (Ramos *et al.*, 1996).

As a reliable universal test of adsorptive properties does not exist for activated carbons, they must be selected under application conditions. However, in characterizing activated carbons several physicochemical parameters can be considered (Galvano *et al.*, 1996a). Indeed, it is known that the adsorption properties are roughly correlated with the total surface area measured by adsorption of a very small molecule (nitrogen). The pore size distribution of activated carbon is another important characteristic affecting the accessibility of the internal carbon surface. As diffusion effects inside the pores can slow down the adsorption process, the effective pore size distribution of activated carbon can influence it as a function of the molecular size of the adsorbate. Information about mesopores and macropores can be obtained by mercury porosimetry, which allows determination of the size distribution of pores of inside diameter greater than 75 Å. Iodine number is a relative indicator of activated carbon microporosity and is often used as an approximation of surface area. Methylene blue index is a test which establishes the medium size pore (mesopores) range and is an important indicator in practice of activated carbon ability to adsorb organic molecules of medium-large size from a solution (Galvano *et al.*, 1996a).

In a series of preliminary *in vitro* tests we investigated the adsorption ability of 19 experimental activated carbons from different source materials (i.e., spent olive residues, peach stones and almond shells) obtained with laboratory equipment by several experimental activation processes appropriately selected to obtain the desired physicochemical parameters. In addition, we investigated four commercial activated carbons produced in industrial processing equipment.

An overall evidence of the high ability of activated carbon in binding mycotoxins *in vitro* was observed in our studies (Galvano *et al.*, 1996a,b 1997, 1998). The highest abilities were noted in the adsorption of aflatoxin $B_1$ and ochratoxin, whereas the lowest were seen in the adsorption of deoxynivalenol (Table 1). In addition, activated carbons have been shown to efficiently adsorb fumonisin $B_1$ and aflatoxin $B_1$ simultaneously. When compared to HSCAS, activated carbons showed much higher adsorption abilities toward all the tested mycotoxins. Thus, activated carbons are capable of binding several mycotoxins *in vitro* and it is reasonable to consider their potential use as multi-mycotoxin sequestering agents.

**Table 1.** *In vitro* adsorption (saturation limits) of mycotoxins from standard solutions by activated carbons or activated carbons or (HSCAS) (μg of mycotoxin/g of sorbent).[1]

| Sorbents | Aflatoxin B$_1$ | Fumon- isin B$_1$ | Aflatoxin B$_1$ + fumonisin B$_1$[2] | Ochratoxin | Deoxyn- ivalenol |
|---|---|---|---|---|---|
| Activated carbon sources | | | | | |
| Commercial 1 | 123.0 | 3.8 | 25.0+2.1 | 115.0 | 2.0 |
| Commercial 2 | 123.0 | 9.9 | 25.0+5.0 | 119.0 | 1.8 |
| Commercial 4 | 95.0 | 9.6 | 25.0+4.7 | 91.0 | 1.9 |
| Olive residue 32 | 112.0 | 3.4 | 25.0+1.8 | 80.0 | 2.0 |
| Olive residue 48 | >125.0 | 9.8 | 25.0+5.0 | 121.0 | >2.0 |
| HSCAS | 79.0 | 0.3 | Not assayed | 1.3 | 0.8 |

[1]Galvano *et al.*, 1998.
[2]Simultaneously.

The molecular size and physicochemical properties of the mycotoxins clearly affect binding efficiency. For this reason further studies on the binding mechanism such as chemisorption indices are needed to clarify and improve adsorption.

Following the preliminary tests we performed two studies intended to verify *in vivo* the binding ability of one of the activated carbons that had the highest potential in *in vitro* adsorption. In an experiment on dairy cows we compared the abilities of activated carbon and HSCAS in reducing carryover of aflatoxin B$_1$ from feed to milk. Activated carbon reduced carryover up to 50%, whereas HSCAS reduction of carryover was 36% (Galvano *et al.*, 1996b). In rats given a fumonisin-contaminated diet toxin bioavailability was indirectly monitored by measuring the sphinganine concentration and the sphinganine/sphingosine ratio in urine, liver and kidney. The addition of 2% activated carbon prevented the increase in liver weight, reduced the sphinganine concentration in liver and the sphinganine concentration and sphinganine/sphingosine ratio in kidneys (Solfrizzo *et al.*, 1998). Even though some of these responses only approached statistically significance, the data are promising and further studies are in progress in our laboratory. In any case, that is the first report of an *in vivo* protective action of a sorbent toward fumonisin B$_1$. Although the tests are strongly encouraging, we are extremely conscious that further *in vivo* studies are required to confirm the efficacy of activated carbon in preventing or reducing the toxic effects of mycotoxins. We assume that the *in vivo* efficacy of activated carbon will be lower, since the practical conditions differ widely from the experimental ones. More specifically, the binding sites of activated carbon can be occupied by many other compounds present in the feed.

Assuming that *in vivo* studies would confirm the effectiveness of detoxifying mycotoxins, three questions on whether activated carbon could be added to feeds must be answered. The first is the possible long-term undesired adsorption of essential nutrients such as vitamins and minerals. If long-term *in vivo* studies should confirm it, two strategies could be adopted: 1) addition of supplemental essential nutrients demonstrated to be excessively adsorbed by activated carbon, or 2) increase the selectivity of activated carbon toward mycotoxins by modulating the activation process and the physicochemical properties. The second question, as indicated by Ramos *et al.* (1996), is related to the property of activated carbon to blacken the environment, the animals and the feed. Some manufactures have overcome this problem by producing activated carbon containing up to 65% water with the consistency of brown sugar, thus eliminating the problems associated with the use of the powder form. We suggested that some of these problems can be also eliminated by pelleting the feed. Furthermore, we observed that, at least for aflatoxin $B_1$, pelleting can increase the sorbent efficacy (Galvano *et al.*, 1996b). The third question is the economic viability of adding activated carbon to feed. Today the price of activated carbon is perhaps prohibitive to the feed industry. However, the possibility of using activated carbon in feed should increase the demand and bring about a practical price for this market. In any case, evaluation of the cost/benefit balance is needed.

*Cholestyramine*
Cholestyramine, a bile acid-binding resin, was tested as protective agent against ochratoxin-induced nephrotoxicity in rats (Kerkadi *et al.*, 1998). Cholestyramine decreased the concentration of ochratoxin A in plasma and toxin/metabolite excretion in urine and bile and increased excretion in feces. These results agree with those of Madyastha *et al.* (1992). The authors attributed the decrease in nephrotoxicity to the reduction of ochratoxin A bioavailability and/or enterohepatic circulation. Cholestyramine also bound zearalenone (Trenholm *et al.*, 1996). However, the authors noted that its high cost would make its commercial use economically prohibitive.

*Polyvinylpolypyrrolideoxynivalenole*
Polyvinylpolypyrrolideoxynivalenole (PVPP), a synthetic resin, was shown to bind aflatoxin $B_1$ in feed (Thalib, 1995). The author noted that 0.4 g/kg PVPP can bind up to 50 µg/kg aflatoxin in feed.

*Bovine serum albumin*
Hirano *et al.* (1994) demonstrated that bovine serum albumin provided protection against aflatoxin $B_1$ toxic effects. In studies on day-old chicks the authors observed a marked reduction in histological and biochemical symptoms of exposure to aflatoxin $B_1$ and of the toxin level in the plasma and liver. The authors concluded that bovine serum albumin is able to bind aflatoxin $B_1$ in the intestinal tract and is excreted with it. The binding mechanism occurring between bovine serum albumin and aflatoxin $B_1$ was highlighted by Vyjaynthi *et al.* (1995).

### Biological binding agents

Increasing interest has also been generated in using biological products to reduce the bioavailability of mycotoxins to farm animals, particularly as these overcome the inherent drawbacks associated with inorganic sorbents. *Saccharomyces cerevisiae* 1026, used primarily as an aid to rumen fermentation, was found to have beneficial effects on weight gain and immune response in broilers exposed to aflatoxin $B_1$ (Devegowda *et al.*, 1998). *In vitro* studies showed an aflatoxin dose-dependent binding capacity of *S. cerevisiae* up to 77% (Devegowda *et al.*, 1996). Interestingly, modified mannanoligosaccharide (Mycosorb, Alltech Inc.) derived from the cell wall of *S. cerevisiae* was reported to have even higher binding capacity (95% aflatoxin, 80% zearalenone, fumonisin up to 59%, and vomitoxin up to 12%; Devegowda *et al.*, 1998). This was further confirmed by the addition of 0.11% modified mannanoligosaccharide to the diet of layers receiving 2.5 ppm of aflatoxin $B_1$ (Figure 1). Aflatoxin did not contaminate the egg, but a 46% decrease in aflatoxin level in the liver was observed (4.13 *vs* 2.21 ppb; Rizzi, personal communication).

The transformation of mycotoxins upon fermentation has been reported a number of times. Deoxynivalenol and zearalenone were degraded *in vitro* by the normal bacterial gut flora from the distal sections (cecum, colon, and rectum) of the gastrointestinal tract of pigs (Kollarczik *et al.*, 1994), whereas microorganisms from the proximal segments showed no transformation activity. Deoxynivalenol was de-epoxidated and zearalenone was hydrolyzed to α-zearalenol and an unknown metabolite. These observations appear to be confined to the type of mycotoxin considered. Incubation with up to 1000 mM fumonisin $B_1$ had no effect on growth rate of various Gram-positive and Gram-negative bacteria nor was fumonisin concentration in the media altered (Becker *et al.*, 1997). *Flavobacterium aurantiacum* was the only microorganism that removed aflatoxin from liquid medium and food products in significant amounts

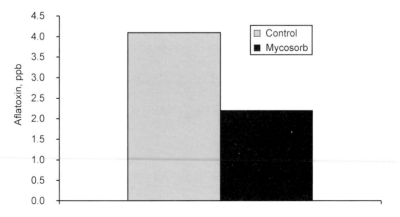

**Figure 1.** Effect of Mycosorb (0.11% of the diet), a modified mannan oligosaccharide, on liver aflatoxin content of layers receiving 2.5ppm of aflatoxin $B_1$.

without the production of toxic by-products (Lillehoj *et al.*, 1967; Line and Brackett, 1995).

More recently, some dairy strains of lactic acid bacteria were found capable of removing aflatoxin $B_1$ from contaminated liquid media via a rapid process involving the removal of approximately 80% of aflatoxin $B_1$ immediately upon contact without further incubation (El-Nezami *et al.*, 1998a). Heat-treated bacteria had the same ability to remove aflatoxin $B_1$ as viable bacteria, consequently metabolic degradation by viable bacteria has been ruled out as a possible mode of action under the experimental conditions tested. All the Gram-positive strains tested were more efficient than *Escherichia coli* suggesting that the ability of bacteria to remove aflatoxin $B_1$ is dependent on cell wall structure. The response was dependent on temperature and bacterial concentration, whereas no difference was observed due to pH variation across the range of pH 4 to 6. Furthermore, treatment with hydrochloric acid, autoclaving or boiling enhanced the binding activity of the bacterial pellets (El-Nezami *et al.*, 1998b), confirming that the type and structure of the cell wall is crucial for an effective binding of mycotoxins.

Megharaj *et al.* (1997) demonstrated the ability of a mixed culture of bacteria to remove zearalenone from culture media while *Pseudomonas aeruginosa* was able to inhibit the growth of *Penicillium citrinum* and the production of citrinin (Giridhar and Reddy, 1997).

## Conclusion

Encouraging results have been obtained in studies on the protective action of a large number of nutrients, food components and additives. Generally, compounds with marked antioxidant properties seem to be potentially very efficacious. However, most of the studies focus on the most known mycotoxins, i.e., aflatoxin $B_1$ and ochratoxin, whereas much less information is available concerning more recently discovered mycotoxins such as fumonisins. Moreover, most of the results are based on *in vitro* studies. Thus, a great deal of work is needed to establish the biochemical mechanisms of action, verify the response *in vivo* and to search for protective compounds against a broader range of mycotoxins. As regards mycotoxin binding agents evaluated in our laboratory, activated carbon seems to have the higher potential as a multi-toxin binding agent. Though more research is needed on activated carbons and other sequestering agents, nutritional strategies to reduce the toxic and economic impact of mycotoxins seem to be the most promising approach.

## References

Aboobaker, V.S., A.D. Balgi and R.K. Bhattacharya. 1994. *In vivo* effect of dietary factors on the molecular action of aflatoxin $B_1$: role of non-nutrient phenolic compounds on the catalytic activity of liver fractions. In vivo 8:1095–1098.

Aboobaker, V.S., N. Sarma, U.C. Goswami and R.K. Bhattacharya. 1997. Inhibition of microsomal activation of aflatoxin $B_1$ by 3–dehydroretinol and 3-dehydroretinyl palmitate. Indian J. Exp. Biol. 35:1125–1127.

Amra, H.A., S.A.Z. Mahmoud, A.H. Taha and M.A. El-Azab. 1996. Destruction of aflatoxin $B_1$ and $G_1$ in bread making. Mycotox. Res. 12:73–78.

Atroshi, F., A. Rizzo, I. Biese, M. Salonen, L.A. Lindberg and H. Saloniemi. 1995. Effects of feeding T-2 toxin and deoxynivalenol on DNA and GSH contents of brain and spleen of rats supplemented with vitamin E and C and selenium combination. J. Anim. Phys. Anim. Nutr. 74:157–164.

Baudrimont, I., R. Ahouandjivo and E.E. Creppy. 1997a. Prevention of lipid peroxidation induced by ochratoxin A in Vero cells in culture by several agents. Chem. Biol. Interact. 104:29–40.

Baudrimont, I., A.M. Betbeder and E.E. Creppy. 1997b. Reduction of the ochratoxin A-induced cytotoxicity in Vero cells by aspartame. Arch. Toxicol., 71(5)290–298.

Becker, B., H. Bresch, U. Schillinger and P.G. Thiel. 1997. The effect of fumonisin $B_1$ on the growth of bacteria. World Journal of Microbiology and Biotechnology, 13:539–543.

Becroft, D.M.W. and D.R. Webster. 1972. Aflatoxins and Reye's disease. Br. Med. J. 4:117.

Bose, S. and S.P. Sinha. 1994. Modulation of ochratoxin-produced genotoxicity in mice by vitamin C. Food Chem. Toxicol. 32:533–537.20

Boutrif, E. and C. Canet. 1998. Mycotoxin prevention and control: FAO programmes. Revue Med. Vet. 149: 681–694

Breinholt, V., M. Schimerlik, R. Dashwood and G. Bailey. 1995. Mechanisms of chlorophyllin anticarcinogenesis against aflatoxin $B_1$ complex formation with the carcinogen. Chem. Res. Toxicol. 8:506–514.

Cavin, C., D. Holzhäuser, A. Constable, A.C. Huggett and B. Schilter. 1998. The coffee-specific diterpenes cafestol and kahweol protect against aflatoxin $B_1$-induced genotoxicity through a dual mechanism. Carcinogenesis 19:1369–1375.

Charmley L.L., H.L. Threnholm, D.B. Prelusky and A. Rosemburg. 1995. Economic losses and decontamination. Nat. Toxins 3:199–203.

Coelho, M. 1996. Optimum vitamin supplementation needed for turkey performance and profitability. Feedstuffs 68:13–21.20

Creppy, E.E., Baudrimont I. and A.M. Betbeder. 1995. Prevention of nephrotoxicity of ochratoxin A, a food contaminant. Toxicol. Lett. 71:869–877.

Creppy, E.E., I. Baudrimont, A. Belmadani and A.M. Betbeder. 1996. Aspartame as a preventive agent of chronic toxic effects of ochratoxin A in experimental animals. Food Addit. Contam. 13:51–52. 20

Dale, N. Mycotoxin binders: It's time for real science. 1998. Poult. Digest. 57:38–39.

Dashwood, R., T. Negishi, H. Hayatsu, V. Breinholt, J. Hendricks and G. Bailey. 1998. Chemopreventive properties of chlorophylls toward aflatoxin B$_1$:a review of the antimutagenicity and anticarcinogenicity data in rainbow trout. Mutat. Res. 399:245–514.

Devegowda, G., Aravind B.I.R and M.G. Morton. 1996. *Saccharomyces cerevisiae* and mannanoligosaccharides to counteract aflatoxicosis in broilers. Proc. Australian Poult. Sci. Symp., Sydney, Australia 8:103–106.

Devegowda, G., Raju M.V.L.N. and H.V.L.N. Swamy. 1998. Mycotoxins: novel solutions for their counteraction. Feedstuffs, December 7, 1998; 12–15.

El-Nezami, H., P. Kankaanpaa, S. Salminen and J. Ahokas. 1998a. Ability of dairy strains of lactic acid bacteria to bind a common food carcinogen, aflatoxin B$_1$. Food and Chemical Toxicology, 36:321–326.

El-Nezami,20H., Kankaanpaa, P., Salminen, S. and J. Ahokas. 1998b. Physicochemical alterations enhance the ability of dairy strains of lactic acid bacteria to remove aflatoxin from contaminated media. J. Food Prot. 61:466–468.

Firozi, P.F. and R.K. Bhattacharya. 1995. Effects of natural polyphenols on aflatoxin B$_1$ activation in a reconstituted microsomal monooxygenase system. J. Biochem. Toxicol. 10:25–31.

Firozi, P.F., V.S. Aboobaker and R.K. Bhattacharya. 1996. Action of curcumin on the cytochrome P450-system catalyzing the activation of aflatoxin B$_1$. Chem. Biol. Interact. 100:41–51.

Galvano, F., A. Pietri, B. Fallico, T. Bertuzzi, S. Scirè, M. Galvano and R. Maggiore. 1996a. Activated carbons: in vitro affinity for Aflatoxin B$_1$ and relation of adsorption ability to physicochemical parameters. J. Food Prot. 59:545–550.20

Galvano, F., A. Pietri, T. Bertuzzi, G. Fusconi, M. Galvano, A. Piva and G. Piva. 1996b. Reduction of carryover of aflatoxin from cow feed to milk by addition of activated carbons. J. Food Prot. 59:551–554.20

Galvano, F., A. Pietri, T. Bertuzzi, M. Bognanno, A. De Angelis, L. Chies and M. Galvano. 1997. Activated carbons: *in vitro* affinity for fumonisin B$_1$ and relation of adsorption ability to physicochemical parameters. J. Food Prot. 60:985–991.20

Galvano, F., A. Pietri, T. Bertuzzi, A. De Angelis, A. Piva, L. Chies and M. Galvano. 1998. Activated carbons: *in vitro* affinity for ochratoxin A and deoxynivalenol and relation of adsorption ability to physicochemical parameters. J. Food Prot. 61:469–475.

Garcia R.P., C.L. Padilla, M. sidik, B.M. Rejesus, R.P. Garcia, B.R. Champ, M. Bengston, O.S. Dharmaputa and H. Halid. 1997. Mycotoxins and its significance in the implementation of general agreement on tariff and trade (GATT). Proceedings of the symposium on20pest management for stored food and feed. Bogor, Indonesia, 5–7 September 1995. BIOTROP Special Publication 59:33–51.

Ghédira Chékir, L, K. Maaroufi, A. Zakhama, F. Ellouz, S. Dhouib, E.E. Creppy and H. Bacha. 1998. Induction of a SOS repair system in lysogenic bacteria by zearalenone and its prevention by vitamin E. Chem. Biol. Interact. 113:15–25.

Giridhar P. and S.M. Reddy. 1997. Efficacy of some bacteria in the control of growth and citrinin production by Penicillium citrinum. Indian Phytopathology 50:1–5.

Goeger, D.E., K.E. Anderson and A.W. Hsie. 1998. Coumarin chemoprotection against aflatoxin $B_1$-induced mutation in a mammalian cell system: a species difference in mutagen activation and protection with chick embryo and rat liver S9. Environ. Mol. Mutagen. 32:64–74.

González de Mejía, E., M. Ramos Gómez and G. Loarca Piña. 1997. Antimutagenic activity of natural xanthophylls against aflatoxin $B_1$ in *Salmonella typhimurium*20. Environ. Mol. Mutagen. 30:346–53.

Gradelet, S., P. Astorg, A.M. Le Bon, R. Bergès and M. Suschetet. 1997. Modulation of aflatoxin $B_1$ carcinogenicity, genotoxicity and metabolism in rat liver by dietary carotenoids: evidence for a protective effect of CYP1A inducers. Cancer Lett. 114:221–223.20

Gradelet, S., A.M. Le Bon, R. Bergès, M. Suschetet and P. Astorg. 1998. Dietary carotenoids inhibit aflatoxin $B_1$-induced liver preneoplastic foci and DNA damage in the rat: role of the modulation of aflatoxin $B_1$ metabolism. Carcinogenesis 19: 403–411.20

Grosse, Y., L. Chekir Ghedira, A. Huc, S. Obrecht Pflumio, G. Dirheimer, H. Bacha and A. Pfohl Leszkowicz. 1997. Retinol, ascorbic acid and alpha-tocopherol prevent DNA adduct formation in mice treated with the mycotoxins ochratoxin A and zearalenone. Cancer Lett. 114: 225–229.20

Hirano, K., Y. Adachi and S. Ishibashi. 1994. Possible role of bovine serum albumin for the prevention of aflatoxin $B_1$-adsorption from the intestinal tract in young chicks. J. Vet. Med. Sci. 56:281–286.

Hoehler, D. and R.R. Marquardt. 1996. Influence of vitamins E and C on the toxic effects of ochratoxin A and T-2 toxin in chicks. Poult. Sci. 75:1508–1515.20

Ibeh, I.N. and D.K. Saxena. 1998. Effect of α-tocopherol supplementation on the impact of aflatoxin $B_1$ on the testes of rats. Exp. Toxicol. Pathol. 50:221–224.

International Agency for Research on Cancer (IARC). 1993. Some naturally occurring substances: food items and constituent, heterocyclic aromatic amines and mycotoxins. IARC Monographs on the evaluation of carcinogenic risks to humans, vol. 56. IARC, Lyon.

Ito, Y., Y. Nakamura, and Y. Nakamura. 1997. Suppression of aflatoxin $B_1$- or methyl methanesulfonate-induced chromosome aberrations in rat bone marrow cells after treatment with S-methyl methanethiosulfonate. Mutat. Res. 393:307–316.

JECFA. 1997. Toxicological evaluation of certain food additives. WHO Feed Additives Series. 49th meeting of JECFA, Geneva, 1997.

Jesval P. 1998. Antidotal effect of grape juice (Vitis vinifera) on ochratoxin A caused hepatorenal carcinogenesis in mice (Mus musculus). Cytobios 93:123–128.

Kerkadi A., C. Barriault, B. Tuchweber, A.A. FrohlichR.R. Marquardt, G. Bouchardand and I.M. Yousef. 1998. Dietary cholestyramine reduces ochratoxin A-induced nephrotoxicity in the rat by decreasing plasma levels and enhancing fecal excretion of the toxin. J. Toxicol. Environ. Health 3:231–250.

Kollarczik, B., M. Gareis and M. Hanelt. 1994. *In vitro* transformation of the Fusarium mycotoxins deoxynivalenol and zearalenone by the normal gut microflora of pigs. Natural Toxins 2:3 105–110.

Kuiper-Goodman, T. 1995. Mycotoxins: risk assessment and legislation. Toxicol. Lett. 82–83:853–859.

Kumari, D. and S.P. Sinha. 1994. Effect of retinol on ochratoxin-produced genotoxicity in mice. Food Chem. Toxicol. 32:471–475.

Lillehoj, E.B., A. Ciegler and H.H. Hall. 1967. Aflatoxin $B_1$ uptake by *Flavobacterium aurantiacum* and resulting toxic effects. J. Bacteriol. 93: 464–471

Lin, Z.H., S.G. Li, L.Y. Wu, S. Sun and Q.W. Lu. 1994. Antagonistic effect of Se on the T-2 toxin-induced changes in the ultrastructure and mitochondrial function of cultured chicken embryonic chondrocytes. J. Clinical Biochemistry Nutrition 17:119–132.

Line, J.E. and R.E. Brackett. 1995. Factors affecting aflatoxin $B_1$ removal by *Flavobacterium aurantiacum*. J. Food Prot. 58: 91–94.

Loarca Piña, G., P.A. Kuzmicky, E. González de Mejía, N.Y. Kado and D.P. Hsieh. 1996. Antimutagenicity of ellagic acid against aflatoxin $B_1$ in the Salmonella microsuspension assay. Mutat. Res. 360:15–21.

Loarca Piña, G., P.A. Kuzmicky, E.G. de Mejía and N.Y. Kado. 1998. Inhibitory effects of ellagic acid on the direct-acting mutagenicity of aflatoxin $B_1$ in the Salmonella microsuspension assay. Mutat. Res. 398:183–187.

Madhyastha, M.S., A.A Frohlich. and R.R. Marquardt. 1992. Effects of dietary cholestyramine on the elimination pattern of ochratoxin A in rats. Food Chem. Toxicol. 30:709.

Manson, M.M., H.W. Ball, M.C. Barrett, H.L. Clark, D.J. Judah, G. Williamson and G.E. Neal. 1997. Mechanism of action of dietary chemoprotective agents in rat liver: induction of phase I and II drug metabolizing enzymes and aflatoxin metabolism. Carcinogenesis 18:1729–1738.

McLeod, R., E.M. Ellis, J.R. Arthur, G.E. Neal, D.J. Judah, M.M. Manson, J.D. Hayes. 1997. Cancer-Research-Baltimore 57:4257-4266.20

Megharaj M., I. Garthwaite and JH. Thiele. 1997. Total biodegradation of the oestrogenic mycotoxin zearalenone by a bacterial culture. Lett. Appl. Microbiol. 24:329–333.

Netke, S.P., M.W. Roomi, C. Tsao and A. Niedzwiecki. 1997. Ascorbic acid protects guinea pigs from acute aflatoxin toxicity. Toxicol. Appl. Pharmacol. 143:429–435.20

Piva, G., F. Galvano, A. Pietri and A. Piva. 1995. Detoxification methods of aflatoxins. A review. Nutr. Res. 5:689–715.

Prelusky, D.B., and B.A. Rotter, B.K. Thompson and H.L. Trenholm. 1997. Effect of the appetite stimulant cyproheptadine on deoxynivalenol-induced reductions in feed consumption and weight gain in the mouse. J. Environmental Science and Health 32: 429–448.

Ramos, A.J., J. Fink-Gremmels and E. Hernàndez. 1996. Prevention of toxic effects of mycotoxins by means of nonnutritive adsorbent compounds. J. Food Prot. 59:631–641.

Reen, R.K., F.J. Wiebel and J. Singh. 1997. Piperine inhibits aflatoxin $B_1$-induced cytotoxicity and genotoxicity in V79 Chinese hamster cells genetically engineered to express rat cytochrome $P4502B_1$. J. Ethnopharmacology 58:165–173.

Rizzi, L., L. Lambertini, L. Marchesini and A. Zaghini. 1995. Affinity sorbent of aluminosilicate for aflatoxin $B_1$: effects on digestibility in growing lambs. Proceedings of 47 Congresso Nazionale SISVet, 1329–1333.

Shi, C.Y., S.C. Chua, H.P. Lee and C.N. Ong. 1994. Inhibition of aflatoxin $B_1$-DNA binding and adduct formation by selenium in rats. Cancer Lett. 82:203–208.20

Shi, C.Y., Y.C. Hew and C.N. Ong. 1995. Inhibition of aflatoxin $B_1$-induced cell injury by selenium: an *in vitro* study. Hum. Exp. Toxicol. 14:55–60.20

Sinha, S.P. and K. Darmshila. 1994. Vitamin A ameliorates the genotoxicity in mice of aflatoxin $B_1$-containing *Aspergillus flavus* infested food. Cytobios 79:85–95.

Smith, J.E., G. Solomons, C. Lewis and J.G. Anderson. 1995. Role of mycotoxins in human and animal nutrition and health. Nat. Toxins. 3:187–192.

Solfrizzo, M., G. Avantaggiato, M.R. Carratu, F. Galvano, A. Pietri and A. Visconti. 1998. The use of biomarkers to assess the *in vivo* effect of activated carbon on fumonisins fed through diets contaminated with *Fusarium moniliforme*. Revue Med. Vet. 149:667.

Soni, K.B., M. Lahiri, P. Chackradeo, S.V. Bhide and R. Kuttan. 1997. Protective effect of food additives on aflatoxin-induced mutagenicity and hepatocarcinogenicity. Cancer Lett. 115:129–133.

Thalib, A. 1995. Detoxification of aflatoxin in feed with a binder of polyvinylpolypyrrolideoxynivalenole. Jurnal Ilmiah Penelitian Ternak Klepu. (Indeoxynivalenolesia) 1:43–48.

Trenholm, H.L., L.L. Charmley, K.L. Underhill and D.B. Prelusky. 1996. Reducing toxicity of mycotoxins in feed. In: Proceedings of the 4th International Feed Production Conference. February 22 –23 Piacenza, Italy. pp. 69–86.

Vyjaynthi, V., A.K. Capoor and R.B. Sashidhar. 1995. Binding characteristics of bovine serum albumin-aflatoxin $B_1$ to polystyrene microtiter plates: importance of hapten to carrier protein molar ratio. Indian J. Exp. Biol. 33:329–332.

Williams, G.M. and M.J. Iatropoulos. 1996. Inhibition of the hepatocarcinogenicity of aflatoxin $B_1$ in rats by low levels of the phenolic antioxidants butylated hydroxyanisole and butylated hydroxytoluene. Cancer Lett. 104:49–53.

Yu, M.W., Y.J. Zhang, W.S. Blaner and R.M. Santella. 1994. Influence of vitamins A, C, and E and beta-carotene on aflatoxin $B_1$ binding to DNA in woodchuck hepatocytes. Cancer 73:596–604.

Zaghini, A., L. Lambertini, L. Rizzi and P. Roncada. 1993. Effects of a bentonite supplemented diet on prevention of aflatoxicosis in growing lambs. Proceedings of 47 Congresso Nazionale SISVet. 1329–1333.

Zaghini, A., P. Roncada, P. Anfossi and L. Rizzi. 1998. Aflatoxin $B_1$ oral administration to laying hens: effects on hepatic MFO activities and efficacy of a zeolite to prevent aflatoxicosis $B_1$. In: Proceedings of Mycotoxins in the Food Chain –20 Processing and toxicological aspects, a satellite symposium of the 8th International Congress of Toxicology, July 2–4, 1998. Toulouse France.

# An association of mycotoxins with production, health and reproduction in dairy cattle and guidelines for prevention and treatment

LON W. WHITLOW[1] and W. M. HAGLER, JR.[2]

[1] Animal Science Department and [2] Poultry Science Department, North Carolina State University, Raleigh, North Carolina, USA

## Introduction

A priority list of mycotoxins was subjectively produced by a survey of mycotoxicologists worldwide and included: aflatoxin, ochratoxin, trichothecenes (primarily T-2 toxin, zearalenone, deoxynivalenol, citrinin, sterigmatocystin, patulin, and cyclopiazonic acid (Hesseltine, 1986a). Fumonisin was identified after this list was compiled (Gelderblom *et al.*, 1988), but undoubtedly it would be included in a current list.

The mycotoxicoses which may be most commonly associated with grazing cattle include ergotism, paspalum staggers, fescue toxicity, sweet clover poisoning, facial eczema and slaframine toxicity. These and other mycotoxicoses are important and have been reviewed by Lacey (1991).

This paper will concentrate on those mycotoxins that are of greatest concern for dairy cattle consuming stored feeds. These include aflatoxin, fumitremorgens, and sterigmatocystin, which are primarily produced by Aspergillus molds; deoxynivalenol, zearalenone, T-2, diacetoxyscirpenol (DAS) and fumonisins, which are produced by Fusarium molds; and ochratoxin, PR toxin and roquefortine, which are primarily produced by Penicillium molds. Several other mycotoxins, produced by these and other molds, are known to be prevalent at times, including derivatives of those listed. It is probable that a lack of observation and simple analytical techniques have prevented us from more fully understanding the prevalence of these mycotoxins and their impact on animal production.

## Mold growth and mycotoxin formation

Molds occur universally in a variety of feedstuffs, including roughages and concentrates and can produce mycotoxins under certain conditions. Molds can grow and mycotoxins can be produced pre-harvest or post-harvest, during storage, processing, or feeding. Mycotoxin production is often related to extremes in weather conditions (causing plant stress or excess hydration of stored feedstuffs), to inadequate storage practices, to low feedstuff quality and to faulty feeding conditions.

Conditions for mold growth and mycotoxin formation are dependent on the specific mold but include the presence of fungal spores, an organic substrate and the proper levels of moisture, oxygen, temperature, and acidity (Moss, 1991). Temperatures may range from -5 to 60 °C. Water activity must generally be above 0.7 $a_w$ (ratio of the vapor pressure of the product to that of pure water or equilibrium relative humidity as a percentage). Mold can begin growing when moisture exceeds about 12%. Higher levels of moisture will support mold growth up to the point where water excludes adequate oxygen. High levels of carbon dioxide can prevent mold growth even when oxygen is at levels high enough to support mold growth. Oxygen as low as 0.5% can support mold growth; thus there can be pockets of adequate oxygen within silage and stored high moisture grain storage, especially near the feed surfaces. A fairly wide range of pH levels will support mold growth, although they do not grow well at extremely low or high pH levels. While silage pH is generally low enough to prevent most mold growth, yeasts are active at a lower pH and their activity can raise the pH to a point conducive to mold growth.

The Aspergillus species grow at lower water activities and at higher temperatures than do the Fusarium species, which generally require higher water activities but are able to grow at much lower temperatures. *Aspergillus flavus* and aflatoxin in corn are favored by the heat and drought stress associated with warmer climates. Aflatoxin seems to be enhanced by insect damage before and after harvest. Penicillium species grow at relatively low water activities and low temperatures and are fairly widespread in occurrence. Since both Aspergillus and Penicillium grow at low water activities, they are considered the more likely storage fungi, with Aspergillus more likely in warm climates and Fusarium and Penicillium more likely in cooler climates.

The Fusarium species are generally considered to be field fungi and more likely to proliferate prior to storage. Fusarium commonly affects corn, causing ear and stalk rot, and small grains, causing field diseases such as head blight (scab). These field diseases are characterized by yield loss, quality loss and mycotoxin contamination. In wheat, excess moisture at flowering and afterward is associated with increased incidence of mycotoxin formation. In corn, Fusarium diseases are more commonly associated with insect damage, warm conditions at silking and wet conditions late in the growing season. Joffe (1986) suggests that the toxic principle in the soil spreads to the plant, first affecting the vegetative parts and then the grain. The grain provides a favorable substrate for toxin accumulation. Trenholm *et al.* (1988) suggest that plowing in plant debris and crop residue left on the field after harvest may reduce fungal disease problems.

It should be noted that the conditions most suitable for mold growth are not necessarily the optimum conditions for mycotoxin formation. For example, the Fusarium molds associated with alimentary toxic aleukia have been reported to grow prolifically at temperatures of 25 to 30 °C without producing much mycotoxin but at near freezing temperatures large quantities of mycotoxins are produced without much mold growth (Joffe, 1986).

## Mycotoxin occurrence

The warm, humid climate of the southern US results in a considerably higher incidence of aflatoxin in feeds. From 1975 to 1980, 34% of corn grain in North Carolina contained more than 20 ppb aflatoxin. Corn grain and peanut meal have been the primary sources of aflatoxin contamination in North Carolina. Cottonseed has seldom been a problem source of aflatoxin for dairymen in North Carolina. Corn samples from the midwestern US representing the 1988 season (severe drought) showed 8% with aflatoxin levels above 10 ppb, 3% positive for zearalenone above 1 ppm, 3% positive for deoxynivalenol above 1 ppm and 7% positive for T-2 above 500 ppb (Russel *et al.*, 1991).

Mycotoxin analysis results from feed samples submitted by North Carolina farmers during a nine-year period and representing more than 2400 samples were summarized (Whitlow *et al.*, 1998). Percentage of corn silage and corn grain samples testing positive were for aflatoxin (>10 ppb), 8 and 9%; deoxynivalenol (>500 ppb), 51 and 52%; zearalenone (300 ppb), 17 and 3%; T-2 (>200), 5 and 4% and fumonisin $B_1$ (>1 ppm), 37 and 60%, respectively. Occurrence was highly variable by year.

## Mycotoxin effects

Mycotoxins can increase disease incidence and reduce production efficiency in cattle. They exert their effects through three primary mechanisms:

1. alteration in nutrient content, absorption and metabolism
2. changes in the endocrine and neuroendocrine function
3. suppression of the immune system (CAST, 1989)

The resulting nonspecific symptoms may therefore be perplexing and make diagnosis difficult. Hesseltine (1986b) and Schilfer (1990) discussed some of the problems encountered in diagnosing a mycotoxicosis. They include:

1. a lack of research reports especially concerning some mycotoxins
2. symptoms that are not specific or unique for the mycotoxin
3. interaction of mycotoxins with other mycotoxins or other stress factors
4. interaction of mycotoxins with immune suppression and thus infectious diseases
5. lack of feed samples or samples improperly collected
6. analysis which is complex and expensive

Our experience suggests that while a definitive diagnosis cannot be made directly from symptoms, specific tissue damage, or even feed analyses, experience with mycotoxin-affected herds greatly increases the probability of recognizing the problem. The following guidelines may be helpful in dealing with a possible mycotoxicosis:

1. Mycotoxins should be considered as a possible primary factor resulting in production losses and increased incidence of disease.
2. Documented symptoms in ruminants or other species can be utilized as a general guide to symptoms observed in the field; however there is a lack of research data, and field observations may differ from those seen in controlled research studies.
3. Systemic effects as well as specific damage to target tissues can be used as a guide to possible causes.
4. Postmortem examinations may indicate no more than gut irritation, edema or generalized tissue inflammation.
5. Ruling out other possible causes such as infectious agents or other toxins is essential.
6. All feeds should be analyzed for common mycotoxins.
7. Responses to simple treatments such as dilution or removal of the contaminated feed are helpful.
8. Diagnosis may be impossible because the clinical situation may be complex and complicated due to interactions with other agents.

Dairy herds experiencing a mycotoxicosis severe enough to reduce milk production will usually display other symptoms. Often there is intermittent diarrhea, sometimes with bloody or dark manure. Cows may not respond well to typical veterinary therapy. Symptoms may be nonspecific and wide ranging and may include reduced feed intake, feed refusal, ill thrift, rough hair coat, undernourished appearance, subnormal production, increased abortions or embryonic mortalities, silent heats, irregular estrus cycles, expression of estrus in pregnant cows and decreased conception rates. Fresh cows perform poorly and generally have an increased incidence of disease, particularly those that are most opportunistic in a dairy herd. There may be a higher incidence of displaced abomasum, ketosis, retained placenta, metritis, mastitis and fatty livers. There may only be a few or many of these symptoms evident.

AFLATOXIN

Aflatoxin, produced primarily by *Aspergillus flavus*, is a mycotoxin of major concern because it is carcinogenic and is commonly found in warm climates such as the southern US. Major efforts are directed at eliminating food residues. The FDA limits aflatoxin in corn grain according to its intended use: not more than 200 ppb for breeding cattle, 300 ppb for finishing beef cattle or 20 ppb for lactating dairy cattle. Aflatoxin is excreted into milk in the form of aflatoxin $M_1$ with residues approximately equal to 1.7% of the dietary aflatoxin level (Van Egmond, 1989). The FDA limits aflatoxin $M_1$ in milk to no more than 0.5 ppb. Since aflatoxin residues can be found in tissues, beef cattle should not be fed aflatoxin contaminated diets for three weeks prior to slaughter. Regulatory pressures and a widespread awareness have helped minimize aflatoxin problems. The GAO (1991) concluded that industry, federal and state programs are effective in detecting and controlling aflatoxin and that it is doubtful that additional programs or limits would reduce the risk of aflatoxin in the food supply. Thus, current surveillance programs aimed at reducing food residues make it very unlikely for aflatoxin to have significant production or health effects on dairy herds.

Aflatoxin can reduce performance and impair health, but this occurs generally at dietary levels greater than the 25 to 50 ppb that can cause illegal milk residues. Although no level of aflatoxin is considered safe, the degree of toxicity is related to level of toxin, duration of feeding, and the amount of other stresses affecting the animal. Levels of 300 to 700 ppb are considered toxic for beef cattle, depending on criteria for toxicity, and other factors affecting toxicity (CAST, 1989). Garrett *et al.* (1968) showed that with beef cattle gain and intake were affected at 700 ppb, but not at 300 ppb aflatoxin; however, levels of no effect cannot be determined from data with such few animals. Trends in the data, especially for increased liver weights, would indicate potential toxicity at levels as low as 100 ppb. Guthrie (1979) showed a decline in reproductive efficiency when lactating dairy cattle in a field situation were consuming 120 ppb aflatoxin and an increase in milk production of over 25% when cows were changed to an aflatoxin-free diet. Patterson and Anderson (1982) and Marsi *et al.* (1969) also suggest that 100 ppb may reduce milk production. Applebaum *et al.* (1982) showed that impure aflatoxin produced by culture reduced production, but equal amounts of pure aflatoxin did not. Several studies suggest that naturally contaminated feeds are more toxic than would be expected from the concentrations of assayed mycotoxins, suggesting the presence of unidentified toxins.

## FUMONISIN

Fumonisin $B_1$ was isolated by Gelderblom *et al.* (1988) and shown to be a cancer promoter. Fumonisin $B_1$ has been shown to cause leukoencephalomalacia in horses (Marasas *et al.*, 1988), pulmonary edema in pigs (Harrison *et al.*, 1990) and hepatoxicity in rats (Gelderblom *et al.*, 1991). A USDA APHIS (1995) survey found an average of 6.9% of 1995 corn samples from Missouri, Iowa and Illinois to contain more than 5 ppm fumonisin $B_1$. While fumonisin $B_1$ is thought to be much less potent in ruminants than monogastrics, work by Kriek *et al.* (1981) suggested that fumonisin was toxic to sheep. Osweiler *et al.* (1993) demonstrated that fumonisin $B_1$ in large amounts (148 ppm) can cause mild liver damage in cattle even when fed for a short term (31 days), but had no effect on feed intake or weight gain. Whitlow (1999, unpublished) has demonstrated that fumonisin $B_1$ is also toxic to dairy cattle. Fed for approximately seven days prior to freshening and for 70 days thereafter, dietary fumonisin $B_1$ at 100 ppm significantly and dramatically reduced milk production (7 kg/cow/day) and affected serum enzymes levels indicative of liver disease.

These results strongly suggest that fumonisin $B_1$ is toxic to dairy cattle and that it is less toxic to beef cattle, or perhaps fumonisin $B_1$ interacts with other factors to produce greatly different effects in beef and dairy cattle under different conditions.

Fumonisin $B_1$ carryover from feed to milk is thought to be negligible. Richard *et al.* (1996) fed fumonisin $B_1$ (about 75 ppm) to dairy cows with no fumonisin $B_1$ or $B_2$ detectable in milk (detection limit of 5 ng/ml). Scott *et al.* (1994) have confirmed this observation.

DEOXYNIVALENOL

Deoxynivalenol (DON) is the proper name for a commonly detected Fusarium-produced mycotoxin often referred to as vomitoxin. Two independent midwestern US studies (Vesonder *et al.*, 1978 and Côté *et al.*, 1984) showed deoxynivalenol to be the primary mycotoxin associated with problems in pigs including feed refusals, diarrhea, emesis, reproductive failure and deaths. In cattle, deoxynivalenol has been associated with reduced feed intake (Trenholm *et al.*, 1985) and lower milk production (Whitlow *et al.*, 1991). Clinical data from 300 herds representing about 40,000 cow records showed that deoxynivalenol was associated with a loss in milk production but did not establish a cause and effect relationship (Whitlow *et al.*, 1991). Deoxynivalenol may simply be a marker for problem feeds. Field observations by others help substantiate these observations (Gotlieb, 1997; Seglar, 1997).

Charmley *et al.* (1993) demonstrated a 13% (2.85 kg) numerical decrease in 4% fat corrected milk production (statistics not available) utilizing 18 mid-lactation dairy cows (average 19.5 kg milk) consuming diets shown to contain no common mycotoxins other than deoxynivalenol, which was at levels of 2.7 to 6.4 ppm in treatment diets. While the decrease in actual milk production (1.35 kg) was not statistically significant, the decrease in fat test (3.92% *vs.* 3.04%) was significant.

Noller *et al.* (1979) utilized 54 lactating dairy cows in a 21-day feeding experiment using corn grain contaminated with *Gibberella zeae* and containing 500 ppb zearalenone (ZEN). Deoxynivalenol was probably present, but it was not analyzed directly. Grain harvested earlier from the same field was contaminated with 12–13 ppm DON. Neither dry matter intake nor milk production (average 22.9 kg) were affected by additions of this grain to the diet. However, compared with controls, cows that received this grain at either 10% (about 1.25 ppm DON and 50 ppb ZEN) or 20% (about 2.50 ppm DON and 100 ppb ZEN) of the diet gained significantly less weight during the study (5.8 or 8.1 kg less weight gain for cows consuming the 10% or 20% diets over 21 days, respectively).

DiCostanzo *et al.* (1995a) cites results by Ingalls (1994) where lactating dairy cows were fed 0, 3.6, 10.9 and 14.6 ppm DON for 21 days, apparently without effect on feed intake or milk production, which averaged about 30 kg daily.

Beef cattle and sheep appear to tolerate relatively large amounts of deoxynivalenol without obvious deleterious effects. Reports from Nebraska indicated similar feed intakes, average daily gains and feed efficiencies when sheep (8.5 ppp dietary DON) or cattle (1 ppm dietary DON) consuming deoxynivalenol-contaminated diets were compared with those consuming diets containing no detectable deoxynivalenol (DeHaan *et al.*, 1984). Nelson *et al.* (1984) fed feedlot steers and heifers diets containing 0.2, 2.3 or 10 ppm DON for 126 days. The low DON diet was corn-based while the other two diets contained wheat. Results reported for the low, medium and high DON diets were similar for dry matter (DM) intake (9.4, 8.7 and 7.8 kg/day), average daily gain (1.54, 1.64 and 1.34 kg/day) and feed efficiency (6.2, 5.6 and 5.7 kg DM intake/kg gain). Results for carcass characteristics, serum biochemistry and tissue histology were similar across treatments. DiCostanzo *et al.* (1995a and 1995b) indicated that feeding up to 18 ppm dietary DON did not affect intake, daily gain, feed efficiency or carcass characteristics of 415 kg steers fed for 166 days. Other recent feeding experiments with beef cattle suggest that they can tolerate large concentrations of deoxynivalenol in a feedlot situation without affecting dry matter intake, average daily gain or feed efficiency (Boland *et al.*, 1994; Windels *et al.*, 1995).

These data suggest that cattle are relatively tolerant of deoxynivalenol. While not compared directly, it appears that beef cattle and sheep may be less sensitive to deoxynivalenol than are dairy cattle. Differences could be related to level of production stress, since mid-lactation, low-producing dairy cattle also appear to be more tolerant of deoxynivalenol than are high-producing dairy cattle in early lactation. Mycotoxins may interact with immune suppression in early lactation to produce more severe effects than would otherwise be expected. Heat or other environmental stresses may be involved. Thus, the early-lactation, high-producing cows which experience greater stress, lower immunity, marginal nutrient deficiencies and a faster rumen turnover (less mycotoxin degradation in the rumen) may be more vulnerable to mycotoxin effects.

Deoxynivalenol is but one causative agent that may be present. Deoxynivalenol may serve as a marker for feed exposed to a situation conducive to mold growth and mycotoxin formation, and thus the possible presence of other mycotoxins or factors more toxic than deoxynivalenol itself. The differences in response to deoxynivalenol may be due to other mycotoxins. Experiments with beef cattle have generally utilized DON-contaminated corn or barley. Deoxynivalenol provided by contamination of a different feed source, such as silage, could result in interactions of different mycotoxins. Mycotoxin interactions are discussed more fully in the section entitled 'Safe levels of mycotoxins'.

T-2 TOXIN

T-2 toxin, a Fusarium-produced mycotoxin, has been associated with gastroenteritis, intestinal hemorrhages (Petrie *et al.*, 1977 and Mirocha *et al.*, 1976) and death (Hsu *et al.*, 1972, Kosuri *et al.*, 1970). Weaver *et al.* (1980) demonstrated that T-2 was associated with feed refusal and gastrointestinal lesions in a cow, but failed to show a hemorrhagic syndrome. Serum immunoglobulins and certain complement proteins were lowered in calves receiving T-2 toxin (Mann *et al.,* 1983). Other data demonstrated a reduction in white blood cell and neutrophil counts in calves (Gentry *et al.,* 1984). A calf intubated with T-2 developed severe depression, hindquarter ataxia, knuckling of the rear feet, listlessness and anorexia (Weaver *et al.,* 1980).

While data with cattle are limited, the toxicity of T-2 toxin in laboratory animals is well-documented (Wannemacher *et al.,* 1991). Our experience suggests that T-2 is a severe gastrointestinal irritant, which can cause hemorrhage and necrosis of the intestinal tract. Diarrhea is usually present but may not be hemorrhagic. With high levels of T-2, there can be congestion and irritation to the liver, lungs and heart. Two dairy herds were observed to receive T-2 contaminated feed from the same supplier and on similar dates. Early lactation cows were more severely affected, showing a lack of appetite, severe and prolonged weight loss, low peak milk production, higher levels of morbidity and death. In another field case, T-2 in corn produced on the farm resulted in approximately 350 ppb in the diet. Cows exhibited diarrhea, which moved in a wave over time through a dairy herd of about 150 Jersey cows. Milk production was erratic for two to three days and then dropped by 15%. The addition of a clay product to the diet appeared to restore production to previous levels after about three weeks. Removal of the clay resulted in an immediate loss in milk production and the clay was again fed, with a positive response.

ZEARALENONE

Zearalenone is a Fusarium-produced mycotoxin that elicits an estrogenic response in monogastrics (Sundlof and Strickland, 1986). However, zearalenone is rapidly converted to α- and ß-zearalenol in rumen cultures (Kiessling *et al.*, 1984) and has been of less toxicity to ruminants. Ruminal degradation of zearalenone was found to be about 30% in 48 hours (Kellela and Vasenius, 1982). A controlled study with cows fed up to 22 ppm ZEN showed no obvious effects except that corpora lutea were smaller in treated cows (Weaver *et al.*, 1986b). In a similar study with heifers receiving about 13 ppm ZEN, conception rate was depressed about 25%. Otherwise, no obvious effects were noted (Weaver *et al.*, 1986a).

Several case reports have related zearalenone to an estrogenic response in ruminants (Khamis *et al.*, 1986; Mirocha *et al.*, 1968; and Roine *et al.*, 1971). Large doses are associated with abortions in cattle (Kellela and Ettala, 1984; Mirocha *et al.*, 1974). Mirocha *et al.* (1968) isolated zearalenone from hay associated with infertility in dairy cattle. Other cattle responses may include vaginitis, vaginal secretions, poor reproductive performance and mammary gland enlargement of virgin heifers. In a field study (Coppock *et al.*, 1990), diets with about 750 ppb ZEN and 500 ppb DON resulted in poor consumption, depressed milk production, diarrhea and total reproductive failure.

New Zealand workers (Towers *et al.*, 1995a; 1995b; Sprosen and Towers, 1995; Smith *et al.*, 1995) have related urinary zearalenone and zearalenone metabolites (zearalenone, zearalanone, α- and ß-zearalenol and α- and ß-zearalanol) which they refer to as 'zearalenone' to intake of 'zearalenone' and to reproductive disorders in sheep and dairy cattle. In sheep, 'zearalenone' was related to lower conception, reduced ovulation, and increased twinning rates. With dairy cattle, herds with low fertility were found to have higher levels of blood and urinary 'zearalenone' and consumed pastures containing higher levels of 'zearalenone'. In addition, within herds, individual cows were examined by palpation and those that were determined to be cycling had lower blood 'zearalenone' levels than did cows that were not cycling. Differences in 'zearalenone' levels were attributed to selective grazing behavior. The reproductive problems in dairy cattle were noted with 'zearalenone' concentrations of about 400 ppb in the pasture samples.

Our observations suggest that zearalenone may be associated with poor conception, early embryonic mortality and increased reproductive tract infections. In most cases, cows have appeared well nourished with average body condition scores but poor reproductive performance. The differences may be attributed to the presence of other mycotoxins or interaction with other factors.

OTHER MYCOTOXINS

Many other mycotoxins may affect ruminants but are thought to occur less frequently or be less potent.

**Fumitremorgens** such as fumigaclavine A and B are produced by *Aspergillus fumigatus* and are thought to be common in silages of the southeastern US. They can cause anorexia, diarrhea, ill thrift and irritability (Cole *et al.*, 1977).

**Sterigmatocystin** is primarily produced by *Aspergillus versicolor* and has been observed as a primary mycotoxin produced by Aspergillus on cereal grains in western Canada (Mills and Abramson, 1986). While it is thought to be infrequent at toxic levels in the US, it was detected in a grain mixture and associated with bloody diarrhea and cow deaths in a field case in Tennessee (Vesonder and Horn, 1985).

**Diacetoxyscirpenol** is a Fusarium-produced mycotoxin. It may occur along with T-2 toxin and causes similar symptoms.

**Ochratoxin**, produced primarily by a Penicillium mold but also by certain Aspergillus molds, has been reported to affect cattle (Vough and Glick, 1993), but it is rapidly degraded in the rumen and thus thought to be of little consequence unless consumed by young pre-ruminant calves (Sreemannarayana *et al.*, 1988). However, high-concentrate diets reduce ochratoxin degradation in the rumen.

**Patulin**, a Penicillium-produced mycotoxin associated with aerobic deterioration of silage, has been incriminated as a possible toxin in Europe and New Zealand (Lacey, 1991).

**PR toxin**, produced by *Penicillium roquefortii*, has been found in silage and was the suspected vector in a case study with symptoms of abortion and retained placenta (Still *et al.*, 1972).

**Roquefortine**, produced by *Penicillium roquefortii*, is a tremorgen that has been found in silage.

**Other mycotoxins** such as rubratoxin, citrinin, cyclopiazonic acid and ergotoxins may be of some importance. Many other mycotoxins are possible.

## Mycotoxin testing

To determine toxicity, feeds should be analyzed for mycotoxins and not just mold content; however the type of mold present may suggest the mycotoxins most likely to be present. The amount or presence of mold or mold spore count is not very indicative of mycotoxin content (Wyatt, 1991). Molds may be present which do not produce, or are not currently producing, mycotoxins. A mold may have produced mycotoxins and is no longer viable resulting in mycotoxin levels without the obvious presence of mold. It is possible that opinions have been formed about the toxicity of mycotoxins based on the presence of mold, which might suggest a low or erratic toxicity.

Analytical techniques for mycotoxins are improving (Chu, 1992). Several commercial laboratories are available and provide screens for a large array of mycotoxins. Cost of analyses has been a constraint but can be insignificant compared with the economic consequences of production and health losses related to mycotoxin contamination. Newer immunoassays have reduced analytical costs.

Collection of representative feed samples is a problem primarily because molds can produce very large amounts of mycotoxins in small areas making the mycotoxin level highly variable within the lot of feed. Sampling of horizontal silos show mycotoxins to be highly variable throughout the silage; however, the silo face appears to have higher and more consistent levels. Because mycotoxins can form in the collected sample, it should be preserved and delivered to the lab quickly. Samples can be dried, frozen or treated with a mold inhibitor before shipping.

## Safe levels of myotoxins

Guidelines for acceptable levels of mycotoxins should be conservatively low due to non-uniform distribution, uncertainties in sampling and analysis, the potential for more than one source in the diet and the limited amount of research. All these factors make it impossible to declare levels of safety.

Hamilton (1984) and Schaeffer and Hamilton (1991) have reviewed the topic of safe mycotoxin levels. They conclude that epidemiological studies coupled with laboratory studies to elaborate the underlying principles may be the best approach to determining safe levels. They state that any level of mycotoxin carries a risk of loss with it and that it is impossible to define a safe level under laboratory conditions that will be accurate under field conditions. This is primarily because of three reasons:

1. Difficulties in conceptualizing and executing experiments to investigate multiple interacting factors simultaneously;
2. The unappreciated fact that the frequency and level of contamination with aflatoxin and other mycotoxins varies unpredictably under field conditions;
3. Animal facilities currently available to investigators do not permit experiments under controlled conditions with the number of animals commonly at risk under field conditions.

Establishing usable or tolerable levels of mycotoxins may be acceptable when all concerned parties are aware of levels and the risks associated.

Interactions with other factors make recommendations difficult. Lillehoj and Ceigler (1975) give an example where penicillic acid and citrinin were innocuous when administered alone but were 100% lethal when given in combination. Fumonisin at 100 ppm has been shown to reduce milk production in dairy cattle (Whitlow, 1999, unpublished), but did not affect average daily gain in beef cattle fed 148 ppm (Osweiler *et al.*, 1993). Aflatoxin produced from culture was more toxic to dairy cattle than pure aflatoxin added to diets (Applebaum *et al.*, 1982). In pigs, Foster *et al.* (1986) demonstrated that pure deoxynivalenol added to diets was less toxic than diets with similar concentrations of deoxynivalenol supplied from naturally contaminated feeds. Smith and MacDonald (1991) have suggested that fusaric acid may occur along with deoxynivalenol to produce more severe symptoms. Many such interactions are possible since Fusarium molds produce many mycotoxins and it is well documented that several mycotoxins may be found in the same feed (Hagler *et al.*, 1984). Abbas *et al.* (1989) demonstrated that *Fusarium* species isolated from Minnesota corn produces an array of mycotoxins. Scott (1990) states that screening methods are needed for the Fusarium-produced mycotoxins and that one approach is to test for deoxynivalenol, diacetoxyscirpenol, T-2 and nivalenol, because other Fusarium mycotoxins seldom occur without one of these four also present. Feeds could then be further tested for other mycotoxins.

There are distinct species differences in tolerance to mycotoxins. Cattle are more tolerant to most mycotoxins than many other animals, probably due to some mycotoxin degradation in the rumen (Kiessling *et al.*, 1984). The rat is much more sensitive to both aflatoxin and T-2 than is the mouse (Wannemacher *et al.*, 1991). Other animal factors include sex, age, environmental and production stress. Certainly duration of exposure is important. The known dietary factors that interact with mycotoxins include most nutrients for which rations are formulated including, fat, protein, fiber, vitamins and minerals. Dietary pellet binders (clay) adsorb some mycotoxins reducing exposure of the animal. Thus, many factors

411

and interactions make it difficult to relate field observations to those from controlled research.

## Prevention and treatment

Prevention of mycotoxin formation is essential since there are few ways to completely overcome problems once mycotoxins are present. Prevention of mycotoxins may begin with selection of crop varieties that are more resistant to fungal foliar diseases along with use of agronomic practices that may reduce fungal infection of the crop. Prevention of mycotoxins in silage includes following accepted silage-making practices aimed at enhancing proper fermentation and eliminating oxygen. Silages should be harvested at the correct moisture content, the silo filled rapidly, the silage packed tightly and the silo sealed completely. Silo size should be matched to herd size to ensure daily removal of silage at a rate faster than deterioration (4–6 inches daily, depending on weather). The face of horizontal silos should be cut cleanly while avoiding loosening more silage than is to be fed. Secondary fermentation can occur very rapidly after loosened silage is exposed to the air. Therefore, silage should be fed directly after removal from the silo and feed bunks should be cleaned regularly. Care should be taken to ensure that high-moisture grains are stored at proper moisture contents and in a well-maintained structure. Grains or other dry feed such as hay should be stored at a moisture content below which molds do not readily grow (<14%). Aeration of grain bins is important to reduce moisture migration and to keep the feedstuff dry.

Some additives may be beneficial in reducing mycotoxins because they are effective in reducing mold growth. Ammonia, propionic acid and microbial or enzymatic silage additives have all shown effectiveness as mold inhibitors. It seems reasonable that additives that enhance fermentation may be added at ensiling, while those which inhibit mold growth may be added as surface treatments when capping off the silo or daily after silage feed-out to reduce molding of the exposed silage surface.

If unacceptably high levels of mycotoxins occur, dilution or removal of the contaminated feed is preferable; however, it is usually impossible to completely replace major forage ingredients. Ammoniation of grains can destroy some mycotoxins but there is no practical method to detoxify affected forages already in storage. Increasing nutrients such as protein, energy and antioxidant nutrients may be advisable (Brucato *et al.*, 1986; Chandler, 1992). In some situations, poultry respond to water soluble vitamins. Acidic diets may exacerbate effects of mycotoxins. Additional research on treatments is needed.

Adsorbent materials are not approved by the FDA for the prevention or treatment of mycotoxicoses. However, favorable research results have been seen when adsorbent materials such as clays (bentonites) are added to mycotoxin-contaminated diets of rats, poultry, swine and cattle (Diaz *et al.*, 1998; Galey *et al.*, 1987; Harvey *et al.*, 1988; Lindemann and Blodgett, 1991; Scheideler, 1990; Hayes, 1990; Smith, 1980; 1984). In most cases, clay was added to the diet at about 1%. Considerable data are also available for other absorbent materials such as charcoal, fiber, and yeast cell components. An esterified glucomannan product (Mycosorb, Alltech, Inc.) was shown to reduce milk aflatoxin concentrations by 58% in dairy cows consuming aflatoxin-contaminated diets when included at 0.05% of the diet dry matter (Diaz *et al.*, 1999; Figure 1). The reduction of milk aflatoxin was similar to that seen for a sodium bentonite product included in the diet at 1.1% of the dry matter. The reduction in milk aflatoxin may be a good indicator of strong binding with dietary aflatoxin, reducing aflatoxin absorption through the intestine of the cow.

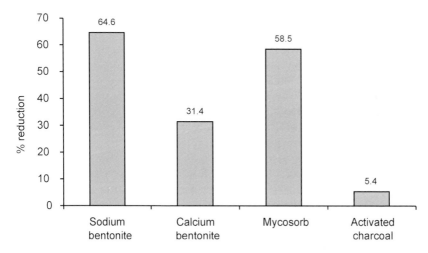

**Figure 1.** Effects of sequestering agents on milk aflatoxin residues (Diaz *et al.*, 1999).

## Areas of needed information

The Council for Agricultural Science and Technology published a list of major needs for research (CAST, 1989). Included in their list were surveillance of feeds for mycotoxin presence and quantity, assessment of control methods, development of resistant plants, improvement of sampling and analysis, improved understanding of effects on animals (particularly on immunosuppression), toxicological evaluation of newly discovered mycotoxins and assessment of economic effects.

## References

Abbas, H.K., C.J. Mirocha, T.Kommedahl, R.F. Vesonder and P. Golinski. 1989. Production of trichothecenes and non-trichothecene mycotoxins by *Fusarium* species isolated from maize in Minnesota. Mycopathologia. 108:55.

Applebaum, R.S., R.E. Brackett, D.W. Wiseman and E.L. Marth. 1982. Responses of dairy cows to dietary aflatoxin: feed intake and yield, toxin content, and quality of milk of cows treated with pure and impure aflatoxin. J. Dairy Sci. 65:1503.

Boland, E.W., V.L. Anderson, H.H. Casper, P.T. Berg and D.V. Dhuyvetter. 1994. The effects of increasing vomitoxin (DON) levels from scab infested barley fed to feedlot steers. Beef Prod. Field Day. Carrington Res. Ext. Ctr. Livestock Unit. North Dakota State University Ag. Expt. Sta. 17:34. (As quoted by DiCostanzo *et al.*, 1995a).

Brucato, M., S. F. Sundlof, J. U. Bell and G. T. Edds. 1986. Aflatoxin B$_1$ toxicosis in dairy calves pretreated with selenium-vitamin E. Am. J. Vet. Res. 47:179.

Chandler, Paul. 1992. Selenium, vitamin E indicate oxidative stress in dairy cattle. Feedstuffs 64(44):10.

Charmley, E., H.L. Trenholm, B.K. Thompson, D. Vudathala, J.W.G. Nicholson, D.B. Prelusky and L.L. Charmley. 1993. Influence of level of deoxynivalenol in the diet of dairy cows on feed intake, milk production and its composition. J. Dairy Sci. 76:3580.

Chu, F.S. 1992. Recent progress on analytical techniques for mycotoxins in feedstuffs. J. Anim. Sci. 70:3950.

Cole, R.J., J.W. Kirksey, J.W. Dorner, D.M. Wilson, J.C. Johnson, Jr., A.N. Johnson, D.M. Bedell, J.P. Springer, K.K. Chexal, J.C. Clardy and R.H. Cox. 1977. Mycotoxins produced by *Aspergillus fumigatus* species isolated from moldy silage. J. Agric. Food Chem. 25:826.

Coppock, R.W., M.S. Mostrom, C.G. Sparling, B. Jacobsen and S.C. Ross. 1990. Apparent zearalenone intoxication in a dairy herd from feeding spoiled acid-treated corn. Vet. Hum. Toxicol. 32:246.

Côté, L.M., J.D. Reynolds, R.F. Vesonder, W.B. Buck, S.P. Swanson, R.T. Coffey and D.C. Brown. 1984. Survey of vomitoxin-contaminated feed grains in Midwestern United States and associated health problems in swine. J. Am. Vet. Med. Assoc. 184:189.

Council for Agricultural Science and Technology (CAST). 1989. Mycotoxins: Economic and Health Risks. Task Force Report No. 116. Ames, Iowa.

DeHaan, K., R. Stock, D. Brink, T. Klopkenstein and N. Schneider. 1984. Scabby wheat influence on performance. Nebraska Beef Cattle Report. MP-47:6.

Diaz, D.E., J.T. Blackwelder, W.M. Hagler, Jr., B.A. Hopkins, F.T. Jones, K.L. Anderson and L.W. Whitlow. 1998. The potential of dietary clay products to reduce aflatoxin transmission to milk of dairy cows. J. Dairy Sci. 80(Suppl. 1):261.

Diaz, D.E., W.M. Hagler, Jr., B.A. Hopkins, J.A. Eve and L.W. Whitlow. 1999. The potential for dietary sequestering agents to reduce the transmission of dietary aflatoxin to milk of dairy cows and to bind aflatoxin *in vitro*. J. Dairy Sci. (Abstract) Southern Branch, American Dairy Science Association, February 1, 1999.

DiCostanzo, A., L. Johnston, H. Windels and M. Murphy. 1995a. A review of the effects of molds and mycotoxins in ruminants. Professional Animal Scientist 12:138.

DiCostanzo, A., J.C. Meiske, M. Murphy, R. Epley, L. Felice, L. Johnson, and H. Chester-Jones. 1995b. Effects of feeding vomitoxin-contaminated barley on performance of feedlot steers. Minnesota Cattle Feeders Rep. B-418, St. Paul, MN. (As quoted by DiCostanzo *et al.*, 1995a).

Foster, B.C., H.L. Trenholm, D.W. Friend, B.K. Thompson and K.E. Hartin. 1986. Evaluation of different sources of deoxynivalenol (vomitoxin) fed to swine. Can. J. Anim. Sci. 66:1149.

Galey, F.D., R.J. Lambert, M. Busse and W.B. Buck. 1987. Therapeutic efficacy of superactive charcoal in rats exposed to oral lethal doses of T-2 toxin. Toxicol. 25:493.

GAO. 1991. Food safety and quality. Existing detection and control programs minimize aflatoxin. Report RCED-91-109.

Garrett, W.N., H. Heitman, Jr. and A.N. Booth. 1968. Aflatoxin toxicity in beef cattle. Proc Soc. Exp. Biol. Med. 127:188.

Gelderblom, W.C.A., K. Jaskiewicz, W.F.O. Marasas, P.G. Thiel, R.M. Horak, R. Vleggaar and N.P.J. Kriek. 1988. Fumonisins: Novel mycotoxins with cancer-promoting activity produced by *Fusarium moniliforme*. Appl. Environ. Microbiol. 54:1806.

Gelderblom, W.C.A., N.P.J. Kreik, W.F.O. Marasas and P.G. Thiel. 1991. Toxicity and carcinogenicity of the *Fusarium moniliforme* metabolite, fumonisin $B_1$, in rats. Carcinogenesis 12:1247.

Gentry, P.A., M.L. Ross and P.K.C. Chan. 1984. Effect of T-2 toxin on bovine hematological and serum enzyme parameters. Vet. Hum. Toxicol. 26:24.

Gotlieb, A. 1997. Causes of mycotoxins in silages. In: Silage: Field to Feedbunk, NRAES-99, Northeast Regional Agricultural Engineering Service, Ithaca, NY. pp. 213.

Guthrie, L.D. 1979. Effects of aflatoxin in corn on production and reproduction in dairy cattle. J. Dairy Sci. 62(Suppl. 1):134.

Hagler, W.M., K. Tyczkowska and P.B. Hamilton. 1984. Simultaneous occurrence of deoxynivalenol, zearalenone and aflatoxin in 1982 scabby wheat from the Midwestern United States. Appl. Environ. Microbiol. 47:151.

Hamilton, P.B. 1984. Determining safe levels of mycotoxins. J. Food Prot. 47:570.

Harrison, L.R., B.M. Colvin, J.T. Greene, L.E. Newman and R.J. Cole. 1990. Pulmonary edema and hydrothorax in swine produced by fumonisin $B_1$, a toxic metabolite of *Fusarium moniliforme*. J Vet. Diagn. Invest. 2:217.

Harvey, R.B., L.F. Kubena, T.D. Phillips, W.E. Huff and D.E. Corrier. 1988. Approaches to the prevention of aflatoxicosis. Proc. Maryland Nutr. Conf. pp. 102–107.

Hayes, S.M. 1990. Counteracting aflatoxin in livestock feed. In: Agricultural Research, USDA, ARS, Washington, D.C. 38(2):18.

Hesseltine, C.W. 1986a. Global significance of mycotoxins. In: Mycotoxins and Phycotoxins. (P.S. Steyn and R. Vleggaar, eds). Elsevier Scientific Publishing Co., Amsterdam.

Hesseltine, C.W. 1986b. Resumé and future needs in the diagnosis of mycotoxins. In: Diagnosis of Mycotoxicoses. (J.L. Richard and J.R. Thurston, eds.) Martinus Nijhoff Publishers, Dordrecht, The Netherlands.

Hsu, I.C., C.B. Smalley, F.M. Strong and W.E. Ribelin. 1972. Identification of T-2 toxin in moldy corn associated with a lethal toxicosis in dairy cattle. Appl. Microbiol. 24:684.

Ingalls, J.R. 1994. Influence of DON on feed consumption by dairy cows. In: Proc. Western Nutr. Conf. P 129. Winnipeg, MB, Canada.

Joffe, A.Z. 1986. Fusarium Species: Their Biology and Toxicology. John Wiley and Sons, Inc., New York.

Kellela, K. and E. Ettala. 1984. The oestrogenic *Fusarium* toxin (zearalenone) in hay as a cause of early abortions in the cow. Nord. Vet. Med. 36:305.

Kellela, K. and L. Vasenius. 1982. The effects of rumen fluid on the content of zearalenone in animal fodder. Nord. Vet. Med. 34:336.

Khamis, Y., H.A. Hammad and N.A. Hemeida. 1986. Mycotoxicosis with oestrogenic effect in cattle. Zuchthyg. 21:233.

Kiessling, K.H., H. Patterson, K. Sandholm and M. Olsen. 1984. Metabolism of aflatoxin, ochratoxin, zearalenone, and three trichothecenes by intact rumen fluid, rumen protozoa and rumen bacteria. Appl. Environ. Microbiol. 47:1070.

Kosuri, N.R., M.D. Grave, S.G. Yates, W.H. Tallent, J.J. Ellis, I.A. Wolff and R.E. Nichols. 1970. Response of cattle to mycotoxins of *Fusarium tricinctum* isolated from corn and fescue. J. Am. Vet. Med. Assoc. 157:938.

Kriek, N.P.J., T.S. Kellerman and W.F.O. Marasas. 1981. A comparative study of the toxicity of *Fusarium verticilloides (F. moniliforme)* to horses, primates, pigs, sheep, and rats. Onderspoort J Vet. Res. 48:129.

Lacey, J. 1991. Natural occurrence of mycotoxins in growing and conserved forage crops. In: Mycotoxins and Animal Foods (J. E. Smith and R. E. Henderson, eds.), CRC Press, Boca Raton, Florida.

Lillehoj, E.B., and A. Ciegler. 1975. Mycotoxin synergism. In: Microbiology - 1975. (D. Schlessinger, ed.) American Society of Microbiology, Washington, DC. pp. 344–358.

Lindemann, M.D. and D.J. Blodgett. 1991. Various clays provide alternative for dealing with aflatoxin. Feedstuffs 63:15.

Mann, D.D., G.M. Buening, B. Hook and G.D. Osweiler. 1983. Effects of T-2 mycotoxin on bovine serum proteins. J. Am. Vet. Med. Assoc. 44:1757.

Marasas, W.F.O., T.S. Kellerman, W.C.A. Gelderblom, J.A.W. Coetzer, P.G. Thiel and J.J. van der Lugt. 1988. Leukoencephalomalacia in a horse induced by fumonisin $B_1$ isolated from *Fusarium moniliforme*. Onderstepoort J. Vet Res 55:197.

Marsi, M.S., V.C. Garcia and J.R. Page. 1969. The aflatoxin $M_1$ content of milk from cows fed known amounts of aflatoxin. Vet. Rec. 84:146.

Mills, J.T. and D. Abramson. 1986. Production of sterigmatocystin by isolates of *Aspergillus versicolor* from western Canadian stored barley and rapeseed/canola. Can. J. Plant Pathol. 8:151.

Mirocha, C.J., J. Harrison, A.A. Nichols and M. McClintock. 1968. Detection of fungal estrogen (F-2) in hay associated with infertility in dairy cattle. Appl. Microbiol. 16:797.

Mirocha, C.J., B. Schauerhamer and S.V. Pathre. 1974. Isolation, detection and quantitation of zearalenone in maize and barley. J. Assoc. Off. Anal. Chem. 57:1104.

Mirocha, C.J., S.V. Pathre, B. Schauerhamer and C.M Christiansen. 1976. Natural occurrence of *Fusarium* toxins in feedstuffs. Appl Environ. Microbiol. 32:553.

Moss, M.O. 1991. The environmental factors controlling mycotoxin formation. In: Mycotoxins and Animal Foods (J. E. Smith and R. S. Henderson, eds.) CRC Press. Boca Raton, Florida.

Nelson, M., N.R. Schneider, A.R. Doster, M.P. Carlson and T. Klopfenstein. 1984. Vomitoxin-contaminated wheat-pathology, toxicity in cattle. Nebraska Beef Cattle Report MP-47:3.

Noller, C.H., M. Stob and J. Tuite. 1979. Effects of feeding *Gibberella zeae*-infected corn on feed intake, bodyweight gain and milk production of dairy cows. J. Dairy Sci. 62:1003.

Osweiler, G.D., M.E. Kehrli, J.R. Stabel, J.R. Thurston, P.F. Ross and T.M. Wilson. 1993. Effects of fumonisin-contaminated corn screenings on growth and health of feeder calves. J. Anim. Sci. 71:459.

Patterson, D.S.P. and P.H. Anderson. 1982. Recent aflatoxin feeding experiments in cattle. Vet. Rec. 110:60.

Petrie, L., J. Robb and A.F. Stewart. 1977. The identification of T-2 toxin and its association with a hemorrhagic syndrome in cattle. Vet. Rec. 101:326.

Richard, J.L., G. Meerdink, C.M. Maragos, M. Tumbleson, G. Bordson, L.G. Rice and P.F. Ross. 1996. Absence of detectable fumonisins in the milk of cows fed *Fusarium proliferatum (Matsushima) Nirenberg* culture material. Mycopathologia 133:123.

Roine, K., E.L. Korpinen and K. Kallela. 1971. Mycotoxicosis as a probable cause of infertility in dairy cows. Nord. Vet. Med. 23:628.

Russel, L., D.F. Cox, G. Larsen, K. Bodwell and C.E Nelson. 1991. Incidence of molds and mycotoxins in commercial animal feed mills in seven Midwestern states, 1988-89. J. Anim. Sci. 69:5.

Schaeffer, J.L. and P.B. Hamilton. 1991. Interactions of mycotoxins with feed ingredients. Do safe levels exist? In: Mycotoxins and Animal Foods (J.E. Smith and R.S. Henderson, eds.) CRC Press. Boca Raton, Florida.

Scheideler, S.E. 1990. Aluminosilicates in poultry rations. Feed Management 41(1):22.

Schilfer, H.B. 1990. Mycotoxicosis of domestic animals and their diagnosis. Can. J. Physiol. Pharmacol. 68:987.

Scott, P.M. 1990. General referee reports: Mycotoxins. J. Assoc. Off. Anal. Chem. 73:98.

Scott, P.M., T. Delgado, D. B. Prelusky, H.L. Trenholm, J.D. Miller. 1994. Determination of fumonisin in milk. J. Environ. Sci. Health. B29:989.

Seglar, B. 1997. Case studies that implicate silage mycotoxins as the cause of dairy herd problems. In: Silage: Field to Feedbunk, NRAES-99, Northeast Regional Agricultural Engineering Service, Ithaca, NY. pp. 242.

Smith, T.K. 1980. Influence of dietary fiber, protein and zeolite on zearalenone toxicosis in rats and swine. J. Anim. Sci. 50:278.

Smith, T.K. 1984. Spent canola oil bleaching clays: potential for treatment of T-2 toxicosis in rats and short term inclusion in diets for immature swine. Can. J. Anim. Sci. 64:725.

Smith, T.K. and E.J. MacDonald. 1991. Effect of fusaric acid on brain regional neurochemistry and vomiting behavior in swine. J. Anim. Sci. 69:2044.

Smith, J., C. Wesselink, J. Parr, J.M. Sprosen, E.A. Fowke, N.R. Towers and D. Laboyrie. 1995. Effect of zearalenone on ewe pregnancy rates. In: Toxinology and Food Safety. Toxinology and Food Safety Research Group, Ruakura Research Centre, Hamilton, New Zealand.

Sprosen, J.M. And N.R. Towers. 1995. Urinary zearalenone metabolite concentrations in herds with fertility problems. In: Toxinology and Food Safety. Toxinology and Food Safety Research Group, Ruakura Research Centre, Hamilton, New Zealand.

Sreemannarayana, O., A.A. Frohlich, T.G. Vitti, R.R. Marquart and D. Abramson. 1988. Studies of the tolerance and disposition of ochratoxin A in young calves. J. Animal Sci. 66:1703.

Still, P., R.D. Wei, E.B. Smalley and F.M. Strong. 1972. A mycotoxin from *Penicillium roqueforti* isolated from toxic cattle feed. Fed. Proc. 31:733.

Sundlof, S.F. and C. Strickland. 1986. Zearalenone and zearalenol: Potential residue problems in livestock. Vet. Hum. Toxicol. 28:242.

Towers, N.R., J.M. Sprosen and W. Webber. 1995a. Zearalenone metabolites in cycling and non-cycling cows. In: Toxinology and Food Safety. Toxinology and Food Safety Research Group, Ruakura Research Centre, Hamilton, New Zealand.

Towers, N.R., C. Wesselink, E.A. Fowke and J.M. Sprosen. 1995b. Plasma *vs* urinary 'zearalenone' concentrations as indicators of 'zearalenone' intake. In: Toxinology and Food Safety. Toxinology and Food Safety Research Group, Ruakura Research Centre, Hamilton, New Zealand.

Trenholm, H.L., B.K. Thompson, K.E. Hartin, R. Greenhalgh and A.J. McAllister. 1985. Ingestion of vomitoxin (deoxynivalenol)-contaminated wheat by nonlactating dairy cows. J. Dairy Sci. 68:1000.

Trenholm, H.L., D.B. Prelusky, J.C. Young and J.D. Miller. 1988. Reducing mycotoxins in animal feeds. Agriculture Canada Publication 1827E.

USDA. APHIS. 1995. Mycotoxin levels in the 1995 midwest preharvest corn crop. Veterinary Services Factsheet N195.1295. The National Veterinary Services Laboratory, Ames, Iowa.

Van Egmond, H.P. 1989. Mycotoxins in Dairy Products. Elsevier Science Pub. Co., Ltd. New York.

Vesonder, R.F., A. Ciegler, R.F. Rogers, K.A. Burbridge, R.J. Bothast and A.H. Jensen. 1978. Survey of 1977 crop year preharvest corn for vomitoxin. Appl. Environ. Microbiol. 36:885.

Vesonder, R.F. and B.W. Horn. 1985. Sterigmatocystin in dairy cattle feed contaminated with *Aspergillus versicolor*. Appl. Environ. Microbiol. 49:234.

Vough, L.R. and I. Glick. 1993. Round bale silage. In: Silage Production from Seed to Animal, NARES-67, Northeast Regional Agricultural Engineering Service, Ithaca, NY. pp. 117.

Wannemacher, R.W., Jr., D.L. Brunner and H.A. Neufeld. 1991. Toxicity of trichothecenes and other related mycotoxins in laboratory animals. In: Mycotoxins and Animal Foods. (J. E. Smith and R. S. Henderson, eds.) CRC Press, Inc., Boca Raton, FL.

Weaver, G.A., H.J. Kurtz, C.J. Mirocha, F.Y. Bates, J.C. Behrens, T.S. Robison and S.P. Swanson. 1980. The failure of T-2 mycotoxin to produce hemorrhaging in dairy cattle. Can. Vet. J. 21:210.

Weaver, G.A., H.J. Kurtz, J.C. Behrens, T.S. Robison, B.E. Seguin, F.Y. Bates and C.J. Mirocha. 1986a. Effect of zearalenone on the fertility of virgin dairy heifers. Am. J. Vet. Res. 47:1395.

Weaver, G.A., H.J. Kurtz, J.C. Behrens, T.S. Robison, B.E. Seguin, F.Y. Bates and C.J. Mirocha. 1986b. Effect of zearalenone on dairy cows. Am. J. Vet. Res. 47:1826.

Whitlow, L.W., R.L. Nebel and W.M. Hagler, Jr. 1991. The association of deoxynivalenol in grain with milk production loss in dairy cows. In: G.C. Llewellyn, W.V. Dashek and C.E. O'Rear. 1994. Biodeterioration research 4. Plenum Press, New York. pp. 131.

Whitlow, L.W., W.M. Hagler, Jr. and B.A. Hopkins. 1998. Mycotoxin occurrence in farmer-submitted samples of North Carolina feedstuffs: 1989-1997. J. Dairy Sci. 81(Suppl. 1):1189.

Windels, H.F., A. DiCostanzo and R.D. Goodrich. 1995. Effect of deoxynivalenol from barley on performance and health of large frame crossbred steers. Minnesota Cattle Feeder Rep. B-417. St. Paul, MN. (As quoted by DiCostanzo *et al.*, 1995a).

Wyatt, R.D. 1991. Measurement of mold growth and mycotoxins in feed: fallacies and innovations. In: Proceedings of the Georgia Nutrition Conference, University of Georgia, Athens.

# NEW ROUTES TO GENETIC POTENTIAL: BIOPEPTIDES

# Bridging the gap between genetic potential and on-farm performance in commercial pigs

EDMUND J. MCCLURE

*Newline Products & Services, Leckhampton, Cheltenham, Gloucestershire, UK.*

## Introduction

Commercial hybrid pigs as found on farms throughout the world today have a much improved potential for growth and a much better ability to convert feed to liveweight gain than their counterparts in the late 1950s. Continuous genetic selection since the early 1960s has been aimed primarily at reducing body fat content to provide the consumer with leaner pig meat in line with changing eating patterns, and more recently in improving the litter size at farrowing.

Given this change in the type of animals being supplied by the breeding companies, have the necessary changes to nutrition, management (including hygiene) and environmental inputs been implemented to allow performance expressed at farm level to move more in line with the true genetic potential? Or, is there a need for more detailed and serious action to quantify and change the various inputs in order to narrow the gap between actual and potential performance? This paper examines the current situation and looks beyond this point as to likely changes required to bring commercial pig farming much closer to true least-cost pig meat production for the future.

## Quantification of some of the effects of genetic selection

A measure of the progress made from ongoing genetic selection programmes and the sale of improved breeding stock to commercial producers in the UK can be gained by examining the change in backfat measurement in UK slaughter pigs. Meat and Livestock Commission (MLC) values (1991a) indicate the progress made in reducing carcass fat in pigs (Figure 1). This reduction in body fat implies needed changes in other nutritional inputs. Modern pigs, by virtue of lower fat insulation, lose heat more easily. As a result closer attention to housing temperature at each stage in the nursing, growing and finishing stages is required. Increased lean tissue deposition (and decreased fat deposition) potential makes it necessary to supply feeds with higher levels of essential amino acids, particularly for the early growing stages, if the improved growth of lean tissue is to be expressed in practice.

A measure of the progress in breeding pig performance over time can be gained from examination of on-farm recording schemes. Evaluation by the Meat and Livestock Commission (1991b, 1998) of breeding herd perform-ance in the UK reveals the performance averages given in Table 1. The recent emphasis on genetic selection programmes to increase numbers of pigs born alive is reflected in commercial herd averages and is a very positive aspect of improving lifetime productivity of the breeding sow. However, increased numbers of pigs born alive are only of real value provided that the pigs can be successfully weaned. Additionally, increasing the numbers born alive has resulted in two practical changes, namely:

- Reduced average piglet birth weight.
- Increased spread in birth weights between the lightest and heaviest littermates.

Major changes at farm level, particularly in the areas of early piglet management and supplementary feeding, are required in order that extra piglets born alive are saved and not accounted for as increased pre-weaning mortality percentages.

## Production and growth potential in pigs

### SETTING TARGETS FOR GROWTH

The introduction of improved pig breeding stock into commercial pig farms requires capital investment. If that investment is to be realized, i.e. more live pigs born with higher growth potential, then standards of feeding and management must be adjusted.

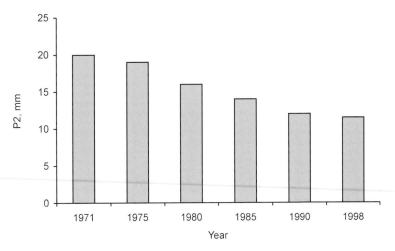

**Figure 1.** Change in backfat (P2) measurements for 60-80 kg deadweight pigs (MLC, 1991a).

**Table 1.  Trends in breeding pig performance[1].**

| Year | 1981 | 1985 | 1990 | 1995 | 1998 |
|---|---|---|---|---|---|
| Litters per sow per year | 2.20 | 2.25 | 2.23 | 2.31 | 2.33 |
| Live piglets per litter | 10.35 | 10.42 | 10.72 | 10.74 | 11.12 |
| Pigs reared per sow per year | 19.90 | 20.90 | 21.10 | 22.20 | 23.16 |
| Pre-wean mortality, % | 12.60 | 11.10 | 12.00 | 10.40 | 10.60 |
| Weaning age, days | 27 | 25 | 25 | 22 | 24 |
| Feed per sow per year, tonnes | 1.15 | 1.14 | 1.21 | 1.15 | 1.16 |
| Weaning to service, days | 23.91 | 22.22 | 23.67 | 21.00 | 17.65 |

[1]MLC/Signet, 1998.

First, what levels of performance are possible given good management and nutrition from modern suckling, growing and finishing pigs at commercial farm level and how does current performance measure up to the potential? Some indications of performance potential may be gained by examining piglet growth trials where intake of highly digestible supplementary feeds are maximised under excellent standards of management and feeding techniques (Table 2). Using these data as a comparison point, pre-weaning piglet performance, both on average and for the better commercial piglet producers in the UK, currently falls short of genetic growth potential by 20–25%. There is clearly a need to re-examine the current management and feeding practices for pigs in the farrowing house.

**Table 2.  Potential versus actual piglet pre-weaning growth performance[1].**

| | Genetic potential | Average | Top 1/3 |
|---|---|---|---|
| Age at weaning, days | 23 | 23 | 23 |
| Weaning weight, kg | 8.65 | 6.50 | 6.6 |
| Calculated : | | | |
|   Daily gain, g | 317 | 224 | 228 |
|   Weight:age index | 100 | 75.14 | 76.30 |
|   Reduced growth, % | 0 | 24.86 | 23.70 |

[1]MLC/Signet, 1998.

The weight-for-age at weaning has a large impact on post-weaning growth performance. Again, examination of post-weaning growth rates in commercial practice as compared to the genetic potential (MLC/Signet, 1998) (Table 3) indicates a widening of the weight-for-age relationship as the growth cycle progresses. It becomes evident from these performance comparisons that maximising early growth rate is critical to controlling the feed cost involved in pig meat production. Higher early growth rate reduces the number of expensive feeding days pre-slaughter (at maximum daily intake and poorer feed efficiency) on *ad libitum* feeding systems employed on most commercial farms.

Table 3. Potential versus actual piglet post-weaning growth performance[1].

|  | Genetic potential | Average | Top 1/3 |
|---|---|---|---|
| Feeding days | 71 | 71 | 71 |
| Weaning weight, kg | 8.65 | 6.50 | 6.60 |
| 94-day weight, kg | 60.32 | 42.80 | 45.14 |
| Calculated: |  |  |  |
| Daily gain, g | 728 | 511 | 543 |
| Weight:age index | 100 | 70.95 | 74.83 |
| Reduced growth, % | 0 | 29.05 | 25.17 |

[1]MLC/Signet Farm Business Consultancy UK data-12 months ending 30/09/1998.

Further information as to the genetic potential for growth of pigs in the later stages of finishing may be gained from carrying out computer growth simulations using feeds of known nutrient density in conjunction with known management and environmental controls at farm level (MLC/Signet, 1998, Table 4). These studies indicate the potential savings in feeding days under typical UK conditions on many commercial farms. The extent of the growth performance gap to be bridged with the finishing pig would appear to be greater than for younger pigs. Some degree of caution is necessary here since the performance and growing time required during this stage is influenced by early piglet growth performance. Thus poorer growth in young pigs results in extended feeding time to reach the final slaughter weight. The changes needed are increases in nutrition and management inputs to bring about higher nutrient intake between birth and 50-60 kg liveweight. The goal is to accelerate early performance when pigs are more efficient followed by closer control of nutrient inputs between 60 kg and slaughter to reduce nutrient wastage.

Table 4. Growth potential versus actual commercial performance in finishing pigs (genetic potential - by growth model prediction[1]).

|  | Genetic potential | Average | Top 1/3 |
|---|---|---|---|
| Age, days |  |  |  |
| Liveweight, kg |  |  |  |
| 94 | 60.32 | 42.80 | 45.14 |
| 120 | 90.00 | 60.27 | 64.22 |
| 155 |  | 83.79 | 90.00 |
| 165 |  | 90.00 |  |
| Calculated: |  |  |  |
| Daily gain, g | 1141 | 665 | 735 |
| Weight:age index | 100 | 58.28 | 64.42 |
| Reduced growth, % | 0 | 41.72 | 35.58 |

[1]MLC/Signet, 1998

SETTING TARGETS FOR BREEDING FEMALES

In the overall context of pig meat production it is also necessary to maximise the lifetime productivity of pig breeding stock. Replacement breeding stock represent a major investment in commercial pig production and replacement costs have increased in line with animal potential to produce increased litter numbers born alive and increased carcass leanness. Examination of annual female breeding stock replacement rates within UK herds indicates a continuous and high level of replacement (MLC, 1991b; Table 5). To what extent this is due to a desire to improve carcass quality or output is unclear; however evidence in the field would tend to suggest that the more likely reasons are due to on-farm nutritional shortfalls which adversely affect fertility and/or skeletal defects such as leg problems. Whatever the reason(s), the inescapable fact is that in practical terms lifetime productivity today is the same as it was a decade and a half ago. The key to progress in this area given larger litter numbers born alive must be improved early piglet management with supplementary feeding to reduce pre-weaning mortality coupled with improved nutrition and management of sows to extend the breeding lifetime within the herd.

Table 5.   Female breeding herd replacement rates and their effects upon lifetime productivity of the herd[1].

|  | 1981 | 1985 | 1990 | 1995 | 1998 |
|---|---|---|---|---|---|
| Annual sow replacement, % | 34.90 | 38.10 | 40.00 | 48.40 | 40.70 |
| Litters per sow per year | 2.20 | 2.25 | 2.23 | 2.30 | 2.32 |
| Pigs reared per litter | 9.05 | 9.26 | 9.43 | 9.53 | 10.11 |
| Piglet mortality, % | 12.60 | 11.10 | 12.00 | 12.70 | 11.00 |
| Calculated: |  |  |  |  |  |
| Litters per lifetime | 6.30 | 5.91 | 5.58 | 4.75 | 5.70 |
| Piglets per lifetime | 57 | 55 | 53 | 46 | 58 |

[1]MLC, 1991b.

As a guideline, suggested lifetime productivity targets for female replacement breeding stock are given in Table 6. Achievement of these targets in commercial production is vital for a future in pig meat production and will only be possible provided a much more disciplined approach is taken in terms of:

- Adequate nutrition of gilts pre-breeding to maximise backfat reserves.
- Careful heat detection and natural service or artificial insemination techniques.
- Phase feeding of sows during pregnancy to maximise implantation and foetal growth.
- Adequate trace mineral nutrition during pregnancy and lactation for improved sow fertility and piglet vitality at birth.
- Step feeding to maximise lactation feed intake, milk production and mimimise body weight loss.

- Supplementary feeding of piglets from day 1 with highly digestible dry feed to maximise intake, promote early digestive system development and increase growth rate.

Table 6. Female breeding stock: lifetime productivity targets for 1999 and beyond.

| | |
|---|---|
| Overall output | 65 – 70 + piglets weaned |
| Minimum number of litters | 7 |
| Each pregnancy should result in | 11 – 12 live piglets born |
| Average birth weight of piglets | 1.35 kg |
| Each lactation should result in | 10.50 – 11.00 piglets reared |
| Average weaning weight | 7.00 kg at 24 days |
| Weaning to mating interval | 4 – 7 days maximum |

# The theoretical objectives

Pig producers and those involved directly in giving nutritional and management advice on all aspects of pig production need to clearly focus on the objectives of the commercial exercise. In the case of the breeding female the objective should very clearly be to maximise lifetime productivity as measured by the number of piglets weaned at maximum weight for age. Practically this implies following a management and feeding strategy that results in:

- Production of the maximum number of litters (minimum 7) before culling from herd.
- Maximising piglet numbers born alive.
- Maximising live piglet birth weights.
- Management and feeding of suckling piglets to minimise pre-weaning mortality and maximise dry matter intake both from sow's milk (number 1 priority) and solid creep feed (number 2 priority).

In the case of the growing pig the objectives may be summarised as follows:

- To produce pig meat at minimum total cost.
- To maximise lean tissue deposition from birth to slaughter.
- To minimise fat deposition from 50–55 kg to slaughter.

ACHIEVING THE THEORETICAL OBJECTIVES

*Breeding females*
Laying the foundation for a long and productive breeding life begins at final selection at 80-90 kg (if not before) by feeding to maximise body fat deposition (minimum 20 mm backfat at P2 position) before first service

428

at 130-140 kg and expression of third oestrus. This is best achieved by *ad libitum* feeding of a high energy/low essential amino acid pre-breeder diet to discourage lean tissue growth and maximise fat deposition. Avoid overfeeding of the gestation diet for the first 28 days post-service as this causes rapid body gain leading to increased hepatic blood flow and increased metabolic clearance of progesterone. A decrease in the plasma progesterone concentration will reduce the production of uterine secretory proteins that play an important role in successful attachment of fertilised ova to the wall of the uterus.

Piglet birth weight is influenced by nutrient intake level from day 85 of gestation through to farrowing. Increasing the level of nutrients consumed by the gilt or sow on a daily basis at this stage will have a positive effect on piglet birth weights and will also condition the breeding animal for maximum daily feed intakes during the following lactation. The form of trace mineral supplements during this period will also have a beneficial effect on both breeding female mineral status and piglet viability at birth. Minerals in the organic or Bioplex form are more readily available for absorption and better able to cross the placenta to increase the mineral status of the neonate and thereby improve livability.

The aim in the farrowing house should be to feed the nursing sow in such a way that nutrient intakes increase daily to reach 7 kg of a high density lactation diet by day 10, with further gradual increases to maximise daily intake and milk production by day 21. The overall aim is maximum milk production coupled with minimum weight loss during the nursing period.

### Suckling piglets

Piglets have the potential for fast lean tissue growth from day 1 provided that sufficient nutrients are consumed on a daily basis. Intake of sow's milk is the number 1 priority. It is 'rocket fuel' in terms of digestibility and nutrient availability for the newborn piglet. However during the course of lactation with larger litter sizes, the problem is that sow's milk as a sole source of nutrition limits individual piglet growth owing to the finite amount of milk available and the dry matter which it contributes. *Piglet growth rate is governed by dry matter intake and the digestibility (i.e., available nutrient content) of that dry matter.* It is essential that daily dry matter intake is maximised by the suckling piglet from day 1 for a number of very important commercial reasons:

- To minimise early mortality of healthy but low birth weight piglets.
- To stimulate early development of the digestive system.
- To maximise availability of nutrients to fuel growth at the genetic potential of the animal.

Sow's milk, being low in dry matter, expands stomach volume in the piglet fairly rapidly. Meeting the commercial objective, genetic growth potential, requires occupation of this expanded stomach capacity with increased intakes of the highest quality dry matter in the form of solid feed. The commercial practice of giving small quantities of digestible, highly palatable solid feed in meal form on day 1 and 'nose dipping' of the smallest piglets a few hours post-farrowing will result in increased dry matter intake, reduced early mortality and earlier development of the digestive system. This may be followed after a few days by mixing in increasing quantities of pelleted piglet starter feed and phasing out of the original starter meal by 7–10 days of age. Careful and sensible adoption of this approach increases consumption of high quality piglet feeds between birth and weaning. The earlier the weaning age, the earlier solid feeding should be offered to suckling piglets, otherwise the more severe the growth check post-weaning.

The priority for selection of the raw materials for piglet feeds must be maximum dry matter digestibility of the final feed mix if genetic growth potential is to be achieved from the earliest possible age. Formulation of diets to the highest quality standards (ie., digestibility) is the requirement, not formulation to a cost standard as diet cost in piglet feeds is purely a reflection of raw material quality and nutrient density. Specially selected quality protein sources (such as milk products, fishmeals, biopeptides), cereal sources (cooked to rupture starch grains) and vegetable oils are the basis of successful early piglet feeds (birth to 12–15 kg) to maximise growth rates both pre- and post-weaning.

### Applied biotechnology: production of Ultimate Protein 1672.

Highly consistent protein sources of animal origin such as low temperature dried fishmeals may be difficult to obtain on a regular basis in many areas of the world where direct early piglet feeding is practised. A new alternative to solve this problem is now available in the form of Alltech Ultimate Protein Biopeptides. Peptides consist of variable length chains of linked amino acid (typically 2-50 amino acid units) which result from the hydrolysis of proteins. Wheat gluten and brewer's yeast are blended and subjected to controlled enzyme hydrolysis to produce a consistent highly digestible product containing biologically active peptides targeted to easily cross the intestinal brush border, accelerate intestinal maturation and crypt depth, encourage development of beneficial intestinal flora and contain glutamic acid to improve feed flavor.

The inclusion of Ultimate Protein 1672 to replace more conventional protein sources in piglet feeds fed both before and after weaning has been shown to improve growth performance. In a post-weaning trial in the UK, piglets weaned at 21 days were used to compare a control feed with one in which some of the protein was replaced with Ultimate Protein 1672. There were 65 piglets per treatment. The control group received a feed containing skim milk, fish meal and potato protein sources. The test feed contained 5% Ultimate Protein 1672 as partial replacement for the protein. The feeds had equal energy, protein and essential amino acid levels. Pigs given the feed including Ultimate Protein 1672 had 6.5% higher average daily liveweight gain and 6% higher daily intake (Table 7).

**Table 7.    Effect of Ultimate Protein 1672 on piglet performance.**

|  | Control | Ultimate Protein 1672 |
|---|---|---|
| Start weight, kg | 7.55 | 7.50 |
| Final weight, kg | 8.94 | 8.98 |
| Daily feed intake, g | 218 | 231 |
| Daily liveweight gain, g | 199 | 212 |
| Feed conversion efficiency | 1.10 | 1.09 |

Use of a highly digestible piglet feed ingredient such as Ultimate Protein 1672 during the period from birth to 20+ kg will enable improved growth rates in commercial pigs and allow the producer to take advantage of the reduction in feeding days to slaughter.

Whilst the foregoing briefly outlines the basics of providing quality nutrient sources for the young piglet, maximising growth rates is not just a matter of nutrient supply and consumption *per se*. What is required is adherence to sound nutritional principles coupled with the discipline of ensuring only the highest standards of daily piglet management including animal comfort, temperature levels and control, and hygiene. The gastrointestinal tract of the piglet at birth is sterile and the farrowing house environment influences the pattern of development of the bacterial flora in the gut. Maintenance of strict farrowing pen hygiene standards allied to control of the development of the bacterial flora in the gut of the piglet via the solid feed route eliminates piglet scouring problems, an essential requirement if genetic growth potential is to be achieved. Bacterial scouring in piglets must be avoided as it causes permanent damage to the lining of the intestine resulting in decreased ability to absorb nutrients. Since the ability to absorb nutrients is fundamental to rate of growth, the scouring piglet never catches up and has poorer growth rate and feed conversion efficiency from the point at which scouring occurs to slaughter weight.

## Feed consumption pattern of the pig from birth to slaughter

A brief examination of the feed consumption pattern of the pig from birth through to slaughter at 90 kg illustrates the importance of maximising growth, particularly in the early stages (Figure 2). The important factors to appreciate are:

- 66% of the total feed requirement from birth to slaughter at 90 kg is consumed during the final 33% of the total weight gain.
- Pigs growing from birth to 60 kg are much more efficient than pigs beyond 60 kg.
- Rapid growth from birth to 30 kg has a major effect in the reduction of feeding days at maximum feed intake pre-slaughter, thereby lowering overall feed production cost.

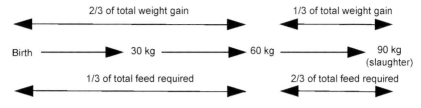

**Figure 2.** Distribution of weight gain and feed intake between birth and slaughter at 90 kg.

- In order to bring pig meat production more into line with least cost, a change in feeding systems and management is needed. Nutrient intake (and lean tissue deposition) must be maximised from birth to approximately 50–60 kg for maximum weight for age followed by a restriction in energy intake to avoid excessive production of carcass fat. This must be done while supplying sufficient intake of energy and essential amino acids to continue to maximise lean tissue deposition through to the desired slaughter point.

- As illustrated in Table 4, the time difference in feeding days between estimated genetic growth potential and actual performance as recorded for the top third of UK pig producers is some 35 days (155 minus 120 = 35 days). With improved piglet management in the farrowing house and increased supplementary feed consumption from day 1 it should be feasible to increase weaning weights by some 500–1000 g. When this is achieved it represents a savings of about seven days feeding at the slaughter end of the production cycle.

- Increased intakes of feed by weaned piglets with more enhanced digestive capability (by virtue of increased feed intake pre-weaning) over the weight range of 10–30 kg will result in further improvements in weight gain, feed conversion efficiency and final feeding days pre-slaughter (Table 8). Cumulatively the effect of improved management and feed intakes pre-and post-weaning can represent 14–21 days savings in feed usage at maximum intake levels pre-slaughter - equivalent to some 35–50 kg of finishing feed.

- Prevention of early piglet scouring and/or looseness can be worth up to 7–10 days reduction in time to slaughter at approximately 90 kg. Again this represents a feed savings of 15–25 kg. Taken overall, the combined effect of improved early feed intake and scour prevention

**Table 8.** Effect of increasing feed intake on post-weaning piglet performance from 10-30 kg liveweight (growth model predictions).

| % Feed increase | Growth response | FCE effect | Reduction in feeding days |
|---|---|---|---|
| +10% | +21% | −7.5% | −7 |
| +20% | +35% | −12% | −14 |

can amount to a time saving of 21–31 days and a saving in feed requirement of some 50–75 kg finishing feed. This is what current pig genetics are capable of delivering at unit level provided improvements can
be made in early management, hygiene, feed quality and feeding
techniques.

## Control of carcass fat content

Current feeding systems for finishing pigs based on *ad libitum* feeding of
a given feed nutrient specification over a wide weight range (eg., 5–90
kg) result in the production of surplus carcass fat due to over-consumption
of energy. This is to be avoided as it usually leads to:

- Increased costs of production since fat is more expensive to produce
  than lean meat.
- Reduced sale value due to downgrading.

Controlling the daily energy intake to supply amounts required for body
maintenance and lean tissue deposition from 50–55 kg onwards will result
in decreased carcass fat content. This may be achieved in practice by:

- Restricted daily feeding to a pre-determined maximum level.
- Frequent and progressive changes in energy density of feed with
  increasing liveweight when feeding *ad libitum*.
- Continuous blending of two feeds with different nutrient densities
  i.e., ratio feeding.

Using the last technique, pigs may be taken from 10–15 kg through to
slaughter by the blending in two stages of a total of three feed specifications (Table 9). Based upon the genetics of the pigs, a computerised
programme may be used to select the appropriate ratios for each stage
in the growth cycle. In practical terms the feed ratios for individual
groups of pigs may be changed on a weekly basis. Depending upon
the feed blends used, pigs may be grown as fast or as slowly as required
according to the market requirements at a given time. In an increasingly diverse marketplace this feeding system is likely to assume increased
relevance and become more widespread in the future as a means of
achieving carcass uniformity.

## Conclusions

Advances in genetics have currently provided commercial producers around
the world with pigs of production potential far in excess of the current
performance levels being achieved. Bridging this gap in performance will
only become possible for the future by appreciation of true production

**Table 9.  General feed specifications for continuous blending of feeds with different nutrient densities.**

Feed Set 1 (from 10–25 kg)
Super Grower: nutrient density set to maximise growth rate for a 10 kg pig fed *ad libitum*.
Grower: nutrient density set to maximise growth rate for a 25 kg pig fed *ad libitum*.

Feed Set 2 (from 25 kg to slaughter weight (90 kg.+))
Grower: nutrient density set to maximise growth rate for a 25 kg pig fed *ad libitum*.
Finisher: nutrient density set to maximise lean tissue deposition for 90+ kg pigs fed *ad libitum*.

potential followed by marked improvements in standards of management, hygiene, environment and feeding. Where this can be achieved in practice, great progress can be made towards true least-cost pig meat production and the necessary return on extra investment involved in the purchase of genetically improved pig breeding stock.

# References

Meat and Livestock Commission. 1991a. In: Pig Yearbook 1991. Meat & Livestock Commission, Milton Keynes, UK. pg.75.

Meat and Livestock Commission. 1991b. In: Pig Yearbook 1991. Meat & Livestock Commission, Milton Keynes, UK Pg. 13.

MLC/Signet Farm Business Consultancy. 1998. 12 Months ending 30/09/1998. Published jointly by MLC, Milton Keynes, UK and SAC COSAS, Ltd. Edinburgh, UK.

# Biologically active peptides: sources, production and nutritional importance

RONAN POWER and RICHARD MURPHY

*European Bioscience Centre, Alltech Inc., Dunboyne, Co. Meath, Ireland*

## Introduction

A wide range of biologically active peptides has been isolated in recent
years from microbial, plant and animal sources. These peptides vary
in complexity from simple dipeptides to large cyclic molecules that may
be extensively modified through phosphorylation, glycosylation or
acylation. Physiological effects ascribed to bioactive peptides include
hormonal, immunomodulatory, antibacterial, antitumor and mineral
binding properties. Natural oligopeptides, derived from enzymatically
hydrolysed protein, are widely used to enhance the sensory characteristics
of food through the recreation of sweet or salty taste sensations; and
several peptides have been implicated in the control of appetite. At a
more fundamental level, it is well accepted that the absorption of di-
and tripeptides from the gastrointestinal tract is an important biological phenomenon and a significant proportion of circulating amino acids
are in the form of small peptides. The demonstration that extracellular
peptide-bound amino acids are preferentially used for protein synthesis
by the lactating mammary gland presents interesting possibilities for
the manipulation of milk protein synthesis through the use of specific
peptides.

Given such an array of biological activities, it is not surprising that the
production and characterisation of biologically active peptides have become
areas of intensive research. The potential use of such biomolecules as
novel therapeutic agents and as dietary supplements in functional foods
or feeds is considerable. It is certain that the use of biologically active
peptides in areas such as the animal feed sector will become increasingly
evident in the early years of the new millennium.

## Biological activities

Although endogenous peptides such as endorphins and enkephalins
constitute a significant proportion of known bioactive peptides, many other

435

peptides with potent biological activity have been isolated from enzymatic digests of various food proteins (Table 1). Several milk protein-derived peptides having for example, mineral binding, anti-thrombotic, antimicrobial and opioid-like activities have been reported (Meisel, 1997; Mullally *et al.*, 1997). These peptides, inactive in the sequence of the parent food protein, may be released from the intact sequence by enzymatic proteolysis. While this will occur to a small extent during normal passage through the gastrointestinal tract, *in vitro* systems that utilise a range of food grade peptidases make it possible to produce and concentrate the bioactive peptide(s) in question.

Once liberated in the body, bioactive peptides perform an impressive array of regulatory functions and display a wide range of other activities, some of which are described below.

**Table 1. Examples of biologically active peptides from various sources.**

| Category | Number of residues | Main activity |
|---|---|---|
| Antimicrobial | | |
|   Lactoferricin | 26 | Enterotoxigenic *E.coli, Listeria monocytogenes* |
|   Nisin | 34 | Inhibits Gram positive bacteria e.g. clostridia and *Listeria* sp. |
| Antioxidant | | |
|   Carnosine | 2 | Inhibits rancidity in cooked meats |
| Antihypertensive | | |
|   ß-casomorphin | 7 | Inhibition of angiotensin-converting enzyme |
| Antithrombotic | | |
|   Casoplatelin | 11 | Inhibition of platelet aggregation and fibrinogen binding |
| Mineral binding | | |
|   Caseinophosphopeptide | 16 - 25 | Calcium binding |
| Neuropeptides | | |
|   Leu-enkephalin | 5 | Opioid |
|   Met-enkephalin | 5 | Opioid |
|   α-endorphin | 5 | Neuromodulator |
| Immunocative peptides | | |
|   Oryzatensin | 9 | Stimulates polymorphonuclear lymphocytes |
|   ß-casein fragment | 2-3 | As above |
| Hormonal | | |
|   Oxytocin | 9 | Contraction of smooth muscle |
|   Vasopressin | 9 | Contraction of vascular muscle |

## PEPTIDES WITH ANTIMICROBIAL ACTIVITY

Antimicrobial peptides are normally associated with antibiotic and antiviral peptides produced by bacteria and fungi. These include cyclic peptides, glycopeptides and lipopeptides such as gramicidin, vancomycin, lactocin, subtilin and nisin (Kleinkauf and Von-Doehren, 1988). Bacteriocins such as nisin offer great potential in the area of food preservation as alternatives to questionable conventional preservatives such as nitrites. These peptides possess potent antimicrobial activity but, because they are produced by naturally occurring strains of lactic acid bacteria used in food fermentations, have no adverse effects upon animals or humans. Nisin, for example, is a relatively short peptide of 34 amino acid residues produced by *Lactococcus lactis*. It is an acidic molecule and exhibits greatest stability under conditions of low pH such as in the stomach. It displays potent activity against Gram-positive food spoilage bacteria and is sporostatic towards clostridium and bacillus species (Delves-Broughton, 1990). Antimicrobial peptides generally display a high degree of heat stability, which render them ideal candidates for preservatives in processed human food and animal feed.

In addition to antimicrobial peptides of microbial origin, in excess of 100 different antimicrobial peptides have been isolated from vertebrates. They share a number of common characteristics:

1.  Such peptides are all relatively small with less than 50 amino acid residues.
2.  They are basic or cationic peptides and tend to be rich in lysine and arginine.
3.  They are amphipathic with their hydrophilic region being necessary for solubility in water while their lipophilic region is required for membrane reactivity with target microorganisms.

The general mode of action observed is the formation of pores in the cell membranes of susceptible microorganisms, which leads to cell leakage, inhibition of growth and/or cell death. Many such peptides are quite potent with minimum inhibitory concentrations (MICs) of 4 ppm or less being reported (Hancock and Lehrer, 1998).

Apart from these endogenous peptides produced by microbes, plants and animals, it is important to realise that effective antimicrobial peptides may also be derived from food proteins via enzymatic hydrolysis. Of particular interest in this regard are antimicrobial peptides produced from milk proteins. Several antimicrobial peptides have been derived from the minor whey protein lactoferrin. Lactoferrin is a well-characterised iron-binding glycoprotein that occurs in mammalian body fluids, most notably milk. As an intact protein, it is considered to be an important host defence against microbial infections. However, its antimicrobial mode of action is more complex than straightforward iron-binding. Three peptides with antibacterial activity towards enterotoxigenic *E.coli* have been purified following enzymatic cleavage of lactoferrin with pepsin. All peptides are cationic and originate from the N-terminus of the molecule in a region distinct from its iron-binding sites. Two of these peptides display antimicrobial activity toward a number of pathogenic and food spoilage microorganisms, while the third peptide has been reported to inhibit the growth of *Listeria monocytogenes* at concentrations as low as 2 µM. Furthermore, the antibacterial effects of these peptides were observable within 30 minutes of exposure (Dionysius and Milne, 1997).

IMMUNOACTIVE PEPTIDES

Endogenous peptides that display immunoactivating activity include the interferons and interleukins, which are central to the activation and regulation of the immune response. In terms of food-derived immunoactive peptides, milk is a favoured source for these molecules. For example, the C-terminal sequence 193-209 of ß-casein, obtained from a pepsin-chymosin digest of bovine casein, induced a marked proliferative response in rat lymphocytes (Meisel, 1997). Further studies have shown that the dipeptide Tyr-Gly and the tripeptide Tyr-Gly-Gly, which are partial sequences in the primary structure of bovine κ-casein and α-lactalbumin, significantly enhanced the proliferation of human peripheral blood lymphocytes at concentrations as low as $10^{-11}$ mol/L (Kayser and Meisel, 1996). Other foods that may offer suitable sources for immunoactive peptides include soybean protein (Yoshikawa *et al.*, 1993). It is possible that such peptides may interact with the Gut-Associated Lymphoid Tissue (GALT). In addition, it is likely that immunoactive di- and tripeptides can pass freely across the intestinal wall and react directly with peripheral lymphocytes. Obviously, this offers rich potential in terms of the identification of other orally bioavailable peptides from food proteins and the study of structure/activity relationships of immunoactive peptides.

NEUROACTIVE PEPTIDES

Peptides in this category include the endogenous opioids, endorphins, enkephalins and other regulatory peptides such as somatostatin and thyrotropin releasing hormone (TRH) (Snyder and Innis, 1979; Lewis *et al.*, 1984). It is not commonly known, however, that neuroactive peptides have been isolated from enzymatic hydrolysates of milk, fish, soya and cereal proteins (Meisel and Schlimme, 1990), with the result that this has become a very active area of research for food pharmacologists and neutraceutical scientists.

PEPTIDES WITH ANTIOXIDANT PROPERTIES

Perhaps the best known peptide in this category is carnosine β-Ala-His) which is a natural dipeptide found in large quantities in animal muscle. Carnosine has been reported to inhibit the oxidation of lipids catalysed by iron, haemoglobin, lipoxidase and singlet oxygen *in vitro* (Chan *et al.*, 1993). It has also found application as an inhibitor of oxidative rancidity in cooked meats during storage. Several low molecular weight peptides have been identified in foods such as mushrooms, potatoes and honey which inhibit polyphenol oxidase (PPO). In addition to inhibiting PPO, these peptides reduce the browning of foods by reacting with the quinonoid products of PPO catalysis thereby preventing the formation of polymeric oxidation products (Iyengar and McEvily, 1992). Certain peptides and protein hydrolysates are known to generally reduce the autoxidative rate and hydroperoxide content of fats by acting as scavengers of heavy metals and promoters of the decomposition of hydroperoxides that would otherwise serve as a source of free radicals (Pokorny, 1991). Antioxidant peptides represent an area of significant potential in the animal feed and human food markets given the present level of consumer awareness and the move towards totally natural preservatives as opposed to artificial additives.


## PEPTIDES DISPLAYING MINERAL BINDING PROPERTIES

The majority of the available research in this area has concentrated on the binding and transport of divalent mineral cations by peptides derived from enzymatic casein digests (Meisel, 1997). It is noteworthy that milk proteins are once more the predominant source of reported mineral-binding bioactive peptides; but substantial evidence also exists that mineral binding peptides may also be generated from other sources of food such as fish, soya and cereal proteins. To date, several mineral-binding casein phosphopeptides have been isolated from enzymatic digests of α- and ß-casein (Maubois and Leonil, 1989; Maubois *et al.*, 1991). Most of these mineral-binding peptides contain a serine phosphate cluster and glutamyl residues in their core sequence. The mineral-binding sites are represented by the negatively charged side chains of these amino acids and, most notably, by the phosphate groups. The binding of minerals such as calcium involves the serine-bound phosphate groups as well as the free carboxyl groups of glutamic acid. Such binding screens the complex from further interactions and this enhances the solubility of the mineral-peptide complex.


## PEPTIDES WITH SENSORY/FLAVOUR PROPERTIES

Without doubt, this category of bioactive peptides is the most important from an historical perspective. For centuries, foods such as cheeses have been organoleptically scored on the basis of sweet, bitter, sour and other tastes. Peptides contribute in a significant manner to the presence of these varied taste perceptions. Hence it is not surprising that a major focal point of bioactive peptide research in the latter part of this century has been the identification and isolation of novel sensory or flavour peptides from varied chemical and biological sources. Typical examples of such peptides include the dipeptides aspartame (Asp-Phe-O-Me) and alitame (L-Asp-D-Ala-NH$_2$) which have gained widespread regulatory approval in many countries and final applications in hundreds of food and pharmaceutical products (Grenby, 1991). Once again, however, consumer resistance to such 'artificial' sweeteners has prompted renewed research into natural sources of peptide-based sweeteners and other flavours. Candidate polypeptides include the plant proteins, thaumatin, monellin, pentadin and mabinlin which are currently being evaluated as natural sweeteners for human foods.

The industrial use of enzymes for the modification of proteins finds its roots in traditional processes such as the fermentation of soya protein to produce oriental foods such as tempei and tofu. Crude extracts of *Carica papaya* yielded the enzyme papain, which has long been used for the production of fish pastes and sauces and in the tenderizing of meats. Extracts of yeast have long been used as a source of flavour. These may be classified as autolysates, plasmolysates or hydrolysates depending on their method of preparation. Predominant flavours associated with yeast extracts are roast meat and cheese-like aromas, many of which are attributed to short flavour peptides. As stated, peptides may impart sweet, bitter, sour and salty flavours; and while bitter peptides are normally avoided in food protein hydrolysates through the judicious use of different enzymes and control of reaction conditions, they are important taste components of foods and beverages such as cheese, coffee and fruit juices. Several bitter peptides have been isolated and characterised from a variety of fermented foods and protein hydrolysates (Tamura *et al.*, 1988, Table 2).

Acidic peptides are generally associated with sour and Umami flavours. The latter display a monosodium glutamate-type taste and generally consist of dipeptides or tripeptides containing the sodium salts of glumatic and aspartic acids. The octapeptide, Lys-Gly-Asp-Glu-Glu-Ser-Leu-Ala, as first isolated from papain-treated beef extract is known as the 'delicious' peptide and represents an excellent example of the Umami taste profile (Yamasaki and Maekawa, 1978). The characteristic beef soup flavour of the delicious peptide has been reported to be due to the combined effect of its N-terminal dipeptide, Lys-Gly, its central acidic tripeptide, Asp-Glu-Glu, and its C-terminal tripeptide, Ser-Leu-Ala. Basic dipeptides, such as Ornithine-β-Ala, display strong salty tastes while oligomers of glutamic acid find many uses as bitterness masking agents in a variety of foods. Obviously, such natural flavouring agents offer significant possibilities for improving the palatability of animal feed and human food. Moreover, they offer safe alternatives to high-sodium seasonings and as a result are gaining widespread favour as components of healthier diets.

NUTRITIVE PEPTIDES

Enzymatic digestion of proteins in the intestinal tract results in the release of free amino acids and peptides. Proteins and peptides, however, appear to have additional value for animal growth beyond the straightforward

Table 2.   Examples of biologically active peptides with sensory and/or flavour properties.

| Activity | Peptide | Structure |
|---|---|---|
| Sweet | Sweet lysine dipeptides | N-Ac-Phe-Lys |
|  |  | N-Ac-Gly-Lys |
|  | Alitame | L-Asp-D-Ala-NH$_2$ |
|  | Aspartame | Asp-PheOMe |
|  | Aminomalonate dipeptides | D-Ama-L-Phe-O-Me |
| Umami (MSG-type) | 'Delicious' peptide | Lys-Gly-Asp-Glu-Glu-Ser-Leu-Ala |
|  | Acidic peptides | Gly-Asp, Gly-Asp-Gly |
|  |  | Ala-Glu, Ala-Glu-Ala |
|  |  | Glu-Leu, Val-Glu-Val |
|  | Fish protein hydrolysates | Glu-Glu, Ser-Glu-Glu |
|  |  | Glu-Ser, Thr-Glu |
|  |  | Glu-Asp, Asp-Glu-Ser |
| Salty/Umami | Basic peptides | Orn-Gly, Lys-Tau |
| Bitter | Soy protein hydrolysates | Gly-Leu, Phe-Leu |
|  |  | Leu-Phe, Leu-Lys |
|  |  | Arg-Leu, Arg-Leu-Leu |
|  | Cheese peptides | Lys-Pro, Phe-Pro, |
|  |  | Val-Pro, Leu-Pro |
|  | Casein peptides | Gly-Pro-Phe-Pro-Val-Ile |
| Bitterness masking agents | Glutamate oligomers | Glu-Glu |
|  |  | Glu-Glu-Glu |

supply of amino acids. For example, synthetic amino acids such as lysine and methionine are extensively used to supplement pig and poultry diets but the amount of intact protein that can be replaced by these free amino acids is limited. While the fact that proteins are merely particular sequences of constituent amino acids suggests that a supply of free amino acids should be capable of replacing protein in the diet, this is not the case. It may be that part of the importance of dietary protein is manifested through intermediate biologically active peptides formed as part of the degrada-tion process in the gastrointestinal tract. Significant evidence may be found in the literature to support the notion of nutritionally important, bioactive peptides. In the case of human nutrition, the use of protein hydrolysates and peptide mixtures as nitrogen sources for patients suffering from diseases such as pancreatitis, short bowel syndrome and Crohn's disease has completely replaced the application of free amino acid or protein mixtures (Siemensma et al., 1993; Schmidl et al., 1994). There is also evidence that supplementation of the diet with protein hydrolysates is beneficial for the elderly, endurance athletes and weight control programmes (Frokjaer, 1994). Several reasons for the nutritional superiority of peptides over free amino acids and intact proteins in these cases have been reported in the literature (Siemensma et al., 1993). These include:

i.   Transport of short peptides across the intestinal wall is facilitated compared to free amino acids.
ii.  Peptides are less hypertonic than free amino acids and this has the net effect of increasing their efficiency of absorption and reduces osmotic problems.
iii. Short peptides, in many cases, are less antigenic than larger polypeptides or the native protein from which they are derived.
iv.  As discussed earlier, short peptides may possess beneficial sensory characteristics.

Superior absorption of dipeptides and tripeptides has meant that short peptides enriched with essential amino acids such as methionine and lysine represent important components of food supplements for patients with special dietary needs. However, the nutritional importance of such peptides is in no way restricted to specific disease states in humans. The concept that peptides may constitute a significant proportion of total amino acid absorption in animals is now well accepted and has been demonstrated by a number of diverse methodologies (Webb and Matthews, 1998; Gardner, 1998). This was first demonstrated in ruminants, where very high concentrations of peptides were observed in the plasma of calves. The ratio of the concentration of peptide amino acids to free amino acids in these studies was approximately 4:1. Furthermore, a high proportion of these circulating peptides was reported to be quite small in size with molecular masses ranging from 500 to 1500 Daltons. While it is very unlikely that circulating peptide-bound amino acids are exclusively of dietary origin, it has been demonstrated that peptides are a more important form of amino acid absorption in ruminants than free amino acids (Webb *et al.*, 1992). Likewise, a convincing body of evidence exists that significant amounts of peptides are absorbed in intact form in monogastric species (Gardner, 1994; 1995). It is important to note that the nature of the peptide preparation seems to be quite critical in this regard. For example, experiments involving luminal perfusion of rat small intestine *in vitro* with enzymatic digests of various proteins showed passage of significant amounts of peptides to the serosal side of the intestinal preparation. However, the amount varied markedly depending on the actual enzyme digest used, indicating that peptide size or peptide sequence are important factors in determining the rate of absorption of peptides (Gardner, 1998). In addition, such experiments indicate that the uptake of peptides is not a passive process and the existence of peptide carriers in brush-border membranes that utilize a proton gradient active transport mechanism is now well recognised. From a nutritional standpoint, the selective uptake of peptides rather than free amino acids from the gastrointestinal tract offers interesting possibilities for improving the utilisation of protein sources by animals through the administration of synthetic peptides or enzymatically–treated proteins. Many studies have suggested that dietary absorption of intact peptides is as important as free amino acid absorption for the supply of amino acids to tissues for protein synthesis. For example, experiments in dairy cows have utilised isotopically-labelled Gly-Phe or Gly-Leu peptides infused into the artery supplying one-half of the mammary gland. Incorporation of the peptide-derived $^{13}$C-labelled amino acids into milk protein from that half of the gland was compared to incorporation of $^{13}$C into milk protein from the non-infused half of the gland over an eight hour period. At all time points, leucine and phenylalanine enrichments were higher in casein secreted from the peptide-infused half (Backwell, 1998). Such findings offer considerable scope for exploitation in animal production situations where the availability of certain amino acids may limit the rates of protein synthesis.

## Sources and production

From the foregoing it is obvious that many common foods represent rich sources of biologically active peptides that may be classified either as nutrients, functional foods, or pharmacologically active substances. At present the understanding of the role peptides play in animal nutrition is not developed to the point where peptides are formulated into diets, however that may not be far away given the research and commercial emphasis on improving nitrogen metabolism. Functional foods are nutrient sources of a specific composition that have functions beyond supplying a nutrient. A functional food might be recognised for its contribution toward prevention of, or recovery from, a disease. It is important to distinguish between health-enhancing functional foods for prevention and pharmacologically active compounds for the direct treatment of disease. Bioactive peptides falling into the latter category include peptides for the treatment of diarrhea (casomorphins), thrombosis (casoplatelins), hypertension (casokinins) and immunodeficiency (immunopeptides) (Meisel, 1997). It is noteworthy that many of the bioactive peptides identified to date are pharmacologically active peptides derived from milk proteins, particularly casein. However, other food proteins have yielded a variety of active peptides upon hydrolysis. These include fish proteins, soya, rice and other cereal proteins (Meisel and Schlimme, 1990). Peptides derived from yeast are, as stated previously, important flavour-enhancing agents; and yeast deserves special mention in this regard given the vast range of processes described in the literature for yeast extraction and hydrolysis (Maltz, 1981).

In terms of peptide production, a clear distinction can be made between naturally produced endogenous peptides such as endorphins and bacteriocins, and peptides produced by deliberate chemical (or other) processes. The main approaches to peptide synthesis are:

i.   Chemical synthesis
ii.  Enzymatic synthesis
iii. Recombinant DNA technology

All have their own unique advantages and the choice of method depends primarily on the desired length and quantity of the peptide in question.

Chemical synthesis of peptides is widely used for the production of high-value, short to medium length peptides of pharmaceutical grade. Disadvantages include the high cost of the substrates and reagents and the hazardous nature of the reactions from a health and environmental perspective. Recombinant DNA technology for the production of bioactive peptides is also widely used but tends to be restricted at present to the production of large peptides and proteins. Many biologically active peptides, particularly those with sensory and nutritive properties, are short and thus the use of recombinant DNA technology is limited in this regard. Another obvious disadvantage of this approach is strong consumer resistance in certain parts of the world to food products derived from genetically modified organisms. Enzymatic approaches to peptide synthesis offer several advantages. Such systems are capable of producing large quantities of short peptides and enjoy relatively inexpensive production costs compared to chemical methods. In addition, substrates, reagents and reaction conditions are non-hazardous and this combination of factors has made enzymatic synthesis of peptides an attractive choice for the production of food or feed additives.

Systems based upon such technology obviously vary in complexity from single step/single enzyme reactions to multistage processes involving several enzymes and complex protected and activated substrates together with deprotection and activation procedures. At a basic level, however, simple hydrolysis using proteases is an attractive means of obtaining better functional properties of food proteins without harming their nutritional value. Quite apart from the release of bioactive peptides of the types discussed previously, the degradation of food into peptides of varying chain lengths generally renders the product more soluble and digestible. However, other functional properties such as viscosity, emulsification capacity and water absorption capacity are also influenced; and by choosing the correct hydrolysis parameters, specific improvements in performance can be achieved. In addition, the food protein in question may contain components with undesirable organoleptic properties and hydrolysis generally facilitates the removal of such components. Indeed, the specific property of taste offers a good example of how a substrate/enzyme combination may be chosen and reaction conditions altered to produce a peptide hydrolysate with the desired characteristics. As discussed earlier, glutamate-containing peptides impart favourable taste characteristics in protein hydrolysates and are used in a variety of human food applications and as palatability enhancers in certain animal feeds. Although there will be a proportion of free glutamic acid released when proteins are hydrolyzed, this will obviously depend on the method of hydrolysis and the actual proportion of glutamate residues present in the substrate protein. It makes sense, therefore, to select substrates which contain a high concentration of glutamate residues and, as shown in Table 3, this can vary considerably among protein sources that one might expect to be almost identical e.g., maize gluten versus wheat gluten. Likewise, commercial proteases normally used for peptide production are not usually well endowed with glutaminase activity. However, several fungal peptidases possess significant glutaminase activity which makes them extremely valuable in the production of highly flavoured hydrolysates. As such it is somewhat surprising that microbially-derived peptidases are often overlooked in the selection processes for enzymes suited to bioactive peptide production.

Table 3.   Typical values for glutamic acid content of proteins.

| Protein substrate | Glutamic acid content approximate % (w/v) |
|---|---|
| Casein | 22 |
| Fish | 16 |
| Gelatine | 11 |
| Haemoglobin | 8 |
| Maize gluten | 25 |
| Meat | 15 |
| Soya flour | 20 |
| Wheat gluten | 40 |
| Whey protein | 20 |

## Conclusions

Peptides have many diverse physiological functions. Activities thus far identified range from antimicrobial and preservative properties to flavour enhancement. From a nutritional perspective, the importance of peptide-bound *versus* free amino acids is well established if not completely understood and offers exciting possibilities for enhancing dietary nitrogen utilization in humans and animals. It is probable that only a fraction of the true potential of biologically active peptides has been realised and tremendous scope exists to develop new products for the food and pharmaceutical areas. Production processes for bioactive peptides are varied. One rapidly developing area of bioactive peptide production is that of enzymatic peptide synthesis that has the added advantage of utilising natural substrates and reagents and, as such, physiologically active peptides destined for use as food or feed additives.

## References

Backwell, F.R.C. 1998. Circulating peptides and their role in milk protein synthesis. In: Peptides in Mammalian Protein Metabolism. (G.K. Grimble and F.R.C. Backwell, eds). Portland Press, London, 69–77.

Chan, K.M., E.A. Decker and W.J. Means. 1993. Extraction and activity of carnosine, a naturally occurring antioxidant in beef muscle. J. Food. Sci. 58:1–4.

Delves-Broughton, J. 1990. Nisin and its uses. Food Technol. 44:100–117.

Dionysius, D.A. and J.M. Milne. 1997. Antibacterial peptides of bovine lactoferrin: purification and characterization. J. Dairy Sci. 80:667–674.

Frokjaer, S. 1994. Uses of hydrolysates for protein supplementation. Food Technol. 48:86–88.

Gardner, M.L.G. 1994. In: The Physiology of the Gastrointestinal Tract. L.R. Johnson, ed). Raven Press, New York, 1795–1820.

Gardner, M.L.G. 1995. In: Absorption of Orally Administered Enzymes. M.L.G. Gardner and K.J. Steffens, eds). Springer-Verlag, Berlin, 1–7.

Gardner, M.L.G. 1998. Transmucosal passage of intact peptides. In: Peptides in Mammalian Protein Metabolism. (G.K. Grimble and F.R.C. Backwell, eds). Portland Press, London, 11–29.

Grenby, T.H. 1991. Intense sweeteners for the food industry: An overview. Trends Food Sci. Technol. 2:2–6.

Hancock, R.E. and R.Lehrer. 1998. Cationic peptides: A new source of antibiotics. Trends Biotechnol. 16:82–87.

Iyengar, R. and A.J. McEvily. 1992. Anti-browning agents: Alternatives to the use of sulfites in foods. Trends Food Sci. Technol. 3:60–64.

Kayser, H. and H. Meisel. 1996. Circulation of human peripheral blood lymphocytes by bioactive peptides derived from bovine milk proteins. FEBS Lett. 383: 18–20.

Kleinkauf, H. and H. Von-Doehren. 1988. Peptide antibiotics, ($\beta$-lactams and related compounds. Crit. Rev. Biotechnol. 8:1–32.

Lewis, M.E., H. Khachaturian and J.M. Walker. 1984. Endogenous opioids – biological functions. Ann. Rev. Neurosci. 7: 223–255.

Maltz, M.A. 1981. In: Protein Food Supplements. (M.A. Maltz. ed.). Noyes Data Corporation, New Jersey, 20–46.

Maubois, J.L. and J. Leonil. 1989. Peptides du lait a activite biologique. Lait 69:245–269.

Maubois, J.L. J.Leonil., R.Trouve and S.Bouhallab. 1991. Les Peptides du lait a activite physiologique. III. Peptides du lait a effect cardiovasculaire. Activities antithrombotique et antihypertensive. Lait 71: 249–255.

Meisel, H. 1997. Biochemical properties of regulatory peptides derived from milk proteins. Biopoly. 43:119–128.

Meisel, H. and E. Schlimme. 1990. Milk proteins: precursors of bioactive peptides. Trends Food Sci. Technol. 2:41–43.

Mullally, M.M., H. Meisel and R.J. Fitzgerald. 1997. Identification of a novel angiotensin-I-converting enzyme inhibitory peptide corresponding to a tryptic fragment of bovine lactoglobulin. FEBS Lett. 402: 99–101.

Pokorny, J. 1991. Natural antioxidants for food use. Trends Food Sci. Technol. 2:223–227.

Schmidl, M.K., S.L. Taylor and J.A. Nordlee. 1994. Use of hydrolysate-based products in special medical diets. Food Technol. 48: 77–80.

Siemensma, A.D., W.J. Weijer and H.J. Bak. 1993. The importance of peptide lengths in hypoallergenic infant formulae. Trends Food Sci. Technol. 4:16–21.

Snyder, S.H. and R.B. Innis. 1979. Peptide neurotransmitters. Ann. Rev. Biochem. 48: 755–782.

Tamura. M., T. Nakatsuka, M. Tada, Y. Kawasaki, E. Kikuchi and H. Okai. 1988. The relationship between taste and primary structure of the "Delicious" peptide from beef soup. Agric. Bio. Chem. 53: 319–325.

Webb, K.E., J.C. Matthews and D.B. DiRenzo. 1992. Peptide absorption: A review of current concepts and future perspectives. J. Anim. Sci. 70:3248–3257.

Webb, K.E. and J.C. Matthews. 1998. Peptide absorption and its significance in ruminant protein metabolism. In: Peptides in Mammalian Protein Metabolism. (G.K. Grimble and F.R.C. Backwell, eds). Portland Press, London, 1–10.

Yamasaki, Y. and K. Maekawa. 1978. A peptide with delicious taste. Agric. Biol. Chem. 42:1761–1765.

Yoshikawa, M., K. Kishi and M. Takahashi. 1993. Immunocirculating peptide derived from soybean protein. Ann. NY Acad. Sci. 685:375–376.

# APPLICATIONS FOR A NON-GMO PHYTASE PRODUCED USING SURFACE CULTURE FERMENTATION

# Enzyme production using surface culture fermentation

SUE E. NOKES

*Department of Biosystems and Agricultural Engineering, University of Kentucky, Lexington, Kentucky, USA*

## Introduction: industrial enzyme use

Enzymes are biological products (usually proteins) that act as catalysts. Enzymes lower the activation energy of the reaction catalyzed and therefore accelerate the reaction on the order of $10^{10}$ times. After the reaction is completed the enzyme is released and is typically available for reuse in the process. Because enzymes highly accelerate reactions, they are widely used in industry to improve process performance and lower costs. Figure 1 presents the breakdown of enzyme use by industry. Roughly half of the enzymes purchased are used in food-related industries including starch processing, dairy, brewing, juice clarifying, milling, and baking. Detergents represent the other major market for industrial enzymes. The textile/paper industries, leather and feed industry constitute the remaining significant markets for enzymes.

Industrial enzyme production is growing rapidly due to the specificity and environmental compatibility of enzyme-catalyzed processes. The US market for industrial enzymes was an estimated $390 million in 1997 and is expected to grow to $685 million by 2006 (Wrotnowski, 1997). Food processing enzymes, predominately α-amylases, glucose isomerase and pectinases, are expected to account for $214 million of the projected enzyme market in 2006. This represents an average annual projected growth rate of 2.4% per year. The detergent enzyme market is expected to experience a 10% annual growth rate during the same period. This growth will most likely be achieved through improved lipases, subtilisin, other proteases and cellulases. Wrotnowski (1997) reported that pulp and paper processing is frequently cited as the next major market for industrial enzymes with an anticipated growth of 15% per year. Xylanases are the major type of enzyme used in this market sector, along with cellulases. Among new applications for enzymes are novel types of enzymes to be used as digestive aids for food and feed supplements.

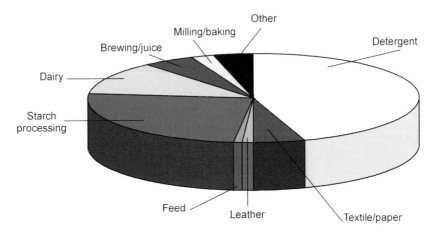

**Figure 1.** Breakdown of industrial enzyme use by industry.

## Enzyme production methods

SUBMERGED FERMENTATION

Table 1 lists some common commercially-important enzymes, the source organisms and the typical applications for the enzyme. Microbially-produced enzymes account for 90% of all enzymes produced for industrial purposes.

Submerged liquid fermentation is traditionally used in the United States for the production of microbially-derived enzymes (Bailey and Ollis, 1986). Submerged fermentation involves submerging the microorganism in an aqueous solution that contains nutrients. Process control is achieved through measuring and adjusting the agitation rate, pH, dissolved oxygen and temperature of the media. These variables are controlled so as to achieve maximum growth rate of the organism or to achieve maximum yields of product. The submerged fermentation reactors can be sterilized and the entire fermentation process is conducted aseptically.

SURFACE CULTURE FERMENTATION

*Definition and history of surface culture fermentation*
An alternative fermentation process known as solid state, or surface culture, fermentation refers to the growth of microorganisms on solid materials without the presence of free liquid (Cannel and Moo-Young, 1980). Figure 2 is a schematic of the interface between the microorganisms and the solid substrate particles. Water is bound to the substrate particle. Microorganisms use the water to grow and to break down the substrate for nutrients. Air and water vapor circulate through the particles, either by natural or

**Table 1. Industrially important enzymes, source organisms, and typical applications[1].**

| Name | Source organism | Application |
| --- | --- | --- |
| Amylase | *Bacillus subtilis, Aspergillus niger* | Starch hydrolysis, glucose production |
| Glucoamylase | *A. niger, Rhizopus niveus,* Endomycopsis | Saccharification of starch, glucose production |
| Trypsin | Animal pancreas | Meat tenderizer, beer haze removal |
| Papain | Papaya | Digestive aid, meat tenderizer, medical applications |
| Pepsin | Animal stomach | Digestive aid, meat tenderizer |
| Rennet | Calf stomach | Cheese manufacturing |
| Glucose isomerase | *Flavobacterium arborescens, B. coagulans, L. brevis* | Isomerization of glucose to fructose |
| Penicillinase | *B. subtilis* | Degradation of penicillin |
| Glucose oxidase | *A. niger* | Glucose conversion to gluconic acid, dried-egg manufacturing |
| Lipases | *Rhizopus pancreas* | Hydrolysis of lipids, flavoring and digestive aid |
| Invertase | *S. cerevisiae* | Hydrolysis of sucrose |
| Pectinase | *A. oryzae, A. niger, A. flavus* | Clarification of fruit juices, hydrolysis of pectin |
| Cellulase | *Trichoderma viride* | Cellulose hydrolysis |
| Xylanase | *Trichoderma longibrachiatum* | Hemicellulose hydrolysis |
| Phytase | *Aspergillus niger* | Degradation of phytic acid |

[1]Shuler amd Kargi, 1992.

forced aeration. Because there is no free liquid (i.e., because the substrate is not standing in water), oxygen can more easily move to the microorganisms than in a liquid submerged fermentation system.

Surface culture fermentation is not a new idea. Three traditional surface culture fermentation products which are still common today are 1) fermented oriental foods, 2) mold-ripened cheese, and 3) compost (Cannel and Moo-Young, 1980). Fermented foods such as soy sauce and miso have been prepared by surface culture fermentation for thousands of years in Japan, China, Indonesia, and other countries in Southeast Asia. The process of surface culture fermentation was active in North America when in 1914 a process was introduced to produce moldy bran to replace malt in distilleries. The liquor produced from this process had an off taste and surface culture fermentation was abandoned for this purpose (Cannel and Moo-Young, 1980; Jain, 1995). Surface culture fermentation was finally

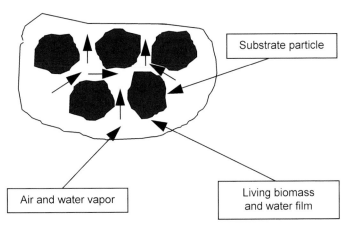

**Figure 2.** Schematic of the surface culture fermentation process.

abandoned altogether in the US during World War II after the development of submerged culture fermentation, which efficiently produced large quantities of penicillin (Cannel and Moo-Young, 1980). The renewed interest in surface culture methods is due to the recognition that many microorganisms, including genetically-modified organisms (GMOs), may produce their end products more cost efficiently using this technique.

While surface culture fermentation has not recently been used commercially in the US, the technology has advanced in some countries, notably Japan, to the point where automated fermentation plants have been established that have significant economic advantages over conventional submerged culture processes. Surface culture production of enzymes on an industrial scale is of interest for two major reasons. First, surface culture has the potential to produce large quantities of inexpensive enzymes, which are essential for use in food and fiber processing industries (Chen and Wayman, 1991). Secondly, surface culture fermentation is a proven technology for waste reduction and/or beneficial reuse and presents an alternative to industries currently facing limited disposal options for organic waste (Evans, 1983).

### The surface culture fermentation process

The steps involved in surface culture fermentation consist generically as follows (Lonsane *et al.,* 1985):

1. Raise inoculum for the surface culture fermentation, either by submerged fermentation or from previous surface culture. Inoculum may be spores or vegetative material.
2. Prepare the solid substrate. This includes adjusting the particle size if necessary, drying to the required water content, and/or adding nutrients and adjusting the pH.
3. Sterilize (or at least pasteurize) the substrate. Adjust to optimal water content.
4. Inoculate the moist solids as shown in Figure 3.

5.  Incubate the moist solids in a culture vessel or chamber. A tray chamber suitable for surface culture fermentation is shown in Figure 4.
6.  Maintain environmental conditions near optimal for microbial growth.
7.  Harvest the solids. Trays which have completed the fermentation process and are ready for harvest are shown in Figure 5.
8.  Dry the solids or extract the product from the solids.
9.  Further downstream processing if necessary.

### Surface culture fermentation bioreactors

Ramana Murthy *et al.* (1993) stated that one of the major reasons why surface culture fermentation has not been used extensively for industrial applications is the lack of information on efficient bioreactor design. They performed an exhaustive literature search and concluded that there is a serious dearth of information on different features of bioreactor design.

Tray and packed-bed bioreactors are used. In a tray reactor, substrate is placed in trays (Figure 6). The trays are placed on racks, which are placed in a controlled environment room. The packed bed (or deep bed) fermentor (Figure 7) has been viewed as the most viable design for widespread industrial adoption, partly because the forced aeration allows for better control of heat removal and oxygen and substrate water content (Durand *et al.*, 1993; Gumbira- Sa'id *et al.*, 1993). However without agitation, the pressure drop through the substrate increases significantly during mycelial growth.

Durand *et al.* (1993) demonstrated the feasibility of intermittently agitating a deep-bed reactor for protein enrichment of sugar beet pulp. Intermittent agitation kept the pressure drop low throughout the fermentation cycle, yet did not break mycelia sufficiently to affect growth. Substrate depth in the bed was reported in this work to be a critical design parameter.

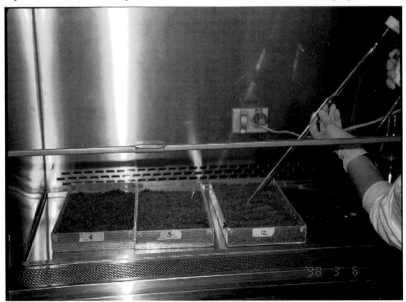

**Figure 3.** Inoculating trays of surface culture fermentation in the laboratory.

**Figure 4.** Tray chamber for surface culture fermentation in the laboratory.

## Advantages of surface culture fermentation

Surface culture fermentation presents many advantages over submerged culture processes, which has fueled renewed interest. One advantage is that the process is typically conducted on readily available, inexpensive substrates. Typically surface culture fermentation is conducted on unrefined agricultural residues. Commonly used substrates include wheat bran, wheat straw, cereal grains, rice hull, and sugar beet pulp. In addition to reducing the cost of producing the product, use of these substrates for surface culture fermentation represents a new use for agricultural residues, and results in value-added products.

Surface culture fermentation typically requires a lower capital investment because very often the equipment and process do not need absolute sterility. Most surface culture fermentation processes perform well under 'semi-sterile' conditions that do not require the technologically sophisticated equipment that sterile cultivations require. The less stringent need for aseptic

**Figure 5.** Trays of fermented wheat bran ready for harvest.

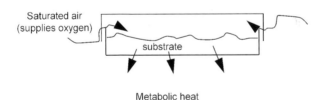

**Figure 6.** Schematic of the surface culture fermentation process in a tray reactor.

conditions results in part from the restricted availability of water in the surface culture fermentation system. The lower water activity selects against undesirable bacterial and yeast contaminants. Along with lower capital costs, surface culture fermentation may require less energy input because it is easier to aerate than submerged cultures. The interparticle spaces allow transfer of fresh air to thin films of water at the substrate surfaces, which allows rapid oxygen transfer. Submerged culture fermentation requires sparging of the oxygen into the aqueous medium, which is difficult due to the low solubility of oxygen in liquid water. Also continuous mixing

457

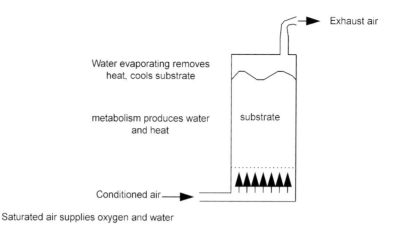

**Figure 7.** Schematic of deep bed fermentor for surface culture fermentation.

is generally not needed in surface culture fermentation. Occasional stirring is typically sufficient (Cannel and Moo-Young, 1980).

Another distinct advantage of surface culture fermentation is that the low moisture levels may favor the production of products which may not be produced (or produced in small quantities) in submerged culture. Evans and Wang (1984) reported a ten-fold increase in red pigment produced in surface culture over that produced in a submerged culture fermentation. Additionally, products may have different properties when produced in surface culture rather than in submerged fermentation. Deschamps and Huet (1984) reported that glucosidase produced in surface culture was more thermostable than that produced in submerged culture fermentation. In addition, surface culture fermentation provided cultivation conditions which favor the production of enzyme complexes more readily than in submerged culture. The complex substrate used in surface culture fermentation requires more diverse enzymes for degradation than does the more refined substrate typically used in submerged culture, thereby encouraging the organism to produce a wider array of enzymes.

Surface culture fermentation generally results in higher volumetric productivity due to high concentration of substrate per unit volume of the reactor. The concentrated substrate allows smaller reactors to be used in surface culture compared to submerged fermentation to produce the same amount of product. Smaller reactor volumes result in lower capital and operating costs (Kumar and Lonsane, 1987).

Downstream processing and waste disposal are often simplified in surface culture fermentation compared to submerged cultures (Mitchel and Lonsane, 1992). If drying is required, less water in the original process results in less drying required for the finished product. Some products are recovered through solvent extraction and less solvent is typically required in surface culture fermentation than in submerged culture processes due in part to the higher volumetric productivity in surface culture.

*Challenges for surface culture fermentation*
Surface culture fermentation has several challenges that have restricted the adoption of this process in the past. These difficulties need to be addressed if it is to be widely adopted.

A major problem with surface culture is that many important basic scientific and engineering aspects are yet poorly characterized (Mitchel and Lonsane, 1992), especially in contrast to submerged culture. Much of the work to date is empirical. Little is known even about the existing commercial surface culture fermentation processes because of the proprietary nature of the information. Process monitoring and control is well established for submerged culture, but not for surface culture fermentation. In surface culture fermentation scientists encounter many challenges even to monitor the process. Sensors and probes developed to monitor submerged fermentations typically are not adequate for surface cultures because of the solid substrate. In addition, surface culture fermentation is by nature a spatially heterogeneous process because of the solid substrate. It is very difficult to ensure even distribution of any substance during the process even with agitation, and as a result pH, moisture, and oxygen control is more difficult.

Probably the challenge most often cited in connection with surface culture fermentation is the difficulty in removing the metabolic heat generated during microbial growth in a large-scale reactor. This can be more difficult in surface culture than in submerged culture because of the limited heat transfer through the solid substrate (Cannel and Moo-Young, 1980). Metabolic heat accumulation can result in microbial death if left uncontrolled.

Surface culture fermentation is restricted to organisms that can tolerate low water activities. Therefore the number of microorganisms and products that are suitable for surface culture fermentation is smaller than for submerged culture. Most applications for surface culture involve fungi, although more recent studies have investigated the use of bacteria and yeast in surface culture fermentation (Kumar and Lonsane, 1987; Lonsane *et al.,* 1985). In addition, culture times are often longer in surface than in submerged culture fermentation due to the lower specific growth rates of the microorganisms (Mitchell and Lonsane, 1992). However despite low growth rates and poor substrate conversion, volumetric productivity may be similar or higher in surface culture due to the highly concentrated solid substrate (Mitchell and Lonsane, 1992).

# References

Bailey, J.E. and D.F. Ollis. 1986. Biochemical engineering fundamentals. Second Edition. McGraw Hill Publishing Company. New York. p. 984.

Cannel, E. and M. Moo-Young. 1980. Solid-state fermentation systems. Process Biochemistry. June/July. pp. 2–7.

Chen, S. and M. Wayman. 1991. Cellulase production induced by carbon sources derived from waste newspaper. Process Biochemistry 26:93–100.

Deschamps, F. and M.C. Huet. 1984. β-glucosidase production in agitated solid fermentation, a study of its properties. Biotechnol. Lett. 6:451–456.

Durand, A., R. Renaud, S. Almarza, J. Maratray, M. Diez and C. Desgranges. 1993. Solid state fermentation reactors: From lab scale to pilot plant. Biotechnol. Adv. 11:591–598.

Evans, C.W. 1983. Rayonier produces animal feed from secondary sludge at sulfite mill. Pulp & Paper. March. pp. 124–126.

Evans, P.J. and H. Y. Wang. 1984. Pigment production from immobilized Monascus sp. Utilizing polymeric resin adsorption. Appl. Environ. Microbiol. 47:1323–1326.

Gumbira-Sa'id, E., P.F. Greenfield, D.A. Mitchell and H.W. Doelle. 1993 Operational parameters for packed beds in solid-state cultivation. Biotechnol. Adv. 11: 599–610.

Jain, A. 1995. Production of xylanase by thermophilic *Melanocarpus albomyces* IIS-68. Process Biochemistry. 30(8):705–709.

Kumar, P.K.R. and B.K. Lonsane. 1987. Potential of fed-batch culture in solid state fermentation for produciton of gibberellic acid. Biotechnol. Lett. 9:179–182.

Mitchell, D.A. and B.K. Lonsane. 1992. Definition, characteristics and potential. In: Solid Substrate Cultivation. (H.W. Doelle, D.A. Mitchell and C.E. Rolz, eds) Elsevier Applied Biotechnology Series. p. 466

Lonsane, B.K., N.P. Ghildyal, S. Budiatman and S.V. Ramakrishna. 1985. Engineering aspects of solid state fermentation. Enzyme Microbiol. Technol. 7:258–265.

Ramana Murthy, M.V., M. S. Thakur and N.G. Karanth. 1993. Monitoring of biomass in solid state fermentaiton using light reflectance. Biosensors and Bioelectronics. 8:59–63.

Shuler, M.L. and F. Kargi. 1992. Bioprocess Engineering: basic concepts Prentice Hall. Englewood Cliffs, New Jersey. pp. 479.

Wrotnowski, C. 1997. Unexpected niche applications for industrial enzymes drives market growth. Gentetic Engineering News. February, 1997. pp. 14.

# Feeding to reduce nutrient excretion: effects of phytase on phosphorus and other nutrients

E. T. KORNEGAY

*Department of Animal and Poultry Sciences, Virginia Polytechnic Institute and State University, Blacksburg, Virginia, USA*

## Introduction

Phytase may well be the 'miracle enzyme' of the 1990s just as soybeans were described as the 'miracle crop' for producing high quality plant protein in the 1960s. Dietary addition of microbial phytase or the inclusion of high phytase ingredients in pig and poultry diets is now well documented to release a large portion of the naturally occurring phytate phosphorus (P), and thus greatly reduce the amount of inorganic phosphorus that must be added to meet the animal's requirement. The net result is a reduction in phosphorus excretion that can range from 20 to 50%.

Microbial phytase was initially used as a tool to reduce phosphorus excretion because modern commercial production of pigs and poultry has led to large amounts of manure that when applied to land in excess results in accumulation of nutrients in and on the soil. This potential for environmental pollution continues to lead to legislation in many countries requiring nutrient management plans for manure.

It is becoming increasingly clear that the use of adequate amounts of phytase in most pig and poultry diets results in improved availability of calcium, zinc, protein/amino acids and energy. This is because seeds or products from seeds, which are the major ingredients in pig and poultry diets, contain 60–80% of the phosphorus in the form of phytic acid or phytate. Phytate is known to complex with other nutrients. Thus, the unavailable phytate phosphorus and nutrients complexed with it cannot be utilized and are excreted.

This chapter will provide a short review of phytate, phytase, and the effectiveness of microbial phytase in pig and poultry diets for enhancing the utilization of phosphorus, calcium, zinc, amino acids/protein and energy so as to reduce nutrient excretion. Factors that influence phytase activity will be briefly discussed.

# Phytate and bioavailability of nutrients

Major ingredients in commercial pig and poultry diets are seeds (cereal grains) or products from seeds (oilseed meal and grain by-products). A large portion (60–80%) of the phosphorus in these ingredients occurs in the form of phytates, the salts of phytic acid (Table 1). Detailed information on the phytic acid content of various foods and feedstuffs can be found in reviews by Oberleas and Harland (1981), Ingelmann *et al.* (1993), Eeckhout and DePaepe (1994), and Ravindran *et al.* (1995b). The bioavailability of phytate phosphorus is generally very low for pigs and poultry because they have limited capability to utilize phytate phosphorus (Table 2). Bioavailability estimates of phosphorus in corn and soybean meal for pigs and poultry range from 10 to 40% (Nelson, 1967; Calvert *et al.*, 1978; Jongbloed and Kemme 1990; Cromwell, 1992).

The phytic acid molecule has a high phosphorus content (28.2%) and large chelating potential (Figure 1). Phytic acid can form a wide variety of insoluble salts with di- and trivalent cations such as calcium, zinc, copper, cobalt, manganese, iron and magnesium at neutral pH (Maddaiah *et al.*, 1963; Vohra *et al.*, 1965; Oberleas, 1973). This binding potentially renders these minerals unavailable for intestinal absorption. Zinc may be the trace element whose bioavailability is most influenced by phytate (Pallauf and Rimbach, 1995). Phytic acid may have a negative influence on dietary protein and amino acids (O'Dell and de Borland, 1976; Knuckles *et al.*, 1985) and inhibits proteolytic enzymes such as pepsin and trypsin under

Table 1. Phytate phosphorus content and phytase activity of some common feed ingredients.

| Ingredient | Phytate P[a] (%) | Phytate P[a] (% of total P) | Phytase activity[b] (units/kg) |
|---|---|---|---|
| *Cereals and by-products* | | | |
| Corn | 0.24 | 72 | 15 |
| Wheat | 0.27 | 69 | 1193 |
| Sorghum | 0.24 | 66 | 24 |
| Barley | 0.27 | 64 | 582 |
| Oats | 0.29 | 67 | 40 |
| Wheat bran | 0.92 | 71 | 2957 |
| | | | |
| *Oilseed meals* | | | |
| Soybean meal | 0.39 | 60 | 8 |
| Canola meal | 0.70 | 59 | 16 |
| Sunflower meal | 0.89 | 77 | 60 |
| Peanut meal | 0.48 | 80 | 3 |
| Cottonseed meal | 0.84 | 70 | NA |

[a]Data adapted from Ravindran (1996) and Ravindran *et al.* (1994, 1995b).
[b]Data from Eeckhout and De Paepe (1994). One unit is defined as that amount of phytase that liberates inorganic phosphorus from a 5.1 mM Na-phytate solution at a rate of 1 μmol/min at pH 5.5 and 37°C (98.6°F).

**Table 2. Bioavailability of phosphorus for pigs and nonphytate phosphorus for poultry.**

| Feedstuff | Bioavailability of P for pigs[a,b] | Nonphytate-P for poultry[c] |
|---|---|---|
| | (%) | (% of total) |
| *Cereal grains* | | |
| Corn | 12 | 28 |
| Oats | 23 | 33 |
| Barley | 31 | 36 |
| Triticale | 46 | 33 |
| Wheat | 50 | 31 |
| Corn, high moisture | 53 | – |
| | | |
| *High protein meals - plant origin* | | |
| Peanut meal | 12 | 21 |
| Canola meal | 21 | 26 |
| Soybean meal, dehulled | 25 | 35 |
| Soybean meal, 44% protein | 35 | 40 |

[a]Adapted from Cromwell (1992).
[b]Relative to the availability of P in monosodium phosphate, which is given a value of 100.
[c]NRC (1994).

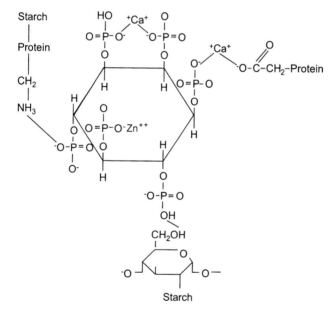

**Figure 1.** Structure of phytate and possible bonds (after Thompson, 1988).

gastrointestinal conditions (Singh and Krikorian, 1982). Phytate-protein or phytate-mineral-protein complexes may reduce the utilization of protein.

Starch is also known to be complexed by phytate. The *in vitro* hydrolysis of either wheat or bean starch incubated with human saliva was retarded when sodium phytate was included in the mixture, but digestion was restored when calcium was added with the sodium phytate (Yoon *et al.*, 1983; Thompson, 1986; Thompson *et al.*, 1987).

The low availability of phytate phosphorus poses two problems for producers: 1) the need to supplement inorganic phosphorus and add higher levels of other nutrients to the diet to ensure that the animal's needs are met, and 2) the excretion of large amounts of phosphorus and other nutrients in the manure.

## Phytases

Phytases are known to occur widely in microorganisms, plants and certain animal tissues (Nayini and Markakis, 1986; Nys *et al.*, 1996). Phytase of microbial origin (3-phytase, E.C. 3.1.3.8) hydrolyzes the phosphate group at the $C_3$ position first, whereas phytase of plant origin (6-phytase, E.C.3.1.3.26) acts first at the $C_6$ position (Pallauf and Rimbach, 1995). Phytase produced by Aspergillus has two pH optima: one at pH 2.5 and the other at pH 5.5. Wheat phytase has only one pH optimum, at 5.2. Aspergillus phytase has been shown to be more effective per unit of activity than wheat phytase, probably due to these differences (Eeckhout and De Paepe, 1996). At least three abbreviations are used in the literature for phytase activity: FTU, PU and U. The latter, U/kg, will be used in this chapter. Contents of the stomach and intestine of pigs (Jongbloed *et al.*, 1992; Yi and Kornegay, 1996) and crop, stomach and small intestine of chickens (Liebert *et al.*, 1993) have negligible phytase activity unless supplemental phytase is fed. The significance of endogenous phytase and phytase produced by exogenous microorganisms and resident bacteria is probably negligible.

It has been known for more than 50 years that plant phytase has the ability to hydrolyze phytate (McCance and Widdowson, 1944; Hill and Tyler, 1954); and its effectiveness for improving phosphorus digestibility in pigs and poultry has been clearly shown (Nelson, 1967; Newton *et al.*, 1983; Bagheri and Gueguen, 1985). Phytase activity has been reported in a wide range of seeds such as rice, wheat, barley, corn, rye, soybean and oil seeds (Gibson and Ullah, 1990; Eeckhout and De Paepe, 1994); however, phytase activity of seeds varies greatly among species of plants (Table 1). With the exception of wheat, rye and triticale, most dormant seeds contain very low phytase activity. Phytase activity in corn and soybean meal is so low that it is not of practical importance. Eeckhout and De Paepe (1991) reported that microbial phytase was 74% more efficient *in vivo* (fed to pigs) than phytase in wheat middlings when added at an equal *in vitro* activity level (500 U/kg). They suggest that microbial phytase may be more active at pH levels present in the stomach than wheat phytase.

Microbial phytases are found in numerous bacteria, yeast and fungi

(Harland and Morris, 1995), but Aspergillus, a genus of Ascomycetous fungi, is probably the one most widely used (Irving and Cosgrove, 1974; Nair and Duvnjak, 1991). Research in the late 1960s and early 1970s by Nelson *et al.* (1971) showed that microbial phytase was effective in improving phytate phosphorus availability for chickens. However, the cost of adding the enzyme was very high and the lack of environmental pressure to reduce phosphorus excretion delayed interest in commercial application until the late 1980s.

The development of commercial phytase that could be economically used in pig and poultry diets was probably a result of advancements in biotechnology that led to genetically modifying fungi, and/or advances in fermentation technology. The mandate that Dutch livestock farmers had to reduce phosphorus excretion was a driving force.

Although some feed ingredients contain native phytase activity, steam-pelleting used in the manufacture of many commercial pig and poultry feeds results in significant losses of this intrinsic phytase activity. Because of variation in phytase activity among and within plant species, damaging effects of pelleting during feed manufacturing, and the lack of availability of feed ingredients of high phytase activity, the presence of residual phytase activity often may not be considered in diet formulation when feeds are pelleted.

There are at least four commercially available microbial phytases, two obtained by fermentation of a genetically modified Aspergillus (Natuphos® and Novo phytase), and two obtained by extraction of media with Aspergillus (Finase™ and Alltech Allzyme Phytase). Patents influence the availability of these in some countries. Most products are available in a powder or granular form and as a liquid. Research is underway to develop more heat stable phytases that could withstand high temperatures during pelleting.

Based on performance, phosphorus utilization and bone mineralization, and general necropsy and histologic examination of liver, kidney and tibial tissues of pigs and poultry fed 5–20-fold higher than recommended phytase levels (500 U/kg), no adverse effects of feeding modified microbial phytase were observed. Small positive improvements in performance, bone mineralization and digestibility of phosphorus were observed at the highest phytase levels (Zhang *et al.*, 1998a,b; Kornegay *et al.*, Virginia Polytechnic Institute and State University, 1998, unpublished data).

Results from several post-slaughter and cannulation experiments with pigs have shown that dietary phytase, whether from plants (Gueguen *et al.*, 1968; Schulz and Oslage, 1972; Lantzsch *et al.*, 1992; Kemme *et al.*, 1998) or fungal sources (Jongbloed *et al.*, 1992; Mroz *et al.*, 1994; Yi and Kornegay, 1996) was predominantly active in the stomach. In pigs, phytase activity or breakdown of phytate phosphorus was generally very low or was not observed in the lower small intestine. Significant amounts of phytate phosphorus (40–50% of the total) would be passed into the large intestine where most of it would be hydrolyzed, but little of the hydrolyzed phosphorus would be absorbed (Jongbloed *et al.*, 1992; Lantzsch *et al.*, 1992; Kemme *et al.*, 1998). Liebert *et al.* (1993) reported in chickens that 69–86% of added microbial phytase activity was detected in the crop and that 31–38% of added phytase activity was detected in the proventriculus. No phytase activity was detected in the small intestine. The disappearance of phytate phosphorus in the crop and proventriculus supports the observation that the crop and proventriculus are the main sites of phytase activity in poultry.

# Effectiveness of microbial phytase in poultry and pig diets

ABILITY OF PHYTASE TO IMPROVE PHOSPHORUS
BIOAVAILABILITY

Supplemental microbial phytase is well known for its effectiveness in improving phosphorus availability from plant ingredients containing high levels of phytate phosphorus. Phosphorus digestibilities were generated using 52 pig experiments representing 32 references in a review reported by Kornegay *et al.* (1998a). Also, 23 poultry experiments representing 13 references were used to generate phosphorus retention equations (Kornegay, 1999). A nonlinear response of supplemental phytase on phosphorus digestibility for pigs and phosphorus retention for poultry was observed (Figure 2). The magnitude of the response per unit of phytase was much greater at the lower phytase levels for both pigs and poultry. This decrease in the magnitude of the response to phytase with increasing amounts of phytase added was previously described in pigs (Kornegay and Qian, 1996; Yi *et al.*, 1996a), broilers (Denbow *et al.*, 1995; Kornegay *et al.*, 1996a) and turkeys (Ravindran *et al.*, 1995a) for growth and bone mineralization.

Digested phosphorus due to microbial phytase supplementation was calculated by multiplying total phosphorus content of the low phosphorus diet (negative control) by the increase in phosphorus digestibility or retention resulting from phytase supplementation (Tables 3 and 4). These values were similar to estimated phosphorus equivalency values of phytase when equivalency values were adjusted downward by the estimated digestibility of inorganic phosphorus that would be replaced by phytase.

For pigs fed 500 U phytase/kg, 0.075% units of phosphorus (0.75 g of P) were digested. In the pig data set, the average total phosphorus level of the low phosphorus diet (negative control) was $0.381 \pm 0.008\%$ (mean $\pm$ SEM) and the calcium (Ca) level was $0.588 \pm 0.020$. The average total Ca:total P ratio was 1.54. For poultry, 0.037% units (0.37 g of P) of phosphorus were estimated to be digested when 500 U phytase/kg were added to the diet. The average total phosphorus level of the low phosphorus diet (negative control) was $0.478 \pm 0.010\%$ (mean $\pm$ SEM) and the calcium level was $0.780 \pm 0.036\%$. The average total Ca:total P ratio was 1.63. Although total phosphorus levels fed are higher and retention coefficients are higher for negative control diets for poultry than for pigs, the

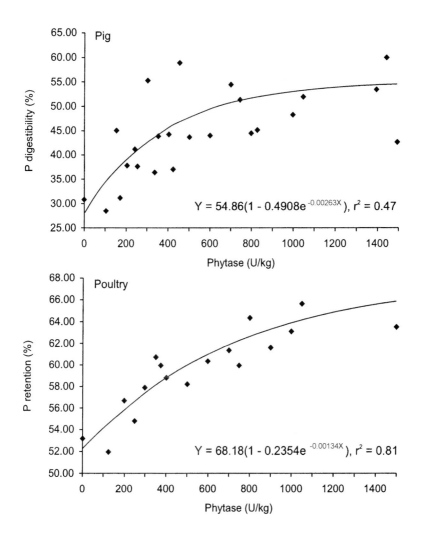

**Figure 2.** Phosphorus digestibility of pigs (top) and retention of poultry (bottom) fed low P, low phytase activity plant-based diets supplemented with microbial phytase (Kornegay *et al.*, 1998a; Kornegay, 1999).

increase of retention coefficients due to microbial supplementation was lower for poultry than the increase of digestibility coefficients for pigs. The percentage utilization of inorganic phosphate appears to be less for poultry than for pigs.

EXCRETION OF PHOSPHORUS

Based on calculations using the digestibility equation from the pig data set, phosphorus excretion can be reduced by 33.2% when 500 U phytase/kg

Table 3. Predicted P digestibility, P digested, and percentage reduction in P excretion based on data generated from the pig data set in this study.

| Supplemental phytase (U/kg) | Total P digestibility[a] (%) | P digestibility[b] by phytase (%) | P digested by phytase[c] (%) | Total P excreted[d] (%) | Decreased P excretion[e] (%) |
|---|---|---|---|---|---|
| 0 | 27.9 | 0 | 0 | 0.275 | 8.3 |
| 100 | 34.2 | 6.2 | 0.024 | 0.251 | 16.3 |
| 200 | 38.9 | 11.0 | 0.042 | 0.233 | 22.3 |
| 250 | 40.9 | 13.0 | 0.049 | 0.225 | 24.8 |
| 300 | 42.6 | 14.7 | 0.056 | 0.219 | 27.0 |
| 350 | 44.1 | 16.2 | 0.062 | 0.213 | 28.9 |
| 400 | 45.5 | 17.5 | 0.067 | 0.208 | 30.6 |
| 450 | 46.6 | 18.7 | 0.071 | 0.203 | 32.1 |
| 500 | 47.6 | 19.7 | 0.075 | 0.200 | 33.2 |
| 550 | 48.5 | 20.6 | 0.078 | 0.196 | 34.5 |
| 600 | 49.3 | 21.4 | 0.081 | 0.193 | 35.5 |
| 650 | 50.0 | 22.1 | 0.084 | 0.191 | 36.4 |
| 700 | 50.6 | 22.7 | 0.086 | 0.188 | 37.1 |
| 750 | 51.1 | 23.2 | 0.088 | 0.186 | 37.8 |
| 800 | 51.6 | 23.6 | 0.090 | 0.184 | 38.4 |
| 900 | 52.3 | 24.4 | 0.093 | 0.182 | 39.4 |
| 1,000 | 52.9 | 25.0 | 0.095 | 0.179 | 40.1 |
| 1,100 | 53.4 | 25.4 | 0.097 | 0.178 | 40.7 |
| 1,200 | 53.7 | 25.8 | 0.098 | 0.176 | 41.1 |
| 1,300 | 54.0 | 26.0 | 0.099 | 0.175 | 41.5 |
| 1,400 | 54.2 | 26.2 | 0.100 | 0.175 | 41.7 |
| 1,500 | 54.3 | 26.4 | 0.101 | 0.174 | 41.9 |

[a]Generated from the equation given in Figure 2 [54.86(1 − 0.4908$e^{-0.00263X}$)].
[b]Calculated by subtracting P digestibility of basal diet without phytase from coefficients at each phytase level.
[c]Calculated by multiplying the P digestibility due to phytase by the average P content (0.381% total P) of the basal diet. The equation of these data is = 0.1026(1 − $e^{-0.00263X}$), where X = phytase level.
[d]Calculated by subtracting total P digestibility coefficients from 100 and multiplying the product by the average P content (0.381% total P) of the basal diet.
[e]Based on an inorganic P digested equation (Y = −0.167 + 0.755X, $r^2$ = 0.24, where X = % P from inorganic source); 0.0245% P was excreted for the 0.1% unit of added inorganic P above the basal diet making the total P excreted by the positive control diet (0.481% total P) equal to 0.2995% P (0.275 + 0.0245). Decreased P excretion was calculated by subtracting the total P excreted by the phytase supplemented diets from the P excreted by the positive control diet (0.2995%) and then dividing by the P excreted on positive control diet and multiplying by 100. For example, at 500 U/kg of phytase, 33.2% =[(0.2995 − 0.200)/(0.2995)*100].

are added to a low phosphorus diet compared with a positive control diet (0.481% P) containing 0.1% units more phosphorus (Table 3). When the phosphorus retention equation from the poultry data set was used to make similar estimates, excretion was reduced 31.9% when 500 U phytase/kg were added to a low phosphorus diet compared with a positive control diet (0.57% dietary P) which would be 0.1% units higher in phosphorus (Table 4). Simply lowering dietary phosphorus by 0.1% will decrease phosphorus excretion about 8.3% in pigs and 18.4% in poultry.

**Table 4.** Predicted P digestibility, P digested, and percentage reduction in P excretion based on data generated from the poultry data set in this study.

| Supplemental phytase (U/kg) | Total P digestibility[a] (%) | P digestibility[b] by phytase (%) | P digested by phytase[c] (%) | Total P excreted[d] (%) | Decreased P excretion[e] (%) |
|---|---|---|---|---|---|
| 0 | 52.1 | 0 | 0 | 0.229 | 18.4 |
| 100 | 54.1 | 2.0 | 0.010 | 0.219 | 21.8 |
| 200 | 55.9 | 3.8 | 0.018 | 0.211 | 24.8 |
| 250 | 56.7 | 4.6 | 0.022 | 0.207 | 26.2 |
| 300 | 57.4 | 5.3 | 0.025 | 0.203 | 27.5 |
| 350 | 58.1 | 6.0 | 0.029 | 0.200 | 28.6 |
| 400 | 58.8 | 6.7 | 0.032 | 0.197 | 29.7 |
| 450 | 59.4 | 7.3 | 0.035 | 0.194 | 30.8 |
| 500 | 60.0 | 7.8 | 0.037 | 0.191 | 31.9 |
| 550 | 60.5 | 8.4 | 0.040 | 0.189 | 32.7 |
| 600 | 61.0 | 8.9 | 0.042 | 0.186 | 33.5 |
| 650 | 61.5 | 9.3 | 0.045 | 0.184 | 34.3 |
| 700 | 61.9 | 9.8 | 0.047 | 0.182 | 35.0 |
| 750 | 62.3 | 10.2 | 0.049 | 0.180 | 35.7 |
| 800 | 62.7 | 10.6 | 0.050 | 0.178 | 36.4 |
| 900 | 63.4 | 11.2 | 0.054 | 0.175 | 37.6 |
| 1,000 | 64.3 | 11.8 | 0.057 | 0.172 | 38.6 |
| 1,100 | 64.7 | 12.4 | 0.059 | 0.170 | 39.5 |
| 1,200 | 65.0 | 12.8 | 0.061 | 0.168 | 40.3 |
| 1,300 | 65.4 | 13.2 | 0.063 | 0.166 | 41.0 |
| 1,400 | 65.7 | 13.6 | 0.065 | 0.164 | 41.6 |
| 1,500 | 66.0 | 13.9 | 0.066 | 0.162 | 42.1 |

[a]Generated from the equation given in Figure 1 $[68.18(1 - 0.2354e^{-0.00134X})]$.
[b]Calculated by subtracting P digestibility of basal diet without phytase from coefficients at each phytase level.
[c]Calculated by multiplying the P digestibility due to phytase by the average P content (0.478% total P) of the basal diet. The equation of these data (%) $= 0.07672(1 - e^{-0.00134X})$, where X = phytase level.
[d]Calculated by subtracting total P digestibility coefficients from 100 and multiplying the product by the average P content (0.478% total P) of the basal diet.
[e]Based on an inorganic P digested (retained) equation ($Y = -0.000936 + 0.484X$, $r^2 = 0.69$, where X = % P from inorganic source); 0.0516% was excreted for 0.1% added inorganic P above the basal diet making the total P excreted by the positive control diet (0.578% total P) equal to 0.2804% P (0.2288 + 0.0516). Decreased P excretion was calculated by subtracting the total P excreted by the phytase supplemented diets from the P excreted by the positive control diet (0.2804%) and then dividing on the P excreted on the positive control diet and multiplying by 100. For example, at 500 U/kg of phytase, 31.9% =[(0.2804 − 0.191)/(0.2804)*100].

## DIGESTED PHOSPHORUS *VS* PHOSPHORUS EQUIVALENCY VALUE OF PHYTASE

Phosphorus equivalency value, a term used to describe the replacement or substitution value of phytase, is defined as the amount of inorganic phosphorus that can be removed by a given amount of added or intrinsic phytase. If one is to directly compare equivalency value of phytase for phosphorus and digested phosphorus, then equivalency values must be adjusted by the estimated digestibility of the inorganic phosphorus sources that phytase replaces. Kornegay *et al.* (1998a) estimated that the phosphorus digestibility of several feed grade phosphorus sources was 76.7% for pigs. The retention of phosphorus from several feed grade sources was estimated to be 46.2% for broilers and turkeys (Kornegay, 1999). Equivalency values (or equations) are usually obtained from nonlinear or linear equations generated from body weight gain, bone mineralization and sometimes digested phosphorus data obtained by feeding multiple levels of phosphorus without phytase addition and multiple levels of added phytase to a low phosphorus diet. These equations are set equal and solved. This procedure was described in detailed by Denbow *et al.* (1995).

For example, some data for pigs suggest an average phosphorus equivalency value of 500 U phytase/kg equals 1.0 g of inorganic phosphorus. The equivalency value of 1.0 g P is multiplied by 76.7% (0.767 g P digested per 1 g of inorganic P fed). The product, 0.767 g P (1 x 0.767), is similar to a digested phosphorus value of 0.75 g (0.075%) obtained from the pig data set shown in Table 3. In poultry, some data suggest that 600 U phytase/kg is equivalent to 1.0 g of inorganic phosphorus. The average phosphorus equivalency of 1.0 g P is multiplied by 46.2% (0.462 g P retained per 1 g of inorganic P). The product is 0.462 g P (1.0 x 0.462). A value of 0.42 g P (0.042%) was obtained from the poultry data set for 600 U phytase/kg (Table 4). Remember that equivalency values must be adjusted by the apparent digestibility of the inorganic phosphorus source being replaced. Jongbloed *et al.* (1996a) estimated that 500 U phytase/kg was equivalent to 0.8 g of digestible phosphorus which was equivalent to 1.0 g P from monocalcium phosphate.

Based on the similarity of digested phosphorus values calculated from equivalency estimates, and values derived from equations generated in the pig and poultry data sets, the estimates of phosphorus excretion should be accurate for a range of situations. However, a larger response than observed in these data sets is possible if careful attention is given to ingredient composition, diet formulation (optimal calcium and phosphorus levels), and quality processing procedures are followed.

RESPONSE OF LAYERS TO PHYTASE SUPPLEMENTATION

In a series of trials reported by Simons *et al.* (1992), Peter and Jeroch (1993), Simons and Versteegh (1993), Vahl *et al.* (1993), Van der Klis *et al.* (1997) and Gordon and Roland (1997), phytase supplementation of a low phosphorus diet for layers was very effective as a replacement for inorganic phosphorus. A range of phosphorus equivalencies, 0.5–1.2 g P as monocalcium phosphate, have been reported for 200–300 U phytase/kg. Van der Klis *et al.* (1997) reported that the effect of phytase supplementation (250 and 500 U/kg) on ileal phosphorus absorption was 12% units greater when added to a low phosphorus basal diet containing 3.0% calcium compared with a low phosphorus basal diet containing 4.0% calcium. Leske and Coon (1998) reported that phytate phosphorus retention was 36.7,

29.0 and 14.8% greater with phytase supplementation (300 U phytase/kg), respectively, for soybean meal, corn, and rice bran, but total phosphorus retention was only 16.6, 16.1 and 7.1% units greater. As has been reported for pigs, broilers and turkeys, the response of phytase supplementation was greater at the lower levels. Phytase supplementation is very effective at releasing phosphorus in layer diets which results in reduced dietary phosphorus levels and reduced phosphorus excretion. The efficiency appears to be greater for layers than for broilers and turkeys. Phytase supplementation of layer diets is also simplified because most diets are fed in a mash form.

## EFFECTS OF PHYTASE ON CALCIUM BIOAVAILABILITY

### Broilers and turkeys
Schoner *et al.* (1991, 1993, 1994) reported improved calcium retention in broilers fed supplemental phytase. In a broiler study designed to measure the effect of phytase on calcium availability, Schoner *et al.* (1994) reported that 500 U of microbial phytase were equivalent to 0.46 g Ca based on body weight gain and phalanx ash. Calcium retention and dry matter digestibility were improved when phytase was added to broiler diets (Kornegay *et al.*, 1996a; 1998c; Yi *et al.*, 1996b). In our study with turkey poults (Kornegay *et al.*, 1996c), estimates based on body weight gain, gain:feed, and digested calcium suggest that 500 U of phytase are equivalent to approximately 0.87 g of calcium. Qian *et al.* (1996b, 1997) reported that both phosphorus and calcium retention were sensitive to the addition of phytase at varying nonphytate levels or Ca:total P ratios. Calcium retention increased linearly as the amount of supplemented phytase increased, and decreased as the Ca:total P ratios became wider and as the level of phosphorus increased.

### Pigs
Radcliffe *et al.* (1995) reported results of two pig trials conducted to determine the effectiveness of microbial phytase for improving calcium bioavailability. Based on these data, Kornegay *et al.* (1996c) estimated calcium equivalency values of 1.08 and 0.38 g Ca per 500 U of microbial phytase for pigs in Trials 1 and 2, respectively, with an average of 0.73 g Ca. Calcium equivalency estimates for phytase were based on daily gain during weeks 3 and 4, digestible calcium and tenth rib ash percentages.

Jongbloed *et al.* (1996b) reported that microbial phytase enhanced not only the apparent total tract digestibility of phosphorus, but also the apparent total tract digestibility of calcium. They estimated that 0.8 g P and between 0.4 and 0.7 g Ca were digested by 500 U phytase /kg. Eeckhout and De Paepe (1991) reported a high positive correlation between calcium and phosphorus digestibilities and phytase supplementation to a low phosphorus pig diet. They suggested that this relationship could be explained by the fact that phytic acid acts as a calcium binding agent in the proximal small intestine. Hydrolysis of phytate in the stomach as a

471

result of phytase activity results in increased digestibility, not only of phosphorus, but indirectly results in increased digestibility of calcium.

## INFLUENCE OF PHYTASE ON ZINC BIOAVAILABILITY

### Broilers and turkeys

The addition of 800 U phytase/kg to a diet containing 27 mg zinc (Zn)/kg increased the retention of zinc and decreased zinc excretion of chicks (Thiel and Weigand, 1992). Thiel *et al.* (1993) reported that the femoral zinc content of chicks fed a diet containing 30 mg Zn/kg plus 700 U of phytase/kg was equal to that of chicks fed a diet containing 39 mg Zn/kg without phytase. Using chicks fed a glucose-soy concentrate diet (13 mg Zn/kg) with multiple levels of added zinc, phytase or 1,25-dihydroxycholecalciferol (di-OH-$D_3$), Biehl *et al.* (1995) reported that both phytase and di-OH-$D_3$ supplementation increased growth rate and tibial zinc to a similar extent. Based on Biehl *et al.* (1995) estimates using tibia zinc, the zinc equivalency of 600 and 1200 U phytase/kg was 3.8 and 5.5 mg, respectively. In contrast, Roberson and Edwards (1994) did not consistently observe an improvement in zinc absorption or retention in broilers when 600 to 750 U phytase/kg was added to a corn-soybean diet containing 32 mg Zn/kg.

In our laboratory, day-old male broilers were fed a corn-soy isolate basal diet containing 20 mg Zn/kg alone and supplemented with multiple levels of zinc and phytase for 21 days (Yi *et al.*, 1996d). Nonlinear or linear response equations of the effects of zinc and phytase levels were generated for body weight gain, feed intake, zinc retention, zinc concentration of toes, tibia, and liver and used to calculate an average zinc equivalency of 5.4 mg Zn/kg for 600 U phytase/kg.

### Pigs

Based on enhanced growth, increased plasma zinc concentration and alkaline phosphatase activity, the bioavailability of zinc for pigs was improved when phytase was added to a low phosphorus (0.3%) and zinc (30 mg/kg) corn-soybean meal diet (Lei *et al.*, 1993). Adding microbial phytase to the diets of young pigs significantly improved apparent absorption of zinc and magnesium (Pallauf *et al.*, 1992). Using a low zinc diet (23 mg Zn/kg) containing 0.8% Ca and 0.62% P, Adeola *et al.* (1995) reported that growth rate and retention of zinc, copper, calcium and phosphorus were increased when 1500 U phytase/kg were added. A zinc equivalency for phytase has not been established for pigs.

## INFLUENCE OF MICROBIAL PHYTASE ON AMINO ACIDS AND NITROGEN BIOAVAILABILITY

Phytate can bind with protein/amino acid (AA) at low and neutral pH (De Rham and Jost, 1979; Cosgrove, 1980; Anderson, 1985; Thompson,

1986; Fretzdorff *et al.*, 1995). Phytate-protein/AA complexes may occur in foodstuffs in the native state and may be formed in the upper gastrointestinal tract. Complexing of phytate with proteolytic enzymes may also occur in the upper gastrointestinal tract. These potential phytate-protein complexes thus may reduce the utilization of proteins and amino acids.

If phytate is hydrolyzed, then its inhibitory effects are reduced. Most of the early research with microbial phytase was conducted to measure the effects of phytase on phosphorus utilization, and when total tract nitrogen digestibility was measured results were inconsistent. Amino acid digestibility was rarely evaluated. Kemme (1998) had a good review in his dissertation.

The opportunity to show improvements in protein/AA utilization is influenced by the dietary level of protein/AA. If the protein/AA retention is at maximum, then the potential to show an improvement is greatly reduced. Furthermore, the use of total tract (fecal) digestibility may not be reliable because of the influence of the microbial population in the large intestine. Ileal digestibility is a more appropriate method of evaluating the influence of phytase on protein/AA utilization.

Binding of free amino acids (particularly lysine) by phytate has been demonstrated *in vitro* (Rutherfurd *et al.*, 1997). Approximately 20% of free lysine HCl was bound following incubation with rice pollard (rich in phytate). Half of that amount was liberated after the addition of phytase. In broilers, Ravindran and Bryden (1997) and Ravindran *et al.* (1999a) reported that dietary addition of phytic acid as rice pollard reduced ileal digestibility of nitrogen and amino acids (lysine, threonine, isoleucine, leucine, valine, phenylalanine and histidine). These adverse effects of phytic acid were effectively overcome by supplemental phytase.

### Broilers and turkeys

Apparent nitrogen retention by broilers was improved when phytase was added to a 23% crude protein corn-soybean meal diet (Kornegay *et al.*, 1996b). Yi *et al.* (1996c), using Large White Turkey female poults fed a corn-soybean meal diet, reported that apparent and true ileal digestibilities of nitrogen and amino acids were generally improved when 750 U phytase/kg was added to both 22.5 and 28.0% crude protein diets containing 0.45% nonphytate phosphorus. Improvements, however, were not observed for birds fed 28.0% crude protein and 0.60% nonphytase phosphorus. Ravindran and Bryden (1997) similarly observed that improvements in amino acid digestibility were higher in low phosphorus wheat-sorghum-soybean meal diets (Table 5).

Using young broilers, Kornegay (1996a) reported that ileal digestibilities of all amino acids were linearly decreased as the crude protein level increased (17, 20 and 23%). Ileal digestibilities of all amino acids except methionine and proline were linearly increased as phytase (250, 500 and 750 U/kg) was added to the 17 and 20% crude protein diets. In a broiler finishing study Kornegay *et al.* (1998b) reported that when dietary

**Table 5.** Changes in apparent ileal digestibility (percentage units) of amino acids in several ingredient combinations as influenced by phytase supplementation in broilers.

| Amino acids | References and diets | | | | | |
|---|---|---|---|---|---|---|
| | Corn SBM[a] | Corn-SBM corn gluten[b] | Wheat-sorghum SBM[c] | Corn SBM[d] | Wheat-middlings[e] | Rice polishings[e] |
| Phytase, U/kg | (750 U) | (450 U) | (400 U) | (600 U) | (1200 U) | (1200 U) |
| Arginine | 0.7 | 1.1 | 2.1 | 1.0 | 1.4 | 3.2 |
| Histidine | 0.7 | 2.1 | 2.6 | 0.8 | 2.13 | 5.1 |
| Isoleucine | 8.4 | 3.9 | 2.7 | 1.0 | 2.4 | 4.0 |
| Leucine | 4.9 | 1.8 | 3.4 | 0.8 | 2.3 | 5.3 |
| Lysine | 0.9 | 2.1 | 2.0 | 0.6 | 1.2 | 3.4 |
| Methionine | 0.3 | 1.8 | 1.1 | 0.9 | – | – |
| Phenylalanine | 0.5 | 1.6 | 2.9 | 0.9 | 2.2 | 5.1 |
| Threonine | 1.4 | 3.5 | 3.6 | 1.5 | 3.7 | 3.7 |
| Valine | 0.9 | 2.3 | 3.0 | 0.9 | 2.5 | 3.2 |

[a]Kornegay *et al.* (1996).
[b]Kornegay *et al.* (1998).
[c]Ravindran *et al.* (1999a).
[d]Kornegay (1999b).
[e]Ravindran *et al.* (1999b).

protein/AA levels were reduced from 95 to 85% of the NRC (1994) recommendation (1.5 to 2.0% units of crude protein), additions of 300–450 U phytase/kg of diet prevented the decrease in performance (slightly lower), breast meat yield, and ileal CP/AA digestibilities observed.

Supplemental phytase (1200 U/kg) was reported by Ravindran *et al.* (1999b) to improve ileal digestibilities of protein/AA of three cereals (corn, sorghum and wheat), four oilseed meals (soybean meal, canola meal, cottonseed meal and sunflower meal), and two cereal by-products (wheat middlings and rice polishings). The magnitude of the response varied among feedstuffs and individual AA (Table 5 and 6).

**Table 6.** Changes in apparent ileal digestibility (percentage units) of amino acids in several ingredient combinations as influenced by phytase supplementation in broilers.[a,b]

| | Corn | Sorghum | Wheat | Soybean meal | Canola | Cottonseed meal | Sunflower meal |
|---|---|---|---|---|---|---|---|
| Arginine | 3.0 | 5.0 | 7.8 | 2.0 | 1.6 | 2.5 | 1.7 |
| Histidine | 2.4 | 4.9 | 7.4 | 3.5 | 1.7 | 2.9 | 3.9 |
| Isoleucine | 2.1 | 4.5 | 5.4 | 2.8 | 2.4 | 4.6 | 3.5 |
| Leucine | 0.9 | 3.3 | 5.3 | 2.1 | 2.2 | 4.0 | 3.5 |
| Lysine | 2.5 | 4.7 | 7.8 | 3.4 | 0.7 | 2.7 | 2.4 |
| Phenylalanine | 1.7 | 5.2 | 5.3 | 3.0 | 2.1 | 3.1 | 3.6 |
| Threonine | 4.4 | 4.5 | 10.4 | 5.7 | 2.9 | 4.3 | 3.5 |
| Valine | 3.1 | 4.9 | 6.8 | 2.8 | 2.6 | 3.9 | 3.7 |

[a]Phytase added at 1200 U/kg.
[b]Ravindran *et al.* (1999b).

Using a low lysine (85% NRC) wheat-sorghum-soybean meal diet with multiple levels of crystalline lysine or microbial phytase and based on body weight gain and feed:gain ratios of broilers, Ravindran and Bryden (1998) reported that 500 U phytase/kg of diet was equivalent to 0.7 g lysine/kg of diet. Apparent metabolizable energy was also linearly increased as phytase was added, but not as lysine was added. Ravindran and Bryden (1998) suggested that body weight gain and feed efficiency responses to phytase may have resulted from both lysine and energy effects. In a similar study using broilers fed multiple levels of crystalline lysine added to a low lysine (0.8%) corn-soybean meal diet, Johnston and Southern (1999) reported an average equivalency of 0.23 g lysine/kg of diet for 600 U phytase/kg of diet based on body weight gain and feed efficiency.

## Pigs

Similar findings have been reported in pigs. Officer and Batterham (1992) and Khan and Cole (1993) reported that microbial phytase improved the apparent ileal and total tract digestibility of crude protein by 2.3–12.8% units. Using cannulated pigs in two studies Mroz *et al.* (1994) and Kemme (1998) reported that microbial phytase (800 and 900 U/kg, respectively) enhanced the apparent ileal digestibility of nitrogen and most amino acids (Table 7). Added microbial phytase generally enhanced the total tract digestibility and retention of nitrogen. Li *et al.* (1998) reported improved dry matter digestibility and nitrogen retention when phytase was added to a corn-soybean meal diet fed to weaned pigs. In a literature review, Jongbloed *et al.* (1996c) reported in 17 experiments using microbial phytase that the average apparent total tract digestibility of protein was enhanced 0.85 ± 1.70% units.

Table 7.   Changes in apparent ileal digestibility (percentage units) of amino acids in complete and low protein diets as influenced by supplemental phytase in pigs.

| | References and diets | | | |
|---|---|---|---|---|
| | Complex diet[a] | Corn-SBM[b] | Low-protein Corn-SBM[c] | Low protein corn-SBM[c] |
| Phytase, U/kg | (800 U) | (900 U) | (500 U) | (500 U) |
| Arginine | 2.5 | 1.5 | 6.3 | – |
| Histidine | 1.4 | 0.7 | 6.0 | 6.3 |
| Isoleucine | −0.3 | 2.1 | 9.5 | 2.9 |
| Leucine | −0.3 | 1.3 | 4.1 | 1.7 |
| Lysine | 0.9 | 1.5 | 12.0 | 3.3 |
| Methionine | 3.9 | 1.1 | 7.1 | 2.2 |
| Phenylalanine | −0.3 | 1.7 | 6.7 | 2.2 |
| Threonine | −1.8 | 2.9 | 10.4 | 4.0 |
| Valine | −0.3 | 2.0 | 8.8 | 3.5 |

[a]Mroz *et al.* (1994) cannulated grow/finish pigs.
[b]Kemme (1998) cannulated grow/finish pigs.
[c]Kornegay *et al.* (1998a) slaughter and cannulated pigs, respectively.

A feeding trial, nitrogen balance study and a cannulation study were conducted using finishing pigs fed diets containing different levels of protein and phytase. The five diets were 1) NRC (1998) crude protein levels, 2) 7.5% crude protein reduction, 3) 15.0% crude protein reduction, 4) diet 3 plus 250 U phytase/kg, and 5) diet 3 plus 500 U phytase/kg (Kornegay *et al.*, 1998a). Fecal nitrogen digestibility, ileal amino acid and nitrogen digestibilities and nitrogen retention were determined. Apparent digestion coefficients for nitrogen and amino acids decreased as dietary crude protein level decreased, but they increased when microbial phytase was added to the 15% reduced crude protein diet. Coefficients were generally equal to or greater than values for pigs fed the 7.5% reduction in crude protein. Using a conservative reduction of crude protein of 1% unit (7.1% reduction), and a nitrogen excretion value (including urinary nitrogen) of 40% of nitrogen intake, nitrogen excretion was estimated to be reduced by 7.1% when phytase is added to pig diets at a level of 500 U/kg.

INFLUENCE OF MICROBIAL PHYTASE ON ENERGY METABOLISM

Thompson and Yoon (1984) indicated that in the native state, phytate could complex with starch. As early as 1969, Rajas and Scott reported that the apparent metabolizable energy (AME) of cottonseed meal and soybean meal for chicks was improved following treatment of the meals with a crude phytase preparation from *Aspergillus ficuum*. Later, Miles and Nelson (1974), using chicks and a similar product reported improvements in the AME value of cottonseed meal and wheat bran, but not soybean meal, when treated with the phytase preparation.

More recent studies, primarily in Australia, used a genetically modified phytase (reviewed by Ravindran, 1999). Small but significant improvements in AME were observed for broilers fed sorghum-soybean meal-based diets (Farrell *et al.*, 1993; Selle *et al.*, 1999), and sorghum-soybean meal-canola meal-cottonseed meal-wheat middling diets (Selle *et al.*, 1999) when phytase was added. The AME values of a sorghum-soybean meal-based diet and in diets with 60% rice bran fed to ducks was improved when phytase was added (Martin and Farrell, 1994).

Findings from three very recent studies (Ravindran *et al.*, 1999a,b; Bryden and Ravindran, 1998) designed to determine the influence of microbial phytase on protein/AA and energy utilization in poultry, clearly show that supplemental phytase improves the AME value of wheat and sorghum-based poultry diets (reviewed by Ravindran, 1999) (Table 8). In agreement, Kornegay and Denbow (Virginia Polytechnic Institute and State University, 1998, unpublished data) observed that phytase supplementation (600 U/kg) improved AME coefficients in 4-week old broilers fed corn-soybean meal, corn-wheat middlings-soybean meal, corn-meat meal-soybean meal or wheat-corn-soybean meal diets. It was suggested, based on literature reported by Ravindran (1999), that phytic acid may exert its effects on starch digestion in one or more ways: 1) by binding $\alpha$-amylase or by chelating $Ca^{+2}$ needed for the normal activity of amylase, and/or

2) by binding starch directly through a protein linkage. Of course, hydrolysis of phytate phosphorus would release the enzyme or free the starch.

**Table 8.** Changes in apparent metabolizable energy (kcal/kg) of diets as influenced by supplemental phytase in broilers.

| Wheat-sorghum-SBM-rice pollards[a] | | | | Wheat-casein basal[b] | |
|---|---|---|---|---|---|
| Low phytate | | High phytate | | Without | With |
| low nP* | adequate nP | low nP | adequate nP | Xylanase | Xylanase |
| 140 | 115 | 45 | 80 | 141 | 247 |

*nP, nonphytate phosphorus.
[a]Ravindran et al. (1999a).
[b]Bryden and Ravindran (1998).

## INFLUENCE OF DIETARY CALCIUM AND CALCIUM:PHOSPHORUS RATIO ON THE EFFECTIVENESS OF PHYTASE

The response to a given level of supplemental phytase will be influenced by dietary calcium level and/or Ca:P ratio, dietary phosphorus level, and dietary phytate level (Lei et al., 1994; Dungelhoef and Rodehutscord, 1995; Kornegay, 1996b). A high molar ratio of Ca:phytate in the diet can lead to the formation of extremely insoluble Ca-phytate complexes under intestinal conditions, making the phytate molecule inaccessible to phytase. The presence of such strong complexes could explain the apparent inactivity of phytase in calcium-rich diets rather than a direct inhibition of the enzyme by $Ca^{2+}$ (Wise, 1983; Bos, 1988). The importance of maintaining a narrow total Ca:total P ratio (or for that matter available Ca:available P) has been recently demonstrated in broilers (Qian et al., 1997), turkeys (Qian et al., 1996b), and pigs (Qian et al., 1996a, Liu et al., 1998).

### Broilers and turkeys
In broilers and turkeys, total Ca:total P ratios of 1.1:1 to 1.4:1 appeared to be equally effective. Feeding diets with wider ratios reduces performance, phosphorus utilization and bone mineralization (Qian et al., 1996b, 1997). In young broilers, using data reported by Qian et al. (1997), a 14.5, 8.5, and 8.3% decrease was calculated for body weight gain, phosphorus retention, and toe ash percentage, respectively, when the Ca:total P ratio was increased from 1.1:1 to 2.0:0. In young turkeys, using data reported by Qian et al. (1996b), an 8.7, 10.8, and 6.6% decrease was calculated for body weight gain, phosphorus retention, and toe ash percentage, respectively, when Ca:total P ratio was increased from 1.1:1 to 2.0:1.

### Pigs
In pig studies, a greater response to phytase (better utilization of phosphorus) is obtained when the total Ca:total P ratio is maintained between 1:1 to 1.1:1 (Qian et al., 1996a). For example, in growing-finishing pigs, Liu et al. (1998) reported a 4.5, 8.2 and 9.7% decrease in

average daily gain, phosphorus digestibility and metacarpal breaking strength, respectively, when the Ca:total P ratio was increased from 1.0.1 to 1.5:1. Lei *et al.* (1994) reported for pigs fed a corn-soybean meal diet with no added inorganic phosphorus (0.31% total P) that the ability of phytase to improve phytate phosphorus availability was greatly reduced at 0.92% dietary Ca (Ca:total P ratio was 3.1) compared with the 0.50% dietary Ca (Ca:total P ratio was 1.6:1). Dungelhoef and Rodehutscord (1995) also observed from their review of the literature that high calcium levels reduce the absorption of phosphorus and the utilization of phytate. Similar findings have also been reported by Jongbloed *et al.* (1996c,d).

The decrease in the effectiveness of phytase as the Ca:total P ratio becomes wider could be explained as follows: 1) phytate phosphorus utilization in corn-soybean diets fed to broilers is influenced by calcium and phosphorus levels in the diet (Edwards and Veltmann, 1983; Ballam *et al.*, 1984); 2) the extra calcium can bind with phytate to form an insoluble complex that is less accessible to phytase; or 3) the extra calcium may directly repress phytase activity by competing for the active sites of the enzyme (Wise, 1983; Pointillart *et al.*, 1985). The negative effect of wide Ca:total P ratios is greater at lower levels of supplemental phytase and at lower levels of available phosphorus or nonphytate phosphorus because a smaller amount of phosphorus would be released from phytate with lower phytase activity which would contribute to a phosphorus deficient environment.

OTHER FACTORS

*Organic acid*
The inclusion of organic acids in the diet will generally lower dietary pH (Kirchgessner and Roth, 1982; Giesting and Easter, 1985; Risley *et al.*, 1992) with a resultant smaller effect on lowering the stomach pH. However, the use of organic acids in combination with phytase to enhance the effectiveness of phytase has produced mixed results (Jongbloed *et al.*, 1996d; Valencia and Chavez, 1997; Boling *et al.*, 1998; Li *et al.*, 1998; Radcliffe *et al.*, 1998b). Further research is needed to understand the relationship between diet acidification and phytase effectiveness.

*Age and physiological status*
The effects of age and physiological status of the pig on the efficacy of phytase in rendering phytate phosphorus available for absorption have been inconsistent. Kemme *et al.* (1997a) reported that the efficacy of phytase for improving digestible phosphorus decreased in the order of lactating sows, growing-finishing pigs, sows at the end of pregnancy, piglets, and sows at midpregnancy. Efficacy of phytase was particularly low in sows on day 60 of pregnancy and high in lactating sows with the growing-finishing pigs intermediate (Kemme *et al.*, 1997b). They suggest that the differences among the categories probably relate to differences in gastric retention time, but also the requirement for digestible phosphorus by the

specific category must be taken into account. Harper *et al.* (1997) reported slightly higher apparent digestibility coefficients for finisher pigs compared to grower pigs in one trial, but the opposite effect was observed in a second trial. Rodehutscord *et al.* (1998) recently compared the efficacy of microbial phytase fed in combination with a low phosphorus semipurified diet in growing pigs of either 16 or 39 kg body weight. Phosphorus digestibility was very similar for both groups. From these studies there is no indication that the efficacy of microbial phytase is dependent on body weight of pigs.

### Soaking

As pointed out by Helander (1995) in her dissertation review, the positive effect of soaking on phosphorus availability has been reported in many experiments involving different feedstuffs (Irving, 1980). Kemme and Jongbloed (1993) reported that the efficacy of microbial phytase was enhanced by soaking the diet in water in one experiment, but in a second experiment using a pelleted diet and a shorter soaking time, soaking had no effect on phosphorus digestibility. A higher incubation temperature may also have increased phytate hydrolysis (Hill and Tyler 1954; Han and Wilfred, 1988). The pH of the diet is also most important. Tossenberger *et al.* (1993) reported the degradation of sodium phytate was 81% and 93%, respectively for 2.5 and 5.0 hours of soaking in a pH 5.0 solution. The respective values were only 38% and 47% when the pH was increased to 6.0. Beneficial effects of soaking on phosphorus utilization with whey were observed for a barley-rapeseed meal diet fed to growing pigs (Nasi *et al.*, 1994), whereas no effect of soaking a pelleted barley-soybean meal diet was observed by Nasi and Helander (1994). Liu *et al.* (1997) reported improved phosphorus utilization when a soybean meal-based diet was soaked. A soaking by phytase quadratic interaction was observed. Soaking the 250 U/kg diet increased phosphorus absorption similar to that obtained with the 500 U/kg diet fed dry.

Wet feeding of growing-finishing pigs is reported to have increased, especially in Europe, and has the potential of enhancing phytase effectiveness and improving phosphorus digestibility. Although I do not have research data, reports from the industry are that phytase is more efficient in these feeding systems.

## Summary

When pig and poultry diets are formulated using significant amounts of plant based ingredients that are low in native phytase, microbial phytase supplementation is very effective for improving the availability of phytate phosphorus. Because phytate is known to complex a number of other minerals, amino acids/protein, and even starch, bioavailability of these nutrients is enhanced when phytate is hydrolyzed by phytase. Thus, the excretion of phosphorus, calcium, zinc and nitrogen can be reduced significantly when diets are properly formulated using phytase. The dose response curve of phytase for improving phosphorus utilization is non-linear for pigs and poultry (broilers and turkeys) and the response has been described over a wide range of phytase levels. The dose response curves for the effects of phytase on calcium, zinc, amino acid/nitrogen and energy utilization are not as clearly understood as they are for phosphorus.

The dose response of phytase will, however, depend upon: 1) the level of phytase used, 2) the level of total phosphorus in the diet, 3) the level of phytate phosphorus in the diet, 4) the level of calcium and the Ca:P ratio, 5) the intrinsic level of phytase in foodstuffs and, 6) processing and pelleting methods. The effects of physiological age and the influence of organic acid are not clearly understood if they exist.

# References

Adeola, O., B. V. Lawrence, A. L. Sutton and T. R. Cline. 1995. Mineral utilization in phytase-and-zinc supplemented diets for pigs. J. Anim. Sci. 73(Suppl. 1):73 (Abstr.).

Anderson, P. A. 1985. Interactions between proteins and constituents that affect protein quality. In: Digestibility and Amino Acid Availability in Cereals and Oilseeds (G.W. Finley and D.T. Hopkins, eds.), American Association of Cereal Chemists, St. Paul, Minnesota. pp. 31.

Bagheri, S. and L. Gueguen. 1985. Effect of wheat bran and pectin on the absorption and retention of phosphorus, calcium, magnesium and zinc by the growing pig. Reprod. Nutr. Develop. 25:705.

Ballam, G. C., T. S. Nelson and L. K. Kirby. 1984. Effect of fiber and phytate source and of calcium and P level on phytate hydrolysis in the chick. Poultry Sci. 63:333.

Biehl, R. R., D. H. Baker and H. F. DeLuca. 1995. 1a-hydroxylated cholecalciferal compounds act additively with microbial phytase to improve phosphorus, zinc and manganese utilization in chicks fed soy-based diets. J. Nutr. 124:2407.

Boling, S. D., C. M. Parsons and D. H. Baker. 1998. Citric acid improves phytate phosphorus utilization in broiler chicks fed corn-soybean meal diets. Poultry Sci. 77(Suppl. 1):S31 (abstr.)

Bos, K. D. 1988. Degradation of phytate by wheat phytase. In: Proc. ANF-Workshop, Wageningen, Nov. 23–25, 3 pp.

Bryden, W. L. and V. Ravindran. 1998. Effects of enzyme combinations on apparent metabolisable energy and ileal nitrogen digestibility in broiler chickens. Proc. Nutr. Soc. Aust. 22: 180.

Calvert, C. C., R. J. Besecker, M. P. Plumlee, T. R. Cline and D. M. Forsyth. 1978. Apparent digestibility of phosphorus in barley and corn for growing swine. J. Anim. Sci. 47:420.

Cosgrove, D. J. 1980. Inositol Phosphates: Their Chemistry, Biochemistry and Physiology. Elsevier Scientific Publishing Company, New York.

Cromwell, G. L. 1992. The biological availability of phosphorus in feedstuffs for pigs. Pig News Info. 13:2:75N.

De Rham, O. and T. Jost. 1979. Phytate protein interactions in soybean extracts and low-phytate soy protein products. J. Food Sci. 44:596.

Denbow, D. M., V. Ravindran, E. T. Kornegay, Z. Yi and R. M. Hulet. 1995. Improving phosphorus availability in soybean meal for broilers by supplemental phytase. Poultry Sci. 74:1831.

Duengelhoef, M. and M. Rodehutscord. 1995. Wirkung von phytasen auf die verdaulichkeit des phosphors beim schwein (Effects of phytases on the digestibility of phosphorus in pigs). Ubers. Tierernahrg. 23:133.

Edwards, H. M., Jr. and J. R. Veltmann, Jr. 1983. The role of calcium and phosphorus in the etiology of tibial dyschondroplasia in young chicks. J. Nutr. 113:1568.

Eeckhout, W. and M. De Paepe. 1991. The quantitative effects of an industrial microbial phytase and wheat phytase on the apparent phosphorus absorbability of a mixed feed by piglets. Med. Fac. Landbouww. Rijksuniv. Gent, 56:1643.

Eeckhout, W. and M. De Paepe. 1994. Total phosphorus, phytate-phosphorus and phytase activity in plant feedstuffs. Anim. Feed Sci. and Tech. 47:19.

Eeckhout, W. and M. De Paepe. 1996. *In vitro* and *in vivo* comparison of microbial and plant phytase, In: Phytase in Animal Nutrition and Waste Management (M. B. Coelho and E. T. Kornegay, editors), BASF Corporation, Mount Olive, NJ. pp. 237.

Farrell, D. J., E. A. Martin, J. J. Du Preez, M. Bongarts, M. Betts, A. Sudaman and E. Thomson. 1993. The beneficial effects of a microbial phytase in diets of broiler chickens and ducklings. J. Anim. Phys. Anim. Nutr.69:278.

Fretzdorff, B., J. M. Brummer, W. Rocken, R. Greiner, U. Konietzny, K.-D. Jany. 1995. Reduktion des Phytinsaure-Gehaltes bei der Herstellung von Backwaren und Getreidenahrmitteln. AID-Verbraucherdienst 40:12.

Gibson, D. M. and A. H. J. Ullah. 1990. Phytase and their actions on phytic acid. Page 77. in: Inositol Metabolism in Plants. D. J. Morre, W.F. Boss, and F. A. Loewus, ed. Wiley-Liss, Inc., New York.

Giesting, D. W. and R. A. Easter. 1985. Response of starter pigs to supplementation of corn-soybean meal diets with organic acids. J. Anim. Sci. 60:1288.

Gordon, R.W. and D. A. Roland, Sr. 1997. Performance of commercial laying hens fed various phosphorus levels, with and without supplemental phytase. Poultry Sci. 76:1172.

Gueguen, L., P. Besancon and A. Rerat. 1968. Utilisation digestive, cinetique de l'absorption et efficacite le retention du phosphore phytique chez le porc. Ann. Biol. anim. Bioch. Biophys. 8(2):273.

Han, Y. W. and A. G. Wilfred. 1988. Phytate hydrolysis in soybean and cottonseed meals by *Aspergillus ficuum* phytase. J. Agric. Food Chem., 36:259.

Harland, B. F. and E. R. Morris. 1995. Phytate: a good or a bad food component. Nutr. Res. 15:733.

Harper, A. F., E. T. Kornegay and T. C. Schell. 1997. Phytase supplementation of low phosphorus growing-finishing pig diets improves performance, phosphorus digestibility and bone mineralization, and reduces phosphorus excretion. J. Anim. Sci. 75:3174.

Helander, E. 1995. Efficiency of microbial phytases on phosphorus utilization in growing-finishing pigs. Dissertation, Faculty of Agriculture and Forestry of the University of Helsinki, Finland.

Hill, R. and C. Tyler. 1954. The influence of time, temperature, pH, and calcium carbonate on the activity of the phytase of certain cereals. J. Agric. Sci. 44:306.

Ingelmann, H.-J., G. Rimbach, J. Pallauf and Gieben. 1993. Phytinsaure - ein antinutritiver faktor? Ernahrungs-Umschau 40:400.

Irving, G. C. J. 1980. Phytates. In: Inositol Phytates. (D. J. Cosgrove, Ed.) Elsevier, Amsterdam, pp. 85.

Irving, G. C. J. and D. J. Cosgrove. 1974. Inositol phosphate phosphates of microbiological origin. Some properties of the partially purified phosphatases of *Aspergillus ficuum* NRRL 3135. Aust. J. Biol. Sci. 27:361.

Johnston, S.L. and L. L. Southern. 1999. The effect of phytase addition or the reduction of dietary calcium and available phosphorus on lysine bioavailability in growing chicks. Southern Poultry Sci. Society meeting, January 18, Atlanta, GA.

Jongbloed, A. W. and P. A. Kemme. 1990. Apparent digestible phosphorus in the feeding of pigs in relation to availability, requirement and environment. 1. Digestible phosphorus in feedstuffs from plant and animal origin. Netherlands J. Ag. Sci. 38:567.

Jongbloed, A. W., P. A. Kemme and Z. Mroz. 1996a. Effectiveness of Natuphos phytase in improving the bioavailabilities of phosphorus and other nutrients for growing-finishing pigs. In: Phytase in Animal Nutrition and Waste Management (M. B. Coelho and E. T. Kornegay, editors), BASF Corporation, Mount Olive, NJ. pp. 259.

Jongbloed, A. W., P. A. Kemme and Z. Mroz. 1996b. The influence of dietary calcium levels on efficacy of microbial phytase, in: Phytase in Animal Nutrition and Waste Management (M.B. Coelho and E.T. Kornegay, eds.), BASF Corporation, Mount Olive, NJ. pp. 393.

Jongbloed, A. W., P. A. Kemme and Z. Mroz. 1996c. Phytase in swine rations: impact on nutrition and environment. BASF Technical Symposium. Des Moines, IA, January 29. 44.

Jongbloed, A.W., P. A. Kemme, Z. Mroz and R. Jongbloed. 1996d. The effect of organic acids in diets for growing pigs on the efficacy of microbial phytase, in: Phytase in Animal Nutrition and Waste Management (Coelho, M.B. and Kornegay, E.T., editors), BASF Corporation, Mount Olive, NJ. pp. 515.

Jongbloed, A.W., Z. Mroz and P. A. Kemme. 1992. The effect of supplementary *Aspergillus niger* phytase in diets for pigs on concentration and apparent digestibility of dry matter, total phosphorus and phytic acid in different sections of the alimentary tract. J. Anim. Sci. 70, 1159.

Kemme, P.A. 1998. Phytate and phytases in pig nutrition. Impact on nutrient digestibility and factors affecting phytase efficacy. Ph.D. Thesis, University of Wageningen, The Netherlands.

Kemme, P. A. and A. W. Jongbloed. 1993. Effect of *Aspergillus niger* phytase and soaking on the apparent digestibility of P in diets for pigs. J. Anim. Sci. 71(Suppl. 1):181.

Kemme, P. A., A. W. Jongbloed, Z. Mroz and A. C. Beynen. 1997a. The efficacy of *Aspergillus niger* phytase in rendering phytate phosphorus available for absorption in pigs is influenced by pig physiological status. J. Anim. Sci. 75:2129.

Kemme, P. A., A. W. Jongbloed, Z. Mroz and A. C. Beynen. 1998. Diurnal variation in degradation of phytic acid by plant phytase in the pig's stomach. Livestock Prod. Sci. 54:33.

Kemme, P. A., J. S. Radcliffe, A. W. Jongbloed and Z. Mroz. 1997b. The effects of sow parity on digestibility of proximate components and minerals during lactation as influenced by diet and microbial phytase supplementation. J. Anim. Sci. 75:2147.

Khan, N. and D. J. A. Cole. 1993. The effect of dietary inclusions of phytate and yeast on apparent phosphorus digestibility in pigs. Proceedings of winter meeting of the British Society of Animal Production. Scarborough. 2 p.

Kirchgessner, M. and F. X. Roth. 1982. Fumaric acid as a feed additive in pig nutrition. Pig News and Information 3: 259.

Knuckles, B. E., D. D. Kuzmicky and A. A. Betschart. 1985. Effect of phytate and partially hydrolyzed phytate on *in vitro* protein digestibility. J. Food Sci. 50:1080.

Kornegay, E. T. 1996a. Effect of Natuphos® phytase on protein and amino acid digestibility and nitrogen retention of poultry, In: Phytase in Animal Nutrition and Waste Management (M. B. Coelho and E. T. Kornegay, editors), BASF Corporation, Mount Olive, NJ. pp. 493–514.

Kornegay, E. T. 1996b. Natuphos™ phytase in swine diets: digestibility, bone and carcass characteristics. Proceedings of BASF Technical Symposium/Carolina Swine Nutrition Conference, November 12, pp 28.

Kornegay, E. T. 1999. A review of phosphorus digestion and excretion as influenced by microbial phytase in poultry. BASF Technical Symposium following the southern Poultry Sci. meetings (January 18), Atlanta, GA.

Kornegay, E. T. and H. Qian. 1996. Replacement of inorganic phosphorus by microbial phytase for young pigs fed a corn soybean meal diet. Br. J. Nutr. 76:563.

Kornegay, E. T., D. M. Denbow and J. S. Radcliffe. 1996b. Bioavailability of inorganic sources of phosphorus for turkeys. Anim. and Poultry Sci. Res. Rpt. 12:22.

Kornegay, E. T., D. M. Denbow, Z. Yi and V. Ravindran. 1996a. Response of broilers to graded levels of microbial phytase added to maize-soyabean meal-based diets containing three levels of non-phytate phosphorus. Br. J. Nutr. 75:839.

Kornegay, E.T., J. S. Radcliffe and D. M. Denbow. 1996c. Influence of Natuphos® phytase on calcium bioavailability in plant ingredients and development of calcium equivalency values for swine and poultry, In: Phytase in Animal Nutrition and Waste Management (M. B. Coelho and E. T. Kornegay, editors), BASF Corporation, Mount Olive, NJ. pp. 419

Kornegay, E. T., J. S. Radcliffe Z. Zhang. 1998a. Influence of phytase and diet composition on phosphorus and amino acid digestibilities, and phosphorus and nitrogen excretion in swine. BASF Tech. Symp., Carolina Swine Nutr. Conf. (November 16), p. 125.

Kornegay, E. T., J. S. Radcliffe and Z. Zhang. 1998c. Non-phosphorus benefits of feeding microbial phytase to pigs and poultry. Animal Production Systems and the Environment, Des Moines, IA, July 19–22, p. 79.

Kornegay, E. T., Z. Zhang and D. M. Denbow. 1998b. Influence of microbial phytase supplementation of a low protein/amino acid diet on performance, ileal digestibility of protein and amino acids, and carcass measurements of finishing broilers. Poultry Sci. 77(Suppl. 1):S33.

Lantzsch, H. J., S. Hillenbrand, S. E. Scheuermann and K. H. Menke. 1992. Comparative study of phosphorus utilization from wheat, barley and corn diets by young rats and pigs. J. Anim. Phys. Anim. Nutr. 67:123.

Lei, X. G., P. K. Ku, E. R. Miller, D. E. Ullrey and M. T. Yokoyama. 1993. Supplemental microbial phytase improves bioavailability of dietary zinc to weanling pigs. J. Nutr. 123:1117.

Lei, X. G., P. K. Ku, E. R. Miller, M. T. Yokoyama and D. E. Ullrey. 1994. Calcium level affects the efficacy of supplemental microbial phytase in corn-soybean meal diets of weanling pigs. J. Anim. Sci. 72:139.

Leske, K. L. and C. N. Coon. 1998. Effect of phytase on total and phytate phosphorus retention of feed ingredients as determined with broilers and laying hens. Poultry Sci. 77(Suppl. 1):54.

Li, D., X. Che, Y. Wang, C. Hong and P. A. Thacker. 1998. Effect of microbial phytase, vitamin $D_3$, and citric acid on growth performance and phosphorus, nitrogen and calcium digestibility in growing swine. Anim. Feed Sci. and Tech. 73:173.

Liebert, F., C. Wecke and F. J. Schöner. 1993. Phytase activities in different gut contents of chickens as dependent on level of phosphorus and phytase supplementation. In: Enzymes in Animal Nutrition (C. Wenk and M. Boessinger eds.). Proc. 1st Symp. Kartause Ittingen, Switzerland, Oct. 13–16. pp 202.

Liu, J., D. W. Bollinger, D. R. Ledoux, M. R. Ellersieck and T. L. Veum. 1997. Soaking increases the efficacy of supplemental microbial phytase in a low-phosphorus corn-soybean meal diet for growing pigs. J. Anim. Sci. 75:1292.

Liu, J., D. W. Bollinger, K. Zyla, D. R. Ledoux and T. L. Veum. 1998. Lowering the dietary calcium to total phosphorus ratio increases phosphorus utilization in low-phosphorus corn-soybean meal diets supplemented with microbial phytase for growing-finishing pigs. J. Anim. Sci. 76:808.

Maddaiah, V. T., A. A. Kurnick and B. L. Reid. 1963. Phytic acid studies. Proc. of the Soc. for Exp. Biol. Med. 115:391.

Martin, E. and D. J. Farrell. 1994. The effect of a microbial phytase in rice bran based diets fed to grower-finisher diets. Proceedings of the Australian Poultry Sci. Symposium 6, 88.

McCance, R. A. and E. M. Widdowson. 1944. Activity of the phytase in different cereals and its resistance to dry heat. Nature 153:660.

Miles, R.D., Jr. and T. S. Nelson. 1974. The effect of enzymatic hydrolysis of phytate on the available energy content of feed ingredients for chicks and rats. Poultry Sci. 53:1714.

Mroz, Z., A. W. Jongbloed and P. A. Kemme. 1994. Apparent digestibility and retention of nutrients bound to phytate complexes as influenced by microbial phytase and feeding regimen in pigs. J. Anim. Sci. 72:126.

Nair, V. C. and Z. Duvnjak. 1991. Phytic acid content reduction in canola meal by various microorganisms in a solid state fermentation process. Acta Biotech. 11:211.

Nasi, M. and E. Helander. 1994. Effects of microbial phytase supplementation and soaking of barley-soybean meal on availability of plant phosphorus for growing pigs. Sect. A. Anim. Sci. Acta Agric. Scand. 44:79.

Nasi, M., E. Helander and K. Partanen. 1994. The effects of *Aspergillus niger* phytase and soaking with whey on phosphorus utilization in growing pigs on barley-rapeseed meal diet. VI Int. Symp. on Digestive Phys. in Pigs, Bad Doberan, 10/4–6, Proc., Vol. I:89.

Nayini, N. R., and P. Markakis. 1986. Phytases. In: E. Graf (Ed.). Phytic Acid: Chemistry and Applications. Pilatus Press. Minneapolis. p. 101.

Nelson, T. S. 1967. The utilization of phytate P by poultry -A review. Poultry Sci. 46:862.

Nelson, T. S., T. R. Shieh, R. J. Wodzinski and J. H. Ware. 1971. Effect of supplemental phytase on the utilization of phytate phosphorus by chicks. J. Nutr. 101:1289.

Newton, G. L., O. M. Hale and C. O. Plank. 1983. Effect of wheat bran in practical diets on mineral absorption by pigs at two ages. Canadian J. Anim. Sci. 63:399.

NRC. 1994. Nutrient Requirements of Poultry (9th Ed.). National Academy Press, Washington, DC.

NRC. 1998. Nutrient Requirements of Swine (10th Ed.). National Academy Press, Washington, DC.

Nys, Y., D. Frapin and P. Pointillart. 1996. Occurrence of phytase in plants, animals and microorganisms. In: Phytase in Animal Nutrition and Waste Management (Coelho, M.B. and Kornegay, E.T., editors), BASF Corporation, Mount Olive, NJ. pp. 213.

O'Dell, B. L. and A. de Borland. 1976. Complexation of phytase with proteins and cations in corn germ and oilseed meals. J. Agric. Food Chem. 24:804.

Oberleas, D. 1973. Phytates. In: Toxicants Occurring Naturally in Foods. National Academy of Sciences, Washington, D.C. p 363.

Oberleas, D. and B. F. Harland. 1981. Phytate content of foods: Effect on dietary zinc bioavailability. J. Am. Diet. Assoc. 79:443.

Officer, D. I. and E. S. Batterham. 1992. Enzyme supplementation of Linola® meal. Proc. of Wollongbar pig industry seminar of feed enzymes. p. 56.

Pallauf, J. and G. Rimbach. 1995. Recent results on phytic acid and phytase. Proceedings of 5th Forum Animal Nutrition, May 4–5, BASF, p 43.

Pallauf, V. J., D. Hohler and G. Rimbach. 1992. Effect of microbial phytase supplementation to a maize-soya-diet on the apparent absorption on Mg, Fe, Cu, Mn and Zn and parameters of Zn-status in piglets. J. Anim. Physiol. Anim. Nutr. 68:1.

Peter, W. and H. Jeroch. 1993. The effectiveness of microbial phytase addition to layer rations on maize and wheat basis. In: Enzymes in Animal Nutrition (C. Wenk and M. Boessinger eds.). Proc. 1st Symp. Kartause Ittingen, Switzerland, Oct. 13–16. pp 206.

Pointillart, A., N. Fontaine, M. Thomasset and M. E. Jay. 1985. Phosphorus utilization, intestinal phosphatases and hormonal control of calcium metabolism in pigs fed phytic phosphorus: soybean or rapeseed diets. Nutr. Rep. Intern. 32: 155.

Qian, H., E. T. Kornegay and D. E. Conner, Jr. 1996a. Adverse effects of wide calcium:phosphorus ratios on supplemental phytase efficacy for weanling pigs fed two dietary phosphorus levels. J. Anim. Sci. 74:1288.

Qian, H., E. T. Kornegay and D. M. Denbow. 1996b. Phosphorus equivalence of microbial phytase in turkey diets as influenced by calcium to phosphorus ratios and phosphorus levels. Poultry Sci. 75:69.

Qian, H., E. T. Kornegay and D. M. Denbow. 1997. Utilization of phytate phosphorus and calcium as influenced by microbial phytase, cholecalciferol and the calcium:total phosphorus ratio in broiler diets. Poultry Sci. 76:37.

Radcliffe, J. S., E. T. Kornegay and D. E. Conner, Jr. 1995. The effect of phytase on calcium release in weanling pigs fed corn-soybean meal diets. J. Anim. Sci. 73 (Suppl. 1):173 (abstract).

Radcliffe, J. S., Z. Zhang and E. T. Kornegay. 1998b. The effects of microbial phytase, citric acid and their interaction in a corn-soybean meal based diet for weanling pigs. J. Anim. Sci. 76:1880.

Rajas, S. W. and J. L. Scott. 1969. Factors affecting the nutritive value of cottonseed meal as a protein source for chick diets. Poultry Sci. 48:819.

Ravindran, V. 1999. Protein and energy effects of microbial phytase in poultry diets. Presented at the BASF Technical Symposium following the southern Poultry Sci. meetings, Atlanta, GA, January 19.

Ravindran, V. and W. L. Bryden. 1997. Influence of dietary phytic acid and available phosphorus levels on the response of broilers to supplemental Natuphos®. University of Sydney, Report to BASF, 1.

Ravindran, V. and W. L. Bryden. 1998. Lysine replacement value of Natuphos® phytase in broiler diets. University of Sydney, Report to BASF, 1.

Ravindran, V., W. L. Bryden and E. T. Kornegay. 1995b. Phytates: Occurrence, bioavailability and implications in poultry nutrition. Poultry Avian Biol. Rev. 6:125.

Ravindran, V., S. Cabahug, G. Ravindran and W. L. Bryden. 1999a. Response of broilers to microbial phytase supplementation as influenced by dietary phytic acid and non-phytate phosphorus levels. II. Effects on nutrient digestibility and retention. British Poultry Sci. (in review).

Ravindran, V., S. Cabahug, G. Ravindran and W. L. Bryden. 1999b. Influence of microbial phytase on apparent ileal amino acid digestibility of feedstuffs for broilers. Poultry Sci. 78: (in press).

Ravindran, V., E. T. Kornegay, D. M. Denbow, Z. Yi and R. M. Hulet. 1995a. Response of turkey poults to tiered levels of Natuphos® phytase added to soybean meal-based semi-purified diets containing three levels of nonphytate phosphorus. Poultry Sci. 74:1843.

Risley, C. R., E. T. Kornegay, M. D. Lindemann, C. M. Wood and W. N. Eigel. 1992. Effect of feeding organic acids on selected intestinal content measurements at varying times postweaning in pigs. J. Anim. Sci. 70:196.

Roberson, K. D. and H. M. Edwards, Jr. 1994. Effects of 1,25–dihydroxycholecaliciferol and phytase on zinc utilization in broiler chicks. Poultry Sci. 72:1312.

Rodehutscord, M., G. Krause and E. Pfeffer. 1998. The effect of phytase on the availability of phosphorus in different ingredients in swine. Proceedings of BASF Technical Symposium/Carolina Swine Nutrition Conference, November 12, pp 32.

Rutherfurd, S. M., A. C. Edwards and P. H. Selle. 1997. Effect of phytase on lysine-rice pollard complexes. In: Cranwell P.D. (Ed.. Manipulating Pig Production VI. Australasian Pig Science Association, Werribee, Victoria, Australia. pp 248.

Schoner, F. J., P. P. Hoppe, G. Schwarz and H. Wiesche. 1993. Effects of microbial phytase and inorganic phosphate in broiler chickens: performance and mineral retention at various calcium levels. J. Anim. Phys. Anim. Nutr.69:235.

Schoner, F. J., P. P. Hoppe and G. Schwarz. 1991. Comparative effects of microbial phytase and inorganic P on performance and on retention of P, calcium and crude ash in broilers. J. Anim. Physiol. A. Anim. Nutr. 66:248.

Schoner, F. J., G. Schwarz, P. P. Hoppe and H. Wiesche. 1994. Effect of microbial phytase on Ca-availability in broilers, Third Conf. of Pig and Poultry Nutrition in Halle, Germany, Nov. 29–Dec. 1.

Schulz, E. and H. J. Oslage. 1972. Untersuchungen zur intestinalen hydrolyse von inosit-phosphorsaureester und zur absorption von phytinphosphor beim schwein. 2. Mitteilung untersuchungen zur hydrolyse der inositphosphorsaureester im verdauungstrakt beim schwein. Z. Tierphysiol., Tierernahrg. u. Futtermittelkde. 30:76.

Selle, P. H., V. Ravindran, P. H. Pittolo and W. L. Bryden. 1999. An evaluation of microbial phytase in sorghum-based broiler diets. Proceedings of Australian Poultry Symposium 11: (in press).

Simons, P. C. M. and H. A. J. Versteegh. 1993. The effect of the addition of low doses of microbial phytase to layer feed on the technical results and skeleton and eggshell quality. Speiderholt publication no. 589 (NL).

Simons, P. C. M., A. W. Jongbloed, H. A. J. Versteegh and P. A. Kemme. 1992. Improvement of phosphorus availability by microbial phytase in poultry and pigs. Georgia Nutrition Conference (November 19), pp. 100.

Singh, M. and A. D. Krikorian. 1982. Inhibition of trypsin activity by phytate. Journal of Agricultural and Food Chemistry 30:799.

Thiel, U. and E. Weigand. 1992. Influence of dietary zinc and microbial phytase supplementation on Zn retention and Zn excretion in broiler chicks, XIX World's Poultry Congress, Amsterdam, Netherlands, Sept. 20.

Thiel, U., E. Weigand, F. J. Schoner and P. P. Hoppe. 1993. Zinc retention of broiler chicken as affected by dietary supplementation of zinc and microbial phytase. In: Proceedings of 8th Int. Symposium Trace Elements in Man and Animals (TEMA), Anke, M., Meissner, D. and Mills, C. F., Eds., Dresden, Gersdorf, 658.

Thompson, L. U. 1986. Phytic acid: A factor influencing starch digestibility and blood glucose response. In: Phytic Acid: Chemistry and Applications, Graf, E., Ed, Pilatus Press, Minneapolis, p 173.

Thompson, L. U. and J. H. Yoon. 1984. Starch digestibility as affected by polyphenols and phytic acid. J. of Food Sci. 49:1228.

Thompson, L. U., C. L. Button D. J. A. Jenkins. 1987. Phytic acid and calcium affect the *in vitro* rate of navy bean starch digestion and blood glucose response in humans. Am. J. Clin. Nutr. 46:467.

Tossenberger, J., F. Liebert and E. Schulz. 1993. Zum einfluss von phytase auf de bau von phytaten verschiedener herkunfte. In: Vitamine und Weitere Zusatzstoffe bei Mensc Tier. 4th Symposium, p 365.

Vahl, H. A., G. J. Borggreve and H. P. Stappers. 1993. The effect of microbial phytase in layer feed. CLO-Schothorst experimental report No. 374 (NL).

Valencia, Z. and E. R. Chavez. 1997. Phytase and acetic acid supplementation of piglet diets: effect on performance and apparent nutrient digestibility. Can. J. Anim. Sci. 77:742.

Van der Klis, J. D., H. A. J. Versteegh, P. C. M. Simons and A. K. Kies. 1997. The efficacy of phytase in corn-soybean meal-based diets for laying hens. Poultry Sci. 76:1535.

Vohra, P., G. A. Gray and F. H. Kratzer. 1965. Phytic acid-metal complexes. Proceedings of the Society of Experimental Biology and Medicine 120, 447.

Wise, A. 1983. Dietary factors determining the biological activities of phytase. Nutr. Abstr. Rev. (Section B). 53:791.

Yi, Z. and E. T. Kornegay. 1996. Sites of phytase activity in the gastrointestinal tract of young pigs. Anim. Feed Sci. Tech. 61:361.

Yi, Z., E. T. Kornegay and D. M. Denbow. 1996c. Effect of microbial phytase on nitrogen and amino acid digestibility and nitrogen retention of turkey poults fed corn-soybean diets. Poultry Sci. 75:979.

Yi, Z., E. T. Kornegay and D. M. Denbow. 1996d. Supplemental microbial phytase improves zinc utilization in broilers. Poultry Sci. 75:540.

Yi, Z., E. T. Kornegay, M. D. Lindemann, V. Ravindran and J. H. Wilson. 1996a. Effectiveness of Natuphos® phytase in improving the bioavailabilities of phosphorus and other nutrients in soybean meal-based semipurified diets for young pigs. J. Anim. Sci. 74:1601.

Yi, Z., E. T. Kornegay, V. Ravindran and D. M. Denbow. 1996b. Improving phytate phosphorus availability in corn and soybean meal for broilers using microbial phytase and calculation of phosphorus equivalency values for phytase. Poultry Sci. 75:240.

Yoon, J. H., L. U. Thompson and D. J. A. Jenkins. 1983. The effect of phytic acid on *in vitro* rate of starch digestibility and blood glucose response. American Journal of Clinical Nutrition 38:835.

Zhang, Z. B., E. T. Kornegay and H. P. Veit. 1998a. Comparison of genetically engineered microbial and plant phytase for young broilers. Poultry Sci. 77(Suppl. 1):71.

Zhang, Z. B., E. T. Kornegay and H. P. Veit. 1998b. Comparison of genetically engineered microbial and plant phytase for young pigs. J. Anim. Sci. 76(Suppl. 1):178.

# Allzyme Phytase reduces phosphorus and nitrogen excretion by caged broilers and by broilers in conventional housing

F. W. EDENS, C. R. PARKHURST and G. B. HAVENSTEIN

*Department of Poultry Science, North Carolina State University, Raleigh, North Carolina, USA*

## Introduction

There is growing concern that land application of poultry litter will contribute to phosphorus and nitrogen contamination of rivers and estuaries in areas with large poultry industries. Land-applied poultry litter has a special problem because its phosphorus content is generally higher than plants need. In 1997, environmentalists' efforts to control water pollution due to run-off from poultry and livestock farms resulted in legislation being introduced into the 105th US Congress (SB 1323- Animal Agriculture Reform Act and HR 3232- Farm Sustainability and Animal Feedlot Enforcement Act) that would have set national standards on pollution from poultry and livestock farms. These bills did not become law, but new legislative initiatives undoubtedly will be submitted in the 106th Congress and at the state level. Similar legislation was proposed and passed by the Maryland General Assembly (Water Quality Improvement Act of 1998 and the Nutrient Management Practices Act of 1998) mandating that by the end of the year 2000, all feeds for monogastric animals must be supplemented with a phytase enzyme or other additives that reduce phosphorus in poultry and livestock wastes to the maximum extent that is commercially and biologically feasible. In 1995 there was a legislative mandate in The Netherlands that called for a 30% reduction in phosphorus content in manure. This goal was partially attained in the poultry sector by reducing dietary inorganic phosphorus and supplementing the diets with a microbial phytase (Simons *et al.*, 1990; 1992; Van der Klis and Versteegh, 1994).

## Increased phytate phosphorus availability with dietary phytase supplementation

Dietary supplementation of phytase enzymes can affect the concentration of phosphorus in poultry and livestock wastes via its ability to liberate phytate phosphorus contained in the cell walls of feed grains. However,

491

this liberation of phytate phosphorus can only be accomplished if a concomitant reduction is made in supplemented dietary inorganic phosphorus and calcium. Phytate forms acid salts with mineral cations such as calcium, magnesium, copper, zinc, iron and potassium thereby reducing mineral solubility and availability (Erdman, 1979; Kornegay, 1996a,b). When acted upon by phytase enzyme, these cations are released much like phosphorus. Consequently, increased availability of these minerals will result in increased retention by chickens given phytase (Sebastian *et al.*, 1996a,b). Aoyagi and Baker (1995) demonstrated reduced copper utilization in chickens fed phytase supplemented diets. The reduced copper utilization by phytase treated chicks may have been the result of increased zinc release from the phytate (Roberson and Edwards, 1994). Yi *et al.* (1996a,b) reported that phytase improved zinc utilization and retention in broilers fed a low zinc corn-soybean protein isolate diet. Furthermore, Biehl *et al.* (1995) reported that manganese availability was increased in broiler diets supplemented with phytase. Therefore, it appears that phytase incorporation into the diets of chickens can effectively increase retention of certain minerals provided the supplementation of those minerals to the diet is reduced, and this should effectively reduce the level of minerals such as copper, zinc, and phosphorus that can act as water and soil pollutants from land applied poultry litter. Thus, phytase incorporation in poultry and livestock diets makes organic phosphorus in feed grains more available and reduces the amount of inorganic phosphorus that must be routinely added to diets. This nutrient management scheme would decrease the amount of phosphorus in manure and ultimately there would be a reduction in the leaching of this nutrient into ground and surface waters near poultry and animal farms.

Approximately 67% of the phosphorus in plant tissue is in the form of phytate phosphorus (myoinositol hexakisphosphate) (Cromwell, 1980; Heinzl, 1996) which is only minimally available to monogastric animals since they lack the phytase enzyme that hydrolyzes phytic acid to inositol and orthophosphate (Peeler, 1972). Supplementation of phytase enzyme in the primarily corn-soybean meal diet of broiler chickens improves the availability of phytate-bound phosphorus (Nelson *et al.*, 1971; Simons *et al.*, 1990; 1992; Sauveur, 1993; Roberson and Edwards, 1994; Denbow *et al.*, 1995). Phytate phosphorus content of corn is 68% of the total phosphorus, and in soybean meal phytate phosphorus represents 60% of the total phosphorus (Stillborn, 1998). Simons *et al.* (1990) demonstrated that in three week old broilers the availability of dietary phosphorus could be increased up to 65% by means of supplemental dietary phytase while reducing fecal phosphorus by 50%. According to Williams (1997), inclusion of phytase enzyme into the diets of broilers contributes to increased energy and protein density and permits the usage of cheaper feed ingredients. Furthermore, inclusion of feed grains with phytase activity such as wheat, triticale, rye, or their by-products resulted in better phosphorus utilization (Pointillart *et al.*, 1993).

# Poultry fecal phosphorus and nitrogen

Poultry manure, due to higher dry matter content and relatively high amounts of uric acid and other ureides, can be very high in phosphorus and nitrogen in comparison to pig feces, but poultry manure contains less phosphorus and nitrogen than ruminant feces (Stillborn, 1998). Uric acid and other ureides are forms of urea and can be toxic to crops. Schmitt and Rehm (1998) indicated that dry matter content of poultry manure ranged from 22 to 29% (without and with bedding, respectively), total nitrogen from 27 to 20 lbs/ton (without and with bedding, respectively), phosphorus from 20 to 16 lbs/ton (without and with bedding respectively), and potassium from 17 to 13 lbs/ton (without and with bedding, respectively). Therefore, when farmers apply poultry litter to meet plant nitrogen needs, phosphorus often exceeds plant needs. Repeated application of manure on the same fields can result in a significant build-up of soil phosphorus, zinc, and copper which might then become a potential source of surface water contamination as run-off. As a result of Vice President Gore's policy address in October of 1997, in the United States future land application of animal wastes may no longer be based simply on nitrogen content of the wastes, but rather phosphorus may become the limiting factor. Using phosphorus as the limiting plant nutrient for field application of poultry and animal wastes, farmers will be limited to application of 25 to 50% as much manure or be forced to spread manure on fields only one time every three to four years.

## COMPOSTING INFLUENCE ON RELATIVE CONCENTRATIONS OF PHOSPHORUS AND NITROGEN IN POULTRY MANURE

Composting of poultry litter results in significant losses of nitrogen by ammonia volatilization. Schmitt and Rehm (1998) reported 15 to 35% nitrogen loss of daily scrape and haul manure, 20 to 40% loss of nitrogen in manure pack, and a 40 to 60% nitrogen loss when manure was composted in open lot. Thus, the amount of phosphorus in manure relative to nitrogen content can increase significantly depending upon the way poultry manure is handled. The lower the nitrogen concentration in manure, the more phosphorus becomes a limiting factor to land application rates if agronomic nutrient application rates are maintained.

## PHYTASE INFLUENCE ON PHOSPHORUS AND NITROGEN CONCENTRATIONS IN POULTRY MANURE

A significant reduction in poultry manure phosphorus can be achieved via the use of microbial phytase in feed. This can reduce the nitrogen:phosphorus ratio in poultry wastes. Balander and Flegal (1997) studied the effect of feed supplemented with Allzyme Phytase in layer diets and reported a 16% reduction in fecal phosphorus from laying hens fed inorganic phosphorus at 80% of NRC requirements and a 25% reduction in fecal phosphorus from laying hens fed 60% of NRC requirements. A 38% decrease in fecal phosphorus from laying hens given another microbial phytase product at 250 FTU/kg diet was reported by Van der Klis *et al.* (1996; 1997). Similarly, Balander and Flegal (1996) reported decreased phosphorus excretion in market turkeys given Allzyme Phytase. These fecal phosphorus reductions from laying hens and market turkeys with Allzyme Phytase supplemented feeds were similar to the fecal phosphorus reductions found in pigs given another phytase feed supplement (Simons *et al.*, 1990), layers (Simons and Versteegh, 1992; 1993), and broilers (Yi *et al.*, 1996a,b).

## Phytase influence on broiler performance

Several researchers have demonstrated improved production performance of broiler chickens given feeds supplemented with a phytase product. Improved growth performance, assessed by increased body weight, feed intake and better feed efficiency, has been reported consistently in both chickens (Schoner *et al.*, 1991; 1993; Broz *et al.*, 1994; Sebastian *et al.*, 1996a,b) and turkeys (Qian *et al.*, 1996a,b). Qian *et al.* (1996b) further demonstrated improved performance of broilers given supplemental dietary phytase, which was correlated with improved bone growth and mineralization. This response was attributed to increased retention of certain minerals and nutrients in addition to phytase-liberated phytate-phosphorus, and this conclusion was supported by earlier research on phytase (Swick and Ivey, 1990; Simons *et al.*, 1992; Hoppe and Schwarz, 1993).

The efficacy of supplemented microbial phytase is dependent upon dietary calcium (Ca) levels. Sebastian *et al.* (1996b) demonstrated that phytase-supplemented broiler diets with calcium concentrations greater than 1.25% caused less retention of phosphorus and nitrogen. Part of this problem is associated with the fact that calcium and magnesium (Mg) precipitate phytate as an insoluble Ca-phytate or Mg-phytate in the intestine inhibiting the release of phytate phosphorus by phytase (McQuaig *et al.*, 1972; Scheideler and Sell, 1987; Sandberg *et al.*, 1993). Qian *et al.* (1997) reported that phytase, vitamin $D_3$ and calcium:total phosphorus ratios are important factors in degrading phytate phosphorus and improving dietary phosphorus and calcium utilization in broilers.

## Manure nutrient management in cage-reared versus litter-reared broiler chickens

Smith (1972) suggested that in the future broilers would be raised in cages in spite of the fact that at that time technology had not advanced to point where that practice was feasible. From the mid-1960s to the early-1980s many attempts were made to design cage facilities for the rearing of broiler chickens from hatch to market age. Unfortunately, none of these early cage systems allowed economical broiler production because of the overall poor performance (Lloyd *et al.*, 1971; Lloyd and Chaloupka, 1972; Andrews and Goodwin, 1973; Andrews *et al.*, 1975; Bayer *et al.*, 1976). Recently, the Josef Kuhlman Company of Germany (Farmer Automatic of America) designed a cage rearing system (Broilermatic® System) that appears to have eliminated many of the early problems associated with cage rearing of broilers (Havenstein *et al.*, 1998).

The advent of this new caging system holds promise for poultry producers in Europe and in other locations where land prices are so expensive as to preclude the establishment of conventional poultry rearing facilities, but production of chickens in cages poses a new problem in manure nutrient management. In a dynamic microenvironment established in poultry litter, the content of phosphorus can be approximately five-fold the concentration of phosphorus found in fresh raw manure (Zublena *et al.*, 1993; Vest *et al.*, 1994). The litter serves as a source of nutrients that can be recycled by the chicken as it practices coprophagy. While little attention is given to this important source of nutrients for the chicken, when the bird is taken off litter and placed in cages where it does not have access to the nutrients eliminated in feces, one must be concerned about performance of the bird and weigh the potential negative effects of caging against the availability of nutrients in the litter. Additional studies, however, must be conducted to determine the minimum levels of nutrients required by broilers in a cage environment. The Broilermatic® System provided a unique opportunity to study methods of reducing manure disposal volume and nitrogen volatilization while at the same time providing much needed information about minimizing fecal phosphorus and nitrogen output.

MATERIALS AND METHODS

A 2 × 4 factorially arranged completely randomized experimental design was used to test the effects of phytase on broiler chickens reared in replicate pens in conventional litter-covered floor pens and replicate pens in cage rows in the cage-rearing facility (Broilermatic® System). There were 40 chickens in each of the 64 pens (e.g. 8 rows of 8 cages with 320 birds per cage row) in the Broilermatic® System cage-rearing facility and 40 chickens in each of the 32 pens in the conventional broiler house. Using this design, a total of 3,840 broiler chickens were used in the trial. Sexes were grown separately, thus providing a total of 1920 males and 1920 females in this experiment. A total of 1280 chickens (640 males and 640 females) were housed in the conventional house and 2560 (1280 males and 1280 females) were assigned to the Farmer Automatic Cage House.

Allzyme Phytase (Alltech, Inc.) is derived from an *Aspergillus niger*. Additional side activities of the Allzyme Phytase included cellulase, protease, xylanase and acid phosphatase. Allzyme Phytase was incorporated as a dry powder into mash feeds at 11.27 PTU/g or 2 lbs/ton. The broilers were given North Carolina Agricultural Research Service diets (Table

1) for *ad libitum* consumption on the following schedule: starter diet, day 0-18 (3177 kcal ME/kg, 22.5% crude protein), grower diet, 18 to 35 days of age (3168 kcal ME/kg, 19.5% crude protein), and finisher diet, 35 to 42 days of age (3160 kcal ME/kg, 17.4% crude protein). Conventional feeds (NRC requirements) normally contain 0.59, 0.58, or 0.41% total phosphorus with 0.79, 0.80, or 0.46% calcium in the starter and grower. However in these studies, the starter and grower test diets were formulated to contain 0.5%, 0.4% or 0.3% available phosphorus with 1.0%, 0.8% and 0.6% total calcium. This was accomplished via manipulation of the dicalcium phosphate (inorganic phosphorus) concentration in each diet. Finisher diets were not supplemented with inorganic phosphorus (Table 1). Allzyme Phytase was blended dry into the 0.5, 0.4, and 0.3% diets at the level 11.27 PTU/g into all three diets. The influence of the Allzyme Phytase on serum concentrations of phosphorus and total calcium, weight gain, feed conversion, livability, and manure and litter phosphorus and nitrogen were determined. Manure phosphorus and nitrogen content were determined on the basis of pounds per ton of dry matter in the manure or litter and on the basis of g total phosphorus and nitrogen per kg of dry matter intake. Sampling for serum phosphorus and total calcium took place at 3 and 6 weeks of age. Fecal phosphorus and nitrogen content were determined weekly on fresh feces collected from the belts under the cages in the Farmer Automatic Cage house and in litter collected from ten random sites within each sampled pen in the conventional house. An AOAC-certified commercial laboratory (Woodson and Tenent, Goldston, NC) analyzed the litter and manure for phosphorus by a colorimetric procedure and nitrogen by Kjeldahl analysis.

Analyses of variance were conducted for each parameter; and the level of significance was set at P≤ 0.05 or less depending upon the F values generated by the GLM procedure. When differences among treatments were found, the means were separated by least significant difference following the procedures of SAS (1994).

## Results and discussion

### PHYTASE AND PERFORMANCE

Allzyme Phytase supplementation to the diets of broiler chickens had minimal effects on body weights at six weeks of age of broilers grown in cages and in conventional housing (Table 2). Reducing the supplemental inorganic phosphorus and replacement with Allzyme Phytase did not significantly affect body weight of the cage-reared broilers. Feed conversion ratios (FCR) ranged between 1.73 (0.5% P) and 1.81 (0.5% P + Phytase), and likewise, supplementation of Allzyme Phytase for reduced available inorganic phosphorus did not significantly affect FCR. Mortality rates were not different among treatments and ranged between 2.81 % (0.5% P + Phytase) and 2.03 % (0.4% P and 0.3% P + Phytase). In the conventional house, Allzyme Phytase added

**Table 1.  Composition of North Carolina Agricultural Research Service basal broiler diets.**

| Ingredients | Starter | Grower | Finisher |
|---|---|---|---|
| | | *kg* | |
| Corn | 269.09 | 311.82 | 348.64 |
| Soy | 122.73 | 87.73 | 70.00 |
| Subtotal | 391.82 | 399.55 | 418.64 |
| Limestone | 3.18 | 3.18 | 1.82 |
| Dicalcium phosphate[1] | 3.18 | 3.64 | |
| Poultry fat | 15.91 | 8.18 | |
| Poultry meal | 36.36 | 36.36 | 30.91 |
| DL-methionine | 0.82 | 0.82 | 0.18 |
| Lysine | 0.32 | 0.41 | 0.27 |
| Salt | 1.82 | 0.91 | 1.36 |
| Choline chloride | 0.91 | 0.91 | 0.91 |
| Minerals[2] | 0.91 | 0.91 | 0.91 |
| Vitamins[3] | 0.23 | 0.23 | 0.23 |
| Total batch weight | 455.46 | 454.46 | 455.05 |
| Selenium premix | 0.20 | 0.20 | 0.20 |
| | | | |
| *Nutrient analysis:* | | | |
| Total phosphorus, % | 0.5882 | 0.5818 | 0.4068 |
| Nonphytate phosphorus, % | 0.3666 | 0.3751 | 0.2060 |
| % of NRC requirement | 81.5 | 107.2 | 68.7 |
| Sulfur, % | 0.7946 | 0.2945 | 0.2605 |
| Calcium, % | 0.7946 | 0.8044 | 0.4649 |
| % of NRC requirement | 9.5 | 89.4 | 58.1 |
| Ca:Total P | 1.3509 | 1.3826 | 1.1428 |
| Metabolizable energy, Mcal/kg | 3.1773 | 3.1684 | 3.1601 |
| Dry matter, % | 88.0500 | 87.5561 | 86.9629 |
| Crude protein, % | 22.5051 | 19.5003 | 17.4814 |
| Ether extract, % | 6.8655 | 5.4324 | 3.7168 |
| Linoleic acid, % | 2.3124 | 2.0864 | 1.7886 |
| Crude fiber, % | 2.6803 | 2.7278 | 2.8179 |

[1]Basal diets were modified to provide 0.5%, 0.4% or 0.3% available phosphorus by manipulating the amount of dical added to the diets for the Allzyme Phytase studies. The calcium: available P ratio was also modified to yield a 2:1 ratio in the diets in the phytase studies.

[2]Trace mineral (TM-90) premix provided (mg/kg): Manganese, 120; zinc, 120; iron, 80; copper, 10; iodine, 2.5; cobalt, 1.0. Selenium premix as sodium selenite was provided to each diet at a level to assure a concentration of 0.15 ppm.

[3]Vitamin premix (NCSU-90) provided per kg: Vitamin A, 6,600 IU; cholecalciferol, 2,000 IU; Vitamin E, 33 IU; Vitamin $B_{12}$, 19.8 mg; riboflavin, 6.6 mg; niacin, 55 mg; pantothenic acid, 11 mg; Vitamin K, 2 mg; folic acid, 1.1 mg; thiamin, 2 mg; pyridoxine, 4 mg; biotin, 126 mg.

to diets with 0.5% and 0.4% available inorganic phosphorus resulted in slight but nonsignificant depressions in six-week body weights (Table 2), but broilers given 0.3% inorganic phosphorus plus Phytase had body weights slightly higher than those of broilers given the 0.5% available phosphorus diet without phytase. There was a clear trend in the conventional house toward improved FCR with addition of Allzyme Phytase in all treatment groups with the best FCR in groups with the lowest levels of available inorganic phosphorus. The FCR in the cage

**Table 2.    Influence of Allzyme Phytase supplementation on production parameters for broiler chickens.**

| | Diet[1] | Replicate pens[2] | Body weight (kg) | FCR (g/g) | Mortality (%) |
|---|---|---|---|---|---|
| Cage | 0.5% P | 16 | 2.09[a] | 1.73[b] | 2.66[a] |
| | 0.5% P + Phytase | 16 | 2.01[ab] | 1.81[b] | 2.81[a] |
| | 0.4% P + Phytase | 16 | 1.98[ab] | 1.74[b] | 2.03[a] |
| | 0.3% P + Phytase | 16 | 1.97[ab] | 1.78[b] | 2.03[a] |
| Floor | 0.5% P | 8 | 2.00[ab] | 2.06[a] | 2.19[a] |
| | 0.5% P + Phytase | 8 | 1.96[ab] | 2.05[a] | 1.56[a] |
| | 0.4% P + Phytase | 8 | 1.92[b] | 2.04[a] | 2.10[a] |
| | 0.3% P + Phytase | 8 | 2.01[ab] | 2.01[a] | 2.10[a] |

[1]NRC dietary requirement of 0.5% available inorganic phosphorus (P) and 1.0% calcium (Ca); 0.4% P and 0.8% Ca; 0.3% P and 0.6% Ca.
[2] N= 40 birds in each replicate pen in both the cage facility and in pens.
[a,b]In a column, means with unlike superscripts differ significantly (P<0.05).

facility was improved overall by 28 points in comparison to the conventional house. Mortality rates in the conventional house ranged between 1.56 and 2.19% and did not differ among the treatments.

Mixed results have been observed with regard to body weight response of broilers fed phytase. In this study, a decrease was evident in caged broilers fed phytase-supplemented diets. In young broiler chickens, phytase is associated with improved digestibility of amino acids (McKnight, 1998). Kornegay (1996b) did not find improved body weight in broilers fed a finisher diet with phytase from three to seven weeks of age. However, McKnight (1996), summarizing the work of several scientific studies, reported that phytase reversed the negative impact of reducing dietary inorganic phosphorus content. Qian *et al.* (1997) reported that broilers fed very low levels of dietary phosphorus showed depressed weight gain, and even with 600 to 900 FTU phytase supplementation weight gain was not equivalent to controls given NRC-recommended phosphorus levels. Additionally, this reduced weight gain even with phytase was related to the ratio of dietary calcium to total available phosphorus in the diet. Calcium:total phosphorus ratios greater than 1.5: 1.0 were associated with reduced weight gain. Nevertheless, in this experiment broilers in the conventional house demonstrated slight reductions in body weight when given the 0.5% and 0.4% phosphorus diets with phytase while broilers given the 0.3% phosphorus diet with phytase had six-week body weights slightly higher than controls (0.5% phosphorus diet without phytase). It is possible that broilers in the conventional house practiced coprophagy and were obtaining additional nutrients unavailable to the birds in the cage rearing facility. The improved FCR in broilers given the Allzyme Phytase was consistent with observations made when broilers were given other phytase products (Simons *et al.*, 1992; McKnight, 1996).

## PHYTASE INFLUENCE ON SERUM CALCIUM AND INORGANIC PHOSPHORUS CONCENTRATIONS

Allzyme Phytase and lower dietary levels of nonphytate phosphorus did not cause a decrease in serum phosphorus levels at either three or six weeks of age (Table 3). Serum total calcium concentrations were also unaffected in birds given diets where Allzyme Phytase was added to feed in which the calcium along with inorganic phosphorus levels were decreased. Calcium:phosphorus (Ca:P) ratios were maintained at 2:1 for each of the experimental diets in this study. Serum Ca:P ratios ranged between 1.02 and 1.26 at three weeks of age. This was not a departure from ratios normally reported (Edens, 1976) even though values for both serum calcium and phosphorus were elevated at three weeks of age. At six weeks of age, the serum calcium and phosphorus concentrations were lower than at three weeks of age. However, nonphytate phosphorus and calcium in the finisher diets were 50% lower than in either the starter or grower diets, and as a result the serum levels of each were expected to be lower. Nevertheless, serum Ca:P ratios at six weeks of age were higher than at three weeks and ranged between 0.92 and 1.80. At three weeks of age, serum Ca:P ratios were greater in the cage-reared broilers than in the floor-reared broilers, but at six weeks of age the cage-reared broilers had lower Ca:P ratios than the floor-reared broilers. The difference between the cage and floor-reared birds at six weeks of age suggests the possibility of increased coprophagy in the floor-reared birds and a possible recycling of nutrients in the litter.

Table 3. Influence of Allzyme Phytase on serum inorganic phosphorus and total calcium concentrations in broilers.

| Housing | Diet[1,2] | 3 weeks | | 6 weeks | |
|---|---|---|---|---|---|
| | | P (inorganic) | Calcium | P (inorganic) | Calcium |
| | | Serum concentrations, mg/dl | | | |
| Cage | 0.5% P | 8.3[b] | 9.0[c] | 6.0[a] | 5.5[d] |
| | 0.5% P + Phytase | 7.7[c] | 9.7[bc] | 6.2[a] | 7.8[c] |
| | 0.4% P + Phytase | 8.0[bc] | 9.9[b] | 5.1[bc] | 7.4[c] |
| | 0.3% P + Phytase | 8.7[ab] | 10.1[a] | 6.1[a] | 8.0[bc] |
| Floor | 0.5% P | 9.1[a] | 10.1[ab] | 5.3[b] | 9.2[a] |
| | 0.5% P + Phytase | 8.5[ab] | 9.2[c] | 4.8[c] | 8.5[b] |
| | 0.4% P + Phytase | 9.1[a] | 10.6[a] | 5.8[ab] | 8.7[a] |
| | 0.3% P + Phytase | 9.6[a] | 9.8[b] | 5.0[bc] | 7.8[c] |

[1]NRC dietary requirement of 0.5% available inorganic phosphorus (P) and 1.0% calcium (Ca); 0.4% P and 0.8% Ca; 0.3% P and 0.6% Ca.
[2] N= 40 birds in each replicate pen in both the cage facility and in pens in the conventional house.
[a,b,c,d]In a column, means with unlike superscripts differ significantly (P<0.05).

PHYTASE INFLUENCE ON PHOSPHORUS CONTENT OF RAW
MANURE AND LITTER

Allzyme Phytase supplementation of broiler diets significantly lowered
phosphorus content (lbs/ton of manure dry matter) in raw manure from
the birds in the cage facility (Table 4). This observation was most apparent in birds given the 0.3% available phosphorus diet compared to the
0.5% available phosphorus diet. Manure from birds given the 0.3%
phosphorus diet contained from 6.6 to 32.2% less phosphorus during the
feeding of the starter and grower diets. However, during the period when
the finisher diet was given to the birds, there was no decrease in manure
phosphorus in response to phytase supplements. In the conventional house,
birds given phytase without a concomitant reduction in dietary inorganic
phosphorus showed increased rates of litter phosphorus accumulation
(Table 4). Yet, with decreasing dietary inorganic phosphorus and

**Table 4. Influence of Allzyme Phytase supplementation on phosphorus content (lbs/ton dry matter) in raw manure from caged broilers and on accumulation of phosphorus in litter in the conventional house.**

| Housing | | | | | Week | | | | |
|---------|------|---------|---------|---------|---------|---------|---------|---------|
| | Diet[1] | 0[2] | 1 | 2 | 3 | 4 | 5 | 6 |
| Cage | 0.5% P + Phytase | | 14.78[a] | 12.06[a] | 10.71[a] | 10.20[a] | 10.09[a] | 8.61[ab] |
| | 0.5% P + Phytase | | 13.71[ab] | 12.10[a] | 9.29[b] | 8.90[b] | 10.99[a] | 8.09[b] |
| | 0.4% P + Phytase | | 14.37[a] | 11.21[b] | 9.01[bc] | 8.88[b] | 10.80[a] | 9.22[a] |
| | 0.3% P + Phytase | | 11.78[b] | 11.31[b] | 8.10[c] | 8.20[b] | 8.29[b] | 8.89[a] |
| Floor | 0.5% P | 10.50[x] | | 10.20[x] | 10.71[x] | 10.20[y] | 11.10[x] | 12.80[x] |
| | 0.5% P + Phytase | 10.50[x] | | 10.50[x] | 11.00[x] | 11.71[x] | 11.50[x] | 12.80[x] |
| | 0.4% P + Phytase | 10.50[x] | | 10.80[x] | 10.81[x] | 10.40[y] | 10.90[xy] | 11.02[y] |
| | 0.3% P + Phytase | 10.50[x] | | 9.51[y] | 10.09[x] | 10.20[y] | 10.39[y] | 10.11[z] |

[1]NRC dietary requirement of 0.5% available inorganic phosphorus (P) and 1.0% calcium
(Ca); 0.4% P and 0.8% Ca; 0.3% P and 0.6%Ca.
[2] Week 0 values represent the starting concentration of litter phosphorus; values for the cage
facility represent average weekly manure P content; values for the conventional house
represent litter P buildup.
[a,b,x,y,z]Means in a column with unlike superscripts differ significantly (P<0.05).

supplemental phytase there was a clear decrease in litter phosphorus in
the conventional house. In fact, at the end of the six week trial there was
a 26.6% decrease in litter phosphorus accumulation in the conventional
house in pens containing birds given the 0.3% phosphorus diet supplemented with the Allzyme Phytase.

When manure phosphorus content was evaluated as a function of dry
matter intake (Table 5) similar reductions were found when the birds were
given the 0.3% and 0.4% available phosphorus starter and grower diets
with Allzyme Phytase supplementation. Significant decreases in manure
phosphorus ranged between 16.4 and 24% in the manure from birds given

the 0.3% available phosphorus diets and housed in the cages. When given the 0.4% available phosphorus diets with phytase, manure phosphorus was reduced by 5.1 and 8.3% during the feeding of starter and grower, respectively. During the final week of the study in the cage house, manure phosphorus increased in both the 0.3% and 0.4% available phosphorus groups and was no longer different from the control (0.5% available phosphorus). However, during the final week of the study in the conventional house there was a 26.6% reduction in litter phosphorus in pens where broilers were given the 0.3% available phosphorus diet with added phytase. A reason for the lack of a reduction in manure phosphorus in phytase-supplemented chickens in the cage facility at six weeks of age is not readily available. However, Edwards (1993) and Van der Klis and Versteegh (1997a,b) have demonstrated that broiler chickens have the ability to degrade phytate phosphorus as they approach market age. The digestibility of phytate phosphorus can increase from 31% at 14 days of age to 38.2% at 25 days of age in broilers (Van der Klis and Versteegh, 1997a,b). At low levels of dietary inorganic phosphorus, phytate phosphorus becomes more available due to an adaptive increase in phytate digestibility (Moore and Veum, 1983). It has been noted that low levels of dietary phosphorus result in increased activity of intestinal phytase in chicks (Davies *et al.*, 1970; McCuaig *et al.*, 1972), explaining the observations made by Edwards (1993) and Van der Klis and Versteegh (1997a,b). Therefore, the increase in endogenous intestinal phytase in response to decreased dietary phosphorus with Allzyme Phytase activity added to the finisher diet, may have liberated more phytate phosphorus than the birds needed. As a result of increased phytase activity in the intestinal tract, excess inorganic and excess liberated phytate phosphorus were simply eliminated.

During the final week of this study no inorganic phosphorus was added to the experimental diets. The amounts of phosphorus eliminated were substantially lower in all treatments in the cage house and slightly higher in the litter in the conventional house (Tables 4 and 5). Therefore, on inspection of the data, it is clear that there were no treatment differences in phosphorus elimination in the cage house as one might expect given that there was no added inorganic phosphorus in the diet. However, in the conventional house, there were differences among dietary groups with less phosphorus elimination in the groups reared with lower inorganic phosphorus in their diets. This could indicate that there was recycling of nutrients in the floor-reared birds as they practiced coprophagy, or it may indicate that the birds on lower phosphorus intake were able to absorb more phosphorus from the intestinal tract. Answers to these problems are not apparent in the data from this study.

PHYTASE INFLUENCE ON NITROGEN CONTENT IN RAW
MANURE AND LITTER

In both the cage facility and in the conventional house the addition of the Allzyme Phytase to normal and decreased phosphate diets was associated generally with lower output of manure nitrogen (lbs/ton dry matter

501

**Table 5.** Influence of Allzyme Phytase (Phy) supplementation in diets with varying concentrations of available phosphorus (AP%) on total phosphorus (TP%) excreted (g/kg dry matter intake (DMI) in raw manure from caged broilers and on accumulation of phosphorus in litter in the conventional house.

| | Starter[1] | | | Grower[1] | | | Finisher[1] | | |
|---|---|---|---|---|---|---|---|---|---|
| | TP (%) | AP (%) | P excreted[2] | TP (%) | AP (%) | P excreted[2] | TP (%) | AP (%) | P excreted[2] |
| **Cage** | | | | | | | | | |
| 0.5% P | 0.72 | 0.50 | 5.38[a] | 0.70 | 0.50 | 10.28[a] | 0.41 | 0.21 | 5.10[a] |
| 0.5% P+ Phy | 0.72 | 0.50 | 5.16[a] | 0.70 | 0.50 | 9.69[a] | 0.41 | 0.21 | 4.80[a] |
| 0.4% P+ Phy | 0.62 | 0.40 | 5.12[a] | 0.60 | 0.40 | 9.49[a] | 0.41 | 0.21 | 5.46[a] |
| 0.3% P+ Phy | 0.52 | 0.30 | 4.62[b] | 0.50 | 0.30 | 8.29[b] | 0.41 | 0.21 | 5.34[a] |
| | | | | | | | | | |
| **Floor** | | | | | | | | | |
| 0.5% P | 0.72 | 0.50 | 4.14[a] | 0.70 | 0.50 | 10.58[a] | 0.41 | 0.21 | 7.59[a] |
| 0.5% P+ Phy | 0.72 | 0.50 | 4.00[a] | 0.70 | 0.50 | 11.34[a] | 0.41 | 0.21 | 7.59[a] |
| 0.4% P+ Phy | 0.62 | 0.40 | 4.24[a] | 0.60 | 0.40 | 10.48[a] | 0.41 | 0.21 | 6.52[b] |
| 0.3% P+ Phy | 0.52 | 0.30 | 4.32[a] | 0.50 | 0.30 | 10.31[a] | 0.41 | 0.21 | 5.99[b] |

[a,b] Values in a column with unlike superscripts differ from the 0.5% P diet (P<0.05).
[1]DM intake in starter, 0.80kg; in grower, 1.99 kg; in finisher, 1.19 kg.
[2]g/kg DM intake.

in manure) when compared with the control (0.5% available phosphorus diet) (Table 6). This observation was apparent during the time when starter and grower diets were being fed to the broilers. Manure nitrogen content (lbs/ton dry matter in manure) was decreased from 4.8 to 24.6% in the cage facility and 8.0 to 21.5% in the conventional house. At six weeks, the litter nitrogen accumulation and raw manure nitrogen content was increased to the level of the control in birds given the phytase supplement (Table 6).

Litter nitrogen and raw manure nitrogen content were evaluated also on the basis of dry matter intake (Table 7). With this approach, no significant influence of phytase on litter nitrogen accumulation was observed. However, in the cage facility, there were significant reductions in manure nitrogen content in association with Allzyme Phytase supplementation in grower feeds (Table 7).

The changes in raw manure and litter nitrogen content associated with supplemental phytase are consistent with other observations. Caldwell (1992) demonstrated that phytate could inhibit proteolytic enzymes, and this inhibition of proteolysis could lead to decreased performance. Earlier reports had indicated that there was an improvement in protein utilization when dietary phytate was decreased and that dietary phytate was correlated positively with manure nitrogen output (Atwal *et al.*, 1980; Knuckles *et al.*, 1985). McKnight (1998) has shown that phytase can increase digestibility of amino acids leading to a reduction in manure nitrogen. In this case, where Allzyme Phytase was added

**Table 6. Influence of Allzyme Phytase on nitrogen content (lbs/ton of dry matter) in raw manure from caged broilers and on accumulation of nitrogen in litter in the conventional house.**

| Housing | | | | | Week | | | |
|---|---|---|---|---|---|---|---|---|
| Diet[1] | 0 | 1 | 2 | 3 | 4 | 5 | 6 |
| Cage  0.5% P | | 77.49[a] | 62.36[a] | 41.85[a] | 41.84[a] | 41.78[a] | 42.05[ab] |
| 0.5% P + Phytase | | 74.44[a] | 67.86[a] | 38.74[a] | 34.33[b] | 32.51[b] | 39.74[b] |
| 0.4% P + Phytase | | 77.41[a] | 57.07[b] | 38.86[a] | 33.59[b] | 38.37[b] | 44.75[a] |
| 0.3% P + Phytase | | 77.01[a] | 59.48[ab] | 38.85[a] | 39.69[a] | 37.51[b] | 45.30[a] |
| Floor  0.5% P | 27.07[x] | | 35.18[x] | 34.64[xy] | 31.73[y] | 32.73[x] | 36.11[xy] |
| 0.5% P + Phytase | 27.07[x] | | 34.24[x] | 33.67[y] | 32.95[y] | 29.05[xy] | 33.89[y] |
| 0.4% P + Phytase | 27.07[x] | | 32.58[xy] | 36.37[xy] | 33.53[xy] | 27.53[y] | 35.55[xy] |
| 0.3% P + Phytase | 27.07[x] | | 28.96[y] | 37.50[x] | 36.90[x] | 30.62[xy] | 38.04[x] |

[1]NRC dietary requirement of 0.5% available inorganic phosphorus (P) and 1.0% calcium (Ca); 0.4% P and 0.8% Ca; 0.3% P and 0.6% Ca.
[2] Week 0 values represent the starting concentration of litter nitrogen (N); values for the cage facility represent average weekly manure N content; values for the conventional house represent litter N buildup.
[a,b; x,y]In a column, means with unlike superscripts differ significantly (P<0.05).

**Table 7. Influence of Allzyme Phytase (Phy) supplementation in diets with varying concentrations of available phosphorus (AP%) on nitrogen (N) excreted in raw manure from caged broilers and on accumulation of phosphorus in litter in the conventional house.**

| | Starter[1] | | | Grower[1] | | | Finisher[1] | | |
|---|---|---|---|---|---|---|---|---|---|
| Diets | TP (%) | AP (%) | N (g/kg DMI) | TP (%) | AP (%) | N (g/kg DMI) | TP (%) | AP (%) | N (g/kg DMI) |
| **Cage** | | | | | | | | | |
| 0.5% P | 0.72 | 0.50 | 28.0[a] | 0.70 | 0.50 | 41.6[a] | 0.41 | 0.21 | 25.0[a] |
| 0.5% P+ Phy | 0.72 | 0.50 | 28.4[a] | 0.70 | 0.50 | 35.0[b] | 0.41 | 0.21 | 23.6[a] |
| 0.4% P+ Phy | 0.62 | 0.40 | 26.9[a] | 0.60 | 0.40 | 36.8[b] | 0.41 | 0.21 | 26.6[a] |
| 0.3% P+ Phy | 0.52 | 0.30 | 27.3[a] | 0.50 | 0.30 | 38.5[a] | 0.41 | 0.21 | 26.9[a] |
| **Litter** | | | | | | | | | |
| 0.5% P | 0.72 | 0.50 | 12.4[a] | 0.70 | 0.50 | 32.9[a] | 0.41 | 0.21 | 21.5[a] |
| 0.5% P+ Phy | 0.72 | 0.50 | 12.2[a] | 0.70 | 0.50 | 31.7[a] | 0.41 | 0.21 | 20.1[a] |
| 0.4% P+ Phy | 0.62 | 0.40 | 11.9[a] | 0.60 | 0.40 | 32.3[a] | 0.41 | 0.21 | 21.0[a] |
| 0.3% P+ Phy | 0.52 | 0.30 | 12.3[a] | 0.50 | 0.30 | 33.2[a] | 0.41 | 0.21 | 22.5[a] |

[a,b] Values in a column with unlike superscripts differ from the 0.5% P diet (P<0.05).
[1]DM intake in starter, 0.80 kg; in grower, 1.99 kg; in finisher, 1.19 kg.

to diets for broilers in cage or conventional housing there were significant transitory decreases in manure nitrogen (Tables 6 and 7). However at six weeks of age there were nonsignificant increases in raw manure nitrogen or litter nitrogen from pens with broilers given the 0.3% phosphorus diet with Allzyme Phytase. This observation suggests that either other unaccounted influences may be interfering with protein hydrolysis in the intestinal tract or that the additional side activities of cellulase, protease, xylanase and acid phosphatase associated with Allzyme Phytase may have altered mucus secretion or even the microbial populations to an extent that additional nitrogen may have been eliminated in the feces of Allzyme Phytase-fed broilers. This hypothesis may be supported by the observation that there were slight depressions in body weight in all but one of the Allzyme Phytase treatments (Table 2). Additional studies are needed to understand the influence of phytate on protein digestibility in broilers.

## Summary

A worldwide concern about land application of poultry and livestock wastes is resulting in legislation in many countries that could result in national standards on pollution from phosphorus and nitrogen run-off into ground and surface waters. The use of microbial phytase in animal feeds has the potential to reduce significantly the concentration of phosphorus in manure by releasing the phytate phosphorus in the cell walls of feed grains thereby reducing the requirement for supplementation of inorganic phosphorus to animal diets. The phytate phosphorus meets the needs of the animal, and the resulting manure contains less inorganic phosphorus. Using both a novel broiler cage rearing unit, the Farmer Automatic Broilermatic® System, and a conventional litter-covered floor in a conventional broiler house, studies were conducted to ascertain production of phosphorus and nitrogen in manure from beneath broilers in cages and in built-up wood shavings litter. The use of Allzyme Phytase in the diet did not significantly affect performance even though with the lowest inorganic phosphorus diet body weights tended to be slightly lower than in controls with the NRC recommended dietary level of 0.5% available phosphorus. In the conventional environment, FCR was improved between 2 and 5 points with phytase supplementation, but this was not evident in the cage house. The FCR in the cage house was improved by 28 points probably due primarily to the fact that the cage house was tunnel-ventilated using a Kool-Cell. There were no differences in mortality rates between the cage and conventional environments. However, there was a definitive trend toward decreased phosphorus in the wastes of broilers provided supplemental Allzyme Phytase with reductions in manure and litter phosphorus contents ranging to 32.2% in the raw manure from the cage house to 26.6% in litter in the conventional house. The nitrogen content of the manure was reduced in response to Allzyme Phytase suggesting that phytase supplementation can improve nitrogen utilization by the broiler chicken. These data suggest that the use of phytase in diets to replace inorganic phosphorus has a significant place in broiler management in both cage and conventional environments.

# References

Andrews, L. D. and T. L. Goodwin, 1973. Performance of broilers in cages. Poultry Sci. 52:723–728.

Andrews, L. D., G. S. Nelson, G. C. Harris, Jr. and T. L. Goodwin. 1975. Performance of five strains of broilers in a four tier cage system with plastic floors. Poultry Sci. 54:54–58.

Aoyagi, S. and D. Baker. 1995. Effect of microbial phytase and 1,25–dihydroxycholecalciferol on dietary copper utilization in chicks. Poultry Sci. 74:121–126.

Atwal, A. S., N. A. M. Eskin, B. E. McDonald and M. Vaisey–Genser. 1980. The effects of phytate on nitrogen utilization and zinc metabolism in young rats. Nutrition Reports Internat. 21:257–267.

Balander, R. J. and C. Flegal. 1996. The effect of using phosphatase enzyme on the performance of growing market turkeys and excreted phosphorus. Poultry Sci. 75(Suppl. 1):60 (Abstr).

Balander, R. J., and C Flegal. 1997. The effect of phytase on egg production and egg specific gravity in laying hens. Poultry Sci. 76(Suppl. 1):3 (Abstr).

Bayer, R. C., F. V. Muir, C. B. Chawan and A. T. Bryan. 1976. Infected feather follicles in cage reared broilers. Poultry Sci. 55:1194–1200.

Biehl, R. R., D. H. Baker and H. F. DeLuca. 1995. 1–α–hydroxylated cholecalciferol compounds act additively with microbial phytase to improve phosphorus, zinc, and manganese utilization in chicks fed soy–based diets. J. Nutr. 125:2407–2416.

Broz, J., P. Oldale, A. H. Perrin–Voltz, G. Rychen, J. Schulze and C. Simoes Nunes. 1994. Effect of supplemental phytase on performance and phosphorus utilization in broiler chickens fed low phosphorus diets without addition of inorganic phosphates. Br. Poult. Sci. 35: 273–280.

Caldwell, R. A. 1992. Effect of calcium and phytic acid on the activation of trypsinogen and the stability of trypsin. J. Agric. Food Chem. 40:43–46.

Cromwell, G. L. 1980. Biological availability of phosphorus in feedstuffs for swine. Feedstuffs 52(9):38–42.

Davies, M. I., G. M. Ritcey and I. Motzok. 1970. Intestinal phytase and alkaline phosphatase of chicks: Influence of dietary calcium, inorganic and phytate phosphorus and vitamin $D_3$. Poultry Sci. 49:1280–1286.

Denbow, D. M., V. Ravindran, E. T. Kornegay, Z. Yi and R. M. Hulet. 1995. Improving phosphorus availability in soybean meal for broilers by supplemental phytase. Poultry Sci. 74:1831–1842.

Edens, F. W. 1976. Body temperature and blood chemistry responses in broiler cockerels given a single intravenous injection of $Na^+$ or $Ca^{++}$ before an acute heating episode. Poultry Sci. 55:2248–2255.

Edwards, H. M., Jr. 1993. Dietary 1, 25–dihydroxycholecalciferol supplementation increases natural phytate phosphorus utilization in chickens. J. Nutr. 123:567–577.

Erdman, Jr., J. W. 1979. Oil seed phytates: Nutritional implications. J. Am. Oil Chem. Soc. 56:736–741.

Havenstein, G. B., J. L. Grimes, P. R. Ferket, C. R. Parkhurst, F. W. Edens, J. Brake and J. H. van Middelkoop. 1998. Recent experiences with reduced or non–litter systems for growing broilers and turkeys. In: Proceedings: 1998 National Poultry Waste Management Symposium. Springdale, AR. October 19–21, 1998. Pages 225–240.

Heinzl, W. 1996. Technical specifications of Natuphos. In: BASF Technical Symposium: Phosphorus and Calcium Management in Layers. Atlanta, GA. January 23, 1996. Pages 21–36.

Hoppe, P. P. and G. Schwarz. 1993. Experimental approaches to establish the phosphorus equivalency of *Aspergillus niger* phytase in pigs. In: Proceedings of the 1st Symposium, Enzymes in Animal Nutrition. Kartause, Ittingen, Switzerland. Pages 187–192.

Knuckles, B. E., D. D. Kuzmicky and A. A. Betschart. 1985. The effect of phytate and partially hydrolyzed phytate on *in vivo* protein digestibility. J. Food Sci. 50: 1080–1082.

Kornegay, E. T. 1996a. Effect of phytase on the bioavailability of phosphorus, calcium, amino acids, and trace minerals in broilers and turkeys. In: BASF Technical Symposium: Phosphorus and Calcium Management in Layers. Atlanta, GA. January 23, 1996. Pages 39–68.

Kornegay, E. T. 1996b. Phytase supplementation of corn–soybean meal broiler diets. In: BASF Technical Symposium: Use of Natuphos Phytase in Poultry Nutrition and Waste Management. 1996 Carolina Swine Nutrition Conference, Raleigh, NC. November 12, 1996. Pages 63–72.

Lloyd, R. W., G. W. Chaloupka and W. C. Kause. 1971. Incidence of feather follicle infection of broilers grown in cages. Poultry Sci. 50:1598.

Lloyd, R. W. and G. W. Chaloupka. 1972. The effect of plastic mat inserts in plastic coops on broiler performance. Poultry Sci. 51:1829–1830.

McKnight, W. F. 1996. Efficacy of microbial phytase in broiler grower diets. In: BASF Technical Symposium: Use of Natuphos Phytase in Poultry Nutrition and Waste Management. 1996 Carolina Swine Nutrition Conference, Raleigh, NC Pages 46–60.

McKnight, W. F. 1998. Nutritional alternatives to reduce nutrient loading enzymes. In: Proceedings: National Poultry Waste Management Symposium. Springdale, AR, October 19–20, 1998. Pages 160–168.

McQuaig, L. W., M. I. Davis and I. Motzok. 1972. Intestinal alkaline phosphatase and phytase in chicks: Effect of dietary magnesium, calcium, phosphorus, and thyroactive casein. Poultry Sci. 51:526–530.

Moore, R. J. and T. L. Veum. 1983. Adaptive increase in phytate digestibility by phosphorus–derived rates and the relationship of intestinal phytase and alkaline phosphatase to phytate utilization. Br. J. Nutri. 49:145–151.

Nelson, T. S., T. R. Shieh, R. J. Wodzinski and J. H. Ware. 1971. Effect of supplemental phytase on the utilization of phytate phosphorus by chicks. J. Nutr. 101:1289–1294.

Peeler, H. T. 1972. Biological availability of nutrients in feed. Availability of major mineral ions. J. Anim. Sci. 35:695–699.

Pointillart, A., C. Colin, C. Lacroix and J. Radisson. 1993. Reduction chez le pore en croissance de la supplementation en phosphorus mineral par l'utilization de cereales a activite elevee. Jour. Recher. Porcine, France, 25e: 233–238.

Qian, H., E. T. Kornegay and D. M. Denbow. 1996a. Phosphorus equivalence of microbial phytase in turkey diets as influenced by calcium to phosphorus ratios and phosphorus levels. Poultry Sci. 75:69–81.

Qian, H., H. P. Veit, E. T. Kornegay, V. Ravindran and D. M. Denbow. 1996b. Effect of supplemental phytase and phosphorus on histological and other tibial bone characteristics and performances of broilers fed semi–purified diets. Poultry Sci. 75:618–626.

Qian, H., E. T. Kornegay and D. M. Denbow. 1997. Utilization of phytate phosphorus and calcium as influenced by microbial phytase, cholecalciferol, and the calcium:total phosphorus ratio in broiler diets. Poultry Sci. 76:37–46.

Roberson, K. D. and H. M. Edwards. 1994. Effects of 1,25–dihydroxy-cholecalciferol and phytase on zinc utilization in broiler chicks. Poultry Sci. 73:1312–1326.

Sandberg, A. S., T. Larsen and B. Sandstrom. 1993. High dietary calcium levels decrease colonic phytase degradation in pigs. J. Nutr. 123:559–566.

SAS Institute. 1994. SAS® User's Guide: Statistics. SAS Institute, Cary, NC, USA.

Sauveur, B. 1993. Les phytases fongiques dans l'aliment des volailles. INRA Prod. Anim. 4:265–267.

Scheideler, S. E. and J. L. Sell. 1987. Utilization of phytate phosphorus in laying hens as influenced by dietary phosphorus and calcium levels. Nutr. Rep. Int. 35:1073–1081.

Schmitt, M. and G. Rehm. 1998. Fertilizing cropland with poultry manure. University of Minnesota Extension Service Bull. FO–5881–GO, Department of Soil, Water and Climate, Minneapolis–St. Paul, MN.

Schoner, B. R. J., P. P. Hoppe, G. Schwarz and H. Wiesche. 1991. Comparative effects of microbial phytase and inorganic phosphorus on performance and retention of phosphorus, calcium, and crude ash in broilers. J. Anim. Physiol. Anim. Nutr. 66:248–255.

Schoner, B. R. J., P. P. Hoppe, G. Schwarz and H. Wiesche. 1993. Effects of microbial phytase and inorganic phosphate in broiler chickens: performance and mineral retention at various calcium levels. J. Anim. Physiol. Anim. Nutr. 69:235–244.

Sebastian, S., S. P. Touchburn, E. R. Chavez and P. C. Lague. 1996a. The effects of supplemental microbial phytase on the performance and utilization of dietary calcium, phosphorus, copper, and zinc in broiler chickens fed corn–soybean diets. Poultry Sci. 75:729–736.

507

Sebastian, S., S. P. Touchburn, E. R. Chavez and P. C. Lague. 1996b. Efficacy of supplemental microbial phytase at different dietary calcium levels on growth and performance and mineral utilization of broiler chickens. Poultry Sci. 75:1516–1523.

Simons, P. C. M. and H. A. J. Versteegh. 1992. The effect of the addition of microbial phytase to layer feed on the technical results and skeleton and egg shell quality. Spelderholt Publication No. 568.

Simons, P. C. M. and H. A. J. Versteegh. 1993. The effect of the addition of low doses of microbial phytase to layer feed on the technical results and skeleton and egg shell quality. Spelderholt Publication No. 589.

Simons, P. C. M., H. A. J. Versteegh, A. W. Jongbloed, P. A. Keeme, P. Slump, K. D. Bos, M. G. E. Wolters, R. F. Beudeker and G. J. Verschoor. 1990. Improvement of phosphorus availability by microbial phytase in broilers and pigs. Br. J. Nutr. 64:525–540.

Simons, P. C. M., A. W. Jongbloed, H. A. J. Versteegh and P. A. Keeme. 1992. Improvement of phosphorus availability by microbial phytase in poultry and pigs. In: Proceeding Georgia Nutrition Conf. November 17–19, 1992, Atlanta, GA. Pages 100–107.

Smith, W. M, 1972. Whither cages in broilers? Poultry Digest. 31:76–77.

Stillborn, H. 1998. Nutrition influences animal waste output. Feedstuffs, 70(18): 20:42–46.

Swick, R. A. and F. J. Ivey. 1990. Effect of dietary phytase addition on broiler performance in phosphorus deficient diets. Poultry Sci. 69 (Suppl. 1):133 (Abstr).

Van der Klis, J. D. and H. A. J. Versteegh. 1994. Effect of dietary measures to decrease phosphorus excretion by poultry. In: Nutrient Management Symposium: Seed and Feed Formulation Research and Its Implications for Nutrient Management. Harrisburg, Pennsylvania. Pages 1–4.

Van der Klis, J. D. and H. A. J. Versteegh. 1997a. The degradation of inositol phosphates in broilers. 1. The effect of dietary calcium and absorbable phosphorus content. In: WPSA European Symposium on Poultry Nutrition. Faaborg, Denmark. August 24–28, 1997. Pages 465–467.

Van der Klis, J. D. and H. A. J. Versteegh. 1997b. The degradation of inositol phosphates in broilers. 2. The effect of age. In: WPSA European Symposium on Poultry Nutrition. Faaborg, Denmark. August 24–28, 1997. Pages 468–470.

Van der Klis, J. D., H. A. J. Versteegh and P. C. M. Simons. 1996. Natuphos in laying hen nutrition. In: BASF Technical Symposium. Phosphorus and Calcium Management in Layers. Carolina Poultry Nutrition Conference. Pages 71–83.

Van der Klis, J. D., H. A. J. Versteegh, P. C. M. Simons and A. K. Kies. 1997. The efficacy of phytase in corn–soybean meal–based diets for laying hens. Poultry Sci. 76:1535–1542.

Vest, L., B. Merka and W. I. Segars. 1994. Poultry Waste: Georgia's 50 Million Dollar Forgotten Crop. Leaflet 206. Georgia Cooperative Extension Service, Athens, GA.

Williams, P. E. V. 1997. Poultry production and science: Future directions in nutrition. World's Poultry Sci. J. 53:33–48.

Yi, Z., E. T. Kornegay and D. M. Denbow. 1996a. Improving phytate phosphorus availability in corn and soybean meal for broilers using microbial phytase and calculation of phosphorus equivalency values for phytase. Poultry Sci. 75:240–249.

Yi, Z., E. T. Kornegay and D. M. Denbow. 1996b. Supplemental microbial phytase improves zinc utilization in broilers. Poultry Sci. 75:540–546.

Zublena, J. P., J. C. Barker and T. A. Carter. 1993. Soil Facts: Poultry Manure as a Fertilizer Source. North Carolina Cooperative Extension Service, Raleigh, NC. 12

# Phytase applications in commercial broiler diets in Maryland

JEANNINE HARTER-DENNIS

*University of Maryland-Eastern Shore, Princess Anne, Maryland, USA*

## Introduction: The Water Quality Improvement Act of 1998 in Maryland

During the summer of 1997 the state of Maryland experienced outbreaks of Pfiesteria in several of its rivers and tributaries. These dinoflagellate microorganisms were implicated in several fish kills that closed affected rivers to fishing and tourism. Similar outbreaks were experienced in North Carolina and other east coast areas, and although not proven there was thought to be a link between these outbreaks and nutrient over-enrichment of the soil due to manure application and subsequent runoff, as phosphorus runoff into surface water has been identified as one of the possible causative agents. In the fall of 1997 the governor of Maryland established a Blue Ribbon Citizens Pfiesteria Action Commission to study the problem and make recommendations to the legislature. In the spring of 1998, the Water Quality Improvement Act of 1998 was passed by the Maryland Senate and the House and signed by the governor. This bill mandates that any farm using sludge or animal manure must have a nitrogen- and phosphorus-based nutrient management plan. The nitrogen plans must be developed by 2001 and implemented by 2002, while the phosphorus plans must be developed and implemented by 2004 and 2005, respectively. Farms using chemical fertilizers must also have nutrient management plans, but the deadlines are 2001 and 2002, respectively, for nitrogen and phosphorus. One additional regulation included in the Water Quality Improvement Act of 1998 is that all contract feed manufactured for chickens must contain phytase or some other enzyme or additive that reduces phosphorus excretion. This must be implemented by the end of the year 2000.

## Barley utilization and manure phosphorus reduction: research areas on the Delmarva

### INCREASING THE POTENTIAL FOR BARLEY UTILIZATION IN BROILER DIETS

Modern broiler diets are composed in large part of a mixture of corn and soybean meal fortified with vitamins and minerals; however there has been interest in the last few years on the Delmarva peninsula in the use of barley instead of corn. Corn is a high energy ingredient and soybean meal is rich in protein. When these two ingredients are combined the resulting feed provides a relatively good combination of amino acids and a high metabolizable energy (ME) level for maximal growth and feed efficiency. The use of barley in this region is of interest because farmers are able to harvest barley several weeks before wheat, which enables them to plant soybeans earlier to increase yield. Historically, barley has been considered a less desirable grain for use in broiler diets due to its high fiber content and the presence of ß-glucans, which are poorly digested nonstarch polysaccharides (NSP). ß-glucans increase digesta viscosity resulting in reduced intestinal absorption of nutrients as well as causing wet litter. These factors contribute to the low ME value for broilers and limit the use of barley, particularly for young birds. Adding the enzyme ß-glucanase has been shown to improve the digestibility of NSP in barley (Petterson and Aman, 1990); however, this practice increases the cost of the diet and makes it more expensive than using corn.

Part of our research has focused on inclusion of locally-produced barley varieties in diets fed to growing broilers with and without the use of the supplemental enzyme ß-glucanase. Because preliminary studies have shown that younger birds perform poorly when fed barley in comparison to corn, we have concentrated on finding ways to maximize the inclusion levels of the Callao and Nomini barley varieties in broiler chicken diets from 21–42 days of age. We also compared the 1996 and 1997 harvests of these two varieties grown in the same location in Virginia. Samples were submitted for *in vitro* metabolizable energy (ME) determinations at the University of Georgia. These ME values were then used in feeding trials to provide comparisons with the ME values reported by the National Research Council. Supplemental ß-glucanase enzyme was also evaluated in growing broilers fed graded levels of barley.

### PHOSPHORUS REDUCTION IN DIETS CONTAINING CORN AND BARLEY

The Delmarva is a peninsula on the northeastern US coast that separates Chesapeake Bay from Delaware Bay and the Atlantic Ocean. It includes all of Delaware and parts of eastern Maryland and Virginia (Figure 1). There are approximately 625 million commercial broilers produced annually on the Delmarva peninsula resulting in approximately

512

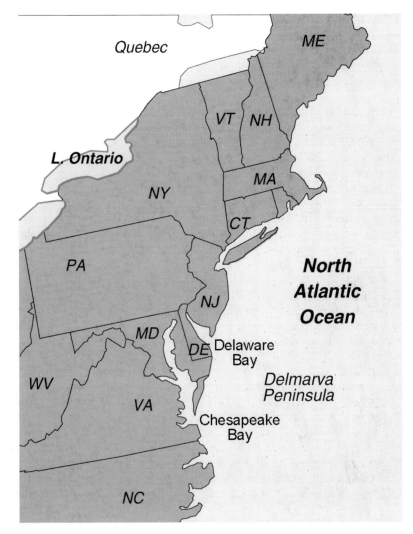

**Figure 1.** The Delmarva Peninsula, between the Chesapeake and Delaware Bays on the eastern coast of the US.

53 million pounds of manure nitrogen and 22 million pounds of manure phosphorus. These figures are based on feeding typical corn-soybean meal based diets formulated to National Research Council recommendations. Simmons *et al.* (1990) reported that 60–80% of the total phosphorus present in many grains, oilseed meals and plant products is bound in the form of phytic acid (myoinositol hexaphosphate) in the material. Since nonruminants contain relatively little intestinal phytase (Nelson, 1976) the phosphorus content of plant-source ingredients is considered to be only 30–40 % bioavailable. Due to this poor bioavailability of plant source phosphorus, nutritionists are forced

to supplement practical feeds with inorganic phosphorus to ensure proper growth and bone development. It has been demonstrated, however, that phosphorus in the phytate ring can be released through the action of phytase enzyme. Typically, phytase has been reported to increase phosphorus bioavailability by 25–50% and reduce phosphorus excretion by 15–40% in grain based diets for swine and poultry.

Factors that also affect the efficacy of the phytase enzyme include dietary calcium and phosphorus levels (Wise, 1983), the age of the birds (Edwards, *et al.*1989) and dietary vitamin $D_3$ (Edwards, 1991; 1993; Mohammed *et al.*, 1991). An additional factor influencing bioavalability of phosphorus in chickens is the types of ingredients in the diet. Several ingredients have been reported to contain endogenous phytase activity (Bartnik and Szafranska, 1987) but the levels vary widely in different cereal grains. Eeckhout and De Paepe (1994) reported that out of 50 feedstuffs analyzed only rye, triticale, wheat and barley contained appreciable amounts of phytase activity (5130, 1688, 1193 and 582 units/kg, respectively). Corn, oats, sorghum and oilseeds were reported to contain little endogenous phytase activity. Templeton *et al.* (1965a,b) demonstrated that diets containing 32–36% wheat and 10% barley without supplemental inorganic phosphorus provided chicks with usable phytate phosphorus due to endogenous phytase in the grains.

With interest in nutrient management becoming more and more important we have also begun to evaluate the availability of phosphorus in broiler diets containing 30% barley. Barley contains endogenous phytase that may result in an increase in phosphorus digestibility and reduce the need for supplemental phosphorus. Ultimately, this would reduce the amount of phosphorus excreted in the manure, resulting in a more favorable nitrogen:phosphorus ratio for soil application if used as a fertilizer.

## Effects of phytase in diets containing either corn or 30% barley and supplemental ß-glucanase

While it is likely that the inclusion of phytase will be commonplace in broiler feeds on Delmarva owing to the provisions of the Water Quality Act, there are no data currently available on its effects in diets containing the types of barley grown in this region. The objective of the following trial is a comparison of barley with corn in the grow/finish diet while using ß-glucanase to reduce gut viscosity and phytase to increase phosphorus bioavailability. Using the two enzyme products in the same diet allowed the opportunity to observe both enzyme response and any interactions that might exist between the two enzymes.

## EXPERIMENTAL PROCEDURES

Four hundred male broiler chicks were fed a commercial starter diet from 0–21 days of age. Following an overnight fast at 21 days of age birds were individually weighed, wingbanded and a homogenous group of 180 birds were selected for the experiment. Birds were allotted to treatments in a manner that ensured similar average weights and weight ranges for all pens. The grow/finish test diets were formulated to contain 0.90% calcium and 0.35 or 0.25% available phosphorus (Table 1). The experimental design

**Table 1. Dietary treatments.**

| Ingredients | Available phosphorus (%) | Enzyme supplement |
|---|---|---|
| Corn/soybean meal | 0.35 | None |
| Corn/soybean meal | 0.35 | Allzyme Phytase |
| Corn/soybean meal | 0.25 | None |
| Corn/soybean meal | 0.25 | Allzyme Phytase |
| 30% Callao barley/corn/soy | 0.25 | None |
| 30% Callao barley/corn/soy | 0.25 | ß-glucanase |
| 30% Callao barley/corn/soy | 0.25 | Allzyme Phytase |
| 30% Callao barley/corn/soy | 0.25 | ß-glucanase + phytase |

**Table 2. Composition of basal diets (%).[1]**

| | Corn/soy-based diets | | 30% barley-based diets |
|---|---|---|---|
| | 0.35%AP | 0.25%AP[2] | 0.25%AP[2,3] |
| Corn | 71.23 | 71.24 | 35.98 |
| Barley | – | – | 30.00 |
| Soybean meal | 25.16 | 25.20 | 26.70 |
| Corn oil | 0.80 | 0.79 | 4.57 |
| Limestone | 1.13 | 1.60 | 1.66 |
| CDP | 1.21 | 0.66 | 0.57 |
| Salt | 0.17 | 0.24 | 0.24 |
| Coccidiostat | 0.10 | 0.10 | 0.10 |
| d,l-methionine | 0.07 | 0.07 | 0.07 |
| Mineral mix | 0.05 | 0.05 | 0.05 |
| Vitamin mix | 0.05 | 0.05 | 0.05 |

[1]Calculated analysis: ME, 3080 kcal/kg, CP=19.25%, lysine=1.01%, sulfur amino acids = 0.69%, calcium = 0.90%
[2]Allzyme Phytase added at 0.20% to supply 11,500 PTU/kg.
[3] ß-glucanase added at 0.10%.

was a randomized complete block with eight treatments (Table 2) with four replicate groups per treatment and five male broilers per replicate. All diets contained the NRC-recommended ME:crude protein ratios of 160; and minimum crude protein:lysine and crude protein:total sulfur amino acid ratios were 20.0 and 27.78, respectively. Feed and water were offered *ad libitum.* Birds were housed in floor pens with wood shaving/sawdust litter.

Growth performance and efficiency during the 21–42 days period were evaluated. At 42 days of age birds were weighed, slaughtered and gut contents were collected (post-duodenum to Merckel's diverticulum), pooled within pen, centrifuged and viscosity of the supernatant determined using a Brookfield Digital Viscometer (Brookfield Engineering Laboratories, Inc., Stoughton, MA). Bone breaking strength and ash content were determined on the right tibias from two birds/pen. Data were analyzed using the General Linear Model with treatment and replicate as sources of variation. Duncan's Multiple Range Test was used to separate treatment means where appropriate.

RESULTS

Reducing available phosphorus (AP) content from 0.35% to 0.25% in the corn/soy diets did not statistically decrease weight gain, however the group given 0.25% without enzyme had the lowest weight gain (Table 3, Figure 2). Bone breaking strength was reduced by lowering available phosphorus (20.63 kg *vs* 18.40 kg) (Table 4). The addition of Allzyme Phytase improved bone breaking strength in both the adequate phosphorus (22.83 kg *vs* 20.63 kg, respectively) and the phosphorus deficient diets (25.57 kg *vs* 18.40 kg, respectively). Bone ash content followed a similar trend.

Table 3.  Effect of dietary available phosphorus level, ß-glucanase and Allzyme Phytase on performance of male broilers from 21-42 days.

| Treatment | Weight gain, (g) | Gain/feed | Feed intake (g) |
|---|---|---|---|
| Corn/soy 0.35% AP | 1458[bc] | 0.445[ab] | 3277 |
| Corn/soy 0.35% AP +Phytase | 1545[abc] | 0.476[ab] | 3248 |
| Corn/soy 0.25% AP | 1399[c] | 0.436[b] | 3227 |
| Corn/soy 0.25% AP +Phytase | 1541[abc] | 0.464[ab] | 3324 |
| 30% barley 0.25% AP | 1616[ab] | 0.480a[b] | 3378 |
| 30% barley 0.25% AP + ß-glucanase | 1665[ab] | 0.496[ab] | 3353 |
| 30% barley 0.25% AP + Phytase | 1559[abc] | 0.432[b] | 3616 |
| 30% barley 0.25% AP + ß-glucanase, Phytase | 1541[abc] | 0.481[ab] | 3217 |
| P>F | P<0.001 | P=0.005 | P=0.074 |

Means in columns with different superscripts differ.

Birds given the diets with 30% barley performed as well or better than those given corn-based diets, particularly when ß-glucanase was added. When available phosphorus was decreased from 0.35% to 0.25% in the diets containing 30% barley there was no significant decrease in either bone breaking strength or bone ash (Figure 3). Birds consuming the 30%

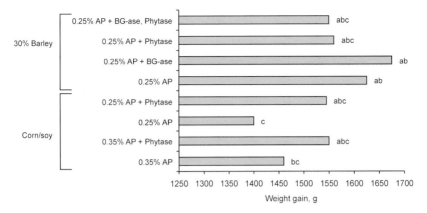

**Figure 2.** Effect of supplemental enzymes on weight gain of broilers fed corn/soy or corn/soy/barley diets.

barley diet formulated to contain 0.25% AP had bone ash values of 51.73% compared to 47.62% when fed the low available phosphorus corn diet. Bone breaking strength followed a similar trend (20.12 kg *vs* 18.40 kg, respectively). Supplemental phytase in the barley diets did not significantly improve either bone breaking strength or bone ash content. These results suggest that phosphorus in barley may be more digestible than phosphorus in corn.

These results suggest that there is no adverse reaction when combining supplemental ß-glucanase and phytase enzymes in the same diet for broiler chickens. Although there were no statistical differences detected, supplemental ß-glucanase tended to reduce gut content viscosity when added to the barley diet.

## Conclusions

The inclusion of barley into broiler grower diets represents a market opportunity for grain producers. With over 2 billion tons of feed fed annually to Delmarva broilers, the industry could absorb all the local barley produced if it were an acceptable ingredient source for broilers. In this trial barley replaced 30% of the corn in a commercial broiler grower diet with no detriment to performance when supplemental ß-glucanase enzyme was added. This work also determined that the ß-glucanase and phytase enzymes can be mixed without any interference in the mode of action of either product. The benefit of endogenous phytase in barley is not clear and additional work may be needed in this area.

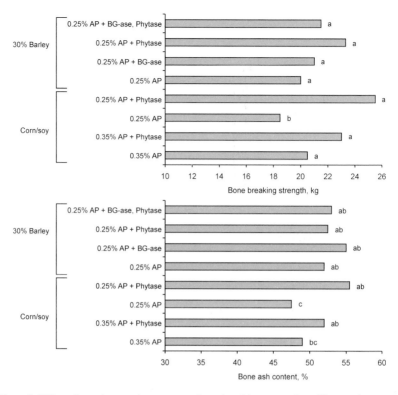

**Figure 3.** Effect of supplemental enzymes on bone breaking strength and bone ash content.

**Table 4. Effect of available phosphorus level, ß-glucanase and Allzyme Phytase on bone break-ing strength, bone ash content and digesta viscosity.**

| Treatment | Bone breaking strength, kg | Bone ash, % | Gut viscosity, cps |
|---|---|---|---|
| Corn/soy 0.35% AP | 20.63[a] | 48.49[bc] | 2.60[a] |
| Corn/soy 0.35% AP +Phytase | 22.83[a] | 51.82[ab] | 2.63[a] |
| | | | |
| Corn/soy 0.25% AP | 18.40[b] | 47.62[c] | 2.43[a] |
| Corn/soy 0.25% AP +Phytase | 25.57[a] | 55.64[ab] | 2.61[a] |
| | | | |
| 30% barley 0.25% AP | 20.12[a] | 51.73[ab] | 4.20[b] |
| 30% barley 0.25% AP + ß glucanase | 20.77[a] | 54.59[ab] | 3.26[ab] |
| 30% barley 0.25% AP + phytase | 23.32[a] | 52.67[ab] | 2.92[ab] |
| 30% barley 0.25% AP + ß-glucanase + phytase | 21.33[a] | 53.00[ab] | 3.21[ab] |
| P value | P=0.003 | P=0.003 | P<0.001 |

[a,b]Means in columns with different superscripts differ.

# References

Bartnik, M. and I. Szafranska. 1987. Changes in phytate content and phytase activity during germination of some cereals. J. of Cereal Sci. 5:23–28.

Edwards, H. M. Jr., Palo, P., Soonchaerenying, S. and M.A. Elliott. 1989. Factors influencing the bioavailability of phytate phosphorus to chickens. In: *Nutrient Availability: Chemical and Biological Aspects* (southgate, D. Johnson, I. and G.R. Fenwick, Eds). The Royal Society of Chemistry, Cambridge, pp. 271–276.

Edwards, H. M. Jr. 1991. Effects of phytase utilization on monogastric animals. Proc. of the Georgia Nutr. Conf. For Feed Manufacturers, Atlanta, pp.1–6.

Edwards, H. M. Jr. 1993. Dietary 1,25-dihydroxycholecalciferol supplementation increases natural phytate phosphorus in chickens. Jour. of Nutr. 123:567–577.

Eeckhout, W. and M. De Paepe. 1994. Total phosphorus, phytate-phosphorus and phytase activity in plant feedstuffs. Anim. and Feed Sci. Tech. 47:19–29.

Mohammed, A., M.J. Gibney and T.G. Taylor. 1991. The effect of dietary levels of inorganic phosphorus, calcium and cholecalciferol on the digest-ibility of phytate-P by the chick. Br. Jour. of Nutr. 66:251–259.

Nelson, T.S., 1976. The hydrolysis of phytate phosphorus by poultry: a review. Poultry Sci. 46:862–871.

Petterson, D. and P. Aman. 1990. Enzyme supplementation of broiler chicken diets based on cereals with endosperm cell walls rich in arabinoxylans or mixed-link (-glucans. Anim. Prod. 51:201–207.

Simons, P.C., H.A.J. Versteegh, A.W Jongbloed, P.A. Kemme, P. Stump, K.D Bos, M.G.E. Wolters, R. F. Beudeker and G.J. Verschoor. 1990. Improvement of phosphorus availability by microbial phytase in broil-ers and pigs. Br. Jour.of Nutr. 64:525–540.

Templeton, H., J. Dudley and G. J. Pickering. 1965a. Phosphorus require-ments of poultry. IV. The effects on growing pullets of feeding diets containing no animal protein or supplementary phosphorus. Br. Poultry Sci. 6:125–133.

Templeton, H., J. Dudley and G. J. Pickering. 1965b. Phosphorus require-ments of poultry. IV. The effects during the subsequent laying year of feeding growing diets containing no animal protein or supplementary phosphorus. Br. Poultry Sci. 6:135–141.

Wise, A. 1983. Dietary factors determining the biological activities of phytate. Nutr. Abs. And Rev. 53:791–806.

# ORGANIC SELENIUM: SCIENTIFIC DATA AND PRACTICAL RESPONSES

# Organic selenium: using nature's model to redefine selenium supplementation for animals

DONALD C. MAHAN

*Department of Animal Science, Ohio State University, Columbus, Ohio, USA*

## Summary

The history of selenium has been plagued with much controversy, but it is now clearly recognized as a dietary essential by both the scientific and lay communities. Organic selenium is the form of the element in plant tissues and thus was the sole form originally consumed by animals and humans. After the deficiency was clinically recognized in the early 1960s, inorganic selenium was used to supplement both animal and human diets. Inorganic selenium was found to be clearly effective in the prevention of some diseases and enhanced the production and activity of the selenoenzymes of the body. Newer discoveries using organic selenium have demonstrated that other benefits can arise from the organic form. Enhanced meat quality, maturity of feathers, increased milk selenium and animal fertility and conception rate are reported to be improved when the organic source is fed. Much has yet, however, to be learned about what organic selenium can do.

## Introduction

Whenever a rumor starts, regardless of its truthfulness, it is often difficult to prevent it escalating, whereupon it can easily get out of control and often results in a reputation that is hard to overcome. In relation to selenium toxicity, that is exactly what happened when it was initially shown to result in the death and malformation of animals (Moxon, 1937; Meyer and Buran, 1995). It was initially identified as a poison, and continued to be perceived that way by much of the public – until in 1957 where it was discovered to be an essential nutrient (Schwartz and Foltz, 1957). From that discovery in history selenium would subsequently be found to prevent some major animal diseases that had plagued the industry for years (Muth *et al.*, 1958; Oldfield *et al.*, 1960). The discoveries that selenium was a component of glutathione peroxidase (Rotruck *et al.*, 1973) and the enzyme iodothyronine 5'deiodinase (Behne *et al.*, 1990) provided solid evidence of biological function. The amount of research demonstrating that selenium is vital for animal performance and health is increasing; but current investigations are also beginning to show it may be helpful in curbing one of the more dreaded human health problems - cancer (Clark *et al.* 1997). The incorporation of the element into the organic structure of amino acids or selenoproteins is now showing evidence that its role in several biological mechanisms may surpass that of the inorganic form of the element. Organic selenium may thus be one of the important nutritional keys to improved human and animal health of the 21st century. Because less research has been conducted with organic selenium than the inorganic form, many questions have yet to be asked and answered before we completely understand its role in animal and human nutrition. It is becoming clear from the existing research that the biological function of organic selenium is basically the same for all species and that this form of selenium may be superior to the inorganic form of the element.

## Organic selenium: nature's source for animals and humans

Selenium found in grains produced in nature is organic. Consequently, its initial discovery as a dietary essential nutrient was established from its use in the organic form. Schwartz and Foltz (1957) discovered by feeding brewer's yeast that a liver abnormality could be corrected. The brewer's yeast that was fed was later found to contain a vital component (i.e. Factor 3) that initially established selenium as a nutritional essential. Olson *et al.* (1970) later demonstrated that selenomethionine was the principal form of selenium in wheat and thus selenomethionine is considered the major form of selenium in most non-accumulator plants. Because it was common practice prior to 1970 to house animals outdoors, particularly reproducing animals, and to formulate diets using animal and forage products (unknowingly with an indigenous source of organic selenium) the deficiency occurrence of this element was not recognized until livestock confinement began. Upon the discovery that liver and white muscle problems encountered with livestock were selenium deficiencies, it was the inorganic form of the element, notably sodium selenite, that became the commonly used form of supplemental selenium. The inorganic form of the element was subsequently approved by the United States Food and Drug Administration (FDA). With introduction of an organic selenium supplement from yeast containing selenium in the protein component of the yeast cell and a similar selenoamino acid profile to grains (Kelly and Power, 1995), an organic source of supplemental selenium is now an option (Sel-Plex, Alltech, Inc., Table 1). Consequently, organic selenium may help to revolutionize the industry by the provision of this element into animal diets if research continues to verify its benefits. The high concentration of selenium (1000 ppm) in this product allows a small quantity to be added per ton of complete feed. As a result of several recent discoveries, the role of organic selenium is now being investigated more vigorously for both animals and humans.

Table 1.    Selenium compounds in Sel-Plex[abc].

| Organic compound | % |
|---|---|
| Selenomethionine | 50 |
| Selenocystine | 15 |
| Selenocysteine | 15 |
| Selenocystathione | 10 |
| Methylselenocysteine | 10 |
| Inorganic selenium | 0.10 |

[a] 1000 ppm Se.
[b] Kelley and Power (1995).
[c] Approximately the same composition as grain.

## Inorganic and organic selenium: differences among species

Although the supplementation of inorganic selenium to livestock feeds was initially of tremendous benefit to the livestock industry, evidence is now emerging that the organic form of the element may have additional benefits that surpass that of the inorganic form. This review will discuss other roles that organic selenium plays while performing many of the same functions as inorganic selenium.

### PIGS

One of the recognized biological needs for selenium (Se) in all animal species is for the production of glutathione peroxidase (GSH-Px). This enzyme contains selenium and has an active antioxidant role in the cytosol of the cell where it prevents the accumulation of superoxide molecules from forming toxic free radicals. An experiment comparing the efficacy of the inorganic (selenite) and organic forms (Sel-Plex) in grower-finisher pigs on serum GSH-Px activity demonstrated that the level of dietary selenium necessary to achieve maximum serum GSH-Px activity was approximately 0.05 to 0.10 ppm Se (Figure 1). Although the inorganic form of selenium generally results in higher GSH-Px values at lower dietary selenium levels, both forms clearly attain maximum GSH-Px activity levels at substantially lower levels than those fed to most pigs, i.e. 0.3 ppm Se (Mahan and Parrett, 1996). Figure 1 also demonstrates that higher dietary levels do not further stimulate production of GSH-Px, and that the activity of the enzyme increases with pig age.

The incorporation of selenium into muscle tissue is largely dependent upon the form of selenium provided and secondarily by the level of selenium in the diet. Figure 2 demonstrates that only a small increase in muscle selenium concentration occurred when inorganic selenium was fed,

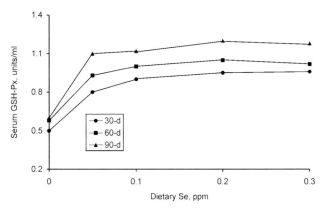

**Figure 1.** Effect of dietary selenium levels on serum glutathione peroxidase activity in grower–finisher pigs at 30, 60 and 90 days postfeeding (Mahan *et al.*, 1999).

whereas when the organic source was provided, there was a linear increase in the selenium content of muscle tissue. This could be important in improving the nutritional quality of pork as well as providing a product with an excellent source and quantity of selenium for humans.

Selenium deficiency in pigs still occurs to some extent during the neonatal and/or post-weaning periods. Inorganic and organic selenium have been found to differ with regard to placental transfer. An experiment evaluated the efficacy of both sources of the element at 0.1 or 0.3 ppm Se (Mahan and Kim, 1996). Figure 3 demonstrates that more selenium from the organic source (Sel-Plex) was transferred to the developing fetus than when the inorganic form was provided to the gestating sow. A higher concentration of selenium was transferred when 0.3 ppm Se level was provided from either selenium source, but the magnitude of increase was higher when the organic source was provided. After the pigs had nursed the sow, pig serum selenium was also higher when organic selenium had

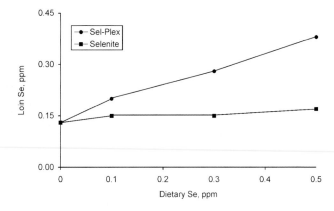

**Figure 2.** Effect of selenium source and level on loin selenium content in grower pigs.

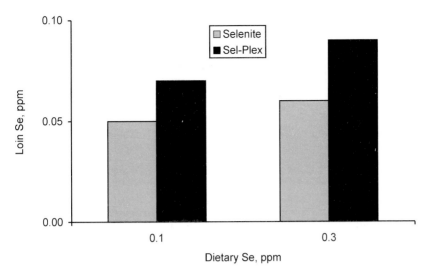

**Figure 3.** Effect of selenium source and level on neonatal pig loin selenium.

been added to the sow's diet (Figure 4). When liver selenium content was evaluated in weaned pigs, there was a higher selenium content when pigs nursed sows fed 0.3 ppm organic Se, but very little difference between the other treatment groups (Figure 5). The data suggest, however, that at low dietary levels some of the organic selenium may be diverted to and incorporated initially into muscle tissue with less being available for incorporation into liver tissue. These data, however, clearly demonstrate that organic selenium was superior for placental and mammary transfer

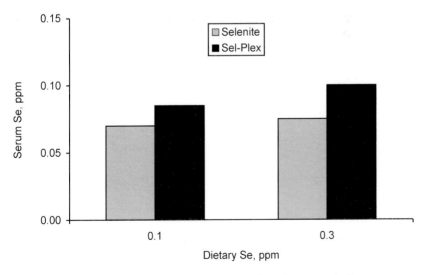

**Figure 4.** Effect of selenium source and level on weanling pig serum selenium content at 21 days.

during gestation and lactation and that pig selenium status at weaning was improved when organic selenium was fed to the female.

To further evaluate the efficacy of selenium forms on selenium transfer to sow milk, an experiment was conducted where various levels of both selenium sources were provided from late gestation through lactation. All sows had been fed 0.3 ppm Se as sodium selenite from breeding to 109 days of gestation whereupon they were fed one of six treatment lactation diets (Mahan, 1999). Both organic (Sel-Plex) and inorganic selenium (selenite) were fed at 0.15 or 0.30 ppm selenium, while another group was fed the combination of organic and inorganic selenium each at 0.15 ppm selenium. The results presented in Figure 6 demonstrate that within four days of feeding the organic form of selenium to sows, the selenium content of the milk increased linearly (P <0.01) as the dietary level increased. When the inorganic form of the element was provided there was a smaller linear increase in milk selenium, whereas the magnitude of the increase when Sel-Plex was provided was much greater. The combination of feeding the sows both organic and inorganic selenium sources resulted in a milk selenium content that was intermediate to that of both groups fed the 0.3 ppm Se. Interestingly, the value of the latter group was almost identical to the milk selenium content when sows had been fed 0.15 ppm Se in the organic form. This suggests that the organic form was readily transferred across the mammary tissue while the inorganic form was not. Additionally, the data demonstrate that organic selenium in the sow diet provided the nursing pig with a higher selenium supply than would have been consumed had the sows been fed sodium selenite. Although it is common in deficiency situations to increase the dietary inorganic selenium level above 0.3 ppm, these results suggest there is little benefit to such an increase.

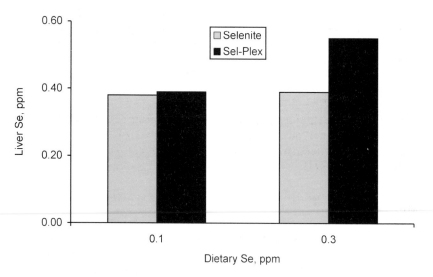

**Figure 5.** Effect of selenium source and level on weanling pig liver selenium content.

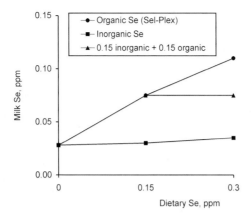

**Figure 6.** Effect of selenium source and level on milk selenium content (average of 7 and 14 days). Sows fed test diets from 109 days gestation through lactation.

POULTRY

The mechanism of selenium absorption and metabolism for poultry is similar to the pig. Glutathione peroxidase and selenium are important in the prevention of exudative diathesis. In this disease, free radical damage of the capillary system results in cellular fluids escaping into the peripheral tissue (Patterson *et al.*, 1957). This condition can be prevented by both inorganic and organic selenium but not vitamin E.

In growing broilers, the rate of feather maturation can be influenced by the dietary source of selenium. The results of Edens (1996) as presented in Figure 7 demonstrate that the inclusion of organic selenium resulted in higher feather scores (i.e. maturity) than when inorganic selenium was fed. The importance of this is two-fold. First, with better feather development the feathers are more easily removed during processing. Secondly, with more mature feathers and better body covering, maintenance energy costs and thus feed requirements are lower. Feeding organic selenium has also resulted in lower broiler mortality than when the inorganic source of the element was provided (Table 2).

The efficacy of feeding inorganic or organic selenium to laying hens is presented in Table 2. Feeding either form of selenium increased the total egg selenium content but feeding organic selenium resulted in a 20% higher selenium content compared to when the inorganic form was provided (Cantor *et al.*, 1997).

MEAT QUALITY

Three reports are helpful in identifying the role of either organic or inorganic selenium in the improvement in meat quality. Munoz and co-workers fed grower-finisher pigs an antioxidant supplement that contained a combination of organic selenium (Sel-Plex), vitamin C and

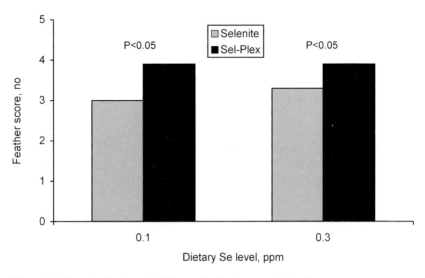

**Figure 7.** Effect of selenite or Sel-Plex on feathering score in broilers.

**Table 2.** Effect of selenium source on egg selenium content[1].

| Item | Basal | + Selenite | + Sel-Plex |
|---|---|---|---|
| Se intake, mg/day | 5 | 34 | 36 |
| Egg selenium (week 6), ppm | 0.06 | 0.20 | 0.24 |
| Total Se/egg, mg | 3.3 | 10.9 | 13.5 |

[1]Cantor (1997).

Vitamin E (cited by Lyons, 1997). Their results demonstrated that the water holding capacity of pork loin was affected by antioxidant supplementation (Figure 8). This was reflected in an increase in the amount of water loss (drip loss) post-slaughter in carcasses from pigs not fed the antioxidant supplement. Other work conducted with poultry by Edens (1996) evaluated the effects of inorganic and organic selenium in two broiler trials (Table 3). They demonstrated that drip loss was lower in both trials when the organic selenium was fed.

**Table 3.** Effect of selenium source on mortality and carcass quality in broilers[1].

| Trial | Treatment | Mortality (%) | Drip loss (%) |
|---|---|---|---|
| 1 | Selenite | 10.2 | 5.3 |
| | Sel-Plex | 7.9 | 4.6 |
| 2 | Selenite | 4.0 | 3.9 |
| | Sel-Plex | 2.0 | 1.9 |

[1]Edens (1996).

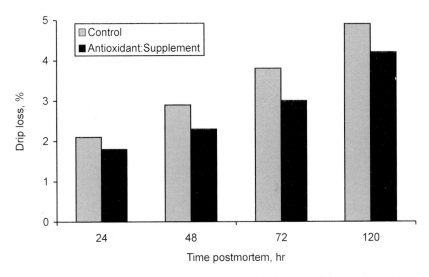

**Figure 8.** Effect of antioxidant supplementation on drip loss from loin muscle in swine.

A recent study by Mahan *et al.* (1999) has demonstrated that there was a trend (P = 0.12) toward a higher drip loss in pork muscle when inorganic selenite was fed, whereas when organic selenium was provided, drip loss was similar to the values from pigs being fed the basal diet without selenium (Figure 9). Drip loss was higher during the 24 to 72 hrs post-slaughter when inorganic selenium was provided, whereas from 72 to 120 hrs there was a minimal effect of selenium source on drip loss. The cumulative values at 120 hrs post-slaughter demonstrated that while organic selenium had no effect on drip loss in pork loin muscle, inorganic selenium had an apparent detrimental effect on water loss from pork loins. Evaluating the effect of selenium source and selenium level on loin color demonstrated an increasingly pale color in pork loins when inorganic selenium was provided. No effect was evident when the organic selenium source was fed (Figure 10).

HUMANS

There is a large variation in the amount of selenium consumed in different regions of the world. With the move of many toward vegetarian-type diets, and the recognition that much of the world's indigenous source of selenium for humans is from selenium-deficient grains or their by-products, the potential for selenium deficiencies in humans will undoubtedly increase. The data available demonstrate that consumption of selenium in most of the world averages <200 μg per day. Perhaps one of the better ways to provide selenium to the human is through the meat and milk food supply. Because pork, poultry meat and milk are consumed in large quantities throughout much of the world, it would appear that this would be an excellent way of providing selenium to the human diet.

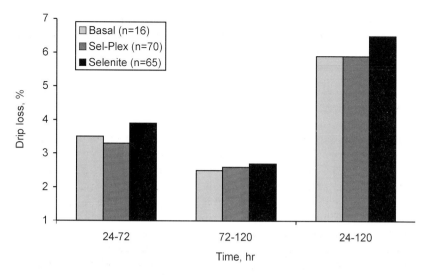

**Figure 9.** Effect of selenium source on drip loss (pork loin) (Loins collected after a 24 hr chill).

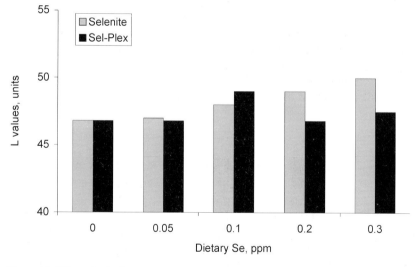

**Figure 10.** Effect of selenium source on pork color (Hunter L value) (Loins collected after a 24 hr chill) (Mahan *et al.*, 1999).

The quantity of selenium needed by humans for normal growth and function has not been accurately determined. Perhaps as important is the amount of selenium that will aid human health. Recent studies have demonstrated that selenium may have an important role in preventing the rate of cancer development in humans. A 10-year study reported by Clark *et al.* (1997) suggested that when 200 µg/day of organic selenium was consumed, the incidence of all cancers was reduced by approximately 50%. The two cancers that were more noticeably reduced were colorectal and prostate cancer (Figure 11).

## RUMINANTS

Inorganic selenium has a reduced bioavailability in the ruminant because of the anaerobic conditions in the rumen. Although some of the oxidized form of selenium (sodium selenite) is reduced in the rumen to the selenide form which is not absorbed through the rumen or the intestinal tract, some of the consumed inorganic selenium is used by rumen microbes for their metabolism. The microbial protein thus formed with selenium can pass into the small intestine and serve as a source of dietary selenium for the ruminant, but overall the bioavailability of inorganic selenium for ruminants is poor. In contrast, organic selenium is in the form of selenoamino acids and generally by-passes the rumen. The selenium-enriched yeast protein is hydrolyzed in the rumen and small intestine to the respective amino acids. These selenoamino acids are absorbed with selenium being retained and effectively utilized. Subsequent research has demonstrated that blood GSH-Px activity in ruminants is lower when the inorganic form of the element is fed to dairy cows (Pehrson *et al.*, 1989; Table 4). Other research has demonstrated that milk selenium can be increased 4–5 fold by feeding organic selenium (Figure 12). It would appear that much of the research conducted with supplemental selenium as sodium selenite may need to be revisited using an organic selenium source.

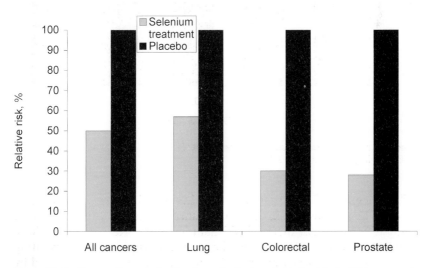

**Figure 11.** Incidence of cancer in placebo and selenium treated subjects (200 μg organic selenium/day for 10 years).

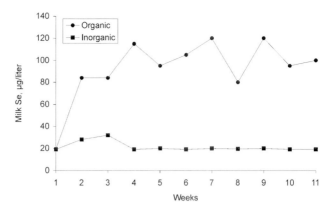

**Figure 12.** Effect of inorganic or organic selenium on milk selenium content of dairy cows (diets contained 0.40 ppm Se).

**Table 4.** Effect of selenium source on GSH-Px activity in dairy cows.

| Se source | Dosage (μg/d) | GSH-Px activity increase (units/liter) |
|---|---|---|
| Sodium selenite | 570 | 747 |
| Sel-Plex | 560 | 253 |

# References

Behne, D., A. Kyriakopoulos, H. Meinhold and J. Kohrle. 1990. Identification of type I iodothyronine 5'deiodinase as a selenoenzyme. Biophys. Res. Comm. 173:1143–1149.

Cantor, A. H. 1997. The role of selenium in poultry nutrition. In: Biotechnology in the Feed Industry, Proceedings of the 13th Annual Symposium. (T.P. Lyons and K.A. Jacques, eds.). Nottingham University Press, UK. p. 199.

Clark, L. C., G. F. Combs, Jr., B. W. Turnbull, E. Slate, D. Chalker, J. Chow, L. Davis, R. Glover, G. Graham, E. Gross, A. Kongrad, J. Lesher, K. Park, B. Sanders, C. Smith, J. Taylor. 1997. Effects of selenium supplementation for cancer prevention in patients with carcinoma of the skin: a randomized clinical trial. J. Am. Med. Assoc. (Cited by Combs, 1997).

Edens, F. W. 1996. Organic selenium: from feathers to muscle integrity to drip loss. Five years onward: no more selenite! In: Biotechnology in the Feed Industry. Proc. of the 12th Annual Symposium. (T.P. Lyons and K.A. Jacques, eds). Nottingham University Press, Nottingham, UK. pp. 165–185.

Kelly, M. P., and R. F. Power. 1995. Fractionation and identification of the major selenium compounds in selenized yeast. J. Dairy Sci 78(Suppl. 1):237 (Abstr.).

Lyons, 1997. The new era in animal nutrition: arrival of scientifically proven natural alternatives. In: Biotechnology in the Feed Industry, Proceedings of the 14th Annual Symposium. (T.P. Lyons and K.A. Jacques, eds). Nottingham University Press, Nottingham, UK.

Mahan, D. C. 1999. Effect of organic and inorganic selenium sources and levels on sow colostrum and milk composition. J. Anim. Sci. (submitted).

Mahan, D.C., and Y.Y. Kim. 1996. Effect of inorganic or organic selenium at two dietary levels on reproductive performance and tissue selenium concentrations in first parity gilts and their progeny. J. Anim. Sci. 74:2711–2718.

Mahan, D.C., and N.A. Parrett. 1996. Evaluating the efficacy of Se-enriched yeast and inorganic selenite on tissue Se retention and serum glutathione peroxidase activity in grower and finisher swine. J. Anim. Sci. 74:2967–2974.

Mahan, D. C., T. R. Cline, and B. Richert. 1999. Effects of dietary levels of selenium-enriched yeast and sodium selenite selenium sources fed to grower-finisher pigs on performance, tissue selenium, serum glutathione peroxidase activity, carcass characteristics and loin quality. J. Anim. Sci. (submitted).

Meyer R. D. and R. G. Buran. 1995. The geochemistry and bio-geochemistry of selenium in relation to its deficiency and toxicity in animals. In: Selenium in the Environment: Essential Nutrient, Potential Toxicant. Proc. of National Symposium. Univ. of CA. p. 38.

Moxon, A. L., 1937. Alkali disease, or selenium poisioning. South Dakota Agriculture . Experiment Station Bulletin 311. South Dakota State University, Brookings 91 p.

Muth, O. H., J. E. Oldfield, L. F. Remmert, and J. R. Schubert. 1958. Effects of selenium and vitamin E on white muscle disease. Science. 128:1090.

Oldfield, J. E., J. R. Schubert, and O. H. Muth. 1960. Selenium and vitamin E as related to growth and white muscle disease in lambs. Proc. Soc. Exp. Biol. and Med. 103:799–800.

Olson, O. E., E. J. Novacek, E. I. Whitehead, and I. S. Palmer. 1970. Investigation on selenium in wheat. Photochemistry 9:1181.

Patterson, E. L., R. Milstrey, and E. L. R. Stokstad. 1957. Effect of selenium in preventing exudative diathesis in chicks. Proc. Soc. Exp. Biol. and Med. 95:617–620.

Pehrson, B., M. Knutsson, and M. Gyllensward. 1989. Glutathione peroxidase activity in heifers fed diets supplemented with organic and inorganic selenium compounds. Swedish J. Agr. Res. 19:53–57.

Rotruck, J. T., A. L. Pope, H. E. Ganther, A. B. Swansown, D. G. Hafeman, and W. G. Hoekstra. 1973. Selenium: Biochemical role as a component of glutathione peroxidase. Science. 179:588–590.

Schwartz, K. and C. M. Foltz. 1957. Selenium as an integral part of factor 3 against dietary necrotic liver degeneration. J. Am. Chem. Soc. 79:3292–3293.

# Selenium for ruminants: comparing organic and inorganic selenium for cattle and sheep

R. L. KINCAID[1], M. ROCK[1], and F. AWADEH[2]

[1]*Department of Animal Sciences, Washington State University, Pullman, Washington, USA;*
[2]*NCARTT, Ammon, Jordan.*

## Introduction

Nutritional deficiencies of selenium (Se) in ruminants result in white muscle disease (Muth *et al.*, 1958), loss of glutathione peroxidase activity and selenoprotein W (Yeh *et al.*, 1997), and suppression of immunity (Yamini and Mullaney, 1985). Newborn ruminants are dependent upon the dam for selenium transfer via the placenta or mammary gland. Because feeds grown in many areas of the world are deficient in selenium for livestock, selenium supplementation is often necessary. Methods that have been used for selenium supplementation include injection, drenching, administering selenium-laden boluses and trace mineral salt mixes. Inorganic selenium salts, primarily sodium selenite, are generally used in selenium supplements. Organic selenium sources, such as plants and selenium yeast (Sel-Plex) contain selenoamino acids that are beneficial as selenium supplements. Differences exist in the utilization of dietary selenium from the various chemical forms. Selenium in sodium selenite can be chemically reduced to insoluble forms by rumen microorganisms, thus lowering selenium absorption. Selenoamino acids can be nonspecifically incorporated directly into body protein (Kincaid, 1995) and presumably serve a selenium storage capacity.

Glutathione peroxidase (GSH-Px) was the first selenoprotein identified (Rotruck *et al.*, 1973), but several additional selenoproteins since have been isolated. Among these selenoproteins are Types I, II, and III deiodinases responsible for peripheral deiodination of thyroxine ($T_4$) to 3,5,3 tri-iodothyronine ($T_3$) and other metabolites. Rats that are selenium deficient have significantly lower concentrations of $T_3$ (Beckett *et al.*, 1987; Behne *et al.*, 1992; and Beckett *et al.*, 1992). Studies by Arthur *et al.* (1988) and Wichtel *et al.* (1996) found that selenium-deficient dairy heifers also have lower concentrations of $T_3$ and elevated $T_4$, resulting in a lower ratio of $T_3$ to $T_4$. Tri-iodothyronine is the metabolically active thyroid hormone and is involved in growth, thermogenesis, and nutrient metabolism. Thus, lowered concentrations of $T_3$ caused by selenium deficiency may contribute to health problems in ruminants.

Selenium is also involved in the immune function of animals. Larsen (1988) observed a trend for increased IgG concentrations in selenium-supplemented ewes and lambs. Calves failing to absorb enough IgG have higher risk of morbidity (McGuire *et al.*, 1976). In addition, Larsen (1988) reported significantly increased titers to tetanus toxoid in selenium supplemented lambs. Similarly, Turner and Finch (1990) reported a decreased lymphocyte response in lambs deficient in vitamin E and selenium.

Thus, there are biological measures beside GSH-Px activity that should be considered when evaluating selenium status of ruminants. Accordingly, two experiments were conducted to determine the effects of level and chemical form of dietary selenium on concentrations of thyroid hormones, selenium in tissues, and immunoglobulin status in dams and newborns.

## Selenium supplementation of beef cows

PROCEDURES

Sixty mature beef cows were assigned to one of four dietary treatments consisting of free-choice access to salt mixes containing 20, 60, or 120 ppm Se as sodium selenite. The fourth treatment was 60 ppm Se as organic selenium from yeast (Sel-Plex). Cows were fed their experimental diets from 90 days prepartum and were maintained on their respective treatments for two calving and breeding seasons. The cows were separated by treatment and rotationally grazed grass pastures during the summers and in winter were fed haylage, a concentrate, and ryegrass seed screening pellets in the first year and cereal graining screenings in the second year. Intakes of the salt mixes were recorded for each group (Awadeh *et al.*, 1998b).

RESULTS AND DISCUSSION

The concentration of selenium in blood of cows at parturition differed significantly ($P \leq 0.01$) among treatment groups with cows fed the 20ppm Se salt mixture having lower concentration of selenium (Table 1). Concentrations of selenium in colostrum in year 1 were similar for all cows, but in year 2, concentrations of selenium in colostrum were higher ($P \leq 0.01$ for cows given salt with 60 ppm Se as Sel-Plex than for control cows. Hemken *et al.* (1998) reported milk selenium tended ($P \leq 0.06$) to be increased more by selenium in Sel-Plex than selenite.

Selenium concentrations in blood of newborn calves were increased by additional selenium in salt for the pregnant cows and were highest for calves of cows fed Sel-Plex in year 1 and higher than 20 and 60 ppm Se

**Table 1.** Effect of level and form of supplemental selenium in salt mixes fed free-choice to pregnant cows on selenium and thyroid hormones in blood and colostrum samples taken immediately postpartum.[1]

| | Concentration and chemical form of selenium in salt mix | | | |
|---|---|---|---|---|
| | 20 ppm Se as selenite | 60 ppm Se as selenite | 120 ppm Se as selenite | 60 ppm Se as Sel-Plex |
| Year 1 | | (µg/ml) | | |
| Se in blood | 0.12[b] | 0.16[a] | 0.15[a] | 0.17[a] |
| Se in colostrum | 0.07 | 0.06 | 0.07 | 0.08 |
| | | | | |
| Year 2 | | (µg/ml) | | |
| Se in blood | 0.14[c] | 0.16[b] | 0.19[a] | 0.17[ab] |
| Se in colostrum | 0.07[b] | 0.09[ab] | 0.08b | 0.11[a] |
| Serum | | (ng/ml) | | |
| $T_3$ | 0.86[b] | 1.0[a] | 0.89[b] | 1.0[a] |
| $T_4$ | 32.6 | 33.9 | 32.4 | 34.1 |
| $T_3:T_4$ ratio | 0.027[a] | 0.031[b] | 0.030[b] | 0.031[b] |

[1]Adapted from Awadeh et al., 1998b.
[abc]Means followed by different superscripts differ, P<0.05.

as selenite in year 2 (Table 2). In year 1, activity of GSH-Px in blood was increased by additional selenium supplementation of cows. The concentrations of selenium in liver of newborn calves were not affected by treatments.

**Table 2.** Effect of maternal intakes of selenium on selenium status and thyroid hormones in day-old calves[1].

| | Concentration and chemical form of selenium in salt mixes | | | |
|---|---|---|---|---|
| | 20 ppm Se as selenite | 60 ppm Se as selenite | 120 ppm Se as selenite | 60 ppm Se as Sel-Plex |
| | | Year1 | | |
| Se in blood, µg/ml | 0.12[b] | 0.14[b] | 0.14[b] | 0.17[a] |
| GSH-Px in blood, EU | 0.6[b] | 0.8[a] | 0.8[a] | 0.9[a] |
| Se in liver, µg/g | 3.1 | 3.9 | 3.1 | 3.4 |
| | | Year2 | | |
| Se in blood, µg/ml | 0.12[c] | 0.14[b] | 0.15[ab] | 0.16[a] |
| GSH-Px in blood, EU | 0.8 | 0.8 | 0.7 | 0.7 |
| $T_3$, ng/ml | 3.4[a] | 3.0[a] | 4.3[ab] | 5.3[a] |
| $T_4$ | 85.3[ab] | 99.2[ab] | 70.1[b] | 116.4[a] |
| Ratio of $T_3:T_4$ | 0.032[b] | 0.033[b] | 0.053[a] | 0.04[b] |

[1]Adapted from Awadeh et al., 1998b.
EU = nmol NADPH oxidized/min/mg hemoglobin.
[ab]Means followed by different superscripts differ, P<0.05.

Treatments affected ($P \leq 0.01$) the concentration of $T_3$, but not of $T_4$, in serum of cows (Table 1). In addition, the ratio of $T_3:T_4$ was increased in cows given added selenium. Calves born to cows supplemented with 60 ppm Se as Sel-Plex had higher $T_3$ concentrations at birth than calves from cows supplemented with 20 and 60 ppm Se as selenite (Table 2). The ratio of $T_3:T_4$ in calves of cows supplemented with 120 ppm Se in the salt mix was higher than that in calves of cows fed salt with 20 and 60 ppm Se. The concentrations of $T_3$ in calves is important because $T_3$ enhances the synthesis of uncoupling protein, necessary for brown adipose tissue thermogenesis (Carstens, 1994).

Concentrations of IgG and IgM in serum of cows and their calves were significantly lower when given salt with 20 ppm Se (Table 3). Serum IgM concentrations were higher ($P \leq 0.05$) in cows given salt with 60 ppm Se as Sel-Plex compared to cows supplemented with 60 ppm Se as selenite. In the present study, salts with 60 or 120 ppm Se enhanced transfer of IgG from cow serum to colostrum but did not affect synthesis of IgM in the mammary gland. Swecker *et al.* (1995) found that cows supplemented with selenium had increased colostral IgG and their calves had increased IgG, but there was no effect of dietary selenium on IgM.

**Table 3.  Effect of maternal intakes of selenium on immunoglobulin concentrations in serum and colostrum of cows and serum of day-old calves.[1]**

| Immunoglobulins | Concentration and chemical form of Se in salt mixes | | | |
| --- | --- | --- | --- | --- |
| | 20 ppm Se as selenite | 60 ppm Se as selenite | 120 ppm Se as selenite | 60 ppm Se as Sel-Plex |
| IgG in serum | —g/l— | | | |
| of cows | 22[a] | 35[b] | 31[b] | 31[b] |
| of calves | 28[a] | 31[ab] | 35[b] | 31[ab] |
| IgG in colostrum | 70[c] | 92[a] | 87[ab] | 78[b] |
| IgM in serum | 2.5[a] | 3.9[b] | 5[c] | 5.2[c] |
| of cows | 2.5[a] | 3.9[b] | 5[c] | 5.2[c] |
| of calves | 2.5[a] | 3.1[ab] | 3.8[b] | 3.9[b] |
| IgM in colostrum | 2.2 | 3.0 | 3.2 | 2.5 |

[1]Adapted from Awadeh *et al.*, 1998b.
[abc]Means followed by different superscripts differ, P<0.05.

# Selenium supplementation of pregnant ewes

PROCEDURES

Pregnant ewes (n = 21) of mixed Ramboulliet and Polypay breeding, 5-6 years old, with an average body weight of 62.7 kg were randomly assigned to treatment. Ultrasound tests were conducted previously (about 60 days gestation) and only ewes suspected of being twin-bearing were used for the study. Ewes were housed in pens of 7 according to treatment groups and fed a mid-gestation diet containing less than 0.02 ppm Se. Treatments were applied via trace mineralized salt mixes and consisted of: 1) control, no supplemental Se; 2) inorganic, 90 ppm Se as $Na_2SeO_3$; and

3) organic, 90 ppm Se as Sel-Plex. Because of a treatment difference in the consumption of the trace mineral salts with added selenium during the first month of the trial, 50% ground corn was added to the trace mineral salt and the ewes were limit-fed the salts to allow for selenium intakes equivalent to about 0.3 mg Se/kg of diet dry matter for ewes supplemented with selenium.

At lambing, rectal temperature and body weight of each newborn lamb were recorded and a colostrum sample was collected from the ewe. One twin lamb was removed before suckling the ewe for eventual tissue collection. The lamb was fed pooled bovine colostrum (25 ml colostrum/kg of body weight) initially and again 6 hrs later. At 12 hrs, blood samples were taken and lambs were euthanized with sodium pentobarbitol. Liver, kidney, heart, gastrointestinal tract and brown adipose tissue from the perirenal and pericardial regions were removed, weighed and frozen.

RESULTS AND DISCUSSION

Intake of selenium was increased by selenium supplementation and was similar between the two supplemented groups. Feed intakes and body weights were similar among treatment groups. Concentrations of selenium in serum were depressed ($P \leq 0.05$) in ewes receiving no selenium supplementation (Table 4). Overall, there was a linear decrease in concentrations of selenium in serum for ewes with length of gestation. The chemical form of the selenium supplement did not significantly affect the concentration of selenium in serum. Van Ryssen *et al.* (1989) reported that while selenium from organic sources increased concentrations of selenium in whole blood of sheep, chemical form of selenium did not significantly affect plasma selenium. This also was reported in cattle by Awadeh *et al.* (1998a). Accordingly, the concentrations of selenium in whole blood were increased ($P \leq 0.0001$) by selenium supplementation with ewes supplemented with Sel-Plex tending to have the highest concentrations of selenium in blood at lambing. The difference in response between serum and whole blood to the selenium supplements indicated greater uptake by the red blood cell of selenium from Sel-Plex than selenite. As expected, GSH-Px activities were greater in ewes given selenium supplements.

Body temperatures and birth weights were not affected by maternal treatments. Concentrations of selenium in whole blood of newborn lambs were increased ($P \leq 0.0001$) 2-fold and 4-fold by the selenite and Sel-Plex supplements, respectively (Table 5). The data are consistent with results of Schamberger (1986), providing further evidence that organic forms of selenium are more readily transported across the placenta. Concentrations of selenium in the liver of lambs were also significantly increased by selenium supplementation. Although the difference between the selenite and Sel-Plex treatments in concentrations of selenium in liver was not statistically different, the trend is consistent with selenium from organic sources being more readily incorporated into protein than inorganic selenium (Kincaid, 1995).

541

**Table 4.** Effect of level and source of dietary selenium on concentrations of selenium, thyroid hormones, glutathione peroxidase activity, and immunoglobulins in ewes at lambing.[1]

| | | Treatment | | Statistical Significance | |
|---|---|---|---|---|---|
| Measure | Control | Selenite | Sel-Plex | Se vs. no Se | Selenite vs. Sel-Plex |
| Se in serum, µg/ml | 0.062 | 0.140 | 0.147 | *** | NS |
| Se in whole blood, µg/ml | 0.091 | 0.196 | 0.242 | *** | NS |
| Se in colostrum, µg/ml | 0.012 | 0.132 | 0.226 | ** | * |
| GSH-Px, EU/ml | 68.7 | 114 | 95 | * | NS |
| $T_3$, ng/ml | 1.12 | 1.44 | 1.67 | * | NS |
| $T_4$, ng/ml | 47 | 58 | 63 | *** | NS |
| Ratio of $T_3$:$T_4$ | 0.024 | 0.026 | 0.025 | NS | NS |
| Serum IgG, g/L | 21.7 | 20.4 | 18.7 | NS | NS |
| Serum IgM, g/L | 1.8 | 2.5 | 3.0 | ** | NS |

[1]Blood samples were taken within 12 hr of parturition, approximately day 100 of the trial.
EU = (moles of NADPH oxidized/min/ml of whole blood.
*P<0.05 **P<0.001 ***P<0.0001.

**Table 5.** Effect of maternal intake of selenium on concentrations of selenium, thyroid hormones, immunoglobulins and activity of glutathione peroxidase in newborn lambs.

| | | Treatment | | Statistical Significance | |
|---|---|---|---|---|---|
| Measure | Control | Selenite | Sel-Plex | Se vs. no Se | Selenite vs. Sel-Plex |
| Se in whole blood, µg/ml | 0.101 | 0.234 | 0.434 | **** | *** |
| Se in liver, µg/g | 0.63 | 1.34 | 1.80 | *** | NS |
| GSH-Px, EU/ml | 145 | 414 | 640 | **** | ** |
| $T_3$, ng/ml | 2.81 | 3.98 | 3.32 | * | NS |
| $T_4$, ng/ml | 87 | 104 | 90 | NS | NS |
| IgG, mg/dl | 2392 | 2940 | 2917 | ** | NS |
| IgM, mg/dl | 196 | 253 | 202 | NS | NS |

EU = (moles of NADPH oxidized/min/ml of whole blood.
NS = nonsignificant, P ≤0.1; *P≤ 0.1; **P ≤ 0.005; ***P≤ 0.001; ****P ≤ 0.0001.

Concentrations of selenium in whole blood of lambs were positively correlated to the selenium concentrations in liver (r = 0.77). Activities of GSH-Px in blood of lambs were greatly increased (P ≤ 0.0001) when the dams were supplemented with selenium during gestation. In addition, ewes given the Sel-Plex had lambs with significantly higher GSH-Px activity than the lambs of ewes given selenite. The GSH-Px activity was highly correlated (r = 0.88) to selenium concentrations in whole blood of lambs.

### Interactions of selenium and thyroid hormones

The concentrations of $T_3$ in serum of control ewes were 39% lower in ewes supplemented with selenium (Table 4). Interestingly, the concentrations of $T_4$ in the control ewes were also lower, thereby resulting in no change in the ratio of $T_3$ to $T_4$. Supplementation of ewes with selenium tended to increase $T_3$ concentrations in the newborn lambs. However, there was no effect due to the chemical form of the added selenium (Table 5).

*Selenium and measures of immunity*
Lambs of control ewes had lower IgG concentrations in serum than lambs of ewes supplemented with selenium (Table 5). Because all lambs were fed equivalent amounts of pooled bovine colostrum, the difference in IgG in the lambs was due to an effect of selenium on the lamb's ability to absorb the IgG from the small intestine. Maternal IgG levels in serum and colostrum were not affected by selenium intake (Table 4). However, IgM was significantly increased in serum of ewes given added selenium. These data indicate that selenium intake during pregnancy can affect maternal synthesis of IgM and the absorption of IgG by the newborn.

# Summary

Some differences in results of these two trials are due to the greater selenium depletion in the ewes compared to the cows, and perhaps due to species differences. In both trials, supplementation of pregnant cows and ewes with selenium generally improved the selenium status and increased concentrations of $T_3$ and immunoglobulins in both the dams and their newborns. Thus, maternal selenium supplementation improved some of the measures predictive of susceptibility of newborn ruminants to disease. The data further showed that selenium in Sel-Plex was transferred more readily to ovine fetus and colostrum than selenium in sodium selenite. Thus, supplements containing Sel-Plex may be particularly beneficial when total intakes of selenium are limited.

# Conclusions

The finding that low, but not deficient, intakes of selenium by pregnant cows and ewes affect Ig and $T_3$ levels has large significance for health and survival of newborns. Passive immunity and heat production from brown adipose are required for newborn survival; and both events may be influenced by maternal selenium intakes.

# References

Arthur, J.R., P.C. Morrice and G.J. Beckett. 1988. Thyroid hormone concentrations in selenium deficient and selenium sufficient cattle. Res. Vet. Sci. 45:122.

Awadeh, F.T., M.M. Abdelrahman, R.L. Kincaid and J.W. Finley. 1998a. Effect of selenium supplements on the distribution of selenium among serum proteins in cattle. J. Dairy Sci. 81:1089.

Awadeh, F.T., R.L. Kincaid and K.A. Johnson. 1998b. Effect of level and source of dietary selenium on concentrations of thyroid hormones and immunoglobulins in beef cows and calves. J. Anim. Sci. 76:1204.

Beckett, G.J., A. Russal, F. Nicol, P. Sahu, C.R. Wolf and J.R. Arthur. 1992. Effect of selenium deficiency on hepatic deiodination of thryoxine is caused by selenium deficiency in rats. Biochem. J. 282:483.

Beckett, G.J., Se. E. Beddows, P.C. Morrice, F. Nicol and J.R. Arthur. 1987. Inhibition of hepatic deiodination of thyroxine is caused by selenium deficiency in rats. Biochem. J. 248:443.

Behne, D., A. Kyriakopoulos, H. Gessner, B. Walzog and H. Meinhold. 1992. Type I iodothyronine deiodinase activity after high selenium intake, and relationship between selenium and iodine metabolism in rats. Nutrient Requirements and Interactions 1542.

Carstens, G. 1994. Cold thermoregulation in the newborn calves. Vet. Clin. North Am. Food Anim. Pract. 10:69.

Hemken, R.W., R.J. Harmon and S. Trammell. 1998. Selenium for dairy cattle: a case for organic selenium. In: Proceedings of the 14th annual Symposium on Biotechnology in the Feed Industry. (T.P. Lyons and K.A. Jacques, Eds.). Nottingham University Press. Nottingham, U.K. pp. 497.

Kincaid, R.L. 1995. The biological basis for selenium requirements of animals. The Prof. Anim. Sci. 11:26.

Larsen, H.J. 1988. Influence of selenium on antibody production in sheep. Res. Vet. Sci. 45:4.

McGuire, T.C., N.E. Pfeiffer, J.M. Weikel and R.C. Bartch. 1976. Failure of colostral immunoglobulin transfer in calves from infectious disease. J. Am. Vet. Med. Assoc. 169:713.

Muth, O.H., J.E. Oldfield and L.F. Rennert. 1958. Effects of selenium and vitamin E on white muscle disease. Science 128:1090.

Rotruck, J. T., A.L. Pope, H.E. Ganther, A.B. Swanson, D.G. Hafeman and W.G. Hoekstra. 1973. Selenium: biochemical role as a component of GSH-Px. Science 170:588.

Schamberger, R.L. 1986. Selenium metabolism and function. Clin. Phy. Biochem. 4:42.

Swecker, W.S., C.D. Thatcher, D.E. Eversole, D.J. Blodgett and G.G. Schurig. 1995. Effect of selenium supplementation on colostrum IgG concentration in cows grazing selenium-deficient pastures and on postsuckle serum IgG concentration in their calves. Am. J. Vet. Res. 56:450.

Turner, R.J. and J.M. Finch. 1990. Immunological malfunctions associated with low selenium-vitamin E diets in lambs. J. Comp. Path. 102:99.

Van Ryssen, J.B.J., J.T. Deagen, M.A. Beilstein and P.D. Whanger. 1989. Comparative metabolism of organic and inorganic selenium by sheep. J. Agric. Food Chem. 37:1358.

Wichtel, J.J., A.L. Craigie, D.A. Freeman, H. Varela-Alvarez and N.B. Williamson. 1996. Effect of selenium and iodine supplementation on growth rate and on thyroid and somatotrophic function in dairy heifers. J. Dairy Sci. 79:1865.

Yamini, B., and T.P. Mullaney. 1985. Vitamin E and selenium deficiency as a possible cause of abortion in food animals. Proc. 28th Ann. Mtg. Am. Assoc. Vet. Lab. Diagn., Madison, WI. pp 131.

Yeh, J., Q. Gu, M.A. Beistein, N.E. Forsberg, and P.D. Whanger. 1997. Selenium influence on tissue levels of selenoprotein W in sheep. J. Nutr. 127:394. 6

# Absorption and metabolism of selenium: differences between inorganic and organic sources

S. WOLFFRAM

*Institute of Animal Nutrition, Physiology and Metabolism*
*Christian Albrechts University of Kiel, Germany*

## Introduction

The essentiality for animals of the trace element selenium was recognized some 40 years ago by the pioneering work of Schwarz and Foltz (1957; 1958) and Schwarz (1961). About 20 years later the discovery of severe selenium deficiency in certain parts of China demonstrated that this trace element is also essential for humans (Keshan Disease Research Group, 1979; Whanger, 1989; Levander, 1991; Ge and Yang, 1993). In animals several selenium deficiency disorders have been characterized, including white muscular dystrophy (white muscle disease), liver necrosis, cardiac myopathy, and exudative diathesis which appear to be essentially related to insufficient protection against oxidative stress (Van Vleet, 1980). Owing to the nature of these disorders it is conceivable that other antioxidative principles within the organism will overlap with selenium's role as antioxidant. Indeed, most of the selenium deficiency syndromes are (at least partially) responsive to an elevated supply of the antioxidant micronutrient vitamin E. Thus, the descriptive term 'selenium/vitamin E deficiency symptoms' might be more appropriate (Van Vleet and Ferrans, 1992). Today, overt selenium deficiency is a relatively rare finding in livestock due to the widespread use of dietary supplementation of selenium with inorganic and organic selenium sources. However, more subtle symptoms of a marginal selenium supply, such as reduced immune defense to viral and bacterial infections, may often occur (Stabel and Spears, 1993).

In the area of human health, knowledge about selenium deficiency symptoms has only been derived from observations of naturally occurring selenium deficiency because unlike in animals, selenium deficiency cannot be experimentally induced in humans for ethical reasons. During the last fifteen years, most emphasis regarding selenium nutrition in humans has been directed to possible anticarcinogenic effects. It should be emphasized, however, that these effects are only observed at supraphysiological doses of selenium, i.e., at levels well above the nutritional requirement (Ip, 1998). However, it cannot be excluded that a preventive effect of selenium against certain types of cancer may even be present at a nutritionally appropriate selenium intake. Although considerable experimental work has been done on the anticarcinogenic functions of selenium in humans during recent years, these aspects of selenium metabolism are beyond the scope of the present contribution.

The present article will deal with the bioavailability of selenium, mainly in animals. Therefore the two most important aspects, namely intestinal absorption and postabsorptive metabolism of selenium, will be considered. Where appropriate, similarities and differences between inorganic and organic forms of selenium will be pointed out.

From a nutritional point of view, the inorganic forms selenate and selenite and the organic forms selenomethionine and selenocysteine might be the most important chemical forms of selenium. In selenoamino acids, the sulfur of the corresponding sulfur-containing amino acids is simply replaced by selenium during synthesis. Whereas most plant- and animal-derived feed and food from natural sources contain organic forms of selenium, e.g., selenoamino acids, the inorganic selenium salts (selenite, selenate) are commonly used for supplementation of livestock rations as a cheap and efficient means to prevent selenium deficiency. However, during recent years organic forms of selenium in the form of selenium-enriched yeast have become available to farmers. It has been assumed that in yeasts cultured in a high-selenium medium the most abundant chemical form of selenium may be selenomethionine. However, recent findings with improved analytical methods indicate that a wide variety of seleno compounds, many of which are unidentified, are present in selenium yeast (Ip, 1998; Bird *et al.*, 1997). Thus the selenium yeast actually contains a cocktail of selenium in a variety of chemical forms. It should be further mentioned in this context, that the specific chemical forms of selenium in most food and feed are unknown.

The importance of an adequate selenium supply to our livestock cannot be overemphasized. Selenium supplementation of low-selenium feed not only prevents deficiency symptoms in animals but also substantially contributes to the selenium intake of humans through animal-derived products such as meat and eggs. It has been estimated, for example, that in Germany about 60% of selenium ingested by humans is derived from animal sources (Oster, 1992).

Before selenium was recognized as an essential micronutrient, its toxic properties were well known. Indeed, there is a relatively small range between the beneficial effects of selenium and selenium toxicity. Concentrations of 0.1 to 0.5 ppm on a dry matter basis are generally accepted as safe and adequate for livestock and poultry whereas signs of chronic and acute toxicity have been described at intake levels of 2–5 ppm (Oldfield, 1992; Edmondson *et al.*, 1993). Although there have been some concerns about hazards to the health of wildlife and even humans by enrichment of selenium in the environment due to selenium supplementation in livestock production (Edmondson *et al.*, 1993; Fan *et al.*, 1988), it should be pointed out that scientific data do not support such conclusions. Presently established animal supplementation uses of selenium are small compared with other sources of the element and do not constitute a hazard to animals, including humans, or the environment (Oldfield, 1992; Edmondson *et al.*, 1993). Indeed, it has been calculated that selenium supplementation of animal diets at a level of 0.3 ppm contributes less than 0.5% of that originating from other man-made and natural sources (Ullrey, 1992).

# Bioavailability of selenium

The term bioavailability has been used to describe different phenomena ranging from the disappearance of a substance from the contents of the gastrointestinal tract, i.e., apparent digestibility, to the accumulation within several organs or the synthesis of a certain enzyme. Bioavailability may be best defined as the part of selenium absorbed from the gastrointestinal tract which is metabolically available for the maintenance of the normal structures and physiological processes of an organism under defined conditions. The author takes the view that measuring tissue accumulation of selenium, e.g., in muscle or liver, without the additional measurement of a functional parameter of selenium, e.g., the activity of glutathione peroxidase, does not sufficiently describe bioavailability of selenium. On the other hand, this does not mean that there is no correlation between tissue accumulation, enzyme activity, and selenium status. It has been repeatedly demonstrated that a good correlation exists between these variables in situations of deficient or marginal selenium supply, whereas the correlation clearly weakens with nutritionally adequate selenium intake.

Numerous exogenous and endogenous factors influence the oral bioavailability of any trace element making trace element metabolism a very complex and dynamic matter (Figure 1). Among others, these factors include the amount and chemical form of the element ingested with feed or food, solubilization within the gastrointestinal contents, the physiological state of the organism (e.g., growth, pregnancy), the bioavailability and metabolism of other elements (e.g., the interaction of selenomethionine and methionine), diseases, drugs and age.

The following sections will deal with the two major aspects regarding the bioavailability of the trace element selenium, namely intestinal absorption and postabsorptive metabolism.

## INTESTINAL ABSORPTION OF SELENIUM

Balance studies based on the disappearance of chemically defined selenium compounds, e.g., selenite or selenomethionine, from the gastrointestinal tract have shown efficient absorption of inorganic (selenate, selenite) as well as organic (selenoamino acids) forms of selenium. Thomson and Stewart (1972) determined in rats a fractional selenium absorption of 91–93% from selenite and of 95–97% from selenomethionine. In another study, Thomson *et al.* (1975) compared the absorption of radioactively

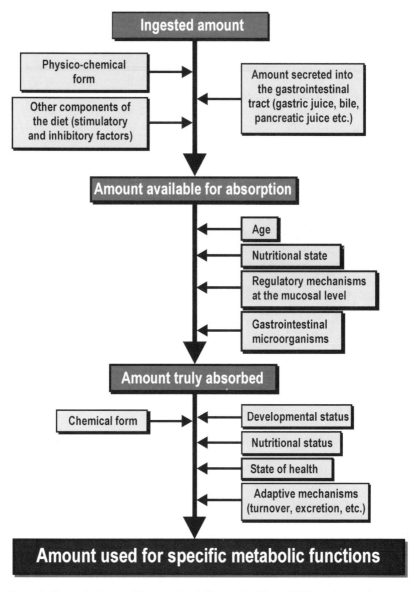

**Figure 1.** General scheme of factors that influence the bioavailability of trace elements.

labeled selenomethionine and selenocysteine. In these experiments, 86% and 81% of the applied dose of selenomethionine and selenocysteine, respectively, were absorbed. Investigations on the absorption of selenium from natural animal sources, e.g., kidneys of rabbits or fish muscle from fish fed labeled selenite or selenomethionine showed that 87% of the selenium from the kidneys of rabbits was absorbed (Thomson *et al.*, 1975) whereas selenium absorption from fish reached only 72–77% of the applied dose (Richold *et al.*, 1977). The authors concluded from these experiments that the chemical form of selenium present in fish was either less available or that the fish meat was incompletely digested by rats. Whanger *et al.* (Butler *et al.*, 1991) incorporated into rat diets muscle, liver and hemoglobin from sheep which had been fed a high selenium diet (1 mg selenium/kg). Selenium as either selenite or L-selenomethionine were used as standards. Tissue selenium levels and glutathione peroxidase activities were used to assess bioavailability. Selenium was found to be more available from muscle than liver or hemoglobin (Butler *et al.*, 1991).

Absorption of selenium in ruminants appears to be less efficient compared with monogastric animals. This might be attributed to the observation that selenium can form insoluble metal selenides or can be reduced to elementary selenium within the contents of the forestomachs, thus rendering selenium less available for absorption (Peterson and Spedding, 1963; Wright and Bell, 1966). In sheep, 66–69% of an orally applied dose of selenium in the form of the inorganic salts selenite and selenate were excreted with the feces (Wright and Bell, 1966; Paulson *et al.*, 1966) whereas a somewhat lower value (54%) was found for organically bound selenium (selenium-rich red clover) (Peterson and Spedding, 1963). In a recent study, Koenig *et al.* (1997) determined the effects of diet composition and chemical form of selenium on intestinal flow, absorption, and retention of selenium in sheep. Animals were fed a forage (alfalfa hay)-based (0.37 mg Se/kg) or concentrate (barley)-based (0.27 mg Se/kg) diet at 90% of *ad libitum* intake and stable isotopes of selenium (enriched [77]Se-yeast, enriched [82]Se-selenite) were administered into the rumen. A larger proportion (51 to 61%) of the selenium tracers flowing to the duodenum was associated with the particulate fraction, mainly as bacteria-associated selenium, than with the fluid fraction. The [82]Se-selenite was more available for absorption and retention than [77]Se-yeast, indicating that inorganic chemical forms of selenium are as available to the ruminant as organic forms of selenium commonly found in feedstuffs (Koenig *et al.*, 1997). Selenium absorption and retention were greater in sheep receiving the concentrate-based diet than in sheep receiving the forage-based diet. Thus, the availability of selenium from inorganic and organic sources in sheep seems to be influenced by diet composition (Koenig *et al.*, 1997).

Taken together, inorganic as well as organic selenium compounds present either in feed and food or used for selenium supplementation seem to be reasonably well absorbed. Thus, gastrointestinal absorption does not limit bioavailability of selenium. Furthermore, in contrast to other trace elements like iron or zinc, absorption of selenium appears not to be influenced by selenium status indicating that intestinal absorption does not play a role in whole body selenium homeostasis (Vendeland *et al.*, 1992; 1994). Balance studies like those cited above do not yield any information on the mechanisms involved in selenium absorption or on the localization of selenium absorption within the gastrointestinal tract. These questions have been addressed in experiments using *in vivo* perfusion and ligated loops of various segments of the gastrointestinal tract as well as by *in vitro* measurements of mucosal uptake and transport into isolated brush-border membrane vesicles. Figure 2 summarizes the major findings on the intestinal absorption of selenium from selenate, selenite and selenoamino acids. Some details will be discussed here.

### Selenate

First evidence for the involvement of specific mechanisms in selenium uptake from selenate derived from *in vivo* experiments in rats. Comparison of the absorption of selenium from either selenate or selenite revealed significantly higher absorption rates for selenate from the perfused ileum but not from other intestinal segments (Wolffram *et al.*, 1985). The presence of an active uptake mechanism for selenate against a concentration gradient was confirmed using everted sacs of various segments of rat small intestine (Ardüser *et al.*, 1985). As in the perfusion experiments, active transport was restricted to the ileum. The presence of sodium clearly enhanced mucosal uptake of selenate but not of selenium from selenite. Again, the effect was most pronounced in the ileum (Ardüser *et al.*, 1986). Using isolated brush-border membrane vesicles from different species (rat, sheep, pig), the nature of active selenate transport was further unraveled (Wolffram *et al.*, 1986; 1988). These experiments revealed that selenate, but not selenite, is transported by co-transport with sodium ions, whereas this mechanism is shared with sulfate. Furthermore, a second transport mechanism appears to exist which co-transports protons together with selenate (sulfate) (Wolffram *et al.*, 1988).

Experimental evidence exists for a competitive interaction of selenate and sulfate as well as some physically and chemically related oxyanions, e.g., thiosulfate, chromate, molybdate. Cardin and Mason (1976) investigated transport of sulfate into everted sacs of rat ileum and found specific inhibition of sulfate uptake by thiosulfate, selenate, molybdate

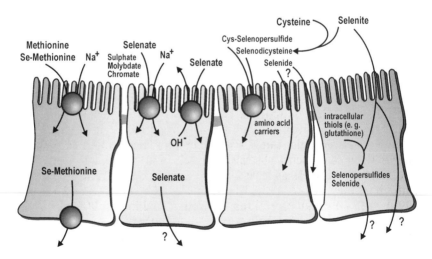

**Figure 2.** Model of the intestinal absorption of different selenium compounds.

and tungstate. Similar results were obtained by Ardüser *et al.* (1985; 1986) who found inhibition of sodium-dependent selenate uptake across the intestinal brush-border in rats and sheep by thiosulfate, sulfate, chromate and tungstate. As already mentioned above, Wolffram *et al.* (1986; 1988) unequivocally demonstrated in experiments with isolated brush-border membrane vesicles that selenate and sulfate share common carrier-mediated mechanisms to cross the intestinal brush-border membrane. It should be mentioned, however, that despite the fact that some competition for common transport mechanisms might exist between selenate and sulfate and some other metal oxides, these findings seem to be of minor practical importance because an influence on the absorption of selenium from selenate might be expected only if toxic levels of these substances are ingested.

### Selenite

Other than selenate, intestinal absorption of selenite *per se* is sodium-independent and seems to occur by simple diffusion (Wolffram *et al.*, 1986; Mykkänen and Wasserman, 1989). Furthermore, absorption of selenium from selenite is not influenced by sulfate and other physically and chemically related oxyanions (Ardüser *et al.*, 1986). However, experiments with isolated brush-border membrane vesicles revealed an extensive binding of selenium from selenite to the membrane surfaces (Wolffram *et al.*, 1986; Mykkänen and Wasserman, 1989). This binding could be explained by the reaction of selenite with thiol groups within the intestinal membranes (Mykkänen and Wasserman, 1990). Reactions of selenite with intracellular thiols may even enhance diffusive uptake of selenium from selenite by maintaining a chemical gradient for selenite directed into the cells. The most abundant intracellular thiol in mammalian cells is the tripeptide glutathione which may occur at concentrations of 0.5–10 mmol/l (Meister, 1981; Meister and Anderson, 1983; Bray and Taylor, 1993; Kelly, 1993). Indeed, Anundi *et al.* (1984) described a rapid decrease of intracellular reduced glutathione in rat enterocytes incubated with selenite. Furthermore, oxidation of intracellular glutathione by the oxidant diethylmaleate prior to incubation with selenite significantly inhibited uptake of selenium from selenite (Anundi *et al.*, 1984). Experiments of Ardüser *et al.* (1986) also indicated a function of intracellular glutathione in the uptake of selenium from selenite. Pre-incubation of mucosal sheets of rat ileum in a glutathione-containing medium stimulated selenium uptake from selenite.

Not only intracellular thiols, but also extracellular thiols present in the intestinal lumen influence absorption of selenium from selenite. This may be of physiological relevance because glutathione and cysteine are secreted with bile (Gregus *et al.*, 1987; Eberle *et al.*, 1981; Ballatori and Truong, 1992) and mucosal secretions (Dahm and Jones, 1994) into the gastrointestinal tract. Anundi *et al.* (1984) found a stimulation of cellular selenium uptake from selenite by isolated enterocytes incubated in the presence of extracellular glutathione. The effect was diminished by the inhibition of the brush-border membrane enzyme $\gamma$-glutamyltransferase.

The authors assumed that selenodiglutathione was formed in the incubation medium which may be transported by γ-glutamyltransferase into the cells. Glutathione as well as cysteine also stimulated selenium transfer from selenite from the intestinal lumen into the blood (Scharrer *et al.*, 1989). Because cysteine-stimulated uptake of selenium from selenite showed a clear sodium dependence and was inhibited by amino acids, e.g., alanine, lysine, leucine, and glutamate, the authors concluded that in the simultaneous presence of selenite and cysteine some amino acid-like metabolites (e.g., selenodicysteine, cysteine selenopersulfide) were formed which may be actively transported across the brush-border membrane by amino acid carriers (Würmli *et al.*, 1989; Senn *et al.*, 1992; Scharrer *et al.*, 1992). Reduction by thiols (e.g., glutathione or cysteine) of selenite to selenide may also contribute to the high bioavailability of selenite because selenide seems to be readily absorbed (Cantor *et al.*, 1975).

### *Selenoamino acids*
In feed and food from natural sources a substantial amount of total selenium is present as free or peptide-bound selenoamino acids, e.g., selenomethionine, selenocystine and selenocysteine. McConnell and Cho (1967) demonstrated active transport of L-selenomethionine but not of selenocysteine across the intestinal wall of the hamster. Furthermore, they described a mutual inhibition between methionine and selenomethionine. Experiments with isolated brush-border membrane vesicles from pig small intestine unequivocally demonstrated that selenomethionine and the sulfur analogue methionine are transported across the intestinal brush-border membrane by the same amino acid carrier(s) (Wolffram *et al.*, 1989a; b) by secondary active sodium-cotransport. This seems also to apply for selenocysteine and cysteine, whereby transport appears to be mediated by the carrier for basic amino acids, because cysteine transport was competitively inhibited by selenocysteine, lysine, and arginine.

POST-ABSORPTIVE METABOLISM OF SELENIUM

In order to fulfill its metabolic roles selenium absorbed from the gastrointestinal contents must enter a metabolically active pool and be transformed into biologically active principles within the organism. Aside from the effects of selenium in cancer prevention, current knowledge indicates that selenium is incorporated into several selenoproteins with specific functions. It is important for an understanding of selenium metabolism to note that all of these selenoproteins contain selenium as one or more selenocystyl residues within the peptide chain. Replacement of selenocysteine by cysteine in these proteins will result in a marked decrease or even complete loss of the specific function.

In this chapter only some major aspects of the functions and synthesis of selenoproteins will be shortly reviewed. A comprehensive treatise of all aspects of selenium metabolism as well as the synthesis and functions of selenoproteins is beyond the scope of the present paper. For further information, the reader is referred to several recent reviews (Sunde, 1990; Zachara *et al.*, 1992; Berry and Larsen, 1993; Burk and Hill, 1993; 1994; Berry and Larsen, 1994; Köhrle, 1994; Larsen and Berry, 1995; Ursini *et al.*, 1995; Daniels, 1996; Low and Berry, 1996; Reddy, 1996; Stadtman, 1996; Gamble *et al.*, 1997; Germain and Galton, 1997; Whanger, 1998).

## Selenoproteins

To date four genetically different selenium-containing glutathione peroxidases (GSH-Px) have been characterized and functionally described (Ursini *et al.*, 1995). The cytosolic form of this enzyme (cGSH-Px), also named "classical" GSH-Px, has been studied for many years. It is the most abundant selenoprotein in most mammalian tissues and has been postulated to be a storage form of selenium in addition to destroying hydroperoxides. Ample evidence reveals that cGSH-Px in concerted action with glutathione (serving as reducing agent), the pentose phosphate cycle (generating $NADPH + H^+$ for reduction of diglutathione) and glutathione reductase (regeneration of glutathione) efficiently metabolizes hydrogen peroxide ($H_2O_2$) as well as unesterified fatty acid hydroperoxides. Recently, another cytosolic GSH-Px has been identified in tissues of the gastrointestinal tract which has been named GSH-Px-GI (Chu *et al.*, 1993; Chu and Esworthy, 1995). Functionally, GSH-Px-GI is indistinguishable from cGSH-Px. Another form of GSH-Px which can finally explain the well known interactions of selenium and vitamin E is the phospholipid hydroperoxide GSH-Px (plGSH-Px). This enzyme is preferentially expressed in reproductive and endocrine tissues. Interestingly, plGSHPx shows a very low affinity for glutathione and a glutathione binding site is completely absent in the catalytic center of this enzyme. Together with vitamin E, plGSH-Px may act as a chain-breaking antioxidant and thus inhibit the peroxy and alkoxy free radical attack on phospholipid membranes. Furthermore, plGSH-Px appears to be the most likely candidate among the different GSH-Px for regulation of leukotriene biosynthesis *in vivo*. The final GSH-Px is an extracellular form present in plasma (pGSH-Px). It appears to be a glycosylated form of cGSH-Px and is secreted by kidney tubular cells and perhaps by several other types of cells. An antioxidant function of pGSH-Px has been ruled out in view of the extremely low extracellular glutathione concentration, the lack of any efficient extracellular glutathione regenerating system, and the comparatively low rate constants for glutathione. It has been speculated that extracellular glutathione levels in the micromolar range could just serve to keep pGSH-Px in a reduced state under undisturbed physiological conditions. An oxidative burst of polymorphonuclear leukocytes or macrophages could keep the active site selenium oxidized long enough to allow a transfer of the oxidant signal onto thiol groups on distant cellular surfaces (Ursini *et al.*, 1995).

Besides the different forms of GSH-Px several other selenoproteins have been identified. These include the deiodinase family of selenoproteins, the thioredoxin reductase, selenoprotein P in plasma, and selenoprotein W in muscle.

Three deiodinase processes, catalyzed by three different enzymes termed deiodinase I, II, and III, have been defined which differ in terms of tissue distribution, reaction kinetics, efficiency of substrate utilization and sensitivity to inhibitors. Whereas type I deiodinase has been clearly identified as a selenoprotein, the presence of selenocysteine in the type II and III deiodinase is still being debated (Berry and Larsen, 1994; Larsen and Berry, 1995; Germain and Galton, 1997). Type I deiodinase can catalyze both outer (5' position) and inner (5 position) ring deiodination; whereas type II deiodinase preferentially functions as a 5'-deiodinase. Although type I deiodinase is capable of inner ring deiodination leading to transformation of thyroxine ($T_4$) into reversed triiodthyronine ($rT_3$), the predominant enzyme for this metabolic function seems to be type III deiodinase. Type II deiodinase seems to be mainly responsible for local (intracellular) transformation of $T_4$ into $T_3$. Together the different deiodinases with their specific tissue distribution and different regulation patterns are responsible for the complex metabolism of the thyroid hormones. Because at least two of the deiodinase enzymes are selenoproteins, interesting links between the metabolism of the two trace elements iodine and selenium have been unraveled (Köhrle, 1994), but the story is still far away from being completely resolved.

Thioredoxin reductases (TR) are $NADPH + H^+$-dependent flavoenzymes. In mammals, this enzymes reduces a variety of substrates in addition to thioredoxin including lipoic acid, selenodiglutathione, selenite, and even lipid hydroperoxides (Hill *et al.*, 1997; Zhong *et al.*, 1998). Thioredoxin is involved in the defense of oxidative stress and provides reducing power for several biochemical processes. Animal and human TR contain a selenocystyl residue at the carboxyl-terminal end of a peptide chain and it has been shown that this selenocysteine is critical for the biological function of the enzyme (Hill *et al.*, 1997; Zhong *et al.*, 1998; Berggren *et al.*, 1997).

Selenoprotein P is a glycoprotein that has been purified from rat and human plasma (Burk *et al.*, 1991; Burk and Hill, 1992; 1994; Burk *et al.*, 1997). In selenium-repleted rats this selenoprotein contains 65% of the plasma selenium and its concentration is 25–30 mg protein/l. In human plasma the concentration of selenoprotein P is only one tenth of that in the rat (Burk and Hill, 1994). It is secreted by the liver into the plasma and turns over rapidly. The plasma half life of $^{75}Se$ in selenoprotein P is 3–4 hours. Selenoprotein P was the first protein described to contain multiple selenocysteines (Burk and Hill, 1992). Purified rat selenoprotein P contains 7.5 ±1 selenium atoms per molecule as selenocysteine. The sequence of the cloned cDNA predicts 10 selenocysteine residues, which suggests that the protein in plasma is a modification of the predicted one (Burk and Hill, 1994). Northern analysis indicates that selenoprotein P is expressed by many tissues. Selenoprotein P is associated with endothelial cells in the liver and is more abundant in central regions than in portal regions. It is also present in kidney glomeruli associated with capillary endothelial cells. Staining of selenoprotein P in the brain is also confined to vascular endothelial cells (Burk *et al.*, 1997). Its localization to the vicinity of endothelial cells is potentially relevant to its oxidant defense function (Burk *et al.*, 1997).

Recently a new selenoprotein has been isolated from the muscle tissue of various species and named selenoprotein W (Vendeland *et al.*, 1993; 1995; Yeh *et al.*, 1995; Beilstein *et al.*, 1996; Yeh *et al.*, 1997). Selenoprotein from rat muscle contains about 0.92 g atoms of selenium per g mol of protein as selenocysteine (Vendeland *et al.*, 1993). Selenoprotein W exists mainly in the cytosol, but very small amounts were also associated with membranes. Western blots revealed selenoprotein W in muscle, spleen, testis, and brain of rats. In a species comparison, the presence of selenoprotein W in muscle of rabbits, sheep, and cattle was confirmed (Yeh *et al.*, 1995). Although the function(s) of selenoprotein W are unknown, the presence of glutathione in isolated selenoprotein W may suggest its involvement in the metabolism of this tripeptide (Beilstein *et al.*, 1996).

## Metabolism of selenium

Plenty of data indicate that organic selenium compounds, e.g., selenomethionine or selenium yeast, are more 'bioavailable' than inorganic selenium sources, e.g., selenite and selenate, in terms of tissue levels of selenium, including meat and milk. Furthermore, selenium concentrations in blood and other tissues as well as glutathione peroxidase activity are maintained for a longer period upon selenium depletion if animals had previously been supplied with organic compounds compared with inorganic sources of selenium. On the other hand, critical evaluation of the literature reveals that inorganic selenium compounds are equally effective or may be even more effective than organic compounds with respect to elevation or maintenance of the activity of selenoproteins, e.g. but only when Se status is marginal glutathione peroxidase (Yeh *et al.*, 1997; Hakkarainen, 1993; Aspila, 1991; Neve, 1995; Mahan and Parrett, 1996). However, as already mentioned, measurement of tissue selenium levels without an appropriate measurement of a biologically active principle of selenium, e.g., glutathione peroxidase, is not fully suitable for the evaluation of the bioavailability of selenium under various conditions.

Figure 3 summarizes the major pathways of the postabsorptive metabolism of inorganic and organic selenium compounds. It should be pointed out that two major pools of selenium appear to exist in the body which are differentially supplied by inorganic and organic selenium compounds ingested with the diet (Daniels, 1996; Janghorbani *et al.*, 1990). This may also explain the above mentioned differences between organic and inorganic selenium sources with respect to selenoprotein synthesis on the one hand, and selenium deposition in tissues on the other hand. One of the pools — termed the exchangeable metabolic pool — incorporates intermediary products that appear during reduction of selenate/selenite, endogenously synthesized selenoproteins as well as compounds derived from methylation of selenide, e.g., methylselenol, dimethylselenide or trimethylselenonium. This exchangeable metabolic pool can also be entered by selenoamino acids. This pool provides metabolism and synthesis of all the functionally important seleno-compounds (Daniels, 1996). The second pool comprises all selenomethionine-containing proteins but has no known function other than perhaps to contribute to selenium stores (Daniels, 1996).

Because selenomethionine is a ready substrate for the enzymes which use methionine, selenomethionine is nonspecifically substituted for methionine in a large number of proteins (especially skeletal muscle protein) particularly when large doses of selenomethionine are supplied (Sunde, 1990; Daniels, 1996; Behne *et al.*, 1991, Butler *et al.*, 1989). Seleno-methionine in skeletal muscle may account for up to 40–50% of total selenium in the body (Daniels, 1996). The extent of unspecific incorpora-tion of selenomethionine instead of methionine in proteins depends on the dietary supply of methionine. With low methionine supply, the percent-age of ingested selenium in the form of selenomethionine immediately available for synthesis of functional selenoproteins may be reduced (Butler *et al.*, 1989). Selenocysteine can also be incorporated into proteins instead of cysteine, but cannot be directly incorporated into specific selenoproteins (Sunde, 1990; Daniels, 1996).

Selenomethionine can be metabolized to selenocysteine analogous to the metabolism of methionine to cysteine via the methionine transsulfuration pathway. Alternatively, methylselenol might be directly released from selenomethionine in animals by a L-methionine-γ-lyase (Sunde, 1990). Selenocysteine does not seem to follow the pathway of cysteine metabolism with oxidative release of selenite; instead a selenocysteine-specific enzyme, selenocysteine-β-lyase, directly releases selenide in the presence of reducing substances (Sunde, 1990; Burk, 1991).

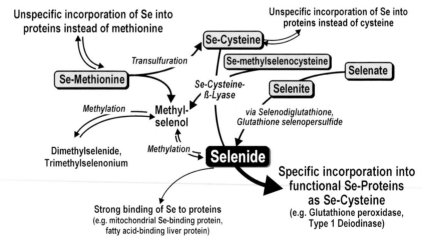

**Figure 3.** Major metabolic pathways of organic and inorganic selenium compounds.

Selenate may be reduced to selenite which may be further reduced to selenide by means of glutathione and glutathione reductase (Ganther and Hsieh, 1974; Ganther, 1986). With respect to the incorporation as well as the excretion of selenium, selenide may hold a central role in selenium metabolism. For excretion, selenide is methylated via methylselenol to dimethylselenide and trimethylselenonium (Ip, 1998; Sunde, 1990; Ganther, 1986; Ganther and Lawrence, 1997). Demethylation of trimethylselenonium and dimethylselenide appears also to be possible (Ip, 1998).

INSERTION OF SELENIUM INTO SELENOPROTEINS

In prokaryotes, synthesis of selenoproteins has been characterized in significant detail (Stadtman, 1996; Böck *et al.*, 1991). In eukaryotes, however, selenoprotein synthesis in animals is much less well characterized (Burk and Hill, 1993; Low and Berry, 1996). Figure 4 depicts the proposed mechanisms of co-translational selenocysteine incorporation (Low and Berry, 1996; Reddy, 1996; Amberg *et al.*, 1996). Several unique molecules are involved, including a structurally unique transfer ribonucleic acid (tRNASec), which is first aminoacylated with serine and further recognized among all other serylated serine isoacceptors by a selenocysteine synthase converting it to selenocysteyl-tRNASec (Amberg *et al.*, 1996). Interestingly, and when first recognized very surprising, insertion of selenocysteine into a peptide chain is coded by the base triplet UGA which normally functions as a stop codon. Insertion of selenocysteine requires

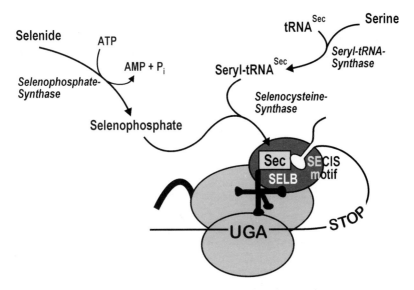

**Figure 4.** Proposed model for cotranslational insertion of selenocysteine into mammalian selenoproteins. Further details are given in the text. Sec = selenocysteine; SELB = specific elongation factor analogous to prokaryotic elongation factor; SECIS motif = selenocysteine insertion sequence motif.

a specific stem loop structure of the mRNA — the so called SECIS motif (SElenoCysteine Insertion Sequence) — which is located in the 3' untranslated regions of the mRNA. A model has been proposed in which a putative quaternary complex is responsible for insertion of selenocysteine. This complex is composed of the selenocysteyl-tRNASec, a specific elongation factor (analogous to the prokaryotic SELB), GTP and the SECIS motif, which interact at the ribosome to decode a UGA selenocysteine codon (Low and Berry, 1996).

## Summary

Although organic and inorganic forms of selenium are absorbed by different mechanisms, intestinal absorption of selenium does not seem to be a limiting factor for the bioavailability of selenium, particularly for nonruminants. Furthermore, intestinal absorption of selenium is not involved in the homeostasis of this essential trace element. Following absorption, both organic and inorganic sources of selenium are utilized for the synthesis of selenoproteins. Whereas selenium from selenate or selenite may be immediately available for these synthetic processes, a varying part of selenium provided as selenomethionine or selenocysteine will be unspecifically deposited in tissue proteins. On the other hand, this "selenium store" may contribute to the synthesis of specific selenoproteins during insufficient dietary selenium supply. If selenium is supplemented to improve animal health and performance, organic and inorganic sources of selenium seems to be equally well suited. However, if selenium is supplied to livestock as a means to improve selenium nutrition in humans by selenium-enriched animal products like meat, eggs or milk, organic selenium sources like selenomethionine or selenized yeast are advantageous.

## References

Amberg, R., T. Mizutani, X.Q. Wu and H.J. Gross. 1996. Selenocysteine synthesis in mammalia: an identity switch from tRNA(Ser) to tRNA(Sec). J. Molec. Biol. 263:8–19.

Anundi, I., J. Högberg and A. Stahl. 1984. Absorption of selenite in the rat small intestine: interactions with glutathione. Acta Pharmacol. Toxicol. 54:273–277.

Ardüser, F., S. Wolffram and E. Scharrer. 1985. Active absorption of selenate by rat ileum. J. Nutr. 115:1203–1208.

Ardüser, F., S. Wolffram, E. Scharrer and B. Schneider. 1986. Transport of selenate and selenite across the brush border membrane of rat and sheep small intestine. Biol. Trace Elem. Res. 9:281–290.

Aspila, P. 1991. Metabolism of selenite, selenomethionine and feed-incorporated selenium in lactating goats and dairy cows. J. Agric. Sci. Finland 6:1–74.

Ballatori, N., and A.T. Truong. 1992. Glutathione as a primary osmotic driving force in hepatic bile formation. Am. J. Physiol. 263:G617–G624.

Behne, D., A. Kyriakopoulos, S. Scheid and H. Gessner. 1991. Effects of chemical form and dosage on the incorporation of selenium into tissue proteins in rats. J. Nutr. 121:806–814.

Beilstein, M.A., S.C. Vendeland, E. Barofsky, O.N. Jensen and P.D. Whanger. 1996. Selenoprotein W of rat muscle binds glutathione and an unknown small molecular weight moiety. J. Inorg. Biochem. 61:117–124.

Berggren, M., A. Gallegos, J. Gasdaska and G. Powis. 1997. Cellular thioredoxin reductase activity is regulated by selenium. Anticancer Res. 17:3377–3380.

Berry, M.J. and P.R. Larsen. 1993. Recognition of UGA as a selenocysteine codon in eukaryotes – A review of recent progress. Bioch. Soc. Trans. 21:827–831.

Berry, M.J. and P.R. Larsen. 1994. Selenocysteine and the structure, function, and regulation of iodothyronine deiodination – Update 1994. Endocr. Rev. 3:265–269.

Bird, S.M., P.C. Uden, J.F.Tyson, E. Block and E. Denoyer. 1997. Speciation of selenoamino acids and organoselenium compounds in selenium-enriched yeast using high-performance liquid chromatography-inductively coupled plasma mass spectrometry. J. Anal. Atom. Spectrom. 12:785–788.

Böck, A., K. Forchhammer, J. Heider, W. Leinfelder, G. Sawers, B. Veprek and F. Zinoni. 1991. Selenocysteine: the 21st amino acid. Molec. Microbiol. 5:515–520.

Bray, T.M. and C.G. Taylor. 1993. Tissue glutathione, nutrition, and oxidative stress. Can. J. Physiol. Pharmacol. 71:746–751.

Burk, R.F. 1991. Molecular biology of selenium with implications for its metabolism. FASEB J. 5:2274–2279.

Burk, R.F. and K.E. Hill. 1992. Some properties of selenoprotein-P. Biol. Trace Elem. Res. 33:151–153.

Burk, R.F. and K.E. Hill. 1993. Regulation of selenoproteins. Annu. Rev. Nutr. 13:65–81.

Burk, R.F. and K.E. Hill. 1994. Selenoprotein P. A selenium-rich extracellular glycoprotein. J. Nutr. 124:1891–1897.

Burk, R.F., K.E. Hill, R. Read and T. Bellew. 1991. Response of rat selenoprotein-P to selenium administration and fate of its selenium. Am. J. Physiol. 261:E26–E30.

Burk, R.F., K.E. Hill, M.E. Boeglin, F.F. Ebner and H.S. Chittum. 1997. Selenoprotein P associates with endothelial cells in rat tissues. Histochem. Cell Biol. 108:11–15.

Butler, J.A., M.A. Beilstein and P.D. Whanger. 1989. Influence of dietary methionine on the metabolism of selenomethionine in rats. J. Nutr. 119:1001–1009.

Butler, J.A., J.T. Deagen, J.B.J. Vanryssen, K.E. Rowe, and P.D. Whanger. 1991. Bioavailability to rats of selenium in ovine muscle, liver and hemoglobin. Nutr. Res. 11:1293–1305.

Cantor, A.H., M.L. Scott and T. Noguchi. 1975. Biological availability of selenium in feedstuffs and selenium compounds for prevention of exudative diathesis in chicks. J. Nutr. 105:96–105.

Cardin, C.J. and J. Mason. 1976. Molybdate and tungstate transfer by rat ileum. Competitive inhibition by sulphate. Biochim. Biophys. Acta 455:937–946.

Chu, F.F., J.H. Doroshow and R.S. Esworthy. 1993. Expression, characterization, and tissue distribution of a new cellular selenium-dependent glutathione peroxidase, GSHPx-GI. J. Biol. Chem. 268:571–2576.

Chu, F.F., and R.S. Esworthy. 1995. The expression of an intestinal form of glutathione peroxidase (GSHPx-GI) in rat intestinal epithelium. Arch. Biochem. Biophys. 323:288–294.

Dahm, L.J. and D.P. Jones. 1994. Secretion of cysteine and glutathione from mucosa to lumen in rat small intestine. Am. J. Physiol. 267:G292-G300.

Daniels, L.A. 1996. Selenium metabolism and bioavailability. Biol. Trace Elem. Res. 54:185–199.

Eberle, D., R. Clarke and N. Kaplowitz. 1981. Rapid oxidation *in vitro* of endogenous and exogenous glutathione in bile of rats. J. Biol. Chem. 256:2115–2117.

Edmondson, A.J., B.B. Norman and D. Suther. 1993. Survey of state veterinarians and state veterinary diagnostic laboratories for selenium deficiency and toxicosis in animals. J Am. Vet. Med. Assoc. 202:865–874.

Fan, A.M., S.A. Book, R.R. Neutra and D.M. Epstein. 1988. Selenium and human health implications in California's San Joaquin Valley. J. Toxicol. Environm. Hlth 23:539–559.

Ganther, H.E. 1986. Pathways of selenium metabolism including respiratory excretory products. J. Amer. Coll. Toxicol. 5:1–5.

Ganther, H.E. and H.S. Hsieh. 1974. Mechanisms for the conversion of selenite to selenides in mammalian tissues. In: Trace Element Metabolism in Animals – 2, Proc. of the Sixth Intern. Symp. on Trace Elem. Metab. in Anim. W.G. Hoekstra, J.W. Suttie, H.E. Ganther and W. Mertz, eds., pp 339–353, Univ. Press, Baltimore.

Ganther, H.E., and J.R. Lawrence. 1997. Chemical transformations of selenium in living organisms. Improved forms of selenium for cancer prevention. Tetrahedron 53:12299–12310.

Gamble, S.C., A. Wiseman and P.S. Goldfarb. 1997. Selenium-dependent glutathione peroxidase and other selenoproteins: Their synthesis and biochemical roles. J. Chem. Technol. Biotechnol. 68:123–134.

Ge, K.Y. and G.Q. Yang. 1993. The epidemiology of selenium deficiency in the etiologic study of endemic diseases in China. Am. J. Clin. Nutr. 57:S259–S263.

Germain, D.L. St. and V.A. Galton. 1997. The deiodinase family of selenoproteins. Thyroid 7:655–668.

Gregus, Z., A.F. Stein and C.D. Klaassen. 1987. Age-dependent biliary excretion of glutathione-related thiols in rats: role of gamma-glutamyltransferase. Am. J. Physiol. 253:G86–G92.

Hakkarainen, J. 1993. Bioavailability of selenium. Norwegian J. Agric. Sci. 65:21–35.

Hill, K.E., G.W. McCollum, M.E. Boeglin and R.F. Burk. 1997. Thioredoxin reductase activity is decreased by selenium deficiency. Biochem. Biophys. Res. Commun. 234:293–295.

Ip, C. 1998. Lessons from basic research in selenium and cancer prevention. J. Nutr. 128:1845–1854.

Janghorbani, M., R.F. Martin, L.J. Kasper, X.F. Sun and V.R. Young. 1990. The selenite-exchangeable metabolic pool in humans: a new concept for the assessment of selenium status. Am. J. Clin. Nutr. 51:670–677.

Kelly, F.J. 1993. Glutathione content of the small intestine – regulation and function. Br. J. Nutr. 69:589–596.

Keshan Disease Research Group of the Chinese Academy of Medical Sciences. 1979. Observations on effect of sodium selenite in prevention of Keshan disease. Chin. Med. J. 92:5471–476.

Koenig, K.M., L.M. Rode, R.D.H. Cohen and W.T. Buckley. 1997. Effects of diet and chemical form of selenium on selenium metabolism in sheep. J. Anim. Sci. 75, 817–827.

Köhrle, J. 1994. Thyroid hormone deiodination in target tissues – A regulatory role for the trace element selenium? Exp. Clin. Endocrinol. 102:63–89.

Larsen, P.R., and M.J. Berry. 1995. Nutritional and hormonal regulation of thyroid hormone deiodinases. Annu. Rev. Nutr. 15:323–352.

Levander, O.A. 1991. Scientific rationale for the 1989 recommended dietary allowance for selenium. J. Am. Diet. Assoc. 91:1572–1576.

Low, S.C. and M.J. Berry. 1996. Knowing when not to stop: Selenocysteine incorporation in eukaryotes. TIBS 21:203–208.

Mahan, D.C. and N.A. Parrett. 1996. Evaluating the efficacy of selenium-enriched yeast and sodium selenite on tissue selenium retention and serum glutathione peroxidase activity in grower and finisher swine. J. Anim. Sci. 74:2967–2974.

McConnell, K.P., and G.J. Cho. 1967. Active transport of L-selenomethionine in the intestine. Am. J. Physiol. 213:150–156.

Meister, A. 1981. Metabolism and functions of glutathione. TIBS 6:231–234.

Meister, A. and M.E. Anderson. 1983. Glutathione. Ann. Rev. Biochem. 52:711–760.

Mykkänen, H.M. and R.H. Wasserman. 1989. Uptake of [75]Se-selenite by brush border membrane vesicles from chick duodenum stimulated by vitamin D. J. Nutr. 119:242–247.

Mykkänen, H.M. and R.H. Wasserman. 1990. Relationship of membrane-bound sulfhydryl groups to vitamin D-stimulated uptake of [$^{75}$Se]selenite by the brush border membrane vesicles form chick duodenum. J. Nutr. 120:882–888.

Neve, J. 1995. Human selenium supplementation as assessed by changes in blood selenium concentration and glutathione peroxidase activity. J. Trace Elem. Med. Biol. 9:65–73.

Oldfield, J.E. 1992. Risks and benefits in agricultural uses of selenium. Environm. Geochem. Hlth. 14:81–86.

Oster, O. 1992. Zum Selenstatus in der Bundesrepublik Deutschland. Univ.-Verl. Jena, BRD.

Paulson, G.D., C.A. Baumann and A.L. Pope. 1966. Fate of a physiological dose of selenate in the lactating ewe: effect of sulfate. J. Anim. Sci. 25:1054–1058.

Peterson, P.J. and D.J. Spedding. 1963. The excretion by sheep of 75selenium incorporated into red clover (*Trifolium pratense* L.) : The chemical nature of the excreted selenium and its uptake by three plant species. N. Z. J. Agric. Res. 6:13–23.

Reddy, P.S. 1996. Biosynthesis of selenoproteins. Curr. Sci. 71:735–737.

Richold, M., M.F. Robinson, and R.DH. Stewart. 1977. Metabolic studies in rats of 75Se incorporated *in vivo* into fish muscle. Br. J. Nutr. 38:19–29.

Scharrer, E., R. Würmli and Wolffram. 1989. Stimulation of intestinal absorption of selenite by cysteine and glutathione. In: Selenium in Medicine and Biology. J. Nève and A. Favier, eds., pp. 55–58, Walter de Gruyter, Berlin, New York.

Scharrer, E., E. Senn and S. Wolffram. 1992. Stimulation of mucosal uptake of selenium from selenite by some thiols at various sites of the intestine. Biol. Trace Elem. Res. 33:109–120

Schwarz, K. 1961. Development and status of experimental work on factor 3-selenium. Federation Proc. 20:666–673.

Schwarz, K. and C.M. Foltz. 1957. Selenium as an integral part of factor 3 against dietary liver degeneration. J. Am. Chem. Soc. 79:3292–3293.

Schwarz, K. and C.M. Foltz. 1958. Factor 3 activity of selenium compounds. J. Biol. Chem. 233:5–251.

Senn, E., E. Scharrer and S. Wolffram. 1992. Effects of glutathione and of cysteine on intestinal absorption of selenium from selenite. Biol. Trace Elem. Res. 33:103–108.

Stabel, J.R. and J.W. Spears. 1993. Role of Selenium in Immune Responsiveness and Disease Resistance. In: Human Nutrition — A Comprehensive Treatise, Vol. 8: Nutrition and Immunology. (D. M. Klurfeld, ed.), Plenum Publishing Corp., New York. pp. 333–356.

Stadtman, T.C. 1996. Selenocysteine. Annu. Rev. Biochem. 65:83–100.

Sunde, R.A. 1990. Molecular biology of selenoproteins. Annu. Rev. Nutr. 10:451–474.

Thomson, C.D. and R.D.H. Stewart. 1972. Measurement of intestinal absorption of selenium. Proc. Univ. Otago Med. Sch. 50:63–64.

Thomson, C.D., and R.D.H. Stewart. 1973. Metabolic studies of ([75]Se)selenomethionine and ([75]Se)selenite in the rat. Br. J. Nutr. 30:139–147.

Thomson, C.D., R.D.H. Stewart and M.F. Robinson. 1975. Metabolic studies in rats of [[75]Se]selenomethionine and of [75]Se incorporated in vivo into rabbit kidney. Br. J. Nutr. 33:45–54.

Ullrey, D.E. 1992. Basis for regulation of selenium supplements in animal diets. J Anim. Sci. 70:3922–3927.

Ursini, F., M. Maiorino, R. Brigeliusflohe, K.D. Aumann, A. Roveri, D. Schomburg and L. Flohe. 1995. Diversity of glutathione peroxidases. Meth. Enzymol. 252:38–53.

Van Vleet, J.F. 1980. Current knowledge of selenium-vitamin E deficiency in domestic animals. J. Am. Vet. Med. Assoc. 176:321–325.

Van Vleet, J.F. and V.J. Ferrans. 1992. Etiologic factors and pathologic alterations in selenium-vitamin-E deficiency and excess in animals and humans. Biol. Trace Elem. Res. 33:1–21.

Vendeland, S.C., J.A. Butler and P.D. Whanger. 1992. Intestinal absorption of selenite, selenate and selenomethionine in the rat. J. Nutr. Biochem. 3:359–365.

Vendeland, S.C., M.A. Beilstein, C.L. Chen, O.N. Jensen, E. Barofsky and P.D. Whanger. 1993. Purification and properties of selenoprotein-W from rat muscle. J. Biol. Chem. 268:17103–17107.

Vendeland, S.C., J.T. Deagen, J.A. Butler and P.D. Whanger. 1994. Uptake of selenite, selenomethionine and selenate by brush border membrane vesicles isolated from rat small intestine. Biometals 7:305–312.

Vendeland, S.C., M.A. Beilstein, J.Y. Yeh, W. Ream and P.D. Whanger. 1995. Rat skeletal muscle selenoprotein W: cDNA clone and mRNA modulation by dietary selenium. Proc. Nat. Acad. Sci. USA 92:8749–8753.

Whanger, P.D. 1989. China, a country with both selenium deficiency and toxicity: some thoughts and impressions. J. Nutr. 119:1236–1239.

Whanger, P.D. 1998. Metabolism of selenium in humans. J. Trace Elem. Exper. Med. 11:227–240.

Wolffram, S., F. Ardüser and E. Scharrer. 1985. *In vivo* intestinal absorption of selenate and selenite by rats. J. Nutr. 115:454–459.

Wolffram, S., E. Anliker and E. Scharrer. 1986. Uptake of selenate and selenite by isolated brush border membrane vesicles from pig, sheep and rat intestine. Biol. Trace Elem. Res. 10:293–306.

Wolffram, S., B. Grenacher and E. Scharrer. 1988. Transport of selenate and sulphate across the intestinal brush border membrane of pig jejunum by two common mechanisms. Quart. J. Exp. Physiol. 73:103–111.

Wolffram, S., B. Berger, B. Grenacher and E. Scharrer. 1989a. Transport of selenoamino acids and their sulfur analogues across the intestinal brush border membrane. J. Nutr. 119:706–712.

Wolffram, S., B. Berger and E. Scharrer. 1989b. Transport of selenomethionine and methionine across the intestinal brush border membrane. In: Selenium in Biology & Medicine, Proceedings of the

4th International Symposium on Selenium in Biology & Medicine. (A. Wendel, ed.), pp. 109–113, Springer Verlag, Berlin, Heidelberg, New York.

Wright, P.L. and M.C. Bell. 1966. Comparative metabolism of selenium and tellurium in sheep and swine. Am. J. Physiol. 21:6–10.

Würmli, R., S. Wolffram, Y. Stingelin and E. Scharrer. 1989. Stimulation of mucosal uptake of selenium from selenite by L-cysteine in sheep small intestine. Biol. Trace Elem. Res. 20:75–85.

Yeh, J.Y., M.A. Beilstein, J.S. Andrews and P.D. Whanger. 1995. Tissue distribution and influence of selenium status on levels of selenoprotein W. FASEB J. 9:392–396.

Yeh, J.Y., Q.P. Gu, M.A. Beilstein, N.E. Forsberg and P.D. Whanger. 1997. Selenium influences tissue levels of selenoprotein W in sheep. J. Nutr. 127:394–402.

Zachara, B.A. 1992. Mammalian selenoproteins. J. Trace Elem. Electrol. Hlth. Dis. 6:137–151.

Zhong, L., E.S. Arner, J. Ljung, F. Aslund and A. Holmgren. 1998. Rat and calf thioredoxin reductase are homologous to glutathione reductase with a carboxyl–terminal elongation containing a conserved catalytically active penultimate selenocysteine residue. J. Biol. Chem. 273:8581–8591.

# The effects of conventional *versus* cage housing and inorganic *versus* organic selenium on feathering in broilers

F.W. EDENS, C.R. PARKHURST AND G.B. HAVENSTEIN

*Department of Poultry Science, North Carolina State University, Raleigh, North Carolina, USA*

## Introduction

It has been suggested that in the not too distant future broilers will be produced in cages (Smith, 1972). From the mid-1960s to the early 1980s, many attempts were made to design cage facilities for the rearing of broiler chickens from hatch to market age. Unfortunately, none of these early cage systems allowed economical broiler production because there were high incidences of downgrades (Lloyd, 1969), breast blisters (Andrews and Goodwin, 1973), soft, distorted and broken bones (Merkley, 1976), poor feathering (Andrews *et al.*, 1975; Bayer *et al.*, 1976) and overall poor performance (Andrews and Goodwin, 1973; Andrews *et al.*, 1975; Bayer *et al.*, 1976).

Andrews and Goodwin (1973) reported that the primary cause for lack of success in rearing broilers in cages was due in part to the lack of proper materials for the development of cages. Recently, a cage rearing system was designed (Broilermatic® Cage System, Farmer Automatic of America) that appears to have eliminated many of the early problems associated with cage rearing of broilers (Havenstein *et al.*, 1998). This caging system is gaining popularity around the world but many questions have been raised concerning production and performance of broilers reared in the system.

Selenium supplementation of poultry rations is a routine procedure. Sodium selenite has been the traditional source of supplementation (Leeson and Summers, 1991). Recently, organic selenium from yeast (Sel-Plex, Alltech Inc.), a more active form of selenium in chickens than selenite (Cantor *et al.*, 1975; Collins *et al.*, 1993), has become widely used in several countries, e.g., Japan, Switzerland, and Finland to name but a few. Thompson and Scott (1969), Scott *et al.* (1982) and Leeson and Summers (1991) have shown that selenium is required for maximum performance of chickens.

Edens (1996, 1998) reported that feathering rate of auto-sexed, slow feathering males was enhanced significantly with dietary supplementation of organic selenium (Sel-Plex). Enhanced feathering with Sel-Plex

567

compared to sodium selenite at levels of 0.1, 0.2, or 0.3 mg/kg of diet was observed in trials conducted in both the spring and summer seasons. These observations were unexpected even though it had been reported that selenium apparently was involved in feathering and feather development (Thompson and Scott, 1969; Supplee, 1966). Since poor feathering has been associated with production of broilers in cages (Andrews *et al.*, 1975; Bayer *et al.*, 1976), an investigation was conducted to determine if organic selenium as Sel-Plex could influence the feathering rate of both females and slow feathering males reared either in a Broilermatic Cage System or in a conventional litter covered floor, curtain sidewall rearing environment.

## Materials and methods

A summer experiment used feather-sexable broiler chickens (Arbor Acres X Arbor Acres) placed in litter covered floor pens or in pens in the Broilermatic® Cage System at standard stocking densities. Males and females were reared separately in this experiment. The diets were supplemented with two selenium sources: sodium selenite and selenium yeast (Sel-Plex, Alltech, Inc) at a level of 0.2 mg/kg of feed for each of these two selenium forms. Brooding temperature and light management within the Broilermatic® Cage System (Havenstein *et al.*, 1998) and the conventional houses were consistent with current broiler management practices. The litter in the conventional broiler house consisted of pine wood shavings top-dressed over built-up litter. The experimental diets consisted of the North Carolina Agricultural Research Service starter diet: 3154 kcal/kg metabolizable energy (ME), 21% crude protein (CP) (1–3 weeks); grower diet: 3135 kcal ME/kg, 18.1% CP (4–5 weeks), and finisher diet: 3172 kcal ME/kg, 15.4% CP (6 weeks).

Body weights and feed conversions (FCR) were determined at 3 and 6 weeks of age (6 week data are presented here), and mortality was recorded on a daily basis. At 2, 3, 4, 5 and 6 weeks of age, feather tracts on the back (interscapular cape, dorsal, pelvic, dorsal caudal tracts combined), breast (pectoral and sternal tracts combined), thigh (femoral tract- rear body and lower thigh, combined), neck (dorsal cervical and ventral cervical combined), tail (greater and lesser sickle feathers), and wings (upper coverts) were scored subjectively on the basis of feather size and skin surface covered. Feathering scores ranged from 0 (poorest) to 5 (best) for each tract. The regional feathering scores were determined, and scores for the different feather tracts were averaged for a whole body feathering score. Data on feathering were partitioned by sex, dietary selenium source and housing environment.

Data were subjected to statistical analysis using the General Linear Models Procedure of SAS (1994). Analysis of variance was conducted for each parameter, and the level of significance was set at a minimum at $P<0.05$.

# Results and discussion

Body weights were equivalent between sodium selenite and Sel-Plex fed broilers in both the conventional and cage house (Table 1). Broilers in the cage house tended to be slightly, but not significantly, heavier than those in the conventional house. Feed conversion ratios (FCR) were equivalent for birds within a housing environment even though there were very small increases in FCR for those birds given Sel-Plex (Table 1). However, the major difference in FCR was between housing environments with the birds in the cage house showing an improvement in FCR of 80 points. There were no mortality differences between housing environments or selenium forms (Table 1). These observations on performance were consistent with earlier observations on the performance of broilers given either sodium selenite or Sel-Plex (Edens, 1996, 1998).

**Table 1.** Effect of housing and selenium form (sodium selenite *vs* Sel-Plex) on performance of broiler chickens at 41 days of age.

| Housing environment | Selenium form | Body weight, kg | FCR, g/g gain | Mortality, % |
|---|---|---|---|---|
| Broilermatic® | Sodium selenite | 2.02[a] | 1.750[b] | 2.18[a] |
| | Sel-Plex | 2.00[a] | 1.760[b] | 2.57[a] |
| House mean | | 2.01[x] | 1.755[x] | 2.38[x] |
| Conventional | Sodium selenite | 1.99[a] | 2.031[a] | 1.83[a] |
| | Sel-Plex | 1.99[a] | 2.039[a] | 2.14[a] |
| House mean | | 1.99[x] | 2.035[y] | 1.99[x] |

[a,b; x,y] In a column, means with unlike superscripts differ significantly (P ≤0.05).

The data from this experiment showed that Sel-Plex induced more rapid whole body feathering in the slow feathering males as well as in the normal feathering females (Figure 1). This influence of selenium yeast was evident at three weeks of age and persisted through six weeks of age. These data show that the females had a greater feathering rate than the males throughout the six weeks of the experiment. Females approached full feathering at five weeks of age, but males were still lagging behind females even at six weeks of age.

Data were partitioned to study the feathering rate on different body regions (Figures 2–7). There was an effect of Sel-Plex on female back feathering at only three weeks of age (Figure 2). At five weeks of age, nearly complete feathering of the backs of females was evident in groups given either sodium selenite or Sel-Plex. In males, back feathering was very slow in comparison to females (Figure 2). However, there was a significant Sel-Plex effect causing faster back feathering in males from three weeks of age through six weeks of age. Full back feathering in males with Sel-Plex supplementation was evident at six weeks, but those males given sodium selenite were not fully back feathered even at six weeks of age.

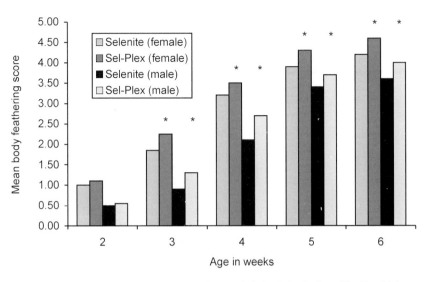

**Figure 1.** Effect of sodium selenite and Sel-Plex on whole body feathering of broiler chickens. (* P<0.05).

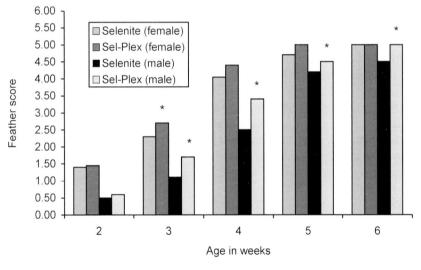

**Figure 2.** Effect of sodium selenite and Sel-Plex on back feathering in broiler chickens (*P<0.05).

Breast feathering was slower than back feathering (Figure 3). The slower feathering rate on this body surface possibly may be related to the fact that the birds spend a great deal of their time resting on sternal feathers and may actually suffer a feather loss on this region due to increased contact with the cage or litter floor. Pectoral feathering, which was not scored separately, developed rapidly in females and in many males. There was,

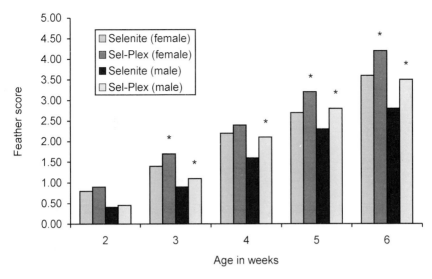

**Figure 3.** Effect of sodium selenite and Sel-Plex on breast feathering in broiler chickens (*P<0.05).

however, a Sel-Plex stimulation of faster feathering in both males and females (except at four weeks of age) when comparisons were made with the sodium selenite effect on feathering. However, breast feathering, even with Sel-Plex, was still slower in males than in females.

Thigh feathering was slower than back feathering but faster than breast feathering in both males and females (Figure 4). Nevertheless, Sel-Plex in both males (except at two weeks of age) and females caused more rapid thigh feathering than did sodium selenite through six weeks of age.

Feathering of the wings was faster in Sel-Plex treated females and males than in birds given sodium selenite (Figure 5). This increased feathering rate was evident at three weeks of age and persisted through six weeks of age. As seen in other regions of the body surface, females feathered their wings faster than did the males.

Neck feathering was delayed until three weeks of age in both males and females when the first growth of feathers in this region became evident (Figure 6). Females feathered the neck faster than did the males. At three weeks of age the females showed a significantly increased feathering of the neck, but from four through six weeks of age, there were no differences between feathering rates of sodium selenite and Sel-Plex supplemented birds (Figure 6). By five weeks of age, neck feathering was nearly complete in the females, but even at six weeks of age the males had not attained complete neck feathering.

Tail feathering rates in females (Figure 7) was stimulated by Sel-Plex as early as two weeks of age and persisted through six weeks of age. Tail feathering in females was significantly faster than feathering of the tail in the males (Figure 7). Even though feathering in the males was

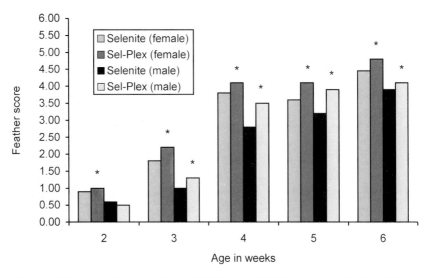

**Figure 4.** Effect of sodium selenite and Sel-Plex on thigh feathering in broiler chickens (*P<0.05).

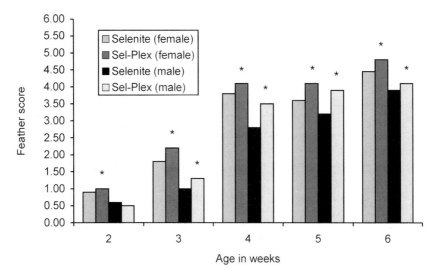

**Figure 5.** Effect of sodium selenite and Sel-Plex on wing feathering in broiler chickens (*P<0.05).

significantly slower in males than females, there was still a significant stimulation of feather growth at three and four weeks of age in the males given Sel-Plex.

There was also a significant housing effect on feathering rate. Generally, whole body feathering was stimulated more by Sel-Plex in females reared in the conventional broiler house (Figure 8). Even in females given

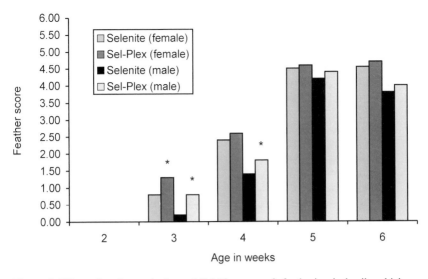

**Figure 6.** Effect of sodium selenite and Sel-Plex on neck feathering in broiler chickens (*P<0.05).

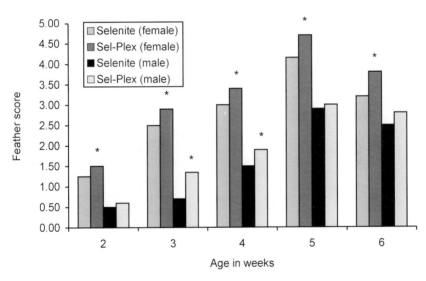

**Figure 7.** Effect of sodium selenite and Sel-Plex on tail feathering in broiler chickens (*P<0.05).

sodium selenite, there was an increase in feathering rate in those birds in the conventional house compared with those in the cage house.

In males, Sel-Plex caused a faster feathering rate than did the sodium selenite (Figure 9). A difference between conventional and cage rearing in feathering rate was not evident until five weeks of age, and this advantage persisted through six weeks of age. Overall, whole body

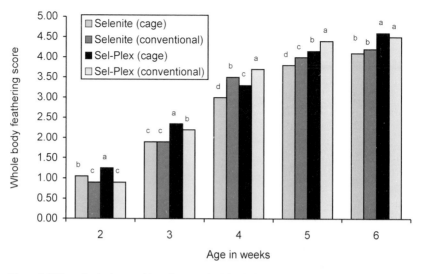

**Figure 8.** Effect of selenium and housing on whole body feathering of female broiler chickens. ([a,b,c,d] P<0.05).

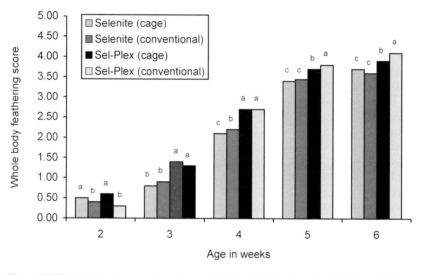

**Figure 9.** Effect of selenium and housing on whole body feathering of male broiler chickens ([a,b,c] P <0.05).

feathering was fastest in the conventional house in birds given Sel-Plex.

The mechanism associated with increased feathering rates of broiler chickens supplemented with Sel-Plex in their diets has not been established. Improvement in feathering with Sel-Plex was seen as early as three weeks of age, and this improvement was evident through six weeks of age. In this case, for summertime feathering, Sel-Plex produced better feathering than did sodium selenite. These data suggest that the improved feathering was directly related to the improved retention of organic selenium, and that selenoamino acids such as selenomethionine or selenocysteine were used for keratin synthesis in feather production thereby sparing the cysteine pool in liver and muscle glutathione which is normally used (Goto and Okamoto, 1965; Murphy and King, 1985). Since organic selenium is retained in tissues to a greater degree than is selenite selenium (Cantor *et al.*, 1975; Collins *et al.*, 1993), it stands to reason that during times when there is a demand for feather synthesis, selenium yeast would be a better source of selenium than selenite. Sel-Plex feed supplementation was reported to facilitate better feathering rates during both cool and hot seasons in slow feathering males (Edens, 1996; 1998), and currently we find that not only males but females feathered better when fed Sel-Plex.

Selenium is a structural component of the glutathione peroxidase system which acts as an antioxidant decreasing numbers of intracellular reactive oxygen metabolites (Tappel, 1987). In order for selenium to be effective in the activation of this enzyme system, the selenite and selenate forms must be converted to the selenide form before selenoproteins are synthesized. Cysteine must combine with selenide to form selenocysteine via a tRNA-mediated process, and this is a very limiting process in mammals (Esaki *et al.*, 1979). Selenocysteine then serves as the active precursor of selenoproteins including glutathione peroxidase. Therefore, it is possible that the improved feathering rate in broilers supplemented with Sel-Plex organic selenium may be related to improved antioxidant activity, but this remains to be elucidated.

The improved feathering rate in broilers, especially in the slow feathering males, suggested that organic selenium might be modifying gene action. Slow feathering is regulated by a dominant sex-linked *K* gene whereas the *k+* recessive allele regulates rapid feathering found in females. The slow feathering K gene is expressed in feather-sexed male broiler chickens and the slow feathering trait in these birds is evident for several weeks after hatch. The slow feathering trait in broilers apparently does not affect performance in well maintained flocks (Dunnington and Siegel, 1986; Lowe and Merkley, 1986; Merkley and Lowe, 1988). Therefore, the supplementation of organic selenium, a more active form of selenium than sodium selenite (Cantor *et al.*, 1975; Collins *et al.*, 1993), may suppress the expression of a K gene product or it may be facilitating a *k+* gene product releasing the birds to show more rapid feathering. If this is the case, selenium from the organic selenium Sel-Plex source also could be affecting the expression of other genes. Additional studies are required to elucidate the mode of action of selenium yeast on feathering rates in poultry.

## Summary

Performance parameters such as feed conversion ratios, body weights, and mortality were unaffected by selenium source. However, Sel-Plex induced more rapid whole body feathering in the slow feathering males as well as in the normal feathering females. This influence of Sel-Plex was evident at three weeks of age and persisted through six weeks of age. Females had a greater feathering rate than the males throughout the 6 weeks experiment. Females approached full feathering at five weeks of age, but males were still lagging behind females even at six weeks of age. Feathering of broilers in the conventional house was slightly better than the feathering of broilers in the cage house. The mechanism for improved feathering rate in normal feathering females and slow feathering males given Sel-Plex has not been determined. However, Sel-Plex may be decreasing oxidative stress, or organic selenium may be a required component of a biochemical pathway involved in feathering that may be blocked by the presence of the $K$ gene on the $w$ chromosome.

# References

Andrews, L. D., and T. L. Goodwin. 1973. Performance of broilers in cages. Poultry Sci. 52:723–728.

Andrews, L. D., G. S. Nelson, G. C. Harris, Jr. and T. L. Goodwin. 1975. Performance of five strains of broilers in a four tier cage system with plastic floors. Poultry Sci. 54:54–58.

Bayer, R. C., F. V. Muir, C. B. Chawan and A. T. Bryan. 1976. Infected feather follicles in cage reared broilers. Poultry Sci. 55:1194–1200.

Cantor, A. H., M. L. Langevin , T. Naguchi and M. L. Scott. 1975. Efficacy of selenium in selenium compounds and feedstuffs for prevention of pancreatic fibrosis in chicks. J. Nutri. 105:106–111.

Collins, V. C., A. H. Cantor, M. J. Ford and M. L. Straw. 1993. Bioavailability of selenium in selenized yeast for broiler chickens. Poultry Sci. 72 (Suppl. 1):85.

Dunnington, E. A. and P. B. Siegel. 1986. Sex-linked feathering alleles (K, K+) in chicks of diverse genetic backgrounds. 1. Body temperatures and body weights. Poultry Sci. 65:209–214.

Edens, F. W. 1996. Organic selenium: from feathers to muscle integrity to drip loss: five years onward no more selenite! In: Biotechnology in the Feed Industry. Proc. of the 12th Annual Symposium. (T.P. Lyons and K.A. Jacques, eds). Nottingham University Press, Nottingham, UK. pp. 165–185.

Edens, F. W. 1998. Feathering rate affects male broiler performance. Misset-World Poultry 14(6):20–22.

Esaki, N., H. Tanaka, S. Uemura, T. Suzuki and K. Soda, 1979. Catalytic action of L-methionine-g-lyase on selenomethionine and selenols. Biochemistry, 19:407–410.

Goto, I. and S. Okamoto. 1965. Blood reduced glutathione levels and plasma protein constituents in molting hens. Japan Poultry Sci. 2:33–36.

Havenstein, G. B., J. L. Grimes, P. R. Ferket, C. R. Parkhurst, F. W. Edens, J. Brake and J. H. van Middelkoop. 1998. Recent experiences with reduced or non-litter systems for growing broilers and turkeys. In: Proceedings: 1998 National Poultry Waste Management Symposium. Springdale, AR. October 19–21, 1998. pp. 225–240.

Leeson, S. and J. D. Summers. 1991. Commercial Poultry Nutrition. University Books, Guelph, Ontario, Canada.

Lloyd, R. W. 1969. Growing broilers in cages. Poultry Digest, 28:542–545.

Lowe, P. C. and J. W. Merkley. 1986. Association rate of feathering genotypes in broilers with production and carcass composition traits. 1. Effect of genotypes, sex, and diet on growth and feed conversion. Poultry Sci. 65:1853–1858.

Merkley, J. W. 1976. Increased bone strength in coop-reared broilers provided fluoridated water. Poultry Sci. 55:1313–1319.

Merkley, J. W. and P. C. Lowe. 1988. Association rate of feathering genotypes in broilers with production and carcass composition traits. 2. Effect of genotypes and diet on processing traits and lipid deposition. Poultry Sci. 67:914–919.

Murphy, M. E. and J. R. King. 1985. Diurnal variation in liver and muscle glutathione pools of molting and non-molting white-crown sparrows. Physiol. Zool. 58: 646–654.

SAS Institute. 1994. SAS User's Guide: Statistics. SAS Institute, Cary, NC USA.

Scott, M. L., M. C. Nesheim and R. J. Young. 1982. Nutrition of the Chicken. 3rd Edition. M. L. Scott & Associates, Ithaca, NY.

Smith, W. M. 1972. Whither cages in broilers? Poultry Digest, 31:76–77.

Supplee, W. C. 1966. Feather abnormality in poults fed a diet deficient in vitamin E and selenium. Poultry Sci. 45:852–854.

Tappel, A. L. 1987. Glutathione peroxidase and other selenoproteins. In: Selenium in Biology and Medicine. G. F. Combs, Jr., O. A. Levander, J. E. Spallholz and J. E. Oldfield, ed. Van Nostrand Reinhold Co., New York, NY. pp 122–132.

Thompson , J. N. and M. L. Scott. 1969. Role of selenium in the nutrition of the chick. J. Nutri. 97:335–342.

# Effect of selenium source on selenium digestibility and retention in exercised Thoroughbreds

J.D. PAGAN[1], P. KARNEZOS[2], M.A.P. KENNEDY, T. CURRIER[1], and K.E. HOEKSTRA[1]

[1] *Kentucky Equine Research, Inc., Versailles, Kentucky,* [2] *Alltech, Inc., Nicholasville, Kentucky, USA*

## Introduction

Performance horses compete in a wide variety of athletic events ranging from high speed racing to 100-mile endurance rides. These types of exercise are known to induce oxidative stress, leading to the generation of free radicals. An increased generation of free radicals may induce lipid peroxidation and tissue damage in both the respiratory system and working muscle. This is particularly true if the animal has a deficient or impaired antioxidant status. Reddy *et al.* (1998) studied the role of vitamin E and selenium during exercise-induced oxidative stress in the pulmonary tissue of rats. Vitamin E and/or selenium deficiency resulted in generation of free radicals as revealed by electron spin resonance (ESR) spectra in lung tissue, indicating the onset of oxidative stress. When the rats were subjected to a single bout of exhaustive exercise, there was an additional increase in the generation of oxygen free radicals. However, no such signals were recorded in the lung tissue of vitamin E and selenium-supplemented animals when subjected to a similar exercise program, suggesting that protection is offered by vitamin E and selenium in combating oxidative stress. Many antioxidants, including glutathione peroxidase (GSH-Px), are selenoproteins making selenium an extremely important mineral for performance horses.

Although the Food and Drug Administration (FDA) has approved maximal selenium supplementation at 0.3 mg/kg of dry matter in complete feeds for cattle, sheep, and swine (FDA, 1987), selenium supplementation of equine feeds is restricted only by nutritional recommendations and industry practices (NRC, 1989). The selenium requirement for mature idle horses was estimated by the NRC to be 0.1 mg/kg of diet. This requirement is based on studies that evaluated the relationship between selenium intake and blood selenium in mature idle horses (NRC, 1989). Shelle *et al.* (1985) investigated the effect of supplemental selenium on plasma selenium and on glutathione peroxidase in Arabian and crossbred horses subjected to a conditioning program. They reported that conditioning increased erythrocyte glutathione peroxidase activity and suggested that horses at high work intensities may have higher requirements for selenium than the 0.1 ppm requirement suggested by the NRC. Stowe (1998) has suggested that the appropriate concentration of selenium in the total diet of a horse is 0.3 ppm. This would mean that if a concentrate mix was 50% of the diet and the forage component of the diet supplied 0.06 ppm Se, the grain mix would need to be roughly 0.6 ppm.

Selenium in forages and seed grains is normally present as organic selenium in the form of selenocystine, selenocysteine, and selenomethionine. Sodium selenite and sodium selenate are common inorganic sources of supplemental selenium for horses; and evidence in horses (Podoll *et al.*, 1992) indicates there is no difference between them in potency as measured by blood selenium status. Measurement in laboratory animals, however, shows that organic plant sources of selenium are more potent than inorganic (Frape, 1998). No studies have measured the digestibility and retention of selenium from different selenium sources in horses. Therefore, the following study was conducted to evaluate how exercised Thoroughbreds digest and retain selenium from either sodium selenite or organic selenium from yeast.

## Materials and methods

Four mature trained Thoroughbred geldings were used in a two-period switch back design trial. During each period, two horses were fed hay and unfortified concentrate supplemented daily with 2.90 mg of selenium from sodium selenite. Selenite-supplemented rations averaged 0.41 ppm Se with ~77% of the total selenium provided by the selenite. The other two horses received hay and unfortified concentrate supplemented daily with 2.76 mg of organic selenium from a selenium yeast (Sel-Plex, Alltech, Inc.). Organic selenium rations averaged 0.40 ppm Se with ~75% of the total selenium provided from the yeast.

During period 1, the horses were fed the selenium supplemented diets for five weeks. During the first four weeks, the horses were exercised three days per week on a high speed treadmill and three days per week on a mechanical horse walker. The horses were housed in box stalls at night and were turned out into paddocks during the day with muzzles to prevent grazing.

During week 5 of period 1, a five-day complete collection digestion trial was conducted. The horses were fitted with collection harnesses that allowed the complete and separate collection of feces and urine. Daily fecal and urinary output was measured and daily samples of each were frozen for later selenium analysis. On day three of the digestion trial, the horses completed a competition exercise test (CET) on the high speed treadmill which was designed to simulate the physiological and metabolic stresses of the speed and endurance test of a three-day event (Marlin *et al.*, 1995). The CET was performed on an inclined treadmill (3°) and consisted of a 10-minute walk (Phase A, 1.4 m/s), 10-minute trot (Phase

A, 3.7 m/s), 2-minute gallop (Phase B, 10.7 m/s), 20-minute trot (Phase C, 3.7 m/s), 10-minute walk (Phase C, 1.4 m/s) and 8-minute canter (Phase D, 9.0 m/s). Following exercise, the horses were hand-walked for an additional 30 minutes. Whole blood and plasma samples were taken from the horses immediately before and after the CET and 4 hrs and 24 hrs post-exercise. Packed cell volume (PCV) was measured in each blood sample using a Coulter Counter S560 (Coulter Electronics, Hialeah, FL, USA). Feed, feces, urine and blood were analyzed for selenium according to the fluorometric method of AOAC (1995). Red blood cell (RBC) selenium was calculated using the following equation:

$$RBC\ Se = [Whole\ blood\ Se-(plasma\ Se*(1-PCV))]/PCV.$$

Following period 1, the selenium supplementation received by each horse was switched for an additional three week period. During the first two weeks of period 2, the horses followed the same exercise schedule as they had during period 1 followed by a complete collection digestion trial and CET during week 3. The digestibility and retention of selenium from the two supplements were calculated and compared using least squares analyses of variance with general linear models procedures. Data were analyzed using a model that included horse, period and treatment as main effects.

# Results and discussion

## SELENIUM DIGESTIBILITY AND RETENTION

Horses supplemented with inorganic selenium excreted more fecal selenium than when supplemented with Sel-Plex Se (P<0.05) (Table 1). The apparent absorption of selenite selenium and Sel-Plex selenium averaged 51.1% and 57.3%, respectively. These digestibility values are intermediate between those reported for pigs and ruminants. In ruminants, selenium absorption is around 35% while in pigs, absorption values of 75-85% have been reported (Levander, 1986). Mahan and Parrett (1996) measured selenium digestibility in growing pigs weighing around 52 kg. They found that the apparent selenium digestibility of both selenite and organic selenium averaged about 75% when fed at supplemental levels of 0.3 ppm.

Selenium retention was increased when Sel-Plex was the added dietary selenium source (P<0.05). Most of the difference in selenium retention was the result of increased selenium absorption since there was no difference in average daily urinary selenium excretion between the two supplemental sources. Mahan and Parrett (1996) also found increased selenium retention with Sel-Plex in growing pigs; but in contrast to the present study, the difference was due to increased urinary excretion of selenium in the selenite-supplemented animals.

While average daily urinary selenium excretion was not different between treatments, selenium excretion following a bout of exercise was affected by selenium source. The horses completed the competition exercise test (CET) on the morning of day 3 of the five-day collection. Following

**Table 1.** Effect of selenium source on balance measurements in exercised horses.

| | Inorganic selenium (sodium selenite) | Organic selenium (Sel-Plex) | SEM | Treatment effect |
|---|---|---|---|---|
| Selenium balance, mg/d | | | | |
| Intake | 3.76 | 3.72 | 0.05 | NS |
| Urine | 1.16 | 1.10 | 0.05 | NS |
| Feces | 1.85 | 1.58 | 0.02 | P<0.05 |
| Retention | 0.75 | 1.04 | 0.07 | P=0.11 |
| Apparent absorption, % | 51.1 | 57.3 | 1.4 | P<0.10 |
| Retention, % of intake | 20.4 | 27.8 | 1.3 | P<0.05 |
| Retention, % of absorbed | 39.3 | 48.6 | 1.4 | P<0.05 |

exercise, selenium excretion in horses given inorganic selenium was higher than during day 1 or day 2 of the collection period (P<0.01) (Figure 1). A similar increase in excretion did not occur when horses were given organic selenium and during day 3 urinary selenium excretion was lower in the Sel-Plex group compared to the horses given selenite (P=0.06).

WHOLE BLOOD AND PLASMA SELENIUM

Before exercise, mean plasma values were slightly higher than reference values reported by Stowe and Herdt (1992), but similar to values reported by Shelle *et al.* (1985) and Snow *et al.* (1987) (Table 2, Figure 2). Whole blood values were typical for horses receiving selenium supplementation (Shellow *et al.*, 1985; Stowe and Herdt, 1992).

Both plasma and whole blood selenium increased post-exercise (P<0.01).

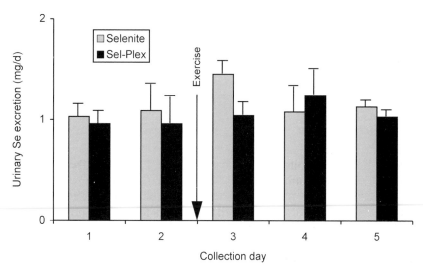

**Figure 1.** Effect of selenium source on daily urinary selenium excretion.

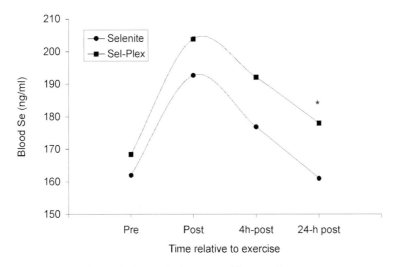

**Figure 2.** Plasma selenium before and after competition exercise test

**Table 2.** Blood selenium before and after the competition exercise test.

| | Inorganic selenium (selenite) | Organic selenium (Sel-Plex) | SEM | Treatment effect |
|---|---|---|---|---|
| Whole blood Se, ng/ml | | | | |
| Pre | 205.1 | 201.0 | 19.4 | NS |
| Post | 216.8 | 224.5 | 16.4 | NS |
| 4 h | 209.2 | 222.1 | 17.7 | NS |
| 24 h | 202.8 | 198.8 | 8.2 | NS |
| RBC Se, ng/ml | | | | |
| Pre | 277.7 | 256.9 | 35.9 | NS |
| Post | 239.5 | 244.4 | 20.1 | NS |
| 4 h | 265.2 | 273.6 | 39.8 | NS |
| 24 h | 276.2 | 235.3 | 15.7 | NS |
| Plasma Se, ng/ml | | | | |
| Pre | 162.0 | 168.4 | 12.3 | NS |
| Post | 192.7 | 203.9 | 12.7 | NS |
| 4 h | 176.9 | 192.1 | 6.5 | NS |
| 24 h | 161.0 | 178.0 | 3.8 | P=0.08 |

This agrees with Gallagher and Stowe (1980) who reported an increase in serum selenium following a training jog in 45 Standardbred horses. Red blood cell selenium was similar between treatment groups and there was a trend towards a decrease in RBC selenium post-exercise. Plasma selenium remained elevated in both treatments four hours post-exercise (P<0.05). By 24 hrs post-exercise, the plasma selenium in horses given inorganic selenium had returned to pre-exercise levels, while plasma selenium from the Sel-Plex-supplemented group remained elevated. At this time, plasma selenium in horses given Sel-Plex was higher than in the horses given selenite (P=0.08).

## Conclusions

The digestibility of selenium in horses appears to be intermediate between ruminants and nonruminants. Selenium from yeast was more digestible than from sodium selenite, leading to a greater positive selenium balance in these horses. The level of selenium supplementation in this study was probably above the horse's requirement since every horse was in positive selenium balance and blood selenium values were on the high side of normal reference ranges. Since only one level of selenium was fed, it is not possible to establish a selenium requirement from these data.

Increased urinary selenium excretion following exercise in the inorganic selenium group suggests that the requirement for selenium by exercised horses may be dependent on selenium source and exercise frequency. The exercise intensity used in this study resulted in an increase in plasma selenium in both treatment groups. The source of this increased plasma selenium may have been the red blood cells, since there was a trend towards lower RBC selenium following exercise. Following exercise, plasma selenium in those fed the inorganic source returned to pre-exercise levels while plasma selenium in those given Sel-Plex remained elevated at 24 hrs post-exercise. Perhaps part of the selenium that mobilized from the RBC in the selenite group during exercise was voided in the urine, leading to an increase in urinary selenium excretion during the subsequent 24 hr collection period.

After absorption, red blood cells take up inorganic selenium and return it to plasma in the reduced (i.e., hydrogen selenide) form, where it binds to plasma proteins and is transported to the liver to become part of the selenium pool for selenoprotein formation (Combs and Combs, 1986). Some travels to the kidney and is excreted via urine. Organic selenium (selenoamino acids) travels in the blood by amino acid transport mechanisms and is less likely to be lost through urinary excretion.

More research is needed to quantify the selenium requirement of horses at different exercise intensities and to determine how the form of dietary selenium affects antioxidant status.

## References

AOAC. 1995. Official Methods of Analysis (16th Ed.). Association of Official Analytical Chemists, Arlington, VA.

Combs, G.F. and S.B. Combs. 1986. Absorption and transfer. In: The Role of Selenium in Nutrition. Academic Press, New York.

Food and Drug Administration. 1987. Food additives permitted in feed and drinking water of animals. Fed. Reg. 52 (Part 573, No. 65):10887.

Frape, D. 1998. Equine Nutrition and Feeding. (2nd Ed.). Blackwell Science Ltd, UK.

Gallagher, K. and H.D. Stowe. 1980. Influence of exercise on serum selenium and peroxide reduction system of racing Standardbreds. Sm. J. Vet. Res. 41:1333.

Levander, O.A. 1986. Selenium. In: Trace Elements in Human and Animal Nutrition Vol. 2 (5th Ed.). (W. Mertz, ed.). Academic Press, Inc. Orlando, FL. pp 209–279.

Mahan, D.C. and N.A. Parrett. 1996. Evaluating the efficacy of Se-enriched yeast and sodium selenite on tissue Se retention and serum GSH-Px activity in grower and finisher swine. J. Anim. Sci. 74: 2967–2974.

Marlin, D.J., C.M. Scott, R.C. Harris, R.C. Schroter, P.C. Mills, P.A. Harris, C.E. Orme, C.A. Roberts, C. Marr, and F. Barrelet. 1995. Physiological responses of non-heat acclimated horses performing treadmill exercise in cool (20°C/40% RH), hot/dry (30°/40% RH) or hot/humid (30°/80% RH) conditions. Equine Vet J., Suppl. 22.

NRC. 1989. Nutrient Requirements of Horses, (5th Ed.). National Academy Press, Washington, DC.

Podoll, K.L., J.B. Bernard, D.E. Ullrey, S.R. DeBar, P.K. Ku and W.T. Magee. 1992. Dietary selenate versus selenite for cattle, sheep, and horses. J. Anim. Sci. 70:1965–1970.

Reddy, K.V., T.C. Kumar, M. Prasad and P. Reddanna. 1998. Pulmonary lipid peroxidation and antioxidant defenses during exhaustive physical exercise: The role of vitamin E and selenium. Nutrition 14(5):448–51.

Shelle, J.E., W.D. Vanhuss, J.S. Rook and D.E. Ullrey.1985. Relationship between selenium and vitamin E nutrition and exercise in horses. In: Proc. 9th Equine Nutr. And Physiol. Soc. Symp., Lansing, MI. pp 104–109.

Shellow, J.S., S.G. Jackson, J.P. Baker and A.H. Cantor. 1985. The influence of dietary selenium levels on blood levels of selenium and glutathione peroxidase activity in the horse. J. Anim. Sci. 61:590.

Snow, D.H., S.P. Gash,.and D. Rice. 1987. Field observations on selenium status, whole blood glutathione peroxidase and plasma gamma-glutamyl transferase activities in thoroughbred racehorses. In: Gillespie and Robinson (Ed.). Equine Exercise Physiology 2. ICEEP Publications, Davis, CA. pp 494–505.

Stowe, H.D. 1998. Selenium supplementation for horse feed. In: Advances in Equine Nutrition. (J.D. Pagan, ed.) Nottingham University Press, UK. pp 97–103.

Stowe, H.D. and T.H. Herdt. 1992. Clinical assessment of selenium status of livestock. J. Anim. Sci. 70:3928–3933.

# Subject Index

# ALLTECH AROUND THE WORLD

## A Listing of Alltech International Offices and Distributors

ARGENTINA
ALLTECH ARGENTINA
Patricia Caporaso, Ing. Agr.
Arce 348 P.B. "B"
1426 Buenos Aires
TEL: 54-1-775-4923 FAX: 54-1-776-2129

AUSTRALIA
ALLTECH AUSTRALIA
Kim Turnley
Unit 9, No. 810 Princes Highway
Springvale, Victoria 3171
TEL: 61-3-9574-2333 FAX: 61-3-9574-2444

BOLIVIA
ALLTECH BOLIVIA, LTDA
Clodys A. Menacho R., Ing.
Calle Los Claveles #3
Barrio Sirari, Casilla 1450 Santa Cruz
TEL: 591-343-2422 FAX: 591-343-5482

BRAZIL
ALLTECH DO BRASIL
Marc Larousse
Rua Said Mohamad El Khatib 280 CIC
Caixa Postal 10808, 81170-610
Curitiba PRCep
TEL: 55-41-347-9291 FAX: 55-41-347-9894

CANADA
ALLTECH CANADA
Nick Smit
449 Laird Road
Guelph, Ontario, N1G 4W1
TEL: 519-763-3331 FAX: 519-763-5682

CHILE
ALLTECH CHILE
Mario Román
Padre Orellana 1315
Las Condes, Santiago
TEL: 56-2-551-9041 FAX: 56-2-201-2986

CHINA
ASIA PACIFIC BIOSCIENCE CENTER
Lan Luo, Ph.D.
P.O. Box 92
No. 30 Baishiqiao Road
Beijing 100081
TEL: 86-10-6218-7751
FAX: 86-10-6218-7750

COLOMBIA
INVERSIÓNES AMAYA
(INVERAMAYA)
Luis Londoño, Ph.D.
Carrera 38 #134-06
Bogotá
TEL: 57-1-627-5484 FAX: 57-1-625-0457

COSTA RICA
NUTEC, S.A.
Ing. Carlos Lang
Apartado 392, P.O. Box 392
Tibas
TEL: 506-2-33-31-10 FAX: 506-2-33-31-10

CROATIA
ALLTECH BIOTECHNOLOGY d.o.o.
Nenad Fuchs
Nodilova 17
10000 Zagreb
TEL: 385-1-464-93-36 FAX: 385-1-299-55-99

591

CYPRUS
CHRONEL BIOTECHNOLOGY Ltd.
Christoforus Kyriacou
21 Gen. Timayia Avenue
P.O. Box 2792, 6503 Larnaca
TEL: 357-4-638082 FAX: 357-4-636251

CZECH REPUBLIC
ALLTECH CZECH REPUBLIC
Vladimir Šiške, Ph.D.
Mezirka 13, 60200
Brno
TEL: 42-0-541-21-57-40
FAX: 42-0-541-21-57-41

DENMARK
ALLTECH DENMARK
Peter Villadsen
Gråbrødrestræde 2
DK 8900 Randers
TEL: 45-86-439700 FAX: 45-86-429300

DOMINICAN REPUBLIC
SANUT, S.A.
Miguel A Lajara P.
Km 10 1/2 Aut. Duarte
Apartado Postal 30-004
Santo Domingo
TEL: 809-560-5840 FAX: 809-564-4070

ECUADOR
ALLTECH ECUADOR
John Weir
Cdla. Albatros
Calle N Entre Gaviota y Ostrero
MZZ 8 Villa 6
Guayaquil
TEL/FAX: 593 4 296-791

EGYPT
INTERNATIONAL FREE TRADE Co.
Magdy Hassan
15 El Mahad El Eshtraky Street
Merryland-Heliopolis
Cairo 11341
TEL: 202-25-800-28 FAX: 202-25-827-93

FINLAND
BERNER LTD.
Antti Rinta Harri
Jukka Klemola
Eteläranta 4B
SF 00130 Helsinki
TEL: 358-9-134-511 FAX: 358-9-134-51380

FRANCE
ALLTECH FRANCE
Denis Gallet
2-4, Avenue du 6 juin 1944
95190 Goussainville
TEL: 33-1-398-86351 FAX: 33-1-398-80778

GERMANY
ALLTECH DEUTSCHLAND GmbH
Manfred Pietsch, Ph.D.
Esmarchstraβe 6
23795 Bad Segeberg
TEL: 49-4551-88700 FAX: 49-4551-887099

GHANA (WEST AFRICA)
BIOTRADE LTD.
Felicio Baëta
No. 4, First Rangoon Close
P.O. Box 7383
Accra-North
TEL/FAX: 233-21-774444

HUNGARY
ALLTECH HUNGARY
Levente Gati
Szugló u 9-15
Budapest, H-1145
TEL: 36-1-267-1408 FAX: 36-1-207-1409

INDIA
VETCARE
Bharat Tandon
IS-40 KHB Industrial Area
Yelahanka New Town
Bangalore 560-064
TEL : 91-80-8461241 FAX: 91-80-8461240

INDONESIA
P.T. ROMINDO PRIMAVETCOM
Dr. Lukas
Dr. Saharjo
No. 266
Jakarta 12870
TEL: 62-21-830-0300 FAX: 62-21-828-0679

IRAN
DAROU GOSTAR CO.
H. Morakabi, Ph.D.
No. 66 Pardis Street, Shiraz Square
Vanak Avenue, Tehran 19916
TEL: 98-21-804-6163 FAX: 98-21-803-2017

IRELAND
EUROPEAN BIOTECHNOLOGY
CENTRE
Sarney, Summerhill Road
Dunboyne, County Meath
TEL: 353-1-825-2244 FAX: 353-1-825-2251


ISRAEL
LUXEMBOURG PHARMACEUTICALS,
Ltd.
Zvi Kaufman
4 Kaufman Street, Tel Aviv 68012
P.O. Box 13, Tel Aviv 61000
TEL: 972-3-5107373 FAX: 972-3-5100882


ITALY
ASCOR CHIMICI, S.R.L.
Arnaldo Valentini
Via Piana, 265
47032 Capocolle (FO)
TEL: 39-543-462464 FAX: 39-543-448644


JAMAICA, W.I.
WINCORP
Teresa Mollinedo-Thomas
38-39 Caracas Avenue
Kingston Export Free Zone, Kingston 15
TEL: 809-923-6894 FAX: 809-923-6856


JAPAN
BUSSAN BIOTECH CO., LTD.
Nick Koyama
3rd Fl, Shiba Daimon
Makita Bldg 5-8
2-Chome Shiba Daimon
Minato-Ku, Tokyo
TEL: 81-3-5470-6601 FAX: 81-3-5470-6606


KENYA
ALLTECH EASTERN AFRICA, Ltd.
Karwitha Kiugu, Tarnya Fasol
P.O. Box 13995, Nairobi
TEL/FAX: 254-2-449082

KOREA
ALLTECH KOREA
Myun-Soo Han, Ph.D.
714 Hyundai Officetel
1589-8 Seocho Dong, Seocho-Ku
Seoul, 137-070
TEL: 82-2-584-6203 FAX: 82-2-584 6202

I.E. SUNG INTL.
C.Y. Chang
C. Jang
ILBok Bldg 2f.
#1602-4, Seocho-Dong
Seocho-Ku, Seoul 137-070
TEL: 82-2-521-0501-4, FAX: 82-2-521-1300

YOONEE CHEMICAL CO., Ltd.
Jung Jooe Lee, D.V.M.
ILBok Bldg 2f.
#1602-4, Seocho-Dong
Seocho-Ku, Seoul 137-070
TEL: 82-2-585-1801 FAX: 82-2-584-2523

LEBANON
YOUSEF FREIHA & SONS
Ralph Freiha
Industrial City
P.O. Box 90261
Sed El Bouchrieh
Beirut
TEL: 961-1-499721 FAX: 961-1-497171

MALAYSIA
FARM CARE SDN. BHD.
Ong Seng Say
No. 48-3, Jalan Radin Tengah, Seri Petaling
57000 Kuala Lumpur
TEL: 60-3-957-3669 FAX:60-3-957-3648

MALTA
ANDREWS FEEDS LTD.
Martin Debasttista, Ph.D.
P.O. Box 134
G.P.O.
Marsa
TEL: 356-234400 FAX: 356-232163

MEXICO
ALLTECH DE MEXICO, S.A. DE C.V.
Gladys Hoyos, Ph.D.
Dr. Enrique Gonzalez Martinez No. 244
Col. Sta. Maria La Ribera
C.P. 06400, Mexico D.F.
TEL: 52-5-547-5040 (to 44)
FAX: 52-5-547-2443

NETHERLANDS
ALLTECH NETHERLANDS B.V.
Timm Neelsen
Hollandsch Diep 63
2904 EP Capelle aan den Ijssel
TEL: 31-10-450-1038 FAX: 31-10-442-3798

NEW ZEALAND
CUNDY TECHNICAL SERVICES
Mike E. Cundy
5 Siebel Road
RD 1
Henderson, Auckland 8
TEL: 64-9-837-3243 FAX: 64-9-837-3214

PERU
ALLTECH PERU
Ricardo Sahagun
Calle Mario Valdivia # 180
San Miguel, Lima 32
TEL: 51-1578-0003 FAX: 51-1578-2131

PHILIPPINES
ALLTECH PHILIPPINES
Ben Vreeburg
Room 301, Lalaine Bldg.
#469 Real St., Alabang-Zapote Rd.
Las Piñas, Metro Manila
TEL: 63-2-800-9153 Fax: 63-2-800-9145

POLAND
POLMARCHÉ
Wojciech Zalewski, Ph.D.
Ul Szczesliwicka 29/31
02-353 Warszawa
TEL/FAX: 48-22-722-9950

PORTUGAL
ALLTECH PORTUGAL
Jorge Cardoso
Rua Pedro Alvares Cabral, 5
R/c/Leceia
2745 Barcarena
TEL: 351-1422-8029 FAX: 351-1-421-8100

ROMANIA
ALLTECH ROMANIA
Liviu Panta
Sos Panduri 25
BI P3A ET 1
Sector 5, A.P. 5
Bucuresti
TEL/FAX: 40-1-410-47-79

RUSSIA
ALLTECH RUSSIA
Ul. Novaya Basmannaya, 12
Office 111
107078 Moscow
TEL: 7-095-265-1645 FAX: 7-095-265-4576

SAUDI ARABIA
ARASCO
A. Al-Rubaian
P.O. Box 53845
Riyadh 11593
Al-Akariyah Shopping Center
Suite No. 625
TEL: 966-1-4191933 FAX: 966-1-419-1520

SLOVAKIA
ALLTECH SK, s.r.o.
Rastislav Bobcek
Jana Mrvu 28
949 01 Nitra
TEL: 421-87-519-358 FAX: 421-87-517-209

SOUTH AFRICA
ALLTECH BIOTECHNOLOGY
Derek Foster/Pat Charlton
P.O. Box 2654, Somerset West 7129
TEL: 27-21-8517-052 FAX: 27-21-8517-000

SPAIN
PROBASA
Valentin Rosell, Ph.D.
Juan Rosell Lizana
c/o Argenters 9 Nave 3
Pol Ind Satiga
Sta. Perpetua de la Moguda
Barcelona
TEL: 34-93718-2215 FAX: 34-93719-1307

SWEDEN
VETPHARMA, AB
Thord Bengtsson
Annedalsvägen 9
S-227 64 LUND
TEL: 46-46-12-81-00 FAX: 46-46-14-65-55

SWITZERLAND
INTERFERM AG
Fritz Näf, Ph.D.
Hardturmstrasse 175
CH-8005 Zürich
TEL: 41-1-272-8024 FAX: 41-1-273-1844

594

TAIWAN
JARSEN COMPANY, LTD.
T.Y. Lin
12 Fl., No. 1377, Chung Cheng Road
Taoyuan
TEL: 886-3-356-6678 FAX: 886-3-356-5529

THAILAND
ALLTECH THAILAND
David Faulkner
2533 Sukhumvit Road, Bangchack
Prakhanong, Bangkok, 10250
TEL: 66-2-742-4545 FAX: 66-2-742-4547

DIETHELM TRADING CO., LTD.
2533 Sukhumvit Road, Bangchack
Prakhanong, Bangkok, 10250
TEL: 66-2-332-7140 FAX: 66-2-332-7166

TURKEY
ARES GIDA TARIM HAYVANCILIK
SAN. TIC. LTD. STI.
206 Sokak No. 4/C 35040
Rasit Kayira
Bornova
Izmir
TEL: 90-232-339-0288
FAX: 90-232-342-0656

UNITED KINGDOM
ALLTECH UK
Jem Clay
Alltech House, Ryhall Road
Stamford, Lincolnshire, PE9 1TZ
TEL: 44-1780-764512 FAX: 44-1780-764506

USA
ALLTECH, INC.
CORPORATE HEADQUARTERS
3031 Catnip Hill Pike
Nicholasville, Kentucky 40356
TEL: 1-606-885-9613 FAX: 1-606-885-6736

VENEZUELA
ALLTECH VENEZUELA
Jorge Arias, Ph.D.
Urbanización Industrial Terrazas de
Castillito
Calle 98. Parcela L/123
Valencia. Edo. Carabobo
TEL/FAX: 58-14-23-20-06

VIETNAM
BAYER AGRITECH SAIGON
Nicholas Brand
1/3 Xom Moi Hamlet
Phuong Long Village
Thu Duc District
Ho Chi Minh City
TEL: 84-8-960127 FAX: 84-8-961-523

YUGOSLAVIA
ALLTECH YUGOSLAVIA
Marina Vukic Vranjes, Ph.D.
Somborska 57
Yu-21000 Novi Sad
TEL/FAX: 381-21-301-083

ZIMBABWE
S.A.F.C.O.
Bruce Grant
P.O. Box ST324, Southerton
Harare
TEL: 263-4-620-486/7/8
FAX: 263-4-620-558/620-485

595